JOHN PAUL JONES

CAPTAIN PAUL

CAPTAIN PAUL

by

COMMANDER
EDWARD ELLSBERG

THE LITERARY GUILD OF AMERICA, INC.

NEW YORK 1941

Endpaper illustration of bust of John Paul Jones by Houdon
reproduced by courtesy of the Office of Naval Records and
Library, Navy Department.

To

THAT IDEAL

FOR WHICH

CAPTAIN PAUL

FOUGHT

1

IT is a trait clearly observable amongst us that we Americans are prone to go to most amazing lengths in suffering injury, to avoid envolvement in war. I refer not alone to the Quaker brethren surrounding me on this island of Nantucket, with whom my lot has been thrown since my earliest boyhood, when we here were but colonials and loyal subjects of King George. No, it is not of the Quakers alone I speak. Let my non-resisting Quaker neighbors have their non-resistance. Within some limits, should they carry it not too far, it may help preserve them.

No, it is not on them nor on their peculiar doctrines that I meditate, in this year of grace 1808 as I look down on our harbor of Nantucket to witness there a sight to break the heart of any seaman. Ships, aye—a harbor full of ships, God help us! Never in my seafaring life do I recall in any port—London, Brest, nor Boston—having seen so many vessels all at once. But there now they lie, my neighbor's ships and mine, the waters of Nantucket harbor invisible for their crowding hulls. And the wide horizon, unless one lifts one's eyes vertically to Heaven (as indeed where else may one look in these anguished days for any wisdom) is almost blotted out by a maze of soaring masts, of wide-spread yards, of crisscrossed ratlines and of rigging, making a tangled web of the sky in which all our ships and we with them are caught like trapped flies, helplessly, immovably, unescapably, until we perish.

Bitterly, I look down from my house each day upon those dying ships. Empty of their crews, their holds empty of the casks of precious whale oil which we of Nantucket have hazarded our limbs and long months of our lives in cockle

[1]

shells against the leviathans of the deep to gain. Aye, and our warehouses empty too of those huge bales and bulky cases of merchandise for which in London, in Amsterdam, or in Brest, we of this island have been wont before this madness struck us, to exchange the products of our whaleship try-pots.

In the harbor our useless ships idly chafe each other, hull against hull, while aloft their yards creak dismally in the slings and their rotting rigging groans mournfully to the winds whistling to no purpose past their furled sails. Ashore, every warehouse is locked. Empty drays and wains stand abandoned on the docks. Our waterfront is deserted. In every cooperage, the clatter of maul against hoop and stave is stilled. In every smithy, the clang of sledge on glowing iron is silenced. In every ropewalk, the cheerful hum of brown hemp and golden manila fiber miraculously spinning into stout cable or flexible harpoon line, has long since faded into dismal quiet.

The silence of the grave, the like of which I never thought to know till it pleased God at last to lay me there, hangs now over Nantucket. Seaman, harpooner, cooper, smith, rope-maker and merchant alike—all are idle, stricken from their posts by that weird interdict born of our weakness which has fallen on us from Mr. Jefferson in Washington.

Embargo!

Only with difficulty can I phrase my thoughts in the sober terms becoming to my years when I gaze now about me upon the ruin that embargo has wrought. Nor, save for the influence of my good wife, Delight, could I, Thomas Folger, sufficiently curb my tongue to speak of it amongst my neighbors in language meet to be heard from the lips of a staid merchant who fears the Lord, rather than the vigorous manner of my youth when, thrown only with rough seamen, like them I feared neither man nor God and swore accordingly.

It is true that abroad Napoleon and George III have made a charnel house of Europe, and in their insane struggle for supremacy neither French nor British have had due regard (nor indeed, any at all) for the rights of Americans

[2]

as neutrals. Orders in Council from George's ministers and Decrees in reprisal from Napoleon have been rained down upon us in this tiny island of Nantucket to the grave distress of our lawful commerce, with both combatants alike heedless of the harm they do us, in their mad anxiety to bleed each other. May our Lord judge between them as to which has justice with his cause, though I, who in my younger days risked my own life to fight King George and his stiff-necked Ministers, have little reason to believe there may be righteousness behind any cause they have espoused.

I have lived through too much warfare to indulge any vain hope that our ships, our goods and our Nantucket seamen might escape injury amidst all this slaughter. But who is there acquainted with the sea so witless as to believe that at any time he may entrust himself and his goods to the perils of the deep without grave risk? Indeed, amongst all those of any nation who adventure upon the seas, who knows better than we whalers of Nantucket that there is always danger on the wave, accustomed as we are to dare death from sweeping flukes and crunching jaws each time a tiny boat of ours steers close aboard the dripping flanks of leviathan that the harpooner may truly strike the whale? From Greenland to the Falkland Islands in the Atlantic, and from Chile to far Japan in the Pacific, the ocean depths are littered with the wrecks of our Nantucket ships. And which of us here in Nantucket does not sustain the hapless widow and the orphaned children of some near relative who has sunk to an unmarked grave amongst the splintered planking of his stove whaleboat?

Aye, there is danger on the sea—from wind, from wave, from reef, from whale. Who that may call himself a seaman knows it not? Then should we of Nantucket shrink from the puny dangers that foreigners engaged in war throw in the paths of our ships? Do we need Thomas Jefferson, a landsman who knows less of the perils of the sea which are our daily life than I know of his tobacco planting on the slopes of his peaceful hills in western Virginia, to save us from these added man-made terrors?

In what age has weakness ever been defense against him who would be Caesar? What weird delusion do we suffer that we think by allowing our ships-of-war to decay and rendering ourselves thus impotent, we procure our safety against the conqueror?

And now as the crowning folly of our weakness, instead of resistance, comes this embargo! What madness has seized us, that anticipating every injury which Napoleon or George III might in some degree inflict upon us, we can find no better remedy than by embargo to inflict it in full measure upon ourselves? A common ruin now engulfs us all as a result.

Life, liberty, and the pursuit of happiness! Well do I remember the days when Mr. Jefferson proclaimed them in that Declaration of Independence to which I as a youth with cutlass and gun fought to give reality as the objects for which we were battling George III. But are they less worth fighting for because this is the year 1808 than they were in 1776? What alchemy have independence and the thirty-odd years between wrought in Mr. Jefferson that we must now suffer supinely the injuries against which he once urged us to rebel and take up arms against our lawful King? But by Mr. Jefferson's fiat, now that George is no longer our liege lord, we must bear at George's hands the tyrannies which as his subjects we could not stomach!

I had thought a few months ago when the British man-o'-war *Leopard* treacherously loosed her flaming broadsides upon our unsuspecting frigate *Chesapeake* to slaughter in cold blood our fellow citizens, and then impudently pressed from her crew part of her seamen to fight the King's battles for him, that the depths of our national degradation had been plumbed. But I was wrong. The *Chesapeake*, taken unawares and unprepared in time of peace for the *Leopard's* murderous attack and unable to fire a shot in return, at least hauled down her flag only when her decks were littered with dying sailors.

But now who can find any excuse at all for us as a nation? To what nether depths of Hell have we sunk indeed when

[4]

we can find no answer to foreign arrogance in looting our ships and murdering our seamen, save by our own act of embargo to proclaim ourselves before the world as craven poltroons, unwilling to defend ourselves, abandoning the seas which are our right and our heritage lest the presence of our ships there offend some petty tyrant flouting every law of man and God?

My greying head sags in shame. That I, who but a few brief years ago fought beneath the banner of John Paul Jones for the liberty of my country and the rights of men, should ever have lived to witness this, seems unbelievable to me. Yet to my sorrow is it so. Looking down from my windows in this desolated town upon our rotting ships, I ponder mournfully what has brought us to such decadence that we slink shamefaced from the seas. I must conclude bitterly that this nation's memory is a fickle thing from which the recollections even of thirty years ago have swiftly slipped, and that what we under Jones dared on the seas for America against the overwhelming might of Britain's Navy, already has faded into the mists of time. It may well be.

But never for any man who scourged the British seas with John Paul Jones will the memory fade. Least of all will I forget, whom fate first threw into his path when he was still plain Captain Paul, ex-slaver, merchantman, and fugitive Scottish buccaneer, to stay by his side till all England trembled at his name. Under him we of Nantucket, far from abandoning the seas as we now have, earned the respect even of Britain's towering men-of-war in the very chops of the English Channel!

None knew Captain Paul better than I, who, in my youth, close beside him on sea and land, watched him as John Paul Jones flash like a flaming meteor across the dark days of our struggle for independence. But already I sadly note that Commodore Jones, dead these seventeen years, is but a dim legend of the past, unreal, forgotten.

With a heavy heart and an anguished soul as I look upon our dying ships, I recall those days when my neighbors and I, though then but boys, sailed the seas to fight as men be-

[5]

side Paul Jones for that freedom so flamingly set out for us by Thomas Jefferson. Now Jones is gone. And so far have we forgotten his rebellious spirit that in our weakness we supinely acquiesce in the embargo of an aging Jefferson in whom the flaming doctrines of the Declaration seem to be wholly dead. Now they are preserved only as lifeless words on yellowing parchment in some Washington vault, as useless to us today as Jones' lifeless body preserved in alcohol in an unmarked leaden coffin in a long-abandoned foreign cemetery.

Only in the memories of those few survivors who fought with him does Jones live now. Lest when we pass, he fade wholly from the knowledge of America, I shall go back to the days of my youth and those tragic years of the rebellion which made us a nation, to set out the story of my life and how strangely it was entwined with that of Captain Paul, that quixotic genius whose thundering guns, speaking the only language tyrants ever understand, breathed life into the words of our Declaration of Independence.

2

To its young men, our island of Nantucket offers but two alternatives in life—they may go awhaling, or, should that not suit them, they may go westward beyond the Alleghanies to the wilderness of the Ohio. There, having first hacked out of the virgin forest a few acres of cleared land for themselves, they may afterward battle with savage Indians to see which of the twain, red man or white, shall enjoy the fruits of their agricultural efforts.

However, there are but few trees on our island and it happens that none of us has been in his youth afforded adequate opportunity to become skilled with an axe. Furthermore Nature made Nantucket mainly of sand, so that we have never had fair incentive to improve our skill in agriculture. For these good reasons, being thereby much handicapped in early training and unsuited as pioneers to the unexplored wilds of our frontier, few of us Nantucketers have ever been inclined to imitate the adventurous youth amongst our neighbors of Virginia or New York in exploiting the possibilities of becoming perchance landed proprietors at the expense of Pontiac's painted warriors.

It will be plain then that I had but Hobson's choice when hard necessity forced upon my young shoulders the burden of bestirring myself immediately to earn a livelihood lest my bread and that of my mother be dependent upon the charity of relatives. That the decision had so suddenly to be made and even more promptly to be acted upon, was a shock for which my sixteen years had ill-prepared me.

I had been loitering one fine May day on Straight Wharf, sprawled out atop a huge heap of barrel staves alongside Henry Gardner, while we two lads idly watched the sweating

[7]

seamen of the *Beaver* laying back on the inboard end of a whip suspended from her main yard, ceaselessly hoisting aboard casks of provisions for her coming voyage. Speculatively I regarded the diminishing bulk of the array of casks of beef and bread on the dock beneath the yardarm, wondering how soon the last of them might be whipped up to the yard, swung inboard, and dropped down the *Beaver's* hatch; for then no doubt the seamen on the dock would commence whipping aboard the staves upon which we reclined, unceremoniously dethroning Henry and me, and perhaps even chasing us both from the wharf to boot.

Henry regarded the huge bulk and towering masts of the ship alongside the dock with the eager eyes of boyhood. The *Beaver* was a noble vessel, of full two hundred and forty tons, the largest whaler of any owned in Nantucket, which meant of course the largest of any in the entire world. Bluff in the bows, full in the waist, her three masts, each topped off by the crow's nest which marked her as a spouter, set squarely perpendicular to her waterline with none of that rake aft which is supposed to denote speed. The *Beaver* as a vessel was certainly no beauty. But in her every line she bespoke her sole purpose—to provide within her stout hull stowage for the maximum number of casks of sperm oil that her buoyancy might safely sustain, with little regard either to appearance, comfort, or speed, qualities which in a whaler never earned a farthing for her owners.

"Next voyage," announced Henry proudly from his perch beside me on the pile of staves, "I have the promise of yon shad-belly Captain on the quarterdeck there, that I may ship with him and for the two-hundredth lay besides. In such a large ship, should they have a greasy voyage, even the two-hundredth lay may well exceed ten barrels for my share of the cargo."

"I would speak somewhat more respectfully of Cap'n Hezekiah Coffin there did I ever hope to sail with him, Henry," I cautioned him. "Shad-belly indeed! Though that Quaker costume of his makes you laugh, and the sober waistcoat shrouding him may well remind you of the belly of a shad, still should he hear you, I doubt he would see anything mirthful in the comparison, and your chances of ever being shipped with him for the two-hundredth lay or even any smaller fraction of the cargo would swiftly go by the board. What would you have him wear aboard a spouter? Gold buttons on a scarlet waistcoat, and a gold laced jacket as if he were an idling officer in the King's Navy, to soak his finery in the oily fumes of those try-pots amidships on the *Beaver* the minute he starts trying out the blubber of his first spermaceti? Mind your speech, Henry, or you'll be lucky to go out on some trifling schooner where your lay won't amount to a barrel, let alone ten!"

Henry Gardner, a well-knit lad for his seventeen years, looked lazily across the wharf at Captain Coffin, who in solitary state on the quarterdeck just abaft the mizzenmast was keeping a watchful eye on the lading of his ship, then turned back to me.

"With all the creaking of blocks and falls and the bellowing of those men heaving in the stores, he'll never hear me," replied Henry, adding a little longingly as he surveyed the *Beaver*, "I was to have gone out with him this voyage, and was indeed practically shipped when my mother fell ill and now I must wait the next trip. And that leaves Cap'n Hezekiah there short a hand. How about you, Tom? You're nearly as old as me; why not try your luck with him? He knows your father well and may easily be prevailed on to ship you in my place. And as for me, when I go out with him next cruise, it'll be some comfort to have at least one shipmate aboard besides myself to talk to without all the 'thee's' and 'thou's' of these Quakers."

A little shamefaced at what might seem treason to the customs of our island, I tried to explain why not.

"I can't, Henry," I confessed. "My mother says there are quite enough of us Folgers awhaling now, and she intends I shall not follow in their footsteps. She has indeed a queer idea to get me away from the sea altogether, that I at least may lead what she terms a normal life." I squirmed uncomfortably at the admission, blushing furthermore at the im-

[9]

plication of female dominance.

With all the dignity of his superior years, Henry looked questioningly at me.

"What's wrong with whaling? What's there about it that ain't normal for any Nantucketer? And what's she going to make you then if not a whaler? A farmer?" he finished scornfully.

I cringed down on the staves. A farmer, indeed!

"No," I averred stoutly, defending my mother as best I could against any such slanderous insinuation. "She has indeed no thought of my becoming a farmer. But a printer, maybe. You know Ben Franklin, Henry, don't you?"

"Poor Richard? The man who snatched the lightning from the clouds? Who doesn't?" asked Henry sarcastically. "He's the greatest man in the world! Why, my grandfather says he's over in London as Colonial Agent right now, advising the King and his Ministers they'd better treat these colonies better. But what's Ben Franklin got to do with you and your not going whaling?"

"Well, Ben Franklin's a Folger too, if you know so much, and he's my second cousin," I bragged, proudly conscious that the relationship could easily be proved, for was not Ben's mother that Abiah Folger who came right here from Nantucket? "And my mother says Ben proves what any Folger can do if he'll only quit risking his life chasing whales all over the oceans and stay ashore to use some of the intelligence that's come down to him from old Peter Folger. He was Abiah's father and one of the first settlers of this island along with Tristram Coffin and Thomas Macy and Nathaniel Starbuck and the rest of 'em a hundred years ago! And my mother's written to Cousin Ben about me and she has his promise that, come two years from now when one of his older apprentices finishes his time, he'll take me in his place as apprentice in his shop in Philadelphia and I'll learn to be a printer too!" I ended breathlessly, prudently omitting any mention of that part of the bargain which involved the payment of the huge sum of twenty pounds sterling to the thrifty Doctor as the major inducement for his taking me instead of some Philadelphia lad as apprentice.

That squelched Henry, as I well knew it would. To be destined as apprentice to the eminent Doctor Franklin whose fame filled both the Old World and the New, put my failure to become a whaler beyond all criticism, even amongst my cronies in Nantucket.

"You're going to Philadelphia to work in Ben Franklin's shop?" breathed Henry enviously. "D'ye think you'll ever get a chance to see him?"

"Sure," I boasted carelessly. "He'll probably teach me to set type himself with his own hands. He doesn't worry about he's a Doctor nor how famous he is, my mother says. If he's just written something he thinks the King or anybody important ought to know, like as not he'll come right down into his printing shop and start setting type on it himself so's not to waste time in getting it printed, and then maybe he'll print it himself right off, too. My cousin Ben can do anything better'n anybody else. If he wanted to, he could be a better harpooner than even my father, so my mother says, only he's got more sense'n to spend his life up in the crosstrees keeping a weather eye out for spouting whales just so's he can harpoon 'em. And I'm not going to either, Henry Gardner," I concluded defiantly, "for you nor for nobody! I'm going to be a printer and be famous like Cousin Be—!"

"Sh-h-h!" interrupted Henry, maliciously nudging me sharply in the ribs. "Look you, Tom! For'd on the dock beneath the *Beaver's* bowsprit, where her dolphin striker overhangs the Square. Isn't that another cousin o' yours, Delight Coffin, there in the lee of your Aunt Keziah, trying to hail you?"

Without stirring otherwise, I inclined my head slightly over my right shoulder for a quick glance in the direction indicated, hopeful that Henry might be wrong, for I had little stomach ever for facing my Aunt Keziah save when avoidance was impossible. Of all the Folger tribe, of which there were many on Nantucket, only my formidable Aunt

[11]

Keziah, Quaker though she was, inspired me so. And in this feeling I was not alone, for such was the awe and fear with which that old dragon was regarded by her neighbors that none dared cross her in any opinion.

But now there was no escape. Henry was right. What ill wind, I wondered, had caused Keziah Coffin, that stiff-necked Quakeress who scarce ever looked either right or left in the singleness of purpose with which she went about her business, to incline her head down Straight Wharf along the *Beaver's* starboard side and spot me amongst the staves? But there, alongside her, beckoning vigorously was my cousin Delight, and to make sure apparently that there be no mistake that it was I and not Henry who was wanted, calling out in a girlish voice nearly drowned by the creaking of the block and fall on the *Beaver's* yard,

"Thomas! Thomas Folger!"

"Aye, aye!" Reluctantly I slid off the staves, dodged a swaying cask whipped suddenly aloft almost from under my very feet as I hit the dock. I strolled morosely up the wharf amongst the tangled heaps of sea stores of every description littering it, waiting to be hoisted aboard and stowed snugly below in the cavernous holds of the whaler. What, I wondered, had I done now to warrant Aunt Keziah's reproof? For never, so far as I could recall, had she ever deigned notice me, much less summon me from any distance, save to admonish me for some shortcoming, of which I must ruefully admit, like many another boy, I was guilty enough in her eyes or in anybody's.

The slowness of my progress bespoke my thoughts perhaps, for long before I had covered half the distance up the wharf to where my grim aunt (though but a distantly related one) awaited me beneath the overhanging dolphin striker, my cousin Delight broke from her side and, regardless of the casks, came dancing joyously down the dock to meet me.

"How's thee do, Cousin Thomas?" A bright smile, doubly gay against her prim Quaker bonnet, sparkled in her brown eyes, but brought no response in mine. "Why so glum? What ails thee? Thou'rt so slow in coming when I called that mother sent me to thy assistance lest thy faltering legs fail thee altogether, Cousin Thomas." A little teasingly she stood before me, blocking my path now, which I scarcely resented, seeing that Aunt Keziah still was in the offing. At any time I had far rather converse with my cousin Delight who was well and truly so named, than with her mother whose manner rasped me always as much as her name rasped the ears.

"Morning, Delight," I answered awkwardly, shifting my weight from one foot to the other, while I tried not to gaze past her lest her mother catch my eye with an imperious command I could not ignore. That this was no slight problem may be clearer when I say that despite only sixteen years I was already a lanky youth approaching six feet and promising shortly to go far beyond that height, while Delight, though but a month younger than I, was a dainty maiden, the top of whose bonnet hardly came to my shoulder. "What's the message? I've got to get back to Henry," I muttered forlornly.

"And what is Henry doing that he so badly needs thy help?" asked Delight, mischievously peering past me at Henry, so obviously sprawled idly out on the stack of barrel staves that there could be no equivocation about his occupation.

"Nothing," I mumbled hopelessly.

"Surely then he requires not thy assistance in it," laughed Delight. "Come, Cousin Thomas; my mother hath some news for thee that should gladden thy heart," and grasping me by the sleeve, she started me reluctantly down the wharf.

Like a lamb led to the shearing, I stumbled awkwardly along beside Delight. That any news might gladden me which Keziah Coffin had, save that her spreading business interests at last required her departure permanently from Nantucket, I strongly doubted. For Aunt Keziah, tall, angular, sharp-featured, with a masculine nose and a protruding chin which gave her a witch-like mien, and grimly grey in both eyes and hair, took little interest ever in gladdening anyone save only herself by increasing her material possessions. Amongst all us boys, it was common knowledge, gathered from the talk of our elders, that Keziah Coffin was a business woman the like of whom Nantucket had never seen, even in a community where, owing to the unavoidable absences of most of the men on two and three year long whaling voyages, the business affairs of all were largely left in the hands of their wives. My Aunt Keziah could drive a bargain over a consignment of sperm oil with merchants in both New York and London that left those bewigged worthies to scratch their bewildered pates in puzzled astonishment as to how they might emerge from the transaction with even a farthing's profit. And amongst our neighbors on Nantucket, it was commonly believed that my cousin, Ben Franklin, had derived most of the observations on thrift which he put into Poor Richard's sayings in his almanac, from having kept a keen eye on Keziah's doings.

No one on Nantucket, either man or woman, could ignore Aunt Keziah. Her house on Centre Street, designed by herself, was by all odds the largest and finest in our town, and it is worthy of note as indicating her character that while every other house in Nantucket faced south, hers faced north disregarding the sun, that from her parlor she might better keep a watchful eye on the harbor and the shipping there, where alone her interests lay. Such was her independence of mind and the stiffness of her back, that she only of all the Quaker sect which ruled our island dared ignore both the opinions and the customs of her strait-laced Society of Friends when it so pleased her. Not even their oft-repeated threat to put her "under dealings" and thereby ostracise her from all social intercourse, ever influenced her conduct. For that perhaps, and its incidental influence on my cousin Delight, I should have respected her. For the drab routine of the Quakers appealed little to the "world's people," as they were pleased to denominate my family and such others

[14]

of our community who remained Presbyterians and refused to join the wholesale rush to the tenets of their society which had followed Mary Coffin Starbuck's conversion thereto some three generations before.

But any such admiration of Aunt Keziah on my part was effectively enough obliterated by her vinegary disposition and by what was worse in boyish eyes, her stern adherence to King George, which labelled her an uncompromising Tory. With every boy of my acquaintance filled with the spirit of rebellion over George's blundering efforts to ram the Stamp Act down colonial throats; with Sam Adams, Patrick Henry, and Ben Franklin our idolized heroes for having foiled him at it; and with our youthful minds aflame with "Liberty or death," it is small wonder that we looked with eyes askance at Aunt Keziah's inflexible royalism, more especially as not one of us could ever remember having received in all our hungry days even so much as a broken ginger cookie from those angular hands which so stoutly upheld our tyrannical King and all his hated doings.

"Thou'rt a sad waster of my time, Thomas," Keziah Coffin announced harshly when my laggard feet and Delight tugging at my sleeve finally brought me face to face with her beneath the *Beaver's* bowsprit. " 'Twere a proper punishment for thee not to inform thee of my news, but since I would thereby hurt thy mother more than thee, I shall not withhold it." Her keen grey eyes, flanking her massive nose, bored sharply into me, numbing any response on my part. "Perchance," she continued, "this may cause thee to stir thy lazy stumps. I have it from Captain Rotch that his ship, the *Dartmouth*, in which I own some interest and in which thy father is first mate, hath been spoken south of the shoals beating against head winds, and may indeed arrive tomorrow should the wind turn fair. Does that interest thee?"

The *Dartmouth* due tomorrow? Instantly my languor vanished. Scarce waiting to fling a "Thank'ee, Aunt Keziah!" over my shoulder, I was madly off up State Street.

[15]

homeward bound, my friend Henry and my cousin Delight alike totally ignored in my departure. The *Dartmouth*, my father's ship, gone these two long years, practically home! My lanky legs stirred up the dusty ground under that spur. How my mother would rejoice at that!

3

To many a lad and many a wife on Nantucket, that May morning in 1773 was a day of glad reunion when the *Dartmouth* dropped anchor just outside the bar off Nantucket harbor. But to me, scrambling aboard over the larboard chains the instant the anchor splashed overboard, looking eagerly about for my father, it became suddenly the darkest day of my life. For hardly had I slid over the low bulwark onto the forecastle, all eyes for my father, who as first mate should be forward at the bitts superintending the ground tackle, when Shubael Hussey who had gone out as second mate, spotted me as I hit the deck abreast the foremast and immediately walked over to place a sympathetic arm about my shoulder.

"Look not for thy father here, lad," he said sadly. "See you abreast the try-pots the stern of yon shattered whaleboat? Thy father was in its bow when the jaws of a sparmaceti closed down there. We never saw him again."

Of the rest of that black day, I remember little. I came ashore immediately with Shubael to find my mother amongst the crowd on Straight Wharf, and as best I might, inform her. But there was no need of words when she saw me. One look at my tear-stained face scrambling up the dock from the wherry with Shubael Hussey instead of my father at my side, and my mother, like many another whaleman's wife of Nantucket before and after since whaling began, knew full well what had happened to her man. What mattered any details for her?

Suddenly white but strangely composed, without a questioning word my mother took me by the hand.

"Come, son. 'Twere best we were alone now. We have no

place amongst these joyous greetings." She pushed her way back from the stringpiece of the wharf, leaving Shubael, whose wife, holding a chubby baby, had flung herself forward to clasp him gladly about the neck, torn between his anxiety to follow and comfort his shipmate's widow and his joy at caressing the son he had never seen.

The rest of that sad day was one long succession of condolences with men and women tramping up the dusty road to our house well out on Orange Street—Captain Swain of the *Dartmouth;* the men who had been my father's crew in the fatal whaleboat as he had stood poised in its bow to drive home the lance into a whale maddened already by the harpoon in its side; my mother's friends; nearly every Folger relative we had who was not away at sea. Awkwardly my father's shipmates twisted their broad-brimmed hats in gnarled hands as they sought to convey what had happened without being too gruesome in their recitals. With stoic features my mother listened, neither questioning nor commenting, hardly concerned. My father was dead. Never again would my mother look with straining eyes from the top of Mill Hill across the Sound at the topsails of a homeward bound whaler looming up over the horizon, torn between hope and fear for her man.

The one relief came when it was over, when our little parlor was no longer crowded with sympathetic women weeping at our loss, with embarrassed whalers who in duty bound felt called on to comfort a shipmate's widow ere they departed to settle back alongside their own long-dreamed-of firesides.

Evening came, the last sympathizer departed. With swollen eyes I gazed across the room in the flickering lamplight at my mother, who was still seated from force of habit in the rocking chair which looked out the window northward toward the harbor mouth. With set face and compressed lips she rocked slowly back and forth, her unseeing eyes fixed on the anchor lights of the deserted *Dartmouth*. A muffled sob and the occasional creaking of her rocker were the only sounds as we sat silently facing our loss in greater agony

[18]

than ever, now that the first numbness of the shock was wearing off. What my mother thought I know not as she said nothing, but my own brain was in a tumult between boyish grief at my father's horrible death and the very obvious fact that I must somehow and that immediately take up the burden of supporting my mother as well as myself.

Gone now was my glowing dream of apprenticeship as a printer. For there I should receive not a farthing in wages while I learned the trade till I was twenty-one, five years yet, during the which interval who would support my mother? And now from whom could I obtain the twenty pounds sterling as a prerequisite to such training? Surely not from any part of the thirty pounds due my mother as the lay accruing to my father up to the time of his death early in the *Dartmouth's* cruise. Far more than that, eighty pounds sterling to be exact, was owing already to Aunt Keziah for provisions and goods advanced us these last two years, and what little might be due us from the *Dartmouth*, my mother would certainly need for herself as an anchor to windward till I might earn something. And that I must do without delay, for no longer would our credit with Aunt Keziah or with anyone go so far as formerly. Thirty pounds, even on Nantucket, was no fortune on which one might for long live a life of ease.

What could I do? There was just one answer, but considering the tragedy that had just befallen us, I was loath for my mother's sake to broach the matter. Still I had need of haste were I not to lose my best opportunity. The *Beaver*, short one hand now that Henry was not going on her, was to sail next day; there might not be another ship as promising for months.

"Mother," I said timidly.

My mother stopped rocking, turned from her fixed gaze through the darkness at the *Dartmouth's* riding lights, to look at me with tear-dimmed eyes.

"Yes, my child?"

Child? That term, which she had not used toward me for some years, however unconsciously it came now to her lips

[19]

in her grief, was an ill beginning for what I had in mind, but there was no help for it.

"I'm not a child any more, mother—not after today," I continued. "I must be a man now, whether I would or no, and thank God, I may well pass anywhere as one."

"Yes, my child," agreed mother absently, resuming her rocking, and letting her eyes drift once more harborward, apparently too absorbed in her grief to note what I had said. Well she might be, I thought. Never again from the *Dartmouth* there, marked bow and stern by those gently swaying oil lanterns, nor from any other homecoming ship would my tall father spring ashore to crush her happily in his arms. No longer was the *Dartmouth*, heavily laden though she was with the casks of oil he had given his life to garner, any part of him. But still as the last visible thread tying him to living reality, her gaze clung to the anchored whaler, hardly hearing what I had said.

"Mother," I broke in desperately, "I'm sailing tomorrow with Cap'n Coffin in the *Beaver,* an' he will have me, which I think he will!"

What reply I expected to this outburst I hardly know, but I got none at all, which was perhaps as well. For an instant, the creaking rocker paused in its oscillations while my mother gave me one startled look, then without a word resumed her endless rocking with never another movement except to pass her hands occasionally across her eyes as if clearing them the better to see the lights shining through the darkness from the ships moored in the harbor.

4

ON the outgoing tide with her topsails aback before a light southerly breeze, the *Beaver* slowly fell away from Straight Wharf. From my station on the main yard ready to loose sail at the word, with bare toes desperately clutching the footrope and both hands clinging for dear life to the yardarm, I looked down across the widening gap of eddying water between ship and dock at the multitude of our townsmen waving hats and 'kerchiefs, wishing us God-speed from the fading land.

Anxiously my eyes searched the dock for my mother, but uselessly. The strain of watching her only son depart no doubt was more than she could bear, and evidently she had not come. Only one female figure on that wharf seemed to have any interest in me. Waving her bonnet frantically towards my elevated perch on the swaying yard, with upturned face and starry eyes stood my cousin Delight. As my glance, dizzily sweeping the end of the dock, met hers, I caught faintly through the multitude of shouts her girlish farewell,

"Greasy luck, Thomas!"

Perhaps I should have waved back at her, but just then prudence had to come before gallantry and in my precarious position, I decided I needed both hands for the present for myself. And so I stood motionless while we drew away and the sea of faces on the wharf merged into a vast indistinguishable blur of waving hats and fluttering 'kerchiefs.

We drifted gently out past Brant Point and across the sand bar to clear the harbor. As I tried to twist my toes about the footrope for a more secure grip, my eyes wandered apprehensively from the surging waters beneath me on the end of that main yard protruding far outboard beyond the bulwarks, to the stolid seaman on the other end of the yard who was to be my companion in the task of loosing the mainsail. I looked him over furtively, wondering if he knew any more about the job than I, and in startled amazement noted he was unquestionably an Indian! My heart sank. With an untutored savage on one end of the main yard and a raw landlubber on the other, God help the *Beaver* when the order came, as it did in another moment from the quarterdeck below. Jared Macy, the mate, roared out,

"Make sail! Loose the courses!"

The next few minutes on the *Beaver* were for me a bedlam of hoarsely bawled out orders from the poop, the whining of sheets and braces running through a multitude of creaking blocks as fore and aft, alow and aloft on every mast the heavy canvas fell from the yards and the yards themselves were braced sharply over to put us on the starboard tack. How I managed even to stay on the swinging yard as it slewed sharply forward when the mainsail filled beneath me I hardly know. And I am quite certain I did nothing useful on it other than to avoid crashing to the deck when the canvas suddenly bellied out below me. Everything needful on that yard was being done to my surprise by the nimble Indian inboard me who, apparently realizing my helpless plight, slid across on the footrope to loose the lashings on my end of the sail as well as on his. During all this I clung whitefaced to the erratically swaying spar when the *Beaver* began to roll to the incoming swells.

On deck again at last with the ship underway outward bound, I made myself as inconspicuous as possible in the lee of the mainmast while under the mate's eye the rest of the crew scurried about the deck in response to a stream of orders that were meaningless to me, setting taut innumerable lines on which I dared not lay a hand for fear of heaving on the wrong one and exposing myself to derision (and perhaps worse) for the helpless landlubber that I was. On any other type of vessel, this shirking of mine would hardly have been permitted, but on a whaler, overmanned of necessity by the need of carrying so many men for her whaleboat crews, there was no lack of hands on the sheets and braces, and Jared Macy, knowing well enough my situation, paid little attention to me just then.

We were underway. As the afternoon drew along, and as we rounded Great Point close hauled on the starboard tack and stood to the southward in a fresh breeze, I watched the low hills of Nantucket gradually sinking into the sea astern of us with a leaden heart. Never had I felt any special urge to go awhaling but now here I was, fairly launched upon the waves, with my hoped-for career as a printer sinking into oblivion along with those Nantucket hills dropping below the horizon. Whale oil, not printer's ink, was to be henceforth the fluid from which I must draw my sustenance. But as I leaned over the lee bulwark which was heeled well down to larboard and watched the *Beaver's* boiling wake stretch in a foaming scar across the tumbling waves to Nantucket, in my boyish heart the outlook loomed none too promising. For compared to what printer's ink had brought to my cousin Ben Franklin in the way of eminence, the tragedy that the pursuit of whale oil had already brought to my family bore dismally on my youthful mind. I wondered what my puny hands could do to whales, though I pursued them the rest of my days with harpoon and lance, that could ever remove from my mother's eyes that anguished look which the return of the *Dartmouth* had implanted there?

5

ON my first whaling cruise, I have not great cause to
dwell, nor have I reason to recall it with any pleasure, save
that it swiftly made a seaman of me.

My strange companion on the main yard when getting
underway I soon enough learned was a Gay Header, an Indian from the nearby island of Marthas Vineyard, rejoicing
in the Biblical appellation of Anthony Jeremiah, though in
no spiritual way recalling that Hebrew prophet whose name
he bore. For Red Jerry, as he was familiarly denominated
by his mates, was a seaman *par excellence,* and he it was
who took me in hand to initiate me into the mysteries of
brails and braces, halliards and topping lifts, sheets and
tacks, stu'n'sails and staysails, shrouds and spars, and all
the innumerable lines, whether in the standing or running
rigging, required in the management of the top hamper
which drove our lumbering hull under straining canvas
along through the foaming seas.

I marvel at the adaptability of man, for this red savage
(and savage he was inwardly) was as much at home in the
maze of tarred rigging with which civilization had bedizened
the *Beaver,* as ever his painted Narragansett ancestors were
amidst the trackless forests of our primeval New England.
A good seaman was Red Jerry to whom I owe much thanks,
for no father could ever have shown more genuine solicitude
than he in imparting to a lubberly boy his knowledge of seamanship. From that first instant when Red Jerry saw me
petrified on the yardarm and loosed sail for me, I somehow
became his protégé and his life and mine remained entangled
even, far from the *Beaver's* peaceful decks, amidst the roar
of thundering guns in foreign seas.

[24]

There was little of the noble savage and nothing at all reminiscent of the forest about Red Jerry. Bronzed like all his Indian brothers, but with an odd patina to his coppery complexion which years of facing salt spray in driving hurricanes and speeding whaleboats had overlaid his natural red, I never saw another Indian like him. Not quite so tall as I, he had nevertheless a pair of brawny shoulders and a barrel chest bespeaking amazing strength in his arms. If the resulting physique, giving him a squat appearance, does not meet the popular conception of what an Indian warrior should be for gliding like a shadow noiselessly through the forests after venison or the scalps of his enemies, at least it suited marvellously the pursuit in which Red Jerry found himself. No love of the sea had brought this savage aboard the *Beaver*, but simply that wild love of the chase which had come down to him through endless Indian generations. His Narragansett brethren now sequestered in filthy villages from the whites who had ravished them of their hunting grounds might be content to eke out for themselves a miserable existence by basket weaving and the like futile handicrafts, but not Red Jerry.

That magnificent set of arms and shoulders with which Nature had endowed him, opened for him a vista of the chase to dwarf the puny game his primogenitors had tracked, and of that fact my prudent Quaker neighbors on Nantucket like the keen merchants they were, had duly taken note. For Red Jerry was in their employ a harpooner, the wide oceans his hunting ground, the largest animal that ever breathed on land or sea his prey. The savage delight with which Red Jerry, poised in the bow of a whaleboat, flung his harpoon bespoke the pure joy of the wild hunter in the chase, undiluted with any mercenary considerations as to how many barrels of sperm oil might be boiled in the try-pots out of the blubber stripped from the huge victims of his barbed harpoon.

Out of the rest of the ship's company, I saw next to nothing of our Captain, whom Henry Gardner had so derisively dubbed "shad-belly," as the *Beaver* day after day ploughed

[25]

southward under full sail. To me, the three mates were the Lords of creation, according to whose whims life proceeded. Of these Jared Macy was first, or as custom has it, *the* mate, with Owen Swain and Jedidah Mayhew second and third respectively. Quakers all, it startled me to note, once the anchor was aweigh and they had shipped their seagoing faces, how little they resembled the staid Quakers I had taken them for amongst their friends and families in sober, God-fearing Nantucket.

I came to know Jared Macy best. Lean, sharp featured, hard of face and hard of heart, as the mate he had first choice of harpooners for his boat and he chose Red Jerry. A harpooner (dubbed also a boat-steerer) is himself something of an officer aboard a spouter, living and messing aft with the mates, and relied on by the mate whose boat he heads in the chase, and consequently influential with that mate. As a result apparently of Red Jerry's suggestion, I found myself assigned also to the mate's boat but to my dismay appointed by that worthy, who was deceived no doubt by my lanky frame, to pull the stroke oar in his whaleboat. For the moment, that meant little, as we were not soon likely to lower for any whales, but I looked with much foreboding to the time when directly under the mate's eye as he manned the steering oar, I must justify my size in setting the stroke as we drove headlong after our first whale.

What there is in the exercise of authority that corrupts most men's souls I have often pondered since that boyhood cruise on the *Beaver*, but to no purpose. Many times on land and sea since those days I have seen the unrestrained possession of power turn the wielder thereof into a petty tyrant revelling in his ability to render life a hell for those subordinate to him, and vividly do I remember Jared Macy for that. What need there was for the harsh words and the abuse he spewed out upon the seamen in his watch with his every order, I could never see. And the malignity with which he kept us weary sailors busy on useless tasks passed all understanding.

That a ship should be kept clean, her gear taut and neatly

[26]

flemished down, her boats in order, was as clear to me as that my mother should desire the like in her own housekeeping, but I failed to comprehend what rhyme or reason there might be in driving us endlessly to scrub and swab down decks which were already immaculate merely that we might not have an idle daylight moment on our hands. And to be driven to it amidst a stream of blasphemous oaths, alert all the time to avoid a stinging lash from the stout rope end swinging menacingly in the mate's fist in the direction of any pair of shoulders which seemed to him not to be sufficiently vigorous behind a swab or holystone, soon grew to me to be almost unbearable.

I quickly gathered from the uncomplaining reactions of my shipmates that this custom was common enough at sea. Off their toughened backs both words and blows alike rolled unheeded. Fortunately I managed with Red Jerry's tutelage (who as a harpooner was himself immune from such jobs) to apply myself to my tasks well enough to avoid the rope's end. But the language which I could not escape, even though none of the blows welted my back, seared my youthful soul. I developed for Jared Macy a murderous hatred that would have shocked even Red Jerry had he suspected that as I fingered his harpoon, being instructed in the mysteries thereof, I balanced it in my hand thinking not so much of burying it in the blubbery flank of a whale, as of some day catching Jared Macy in the midst of his blasphemies lined fairly up with the base of the mainmast and pinning him thereto with one powerful cast of that razor-edged iron.

However, under that harsh discipline and the harder work that went with it, my youthful form toughened rapidly as we went south. Watch and watch during the night, four hours on, four hours off, with the broken sleep resulting therefrom, and all hands on deck during the day with never a moment free to catch up on lost slumber, will either toughen a body or very quickly kill him. Each night of my first week when my watch ended, as I wearily dragged my tortured limbs into my bunk, hands blistered and raw from hauling on briny lines, every joint aching from the back breaking toil of handling soaked canvas aloft or muling stores up from the hold, I bemoaned the fate which had made me a sailor instead of a printer.

But after that week, as my hands grew somewhat calloused, my muscles somewhat hardened, and most of all, as my mind absorbed the tricks of the trade in which I found myself and rapidly applied that knowledge to save my back, with the resilience of youth I began to take a keener interest in the real object of our voyage and to consider how, if I was to be a whaler, I might soonest rise in that profession at least to the dignity of harpooner if not indeed to that of officer.

Simple arithmetic made the need of that quite evident, even if I had been wholly lacking otherwise in ambition. During the day, with all hands turned to on deck, there was little opportunity for any thought. But in the interminable night watches, when except for the lookout forward and the helmsman on the quarterdeck aft alongside the mate, the rest of the watch awaiting any order to trim sail was clustered amidships in the lee of the try-pots sheltering themselves from the wind, I had ample time for cogitations on the more commercial aspects of whaling.

We should, with reasonable luck, come home in the *Beaver* after three years with 2400 barrels of oil, worth some thirty shillings to the barrel. Of that cargo, since I had the two-hundredth lay, my share would be 12 barrels, or £18 for my three years work, surely no munificent reward for the racking toil and the hard words I had endured meanwhile, let alone the dangers I had yet to face in gaining it.

But if I could ever rise to the dignity of harpooner, then indeed my situation would improve mightily. For on the skill and recklessness of the harpooners rested heavily the success of our voyage, and to encourage the exercise of those qualities the lay of the harpooners was made alluringly large— the twentieth lay, ten times what I as humble seaman was to receive, being their reward. The twentieth lay! One hundred and twenty barrels of sperm oil, should we have greasy luck, the gain of each harpooner! That was even more than allot-

[28]

ted the three mates, who drew but a twenty-fifth, thirty-fifth, and fifty-fifth lay respectively.

In the dreary night watches as the waves foamed up about the *Beaver's* bluff forefoot and eddied aft in the darkness along her heeled-down lee rail, I fingered imaginatively the rough wood shaft of Red Jerry's harpoon and pictured myself flinging it unerringly into the glistening backs of endless spouting whales with never a miss. I saw my twentieth lay swelling steadily as the oil poured from the try-pots down into the casks below in the hold, to fill them till not another drop of sperm oil could we stow anywhere aboard the overladen *Beaver*, not even in the galley kettles or in the emptied vials of the ship's medicine chest.

Affectionately I fondled that dream in all the confidence of my sixteen years. I must rise as rapidly as possible to harpooner. I was already tall and might well expect at my age quickly to add even a few more inches to my stature. That would give me a leverage for hurling a harpoon that might well compensate for the fact that I could never hope to match the deep-chested breadth of shoulders that distinguished Red Jerry.

But my ambition did not stop at harpooner. After all, there was the Captain with the largest lay of any, exceeding even that of the harpooners. The one-sixteenth lay fell to him, plus a bonus besides from the owners for an unusually successful voyage. What I could do for my mother with the one-sixteenth lay and such a bonus as I should surely earn as Captain, entranced me! In my ignorance I passed lightly over the years of experience in whaling necessary to gain the background that a Captain must have for judging proper whaling grounds as the seasons varied and the migratory whales made passage hither and yon across the trackless seas. What more a Captain needed than a harpooner was quite obvious to me—simply three inhuman mates to relieve him of the care of the ship, and some knowledge of navigation. For the only task on deck I ever saw that engaged the seldom-seen Hezekiah Coffin was a daily shot at the sun just

[29]

before meridian with his cumbrous quadrant to determine our latitude, though how, if at all, he determined our longitude I could not imagine.

My knowledge of arithmetic already acquired was equal I felt sure to that of anyone on board. I had little doubt that if I could only obtain an instructor who took as much interest in me as did Red Jerry, and who knew navigation as well as that savage knew the art of the harpooner, I might swiftly enough gain all I lacked to qualify me as a master mariner.

But before the problem of finding that instructor aboard the *Beaver*, my heart sank. Just two men encompassed in her company had that coveted knowledge—Captain Coffin and the mate. For the second and third mates were themselves hardly more than glorified seamen, knowing no more of navigation than I, and perhaps even less of arithmetic. But in my fierce hatred of Jared Macy, I could as soon have brought myself to asking aid of Satan himself as of the mate. And as for the Captain, to me he was, though the comparison seem somewhat blasphemous, as inaccessible in the sanctity of cabin and quarterdeck as God in Heaven, and very evidently far less interested in my welfare and advancement.

In the face of this Scylla and Charybdis thus guarding, so far as I was concerned, the passage to a knowledge of navigation, I gave up as hopeless the thought of gaining any this voyage and fell back on my dream of becoming a harpooner. After all, I consoled myself, arithmetically there was no great loss in this. The twentieth lay that fell to a harpooner was but slightly inferior to the sixteenth lay that fell to the Captain's lot. The difference between the two was but the equal of the eightieth lay. This I arrived at after some fumbling with my mental arithmetic, there being no pencil at hand for work in vulgar fractions in the midwatch nor indeed any light on that spray-swept deck had I had a pencil.

This trifling difference I was inclined at first to dismiss as insignificant in determining my aspirations in life. Then suddenly I recalled that my actual lay for the voyage was none of the magnificent fractions I was juggling in my dreams but plainly and unmistakably only the two-hundredth lay. The difference in lays between Captain and harpooner which I was so cavalierly dismissing was of itself two and a half times as great as all I could hope to obtain from the voyage. I came sharply down out of the clouds in which my mind had been wandering to lean limply back in the black night against the *Beaver's* awash lee rail and contemplate mentally the vast gulfs which separated my humble position on board from the pecuniary affluence of either Red Jerry or Hezekiah Coffin.

Still at sixteen, even on the heaving deck of a spouter hammering along close hauled through head seas in the darkness, the future ever looks bright, and I soon recovered from the shock which my delving into fractions had dealt me. There was no use butting my head against the impasse of learning navigation this cruise. Obviously then I was not going to return home three years hence at nineteen Captain of the *Beaver* even though in the interim some helpful spermaceti should accommodate me in making the vacancy by fanning Captain Coffin off his own quarterdeck with one mighty sweep of his flukes. Nevertheless, to my young imagination, becoming a harpooner seemed still to be within the bounds of possibility and on that I determined to concentrate. And on the twentieth lay that went with it.

Eight bells, sharp and clear, echoed metallically in pairs through the night. The midwatch was over at last. Down the forecastle hatch echoed the hoarse cry,

"On deck all the starbowlines! Shake a leg below!"

As the new watch tumbled up and relieved us, I stumbled below thankfully to the faintly lighted forecastle, tossed aside my spray-soaked jacket, and with my bared feet still as wet as when they left the deck, clambered hurriedly up into my stuffy bunk in the topmost tier and rolled in. Instantly harpoons, navigation, lays and all their fractional relations were forgotten. Sleep, blessed sleep, was all that mattered to me. Truly the seaman's vision of Paradise is that spot where he may have all night in, with never an ungentle voice bursting raucously out to summon him on deck for the next watch.

6

WE approached the Cape Verde Islands, a favorite whaling ground. Carefully each whaleboat was fitted out for its task. The amount of gear stowed into those boats surprised me. Five oars, of course, of varying lengths, and as many paddles; a long steering oar; mast and sail; two harpoons and two lances; several wood drags; a small cask of fresh water and another of hard biscuit; a boat box; a short handled blubber spade; and most prominent of all objects in the boat, looking like a vast cheese in a tub, the harpoon line.

In fascination I watched Red Jerry coil down that harpoon line into the tub of our boat. Two hundred fathoms in length, almost two inches in circumference, spun of the finest golden brown hemp, strong enough to sustain a three ton strain, was that whale line. I ran one end up the rigging to the masthead, through a block there, and down again to the deck alongside the line tub before Red Jerry deigned to begin the coiling, so finical was he that he have a long fair lead of line free of all twists, turns, or possible kinks.

The coiling commenced. Into the bottom of that three foot diameter wooden tub, Red Jerry laid down a smooth spiral layer of hemp like a huge concentric scroll till the tight coils covered the entire base, then continued to the next layer above. All the time as we hauled down line from the masthead block, he delicately fingered it in his calloused hands for the slightest indication of any twist or turn in the lay of the hempen strands which might, when it uncoiled from the tub, cause it to kink or run out foul in tangled coils.

I needed little imagination to justify the extreme pains taken by Red Jerry in coiling those hempen turns down upon each other till the tub was filled to the top with the

[33]

whole two hundred fathom length of hemp, a most meticulously built up layer cake. For that line, which led from the tub aft to the loggerhead in the stern of our whaleboat and then forward over the oars between the oarsmen to the bow chock where the outboard end of the line was attached to the harpoon, would go singing out like unleashed lightning should the whale sound when he was struck. Any foul turn, if the line did not run out true, might well loop itself about an arm, a leg, or a neck to yank the unlucky possessor thereof overboard into the depths after the sounding whale before he had any knowledge of what was happening to him, let alone the slightest opportunity to do anything to free himself of the deadly coil.

No, neither I nor Manuel Sylvia nor Obed Hussey nor Peleg Coleman (the other three members of that boat's crew) feeding the line carefully along to Red Jerry to be coiled down, begrudged him any second of the long hours he thought proper for the completion of his task. It was past our necks as we sat at the oars, that twisted hemp was going to sing, once the harpoon was darted. Naturally we took the liveliest interest in the skill and care with which it was flaked down.

With all on deck ready, boats stowed, boat falls overhauled and clear for running out from the clumsy wooden davits secured to our bulwarks, the three boat crews told off, nothing needful remained now for the commencement of our labors except the whales.

It must not be believed that the lack of whales was due to any laxity on Captain Hezekiah's part in keeping a weather eye out for any sign of them. We had hardly cleared Nantucket Shoals when the *Beaver's* mastheads were manned, and every daylight hour from then on at both fore and main topgallant crosstrees a seaman was perched, scanning the waves out to the far horizon for the thin crested spout of vapor that denoted a blowing whale.

Fortunately for me, my own first watch at the masthead did not come until we were some two weeks out, and I had had opportunity to gain both some sea legs and some confidence aloft or I might well never have survived it.

To any landsman, even the deck of a vessel rolling and heaving as she breasts the seas and heels to the winds, is an unsubstantial footing, like enough to make him squeamish. What then must be the sensation, over a hundred feet above the waves, perched only on the thin crosstrees, clutching for support only the trifling royal mast behind, with every slightest motion of the hull magnified by the tremendous leverage of practically the whole length of swaying mast swinging like a huge inverted pendulum from the ship below?

There may or may not have been whales spouting about while I stood my first masthead. I was in no way interested in them. With my bared feet pressed firmly down on the fore topgallant crosstrees, my back solidly jammed against that tapering timber behind me called the royal mast, and my two hands clutched in a death grip behind my back about that slippery stick, my sole concern as I swayed there suspended between sky and sea with my jacket streaming in the breeze, was to hang on. Somehow I had managed before to escape seasickness down on deck, but the motion far aloft was too much for me and my stomach immediately revolted at such treatment. A few sharp rolls to leeward and a sudden upward heave as the *Beaver's* forefoot lifted to a wave, set my mouth awatering unpleasantly. I was hardly fully conscious of that when the ensuing dizzy drop into the following trough of the sea brought on catastrophe. Without even a premonitory gulp, my outraged stomach wholeheartedly disgorged its contents, which as best I might I spewed to leeward, the while in my weakened state I strove to maintain my perch.

Completely miserable, from then on I clung to the mast behind me, fearful on each roll of losing my grip and being catapulted off to go hurtling down a hundred feet past bellying sails into the foaming seas below. But even retching proved no relief, for the motion of that lofty masthead continued unabated and it soon seemed my stomach itself was striving desperately with each plunge of our hull to rise up in my throat and separate itself from my tortured body.

[35]

Thoroughly sick physically, thoroughly terrified mentally, gulping and gagging I weaved erratically athwartships and up and down through vast arcs of space with every twist of that swaying mast. Had all the whales in creation spouted round about the *Beaver* then, my glazed eyes and terrified brain would have taken not the slightest note of them.

Befouled by my own retchings and sick from the odors thereof, with mouth soured and teeth set on edge from the passage upwards of half-digested food, with watering eyes and a greenish hue suffusing my face, I lay down from aloft at the end of my first masthead watch as woebegone an object as may possibly be imagined. I was completely heedless of any desire save to crawl immediately into my bunk, and there, should God be merciful to me, to die as speedily as might be. But such is the heartlessness with which such suffering is regarded aboard ship that four hours later, when the next watch was called, I was callously dragged from my bunk by the seaman I was to relieve to stagger feebly on deck. There when I unwittingly passed to windward of Jared Macy, I was promptly soused with a bucket of salt water by the mate whose nostrils were no doubt grossly offended by my aroma, and rudely admonished,

"Keep well to leeward when ye pass me, ye stinking pig, or next time I'll heave thee overboard!"

Gasping and choking from the stinging water, now indeed was the opportune moment when I might with full warrant have seized a harpoon from the rack abreast the mainmast and pinned that devil to it. But no such vengeful gesture even faintly entered my mind. Instead, wan and wretched, I slid feebly down the inclined deck to the *Beaver's* lee rail to hang across it with the eddying water seething past but a few feet beneath me, heaving up my very insides in one agonizing spasm of retching after another.

My plight while seasick was worse on the *Beaver* than is usual. Misery indeed loves company, and it may well be that the sight of others suffering similarly might have ameliorated somewhat my own distress. But being the only landsman aboard, I had not even that slight comfort. As for any sympathy from my mates, I got if anything only derision, for to the seaman nothing is more humorous apparently than this malady in landsmen. Rough jests from Manuel and Obed, with various suggested remedies hinging about coarse foods, the mere mention of which immediately turned my stomach again, were all the help I received as I forlornly staggered from one task to another between involuntary dashes to the rail, until at last I could once again creep into my bunk. Should I ever live to see the shore again—any shore—nothing I knew could tempt me again aboard a vessel.

7

THROUGH somewhat fairer weather, we drove along the following week so that I recuperated amazingly, and, though salt water is no great cleanser and fresh water was not to be had, I managed by long continued scrubbing to restore my body and my clothing to some degree of cleanliness.

The *Beaver's* deck upon the seventh day took on more animation. I turned out with my watch to find the whole after guard—mates, harpooners, and even, wonder of wonders, Captain Coffin—on deck before me, all sniffing the breeze eagerly.

"Mastheads, there! There's whales about!" sang out Captain Coffin, tilting his head far back. "Look alive! A pound of tobacco for the first man sights a blow!"

Whales about? A little apprehensively I hastily scanned the sea. The breeze was moderate; the waves, sparkling beneath the sun, crested here and there with a little foam; the *Beaver* butted along at perhaps six knots as usual. All in all, except that the weather was better than any we had yet had, I could see no difference from any other day when we had seen no whales, and certainly there were no spouts anywhere visible.

Whether the experienced sense of smell of our veteran whalers really detected anything, or whether between our position and the sea conditions their experience indicated the probability of seeing spouts thereabouts, I know not. But there could be no doubt they all believed action imminent, for Red Jerry and the other harpooners were lovingly honing the barbed heads of their harpoons to a razor edge. And nearby them, similarly engaged, Jared Macy and the second and third mates were whetting the heart shaped points of their long lances, those slender iron probes intended, once a fish is fastened to with a harpoon, to let the life out of him by repeated thrusts through blubber and body into his vitals.

When our weapons had been sharpened to everyone's satisfaction, into each boat they went, two harpoons resting handily in a forked crotch protruding over every whaleboat's starboard bow, with the wicked looking points of the lances close beside on the opposite bow.

Still nothing was reported from aloft. But nevertheless as if sure of seeing something soon, the skipper kept on with his preparations. Once the boats were lowered, there would be few men left aboard to handle ship—only the Captain, the cooper, and the cook—and accordingly we briskly shortened sails. The stu'n'sails, which we had set in the light breeze, giving us the appearance of a huge bird with wings spread wide over the seas skimming just above the waves, were struck. The stu'n'sail booms were run in and secured. Up went the courses, to be triced swiftly to the lower yards. Down came the flying jibs. On fore and main the topgallant sails were furled, which also gave those at the mastheads a clearer view all about. In a brief time under topsails, spanker on the mizzen, and jib alone at much reduced speed the bluff-bowed *Beaver* ploughed along.

For the first time in my experience during any daylight hours, once sail was reduced and the topmen all back on deck, we were not greeted by the harsh call,

"Turn to! Scrub down!"

Instead, from aft where Hezekiah Coffin stood with his broad-brimmed hat shielding his wide sheep-like face, staring off to the eastward into the sun on our larboard bow looking for the anticipated spouts, came subtle bribery.

"A golden guinea to the man on deck who sings out for a blow ere the mastheads cry it! 'Tis his, provided only that we take the whale!"

A golden guinea! I caught my breath. That was more than the part of my lay for a whole month's work might bring me. Instantly I sprang into the lower fore shrouds to scan the waves for any puff of vapor. Nor was I alone. Every seaman, including even the cook and the cooper, followed suit to plaster the shrouds with sailors clinging like monkeys to the lower rigging, eagerly searching for spouts. Only the mates, the helmsman, and the harpooners took no part.

So for some hours we sailed on in silence, sighting nothing save an occasional crest breaking here and there to leave a little patch of white foam on the blue sea. At last the cook, grumbling audibly that that guinea would never be his, dropped off the main shrouds to the deck, and disappeared into the galley. He had his meals to get, spouts or no. Among the others, straining eyes began to weary and to blink under the glare of the sun reflected back from the sea, and attention began to wander, though no man left his perch.

But my eyes were young and I had faith that they were keener than any others aboard, enough so perhaps to offset even the advantage height gave those at the mastheads in range of vision. Aside from which, the Captain's offered gold meant more to me than to the others if I should be able to lay that guinea proudly in my mother's hand as the first fruits of my whaling. So with undiminished vigor, sector by sector in order, time and again I searched out endlessly to the very horizon, the vast circle of the heaving seas surrounding us.

A faint iridescence glimmering an instant among the distant waves on our lee quarter caught my eye. For many a man on the *Beaver* it would have been better had my eyes been duller that day and missed that glint, for no one else alow or aloft saw it, and with the ship steadily drawing away from it, would ever have seen it. And radically different would have been my own life had that infinitesimal rainbow in the sun escaped my glance.

But there it was, an instant's glitter topping the far off crests, and then nothing. With eyes riveted on that spot, afraid almost to breathe, I waited some few seconds, to see then a thin stream of vapor rise slightly above the waves, spread like a nebulous umbrella, fade.

"There she blows!" I sang out, almost splitting my throat that no one should get ahead of me in my claim to that guinea. "She blows, she b-l-o-w-s!" Ecstatically to the last breath of air in my lungs I dragged out that "blows" as once again I saw the cresting spout rise up. Our first spout, and I had first sung out for it! "There on the lee quarter! There she blows!"

Instantly the silent *Beaver* came alive, but ere the men clustered in the rigging with me could scramble down, from the quarterdeck came a roar from the skipper.

"Hard up with the helm!" and then, "Man the braces, Mr. Macy! Stand by to wear!" after which Captain Coffin, shedding all his dignity, with surprising agility came rushing forward, coattails flying, to scramble up the fore shrouds beside me, peering off the larboard quarter.

"How far, lad?" he breathed hoarsely.

"Perhaps five miles, sir!" I estimated hastily. "There, again! Near the horizon, broad off the lee quarter!"

But already the lumbering *Beaver* was beginning to pay off to leeward as the helmsman spun his wheel and on deck under the mate's sharp orders, the laboring crew hastily slacked away on the lee sheets and braces of our canvas and hove taut on the windward ones, so that gradually the spouts began to haul forward along our larboard beam.

"Five miles?" Captain Coffin, who had been shading his eyes, straining for a sight of what I saw, dropped his hand. "Too far for my eyes without a glass." Still clutching the ratlines, he lifted his shaggy head.

"Mastheads, there!" he bellowed. "D'ye make it out yet?"

But from both mastheads came the same response,

"Nary a blow, Cap'n!"

That with the ship now swinging, the lookouts should not pick up amongst the waste of waves those tiny far off spouts which they had not previously spotted, was not surprising to me, but it made the Captain furious.

"Down from aloft, ye lubbers!" shrieked the skipper. "Lookouts, indeed! Thou'rt both blinder than bats! Down

[41]

on deck, where at least thy carcasses may serve to heave on the sheets!" Hezekiah Coffin paused a moment for breath the while he observed his order was obeyed, then lowered his massive head and in a much kindlier tone, said to me,

"Thou hast the best eyes on the ship, lad, and the wit to use them too, I see. Thou'lt make a whaler soon, e'en better than thy father who was e'er a credit to the Folgers. Up to the masthead with thee now, and con ship for those spouts as we come about!"

"Aye, aye, sir!" In another second I was skimming up the ratlines to the foretop, there to disregard the lubber's hole, swarm agilely over the outer edge of that platform, and go racing up the topmast shrouds, my heart aflame under the skipper's praise. I literally shot up the swaying ladder to the topgallant masthead, wasting hardly a second to get a grip on the shrouds there before I was searching the sea again, off the larboard beam now, for I judged we had swung off that much from the wind since starting to come about.

From that elevation as against my previous post, I had little difficulty in picking up the spouts. Once again I raised the cry,

"There she blows! Broad off the larboard beam!" as, regularly as clockwork, every ten seconds that far off fountain sprayed amongst the waves.

Below me the yards swayed smartly over as our stern came up into the wind, the jib fluttered over to starboard, and the crew below set taut the sheets and braces to keep the *Beaver* off before the wind on our larboard quarter, headed fairly for those spouts, which in accordance with my directions shouted from the masthead, Captain Coffin soon had lined up dead over our jibboom. But hardly had the *Beaver* steadied on her new course when over the spot where that fountain had been playing, there reared suddenly up some thirty feet above the sea, a glistening tapered tail! I saw a pair of wide black flukes wave gracefully a moment against the horizon, and then swiftly they sank vertically from my sight. The spouting ceased, of course.

Immediately from on deck, where dead ahead of us this sudden apparition was instantly spotted, there came up to me in a rough chorus the cry,

"There goes flukes!"

The whale had sounded.

For some sixty minutes, I knew, that whale would stay below and we should see no more of him. Only a disturbed patch of white water still nearly five miles off marked his vanishing. How near to that spot he would rise no one could tell.

Shortly the cooper, crabbed Zenas Joy, more of a craftsman than a seaman, came toiling up the shrouds to relieve me at the masthead, now that the position of that whale was well established. Disdaining the slow descent on the shrouds, down the royal backstay with legs wound tightly about it to brake my speed somewhat, I dropped like a plummet to the deck, all eagerness to be promptly on hand for my place in the bow boat. But I might have saved myself the burned palms on my hands and the tarred streak on my trousers that swift descent left me with. Not for an hour could we hope for another sight of spouts, and we needed all that hour under our shortened sail to run down the wind to where that whale had last flirted his tail before sounding.

But in my boyish enthusiasm, nothing of this deterred me. Hardly had I swayed inboard as I came streaking down that backstay to clear the bulwark and drop out of the rigging to the deck, than I was running forward to take my place alongside the bow boat, lest it get away without me.

"Good lad," grunted Red Jerry, giving me a pat on the back as I arrived. "Done like seaman."

I flushed with pride. So Red Jerry had noted my avoidance of the lubber's hole in the foretop going up; my avoidance of the ratlines coming down. Somehow I felt that pat on the back from him was my accolade, the recognition of my emergence as a sailor. But too breathless for any answer, I merely leaned against the bulwark beneath our boat swinging overhead from its cranes, ready at the word to leap overboard as it went down.

[43]

Slowly the minutes dragged away till that hour was nearly gone and we had covered some three miles of the space intervening to where my whale had sounded. Except for the groaning of the rigging and the slight splash of the waves rippling under our forefoot, a deep silence shrouded the *Beaver*. No man spoke. I believe even breathing was unconsciously restrained as all about, twenty-one pairs of eyes tensely scrutinized the sea ahead for the first sign of that rising fish.

Then simultaneously from Zenas Joy at the masthead and from every throat on deck rose the cry,

"There she white-waters!"

A mile, perhaps, on our larboard bow came a boiling on the surface of the sea, then a mass of foam and spray falling away from a gleaming black hump, and immediately a fountain sprayed into the air, spread, dissipated like a vagrant mist. There was my whale, smooth and black as a shapeless mound of india rubber, swimming majestically to windward away from us, a solitary bull spouting regularly as he went, apparently at peace with all the world.

Instantly down went our helm to bring us as nearly as might be into his wake; and soon close hauled we followed seemingly at about his speed since, so far as I could judge, the *Beaver* neither closed nor opened on him. A moment thus I gazed ahead at that vast bulk, awestruck and open-mouthed, and then at my elbow I caught a sharp intake of breath. There was Jared Macy, covetously eyeing that whale, muttering,

"The biggest bull in all creation! A hundred and fifty barrels of oil if he's a drop!"

Just then, Captain Coffin, himself manning the wheel, luffed sharply to deaden the ship's headway. As we swung idly up into the wind and our topsails began to flap, with no hint of the Quaker in his voice, he bellowed,

"Remember, lads! A dead whale or a stove boat! Lower away!"

Immediately all along the larboard side, the boat falls started to run out. The bow boat dropped from the davit heads, came abreast the bulwarks. Over the rail into the falling boat in one mass shot the mate, Red Jerry, Obed Hussey and I, while at the davit cleats, Manuel, the Portuguese, and Peleg Coleman slacked sharply off. In another second, the boat hit the water, the falls slackened. Red Jerry at the bow and the mate in the stern cast loose, at which Peleg and Manuel came sliding pell-mell down the side of the ship to join us. A sharp shove bow and stern and we were clear of the hull, towering now alongside us. Out went our sweeps, the mate shipped his long steering oar astern, gave us a sharp sheer out, cried,

"Give way!"

Our five oars splashed into the water, and I lay back with all my weight on mine. Swinging under the *Beaver's* jib-boom, scarce clear of the dolphin striker, we straightened away for the chase, while astern of us I could see our other two boats still struggling on her weather side to swing clear of our ship which was now falling off from the wind to fill sails again and stand on, tacking after us as best she might.

But even that vagrant glance of mine astern was too much for Jared Macy.

"Keep thine eyes on me, lad!" he ordered harshly. "Ye've work to do. Lay back, now!" The mate's body began to sway slightly back and forth in the rhythm of the stroke, speeding it up.

"Pull, all!" shouted Macy. "Heave an' break them oars! Lean into it, ye've hardly bent 'em yet! Pull an' shear the tholepins off! We'll never overhaul that fish this way! Lift her!"

I clenched my teeth, braced my bared heels against the bottom boards, tugged with all my might. That fish was mine, I had first raised his spout, if human endurance could lay a whaleboat alongside him, then that boat should be the one I stroked. I was no weakling, even at sixteen; with my lanky body and long arms, I was fitted for an oarsman if ever anyone was. Back and forth I swung on the thwart, tugging with fierce determination on that ash oar, bending it perceptibly each stroke in spite of what the mate said to the contrary.

Behind me, regardless of how good or poor I might be myself, I had four good oarsmen. The solid thump each stroke of oars against tholepins, muffled though they were in marline mats to deaden the sound, was proof of that, had not the way our whaleboat leaped ahead each lusty heave otherwise showed it. But best of all, there was evidence indisputable astern of us. For aft, unless I closed my eyes wholly, I could not avoid seeing that we were steadily drawing away from our other two boats, in spite of all the lurid profanity which drifted across the waves to me as in those boats, Owen Swain and Jedidah Mayhew urged their respective rowers on in our wake.

Endlessly we heaved. Just behind me, hampered somewhat by the line tub stowed at his feet, I could hear the labored breath of Obed Hussey stroking the larboard side, and even that of Peleg Coleman in the waist behind Obed, pulling the longest oar in the boat, a massive sixteen foot sweep. I gave fervent thanks that as stroke, the oar I had thrust out to starboard was but twelve feet in length, for even that, after some five minutes pulling on it, gave me the feeling that I had hold the butt of a young tree.

But however it felt, I could hardly give it my undivided attention. There in the sternsheets facing me was Jared Macy clinging to the steering oar, not for an instant pausing in his weird harangue. Bullying, pleading, cursing, aye, strangely enough even praying occasionally, he bent over us. Not if the fate of all humanity hung on the result, could he have been more wholeheartedly engrossed in making us pull harder.

"Break something, damn your eyes!" he cursed. "A hundred an' fifty barrels o' sperm ahead o' ye, and ye're letting it open on ye as if ye were backing water! Heave and break something! If ye can't break the oars, break the tholepins then, they're smaller! Only heave, my babies! Carry away something! An' if ye can't break anything else, heave an' break your worthless backs! What? Nothing broken yet?

Afraid to hurt the boat? Pull, damn your lazy hides! Pull, an' tear out the gunwales; the owners won't mind! Oil's all they want, an' the devil take the boat an' all that's in her! Pull an' start her!"

We pulled with panting lungs and straining muscles, rowing our hearts out. It was not that what Jared Macy said made any difference; it was his manner of saying it. Hypnotically almost, he ruled us, with a maniacal gleam in his fiery eyes literally moulding us to his will.

How well we were making out as against our fish, there was, of course, no way of judging. Only the mate could see forward toward the whale, and from his ravings as we bucked into the head seas, I could only guess that we, the worst boat's crew he had ever seen in all his years of whaling, were steadily losing despite the aching muscles, panting lungs, and throbbing temples behind the oars. My heart grew as leaden as my tired hands and my dreams of that golden guinea faded. For there was a catch to Hezekiah Coffin's offer. It was not enough that I had raised a blow; we had to land that whale "fin out" alongside the *Beaver*, ere I earned it. I clenched my teeth hopelessly. So this was whaling! Lavishing our very heart's blood toiling at those oars, only to be cursed by Jared Macy as futile idlers, unable to overhaul a leisurely swimming whale!

But soon by his increasing frenzy, I knew Jared Macy was deceiving us—we were gaining! And to make it certain, mingled with the muffled thumping of our oars I detected now a new sound—an odd puffing from ahead amazingly like a blacksmith's bellows suddenly sucking in and then slowly expelling vast gulps of air. We must be nearing the whale.

I had an irresistible impulse to turn my head for a glimpse, but some infinitesimal motion of my eyes must have betrayed my intention. Ere I had even begun to twist my neck, those eyes glittering fanatically above me in the sternsheets fastened on mine, and Jared Macy snarled,

"Eyes on me an' offen that whale, or I'll lather thy head with the tiller! Lay back on that oar, damn ye!"

That the hysterical mate meant his threat literally and

was prepared instantly to carry it out was perfectly obvious. Prudently I resisted my impulse to look and estimate for myself what danger we were driving ourselves into. Instead, with every remaining ounce of strength, I lay back to drive us after the whale.

Jared Macy leaned against his steering oar, sheered us slightly out to starboard. Immediately I saw we must be close aboard our fish, for there a little to larboard of the wash left by our oars and whaleboat now was a separate wake in the waves. And once we were straightened away again parallel to it and a little clear, an abrupt termination came to the mate's loud exhortations.

"Silence, now!" he whispered, as if before it had been we roaring out like demons possessed instead of himself. "Not a word from any of ye, or ye'll gally that whale! Quiet, only pull now if ye love me!"

The incongruity of this after all which had gone before, at that moment escaped me, for just then out of the corner of my eye in the water to larboard I vaguely glimpsed some massive object slithering forward in a queer corkscrewing motion beneath the surface. Flukes! But obediently I heaved harder as if pleasing Jared Macy were my heart's desire.

"Stand up, Jerry!" hissed the mate. I heard a slight commotion in the bow as Red Jerry shipped his oar, faced hurriedly about, seized his harpoon and braced his left leg against the forward thwart. Abaft him, facing Jared Macy's contorted visage, we four remaining oarsmen clenched our teeth and heaved on our oars, the while Red Jerry, black hair streaming now in the breeze, black eyes glittering as they lighted on that vast shining hump before him, balanced himself in the bow of the leaping whaleboat, both hands clutching the wood shaft of his harpoon poised high above his head.

Jared Macy jerked his steering oar sharply to starboard, sheered the boat suddenly in toward the whale, roared out, all caution gone,

"Once again, lift her! Beach me on yon hump!"

With a last frenzied jerk, we at the oars lay back together. The boat leaped forward, struck something, lifted in the bow as if grounding on a rock.

"Give it to him, Jerry!" shrieked the mate.

Down came the Indian's harpoon. With a wild whoop that fairly split my ear drums, Red Jerry drove home the iron to the hitches, leaving in view only the violently quivering wood shaft protruding from that black skin. And as his hands let go, with one lightning motion he swept from the crotch beside him the second iron, without a pause swung it aloft and darted that also fiercely down into the gleaming back beneath him.

Everything after that happened simultaneously. Alongside us, the startled whale rolled violently sidewise, setting up a terrible wash. Our boat heaved up and then slid dizzily away to starboard, almost pitching Red Jerry out. Jared Macy in the stern, raging like a madman, was shouting,

"Stern all! Stern, for your lives!" and we four oarsmen on the thwarts in that crazily rocking boat were trying desperately to bury our blades in the foaming water that we might obey and get clear. I had hardly got a grip with my oar on something that felt enough like solid water to start to back, when so close beside the careening boat that I might have touched it, there reared suddenly up from the sea the vast tail of the harpooned monster, soaring full forty feet above the surface, flinging both the larboard oars up into the air like straws in the wind.

Too terrified to move a muscle, I gazed upward at the mammoth body topped by those massive flukes waving awesomely against the sky above, expecting momentarily to see them come flailing down on our helpless boat to crush us into jelly. No use to row now. With no larboard oars, neither backing nor pulling ahead on the starboard side would do anything save pivot us about into even closer contact with that vast bulk beside us.

In that horrifying moment, only Red Jerry made any move. Reaching across the larboard gunwale as coolly as if that rearing spermaceti were but an inanimate ebony pedestal, he planted his doubled up left leg solidly against the whale's exposed belly, burying it in the blubber, then straightened it suddenly out with a vicious kick that sent the whaleboat flying astern and clear enough so that the next instant when the whale sounded and those waving flukes shot downward past us we were hardly grazed and in nowise damaged.

Of that, however, I had little time just then to take notice. For now the harpoon line was running out over my oar as if secured to a thunderbolt, streaking by me from the tub behind my thwart to go aft to the loggerhead, and from that shooting forward down the middle of the whaleboat to the bow chock, the flying warp searing my left arm where it rubbed over it so that involuntarily I slid outboard as from contact with a branding iron.

As if this were not commotion enough in the boat for the moment, Jared Macy chose that time to exchange places with Red Jerry, so that to top off all, we on the thwarts had the mate leaping wildly over our oars going forward to starboard, the harpooner tumbling madly aft over the heads of the helpless rowers to larboard, and in between, that singing hempen line vibrating like a plucked harp string between loggerhead and bow chock on its way overboard into the depths.

That all this in that cockle shell tossing like a chip in the broken water left by the sounding whale, did not capsize us, was certainly due to no precaution taken by the mate to avoid it, and I can lay it only to the inbuilt seaworthiness of our whaleboat. At any rate, in another moment, still too dazed to comprehend fully what had happened, I came to, to find Red Jerry now manning the steering oar and in the bow, Jared Macy with a twelve foot lance in his hands, calmly sweeping in with it toward the side of the boat our two drifting larboard oars. Gingerly edging well to larboard to avoid entangling themselves in the flying warp, Obed and Manuel reached overboard to recover them, ship them cautiously beneath the harpoon line, and once again we were ready for action.

The line was still going out, but not quite so fast now.

Red Jerry, eyeing it, let go his steering oar an instant, dexterously caught up the line, flung a turn about the loggerhead, then another, so that he might if desired put a strain on the line. But since it was quite evidently still running out too swiftly for that as yet, he gripped his steering oar again, curtly bade Obed and me to boat our oars, and stand by either to seize the line and hold back on it or to heave in slack, whichever the further actions of the harpooned fish should indicate.

Still panting furiously from my previous exertions, I boated my oar thankfully enough, glad to relieve my aching palms and throbbing muscles of that burden. I swung about on my thwart, prepared to heave in should the occasion warrant, while Obed, on the forward side of the line tub, seized up a pair of quilted canvas cloths to protect his palms and prepared to hold back if ordered.

I glanced at the line tub. Even in those few hectic seconds it was over half empty. A hundred fathoms down at least, our whale had sounded already and still was plummeting into the depths. How much farther would he go? I looked apprehensively again at the fast emptying tub, with the hempen turns, layer after layer, darting upward like a continuous stream of uncoiling cobras striking at their prey. Yes, there unsecured to anything and hanging free and clear over the edge of the tub was the eye splice in the bitter end of the warp. If the sounding whale took out our full two hundred fathoms of line, at least he could not drag us under with him.

Save for the singing of the surging warp, all was quiet again in our boat. Forward in the bow, lance poised, stood Jared Macy, hatless, shirt torn off now and bared to the waist, his legs braced wide apart, eyes glued to the sea beneath the stem where, centered vertically in a little whirlpool, our harpoon line was vanishing. Just abaft him, forehead swathed in a gaudily-colored 'kerchief, sat swarthy Manuel at his recovered oar, silently regarding the waves alongside. On the midship thwart, fingering the only oar now out to starboard, was Peleg, just as fully occupied in peering down his side into the depths. Then, facing each

[51]

other across the line tub, came Obed and I, our gaze riveted on the vibrating hempen line, ready at the word to seize it. And finally in the sternsheets stood Red Jerry, boat-steerer now, gripping his long steering oar awaiting the orders of the mate.

Red Jerry's task as harpooner was over. He had beyond all doubt driven his two harpoons through the blubber into the flesh below to fasten us firmly enough to that whale. Now it was the mate's business to probe with that slender lance of his through oily blubber and tough flesh far into the vitals of the whale where pulsed his huge heart and set him to spouting blood instead of vapor till at last he rolled "fin out." And all we in the boat had left to do when that maddened bull bent probably on our destruction rose, was to keep the boat in close enough contact with him so that Jared Macy, leaning over the bow, might at his convenience proceed with the probing.

Ordinarily a stricken whale, unacquainted with man and his weapons, sounds to full depth to rid himself of the strange enemy piercing his back and stays there till the need for air forces him to rise. He then furiously swims off on the surface, striving only to tear away the lines and free himself, during the which effort he usually falls a relatively easy prey to the keen lance wielded alongside him as the boat is hauled up. But occasionally a fish which has managed to escape one or two such encounters learns better tactics, and such a "fighting whale" we had now to deal with I gathered immediately from Red Jerry's first remark.

"Be wary this fish, mister mate!" sang out the Indian, once he was firmly planted in the sternsheets. "Him fighting whale or me squaw! Two twisted irons already in him back when I strike him. That bull meet whalers before!"

"Aye, aye! Leave him to me!" replied the mate curtly. "I've a long enough lance!" Abruptly the discussion ended.

That brief interchange did nothing to restore in me any of the confidence already blasted from my mind by the close view of the whale I had raised. A fighting whale? His vast bulk was terrifying enough to me already had he been the most unsophisticated whale afloat.

But I was given no time for cogitation over that. Our running line, now three-quarters gone, commenced perceptibly to slow up, then stopped going out altogether.

"Hold it!" ordered Macy.

Immediately Obed gripped the line with both his canvas lined palms, braced himself to hold back on the turns about the loggerhead. There was no need. The mate, tentatively pressing his leg against the line to test its strain, found it altogether slack.

"Heave in lively!" he shouted.

With both fists, hand over hand as fast as I could heave it, I started to haul in on the line. Red Jerry tossed off the two turns he had taken round the loggerhead, and Obed immediately began to coil the slack down in loose loops in the sternsheets. No time now to try restowing the line in the nearly-emptied tub—it was coming in too fast for that. Frantically I heaved in wet hemp dripping with water, soaking myself and everything about me with spray flying from the line. Except for the weight of the soaked warp, there was no strain at all on it as I yanked in and Obed strove to keep abreast of me in coiling down. Our whale was evidently rising fast; much faster indeed than I could heave in slack. Where, I wondered, would he breach? And could we hold him back enough as he strove to rush off with us so that our other two boats, lying on their oars now a short distance astern of us, might pull up close enough to get fast to him also?

In the bow in front of me as I furiously hauled in slack stood the mate, his roving eyes searching the surface all about us for the first spout from the rising whale, his lance poised lightly across his bared chest, ready instantly for a dart should the fish break surface anywhere within reach. Between me and the mate, still peering into the water as they rested on their oars, were Manuel and Peleg, while in a close knot in the sternsheets were Obed at my side, coiling line, and Red Jerry clutching the steering oar, impassive now, awaiting the next move.

As unexpectedly as a bolt of lightning from the placid sky above us and as suddenly, it came. Jared Macy stiffened against the forward thwart, half-turned aft, shrieked,

"Stern all! Ster—!"

I caught a metallic gleam shimmering as it rose beneath the boat. Before the words were fully out of Jared Macy's mouth, a long tapered jaw lined both sides with monstrous ivory teeth shot from the water fifteen feet above our starboard bow and almost simultaneously to larboard of us the mountainous black mass of a sperm whale's blunt snout followed it, gripping the bow of our boat between! Our whaleboat reared suddenly up, I shot as suddenly downward into the stern. Those vast jaws above closed slightly, though in no wise slackening in their rise, and the whole bow of our boat crumpled up, broke from the stern, vanished inside that erupting maw.

Still rising, the body of the whale shot up before me from the depths, blotting out sea and sky and all else as I looked upward through the void, framed in splintered planking, where had an instant before been the bow of our whaleboat and my shipmates. Nothing was there now save the black flank of the whale, rising with incredible velocity vertically from the water, while the broken ends of the cedar planking in what was left of the after half of the boat, thumped irregularly against that dripping hide to bite into it and be carried upward with it.

Tossed on my back into the sternsheets, sprawled helplessly out in the mass of wet line coiled down there, I found myself, whether I would or no, staring vertically up at a sight which froze my blood. There in the jaws of the whale, slowly closing now as its vast form began to describe an arc in air, was Jared Macy! Full half his body from his waist out protruded grotesquely from the whale's mouth, his long arms waving futilely in the air above the useless lance which had dropped from his hands, his face turned downward toward us sprawled out in the remnants of his boat.

Majestically the whale rose to breach completely clear of the sea—its tremendous head, sleek body, and gigantic flukes all at once exposed above the waves, a sight to be seen on but few occasions in a lifetime of whaling. But I had then no eyes for that, nor any thought even of my own danger. Horror-stricken, I followed only the path of that monstrous head as it curved in space above me, my gaze riveted only on Jared Macy.

There he lay, sprawled half in, half out across the lower jaw of that wide-spread coral-colored cavern, staring down at us, at first a look of blank amazement on his face. But that passed swiftly, succeeded by a convulsive gleam of fear, as realizing his desperate predicament, he strove to roll himself free. But apparently his legs, entangled inside that mouth in the wreckage of the boat invisible to us, held him firmly as the jaws began to close.

To my dying day I shall never forget his face, and many a night since in my dreams have I lived that scene again.

With face contorted, neck muscles standing strongly out and arms flailing wildly, the mate twisted his bared torso sharply about, grasped with both hands the huge tooth alongside him, strove to writhe free of his entanglement, only to end as he began, an impotent fragment amongst the ferocious teeth of that lower jaw, save that in his twistings, his eyes had caught a glimpse of the ponderous jaw above him starting to descend.

That ended his struggle. The straining muscles in his chest relaxed, he ceased twisting and hung again head down, his countenance a ghastly white, his eyes staring from far above upon us as if mutely imploring help, for his lips were tightly closed and never moved. In another instant the closing jaws came together about his naked waist. Over Jared Macy's face shot a spasm of frightful agony, his eyes bulged suddenly, and the whale, curving down again toward the water, plunged with a thundering crash back into the sea with his victim. Trailing behind his vanishing flukes in a lofty arc across the sky our harpoon line streamed from the irons planted in his back.

So numbed was I with horror that not till I found myself awash to my neck, sitting in the waterlogged remnants of the stern of the whaleboat, did I do anything consciously for myself. But then as I saw the slack turns of the hempen warp floating idly on the surface, begin suddenly to disappear after the whale, I realized that as I sat there alongside Obed Hussey where we two had been tumbled into the maze of harpoon line, with snarled coils looped about our arms and legs and even our necks, we were any instant like to be dragged down into the ocean depths after that sounding whale to be strangled by the coils about our throats if we did not drown first.

I strove frenziedly to clear myself, but not Laocoon himself and both his sons were more entangled in clinging coils than we. I have no doubt that we would surely have gone to join Jared Macy in the deep had not Red Jerry, floundering in the waves alongside where he had been tossed clear of the upended boat, looked across the awash gunwale and seen us struggling with those deadly coils.

Instantly he flung his body through the water toward a loose turn still floating on the surface where once the bow of the boat had been, and savagely dug his teeth into the hemp. Twisting on his back, he clung thus to the line while he fumbled with one hand beneath the surface for his sheath knife, found it, drew it forth. Then grasping the line with his left hand, he jerked it taut against his teeth, swung up over his face the gleaming blade in his right fist and with one vicious slash across the stout hemp, severed it. And none too soon, for in another second that end of the line disappeared suddenly after the whale, leaving the three of us clinging to the shattered stern of our boat with only our heads above water, a few bits of wreckage about, and our emptied line tub dancing lightly off atop the waves, where perhaps ten seconds before had been the bow boat, the mate and all his crew, awaiting some sign of a rising whale.

8

OWEN SWAIN'S boat picked us up, Red Jerry, Obed and me, and promptly headed back for the *Beaver* with us. Jedidah Mayhew, third mate, and his boat stayed to search amongst the wreckage strewing the roiled surface of the sea for Manuel and Peleg.

But never a sign of either did they see, unless an ominous red tinge in the waves thereabouts be taken as such. What happened to them we never knew. Whether maimed and crushed by that savage uprush which had torn their half of the boat away, they had sunk unnoticed into the sea, or whether, unlike Jared, they had been completely engulfed with the wreckage of the bow in the mouth of that colossal whale, we could not tell. They were simply and completely gone, and after satisfying himself of it, the third mate hastily abandoned that perilous spot lest the whale repeat its tactics, and rowed hurriedly back to the *Beaver*, which was lying to now not a quarter of a mile off.

Unencumbered by any passengers, Jedidah Mayhew, who had not delayed overlong in his search, soon overhauled the second mate's boat, so that practically together we came alongside the hove to *Beaver*. Immediately both boats hooked on their dangling falls, preparatory to sending their crews on deck to hoist away. But before that could be done, Hezekiah Coffin, pausing only long enough to turn the wheel over to the cook, came rushing to the side, roaring,

"Belay hoisting! Stay in the boats!"

Taken full aback by that, both mates looked quizzically up the gunwale, while their crews, already on their feet ready to scramble up the sides, sank heavily back on the thwarts.

[57]

"And why, Cap'n?" asked Swain, speaking first in his new dignity as the mate, now that Jared Macy was dead.

"Why, thou blockhead? Thou askest me why?" Captain Coffin stared down at him in amazed indignation. "To take yon whale, of course, when again he blows! Why else?"

Dripping wet, I sat shivering, though not from cold, on the after thwart beside the stroke oarsman, looking up the towering wood side at our Captain. There was no question but that he was dumbfounded at the mate's query, yet he was not half so dumbfounded as I next was at Owen Swain's immediate reply.

"Not I, Cap'n," said Swain solemnly. "Yon sperm can blow and breach alongside as he pleases, and I'll not lower again for him. I whale it not for glory, and I believe not in fighting whales that too cunningly fight me. Saw ye not with what devilish craft that fiend slew Macy? And where be now his two men and his stout boat? I have a wife and a suckling babe in Nantucket whom I desire to see again. Three good men and a stove boat already that demon hath cost the *Beaver*. 'Tis enough!"

"And to that, I say 'Amen,' Cap'n," added Jedidah Mayhew swiftly from the stern of the other boat. "Belay further pursuit, lest worse occur! Yon old bull is Satan incarnate!"

Startled though I was that both remaining mates should dare to disobey the Captain's orders so flatly, yet I could see that both were simply acting the part of prudent men whose aim was to garner oil, not glory. So I looked for the Captain, in the face of their well-founded opposition, to give way and allow the boats to be hoisted in, but I learned that I had misjudged what iron in his Quaker soul lay behind that shad-belly waistcoat on Hezekiah Coffin.

"Thou'rt wary to match thy brains then, if indeed thou hast any, 'gainst yon dumb tun of oil?" Contemptuously the Captain looked down on his mates. "Nantucket had remained but a barren sand heap nurturing a few grazing sheep had it been for such sons as thou. A hundred and fifty barrels of good sperm close by and ye shrink from it? On deck, then, Owen Swain, and let me take thy place in

[58]

the boat behind the lance. I'll save thee for that suckling babe thou'rt so thoughtful of, the while I myself slay that whale! On deck with thee, I say!"

With alacrity, the mate hastened to obey *that* order, but he was not alone. Up with him as one man scrambled his whole boat's crew, harpooner, oarsmen, all, apparently in no wise desirous of coming again to close grips with those wicked jaws they had last seen closing on Jared Macy. Only we three castaways from his ill-fated craft remained, wet and dripping, in the boat.

That imitation of the mate the skipper had not counted on, but in vain he ordered the crew back. They were all of one mind with their mate, stolidly behind him in his refusal. The Captain raged and stormed at them, there in the rolling *Beaver's* waist, but to no purpose. Not a man of those who close by had witnessed the ferocious ingenuity with which the whale had risen to destroy our boat and half its crew, could be either persuaded or bullied into approaching him again.

The skipper gave up. Leaving the recalcitrant group on deck clustered behind Owen Swain, he once again approached the bulwark, leaned over, looked down into the rocking boat where I still sat.

"Thou, Red Jerry, hast once struck that whale and know he is but a fish. Durst thou dart another harpoon an' I lay thee on him?"

A grim smile played about Red Jerry's lips; a fierce gleam lighted up his savage eyes.

"Aye, Cap'n," replied the Indian. "Maybe one, maybe dozen, till fish roll fin out!"

"Aye, Jerry!" cried Hezekiah. "E'en though thou be a Gay Header and off island, Nantucket can be proud of thee! And thou, Tom Folger, and thou, Obed, wilt pull for me an oar again behind Red Jerry while he strikes that whale?"

I looked dubiously at Obed, pale, wet, and unnerved as he had been dragged from the sea. Would he do it? Just as dubiously Obed looked at me, shivering yet in my bedraggled shirt and clinging canvas trousers. I could not forget in that fleeting instant my father, a sacrifice to some such monster, nor my stricken mother broken now for life as a result, and I was of good mind, having by God's grace been spared to her, to answer no. But ere I could, I glimpsed Red Jerry impassively eyeing me as if weighing of what mettle I might be, and there flashed across me the thought that had that savage, himself well clear of all danger, been less venturesome and swift with teeth and knife in cutting the harpoon line, neither I nor Obed had been in that boat now with him.

"Aye, aye, Cap'n!" I answered soberly, and Obed, his mind resolved by my decision (and perhaps even for the same reason) nodded acquiescence also.

"Good!" exclaimed the Captain. "Give me always Folgers and Husseys for a greasy voyage! And now between thee both and the cooper and the cook, I have my crew." He raised his eyes to the masthead where the cooper swayed on the crosstrees. "Zenas, lay thee down from aloft!" he shouted, and then turning to the mate nearby, ordered brusquely, "Detail one of thy men at the wheel, that the cook may go with me."

Immediately the cook arrived from the wheel and the cooper soon after from the masthead, the Captain hustled them overboard into the boat alongside, giving neither of them any opportunity to discuss the situation with the mate or any of his boat's crew, even had they been so minded, and in another moment came sliding himself down the after fall to seize the steering oar. Hastily, lest even yet he lose some one of his crew, he pushed the boat away from the side and detailed us at the oars, regardless of how we had rowed before, so that now I found myself pulling second bow just abaft Red Jerry, with Zenas Joy before me, Obed once again at the tub oar, and the cook stroking.

A few strokes carried us well clear, when the Captain, bidding us lay on our oars, turned to look back at the *Beaver*. Under her larboard quarter, hooked to the falls, still lay Jedidah Mayhew's boat and all her crew.

[60]

"Cast off and follow," ordered the Captain. "Thou may'st for thy fears play loose boat today, Jedidah, and while we fasten to the whale, perchance thereby be of some use to us in diverting his attention." He turned about again, sang out to us, "Give way!" We leaned forward, laid back together. But I could see from our first stroke that we had neither the power now nor the skill with which in Jared Macy's boat the oars had been plied, and I doubted, should we again have a stern chase after the whale, that we should ever get close enough for Red Jerry to dart a harpoon.

A moderate pull to windward brought us to the reddened water where the whale had breached and then sounded. A few drifting oars, some splintered planking, and the awash stern of our shattered boat marked it sharply enough even had that sickening reddish hue been absent. Just short of that spot, we rested once again on our oars and waited.

I need scarce mention with what trepidation I peered over the side into the water during that wait. I sat now on the thwart next the bow where Manuel in all the brave gaiety of flaming 'kerchief and crimson shirt had sat when the whale had risen before, and where now was Manuel? I shrank from pondering the only two alternatives.

Between attempts to pierce the depths for some indication of the vanished fish, my fleeting glimpses round about the heaving surface showed me Jedidah Mayhew's boat resting prudently on oars some dozen lengths to leeward of us. The *Beaver*, still hove to on the larboard tack, rolled gently amongst the waves several cables off with apparently all those on board save the new lookout and helmsman anxiously lining the weather rail to watch.

How long since the whale had sounded with Jared Macy dangling from his jaws? Certainly far less than the hour his reserve of aerated blood allowed him, but whether it had been ten minutes or thirty, I had only a vague idea and consequently little notion of how long a wait was yet before us. Captain Coffin, as if sure of but a few seconds, with surprising agility for all his years tore off his coat, rolled up his shirtsleeves, and again grasped the steering oar to

[61]

confront us in his drab waistcoat, a stout figure beneath his broad-brimmed hat that was the very antithesis of Jared Macy's lithe leanness.

"There she blows!" breathed Red Jerry softly. Sure enough, a hundred fathoms away, broad off our larboard beam, rose a majestic spout. And immediately following it there also rose vertically from the sea the whole head of our whale, to stand some thirty feet above the surface the while he slowly revolved, scanning the horizon for his late enemies.

Immediately he sighted us, he sank back horizontally, then with a flirt of his tail which sent up a heavy cloud of spray, swung about, and head out, exposing the full blunt cliff that made up his massive snout, started dead for us!

"Give way!" shouted the skipper. Obediently I bent to my oar, my eyes nevertheless fixed sidewise on that terrifying vision to larboard bearing down on us, wondering only in what direction we should flee for safety. To my overwhelming amazement and infinite dismay, instead of fleeing in any direction, Hezekiah Coffin bore sharply down to starboard on his long steering oar, swung the boat about heading us directly for the oncoming spermaceti, and then to top off all, roared out,

"Heave now, my lads! Spring and start her!"

What madness had seized our Captain to drive us headlong into the oncoming jaws of death I could not fathom. But I could do nothing save comply and in a moment we five at the oars were tugging mightily, fairly lifting the boat along through the water.

"Stand up, Jerry!" ordered the Captain.

Just behind me, once again as I labored I heard Red Jerry boat his oar, swing about, grab up a harpoon. But all I saw, looking down the whaleboat over the three oarsmen astern of me, was Hezekiah Coffin, his greying locks flying in the breeze, his thick lips tightly compressed, clinging grimly to the handle of his steering oar, holding us head on for the charging whale!

Suddenly the skipper flung the full weight of his thick body against the steering oar, jamming it hard down to larboard. Instantly the speeding whaleboat shot over to starboard. In that same moment as we swung off diagonally athwart our previous course, there loomed up rushing by close aboard us the head of the whale, towering high above the boat, mouth open, with livid throat and massive teeth in that lower jaw eager to seize upon us.

Hardly had I glimpsed the blunt snout and that terrifying opened mouth beside me than the Captain jerked his steering oar hard to starboard, swung the boat over to straighten it up parallel to the monster once again and only a few feet away, though of course, headed opposite, and roared out,

"Give it to him, Jerry!"

I heard the whir of the line as the harpoon shot sideways by my head through the air and the solid thump with which it landed in the soft blubber. The whale gave a hoarse bellow as if in pain, writhed sidewise, raised his mighty flukes in fury. Red Jerry grabbed up his second iron, hurriedly flung it, but such was the turmoil there of careening boat and infuriated whale speeding past each other, that it missed, going overboard only to dangle on the harpoon line. Another second and we were clear of the whale, fast to him with one iron, as those lifted flukes came down on the water astern of us with a thundering splash.

"Way enough!" shouted the Captain, and immediately let go the steering oar to spring forward over the thwarts and man the lance, while Red Jerry leaped aft to take up the steering. Meanwhile I shrank instinctively outboard against the gunwale to get clear of the surging harpoon line, but there was no need. The line was hardly moving out at all.

Instead of sounding as before or rushing off on the surface into the wind towing us behind, either of which maneuvers would have taken our line out with lightning rapidity, this time the harpooned bull, baffled in his first charge and roaring from that spiracle of his in rage and pain, was lying astern of us in the water. His powerful tail raised a little clear of the surface with wide-spread flukes slowly was

[63]

swinging horizontally to and fro over the waves, delicately feeling over them for any contact with our boat.

A little clear of that astounding tail which spread full fifteen feet from tip to tip over the water, I had my best opportunity to view the whale I had raised close aboard, in the brief interval while I rested on my sweep ere Red Jerry reached the steering oar. Easily more than three boat lengths from snout to flukes, he must have been nearly as long as the *Beaver*. Certainly he was well over eighty feet long, with a breadth across his body of perhaps two fathoms. That we might in our try-pots boil a hundred and fifty barrels of good sperm oil from his blubber, was easily believable.

I hardly got further than that in my estimate when we were in action again. Feeling nothing at all with the tips of those sensitive flukes so daintily feathered over the surface searching for us, the bull dropped his tail into the sea, and started to come about toward us so that he might use his eyes instead.

As he swung broadside I saw his eye for the first time, just above the point of his jaw some twenty feet from his snout. It was a tiny glistening ball hardly larger than that of an ox and seemingly quite insignificant for so vast a creature. He paused a moment in his turning in indecision.

For now while he could see us well enough with that little left eye glaring wickedly at me from the high blank cliff of black skin on that side, he must at the same instant with his right eye on the other side of that soaring mountain which formed his head, have glimpsed Jedidah Mayhew playing loose boat, and thereby had presented to his brain simultaneously two entirely separate pictures for his consideration.

In that moment of his hesitation, Red Jerry dexterously threw two turns of our slack line about the loggerhead, and bade Obed stand by to boat his oar and hold back on the line, while Captain Coffin, bracing himself in the bow with the lance, made ready for battle.

What queer quirk in the two differing images before his mind prompted that bull's decision was, of course, beyond

[64]

me, but what he did was totally unexpected. Wholly disregarding us, he rushed off toward the boat on his right side, starting the line out suddenly from the tub, while Red Jerry yelled,

"Hold it! Hold it!"

And meanwhile he swung hard over on the steering oar to turn the boat about into the wake of the whale.

Obed flung his oar inboard, grabbed his canvas pads, gripped the flying line, heaved back against the turns around the loggerhead. For an instant the tightening hempen turns surged round the wooden post in a wreath of blue smoke, then suddenly they seized hard about it, stopping the line. At the same time our stem was given such a jerk, as the suddenly taut line to the whale brought up sidewise against the bow chock, that it nearly capsized our boat which still lay broadside to the direction of the line.

The next moment our whaleboat, yanked bodily around by the harpoon line, was flying over the waves in the wake of that fish, bounding with sickening concussions of its thin cedar bottom from crest to crest while the spray going by both bows in two wide sheets fairly drenched us all clinging desperately to our thwarts to avoid being tossed out.

But precarious as our situation may have seemed to me, it was safety itself compared to what the third mate was immediately faced with. For Jedidah Mayhew, never expecting a rush from the whale once we had successfully made fast, lay motionless hardly a dozen boat lengths off from the leviathan now furiously charging him. And ere he could get way enough on his boat to maneuver in avoidance, the whale, head lifted high and mouth wide open, was practically upon his boat.

I had a fleeting vision of harpooner and bow oarsman leaping from their thwarts to spring wildly overboard and the next instant the whale had the bow of that boat in his jaws, lifting it high up to spill Mayhew and his remaining men incontinently into the sea. The whale stopped then in his charge, dropped the remnants of the crushed boat, once more closed his maw on the stern to make basket work of that, and then started swinging about, flailing the sea with mighty strokes of his flukes to finish the havoc he had wrought.

"Haul up! Haul up!" shrieked Hezekiah, seeing the ocean before him lashed into swirling foam amidst which bobbed the heads of six men frenziedly striving to swim clear of snapping jaws and pounding flukes while all about them floated smashed planks, broken oars, lance poles, and the tangled coils of their harpoon line.

Desperately Zenas and I, facing forward, heaved in on our line to drag us close aboard, that we might attract the whale's attention and give our unfortunate shipmates a chance to get beyond his reach before it was too late. While we hauled in the wet hemp with set teeth, blanched faces, and straining arms, behind us Obed, the cook, and Red Jerry tensely grasped their oars to maneuver the boat should the whale charge us. And just forward of me in the very bow, brandishing his lance and bellowing across the water at the top of his lungs to attract the attention of that maddened whale, stood Hezekiah Coffin, no sign of any Quaker in his embattled figure now.

The whale paid no attention to us. There were too many floating objects close aboard of greater interest to occupy him fully. As soon as his tail, feathering lightly again over the sea, touched anything, down it came on the water with the thunder of a thousand drums, to demolish whatever was beneath. That he should be so enraged was reasonable enough, seeing that his sleek black back somewhat resembled a huge pin cushion. Atop it and a little to the right of his hump were the two harpoons which Red Jerry had first planted as well as the broken shafts of two badly twisted irons left there in some previous encounters with whalers. Now in addition the harpoon to which our line was attached stood in his left side.

We were enabled to haul ourselves close in on the whale's left flank as a consequence of his concentration. Coming diagonally from astern him just clear of his thrashing flukes we almost brought our bow up to where the harpoon was darted into his side just abaft his fin.

At that point, Captain Coffin waited no longer. Lifting his poised lance high, he lunged fiercely forward, drove its slender iron shaft full six feet into the body of the whale, and started furiously to churn its oval point about inside. The effect on the whale was instantaneous. He rolled suddenly away from us, leaving the lance which the skipper still held firmly clutched, to draw free of his body, followed by a gush of thick blood. And ere, as I sat on the fore thwart, I could lean back to haul in line again so that the Captain might get in a second thrust, or he could order Red Jerry to back water and lie clear a moment should that be what he desired, the ponderous flukes of that writhing whale lifted from the sea, came soaring with incredible speed across the water toward me over the gunwale of the boat to sweep in a gale of wind like a vast black canopy right over my head, blotting the sky from sight.

With a sickening crunch, those flukes caught Hezekiah Coffin as he stood poising himself for another thrust, squarely across his waistcoat, whisking him before my terrified eyes clean out of the boat!

I fell back on my thwart too stunned for conscious action, only to hear Red Jerry shouting,

"Stern all! Stern!"

Automatically I fumbled for my oar, but before my clawing fingers found it, I felt the rushing harpoon line searing my chest. I shrank away instinctively to starboard, lest I be tangled in it. And as I came erect against the gunwale, looking wildly about to orient myself, I heard Red Jerry shrieking,

"Cut line! Cut line!"

The whale was gone, sounded evidently, leaving the surface of the sea an eddying mass of red foam littered with the smashed debris of the other boat, both men and lumber. But we were still fast to him, for there, smoking out through the bow chock, was the singing harpoon line. I reached forward into the empty bow where the Captain had been standing, caught up a hatchet from the floorboards, brought it

[67]

viciously down on the bow chock across the flying hemp, parted the line.

Once we were free of the whale we looked about sick at heart in the swirling froth amidst the wreckage for survivors. Red Jerry caught sight of some hair undulating on the water nearby, reached over the gunwale, dug his fingers into it to drag up, half drowned and wholly unconscious, the third mate, Jedidah Mayhew. In addition, nearby we picked up, still swimming frantically away, two terrified seamen who had managed to get clear to leeward.

But that was all. Of the rest of that boat's crew of six, or of Hezekiah Coffin, we found no trace. Crushed, undoubtedly, by those death-dealing flukes which in the twinkling of an eye had reduced them to bloody heaps of lifeless pulp, they had sunk soundlessly to unmarked graves at the bottom of the sea.

Red Jerry, now in command, stoically surveyed a moment the scene of battle, a turbulent blotch of crimson froth and scattered splinters on the heaving sea, then ordered gutturally,

"Give way all! We go back to ship!"

9

IT was a sad remnant of the *Beaver's* company that lay back on the falls to hoist in on the quarter the solitary remaining larboard boat. On the bow and in the waist, the cranes, standing there gaunt against the bulwarks empty of the boats that a few hours before had swung from those davit heads, were mute reminders for the rest of our voyage of the disaster the ferocious whale I had raised had caused us.

Captain, mate, five of our shipmates from the forecastle, and two stove boats—that was the toll of our encounter. One third of our entire crew, including two officers, killed in that one battle—a slaughter to make many a bloody naval action seem tame indeed by comparison.

We had hardly hoisted our lone remaining boat to the davit heads when the whale rose again to commence spouting off our larboard beam while he savagely disported himself with his flukes, reducing to still smaller kindling the wreckage of our two boats floating thereabouts. But while he spouted and thrashed about in full view of all on deck, and with such thunderous flailings beat the sea with his flukes that had we all been blind, our ears alone could not have left us ignorant of his presence, yet no man raised again the cry,

"There she blows!"

Instead with only imprecations on that fighting whale for the shipmates he had so horribly reft us of, we prudently left him to his own devices.

Under Owen Swain's orders, Captain now, we hastened to make all sail before the wind and get away from there before it should enter the furious monster's mind perhaps to con-

[69]

nect the *Beaver* with the boats he was demolishing and the injuries he had sustained, and as a consequence come churning through the waves to ram us with that vast snout of his, stave in our side, and send the hulk of the *Beaver* to join the body of her Captain in the ooze of the ocean floor.

Our whaling cruise was over. With the responsibility for the ship so unexpectedly thrown upon his shoulders, it was obvious from his every gesture that there was but one idea left in Owen Swain's mind—to get the *Beaver* back (if he could) to Nantucket, and that as quickly as might be. For aside from the loss of Hezekiah Coffin and Jared Macy, which left us without an officer aboard competent to navigate the ship, it was found when we finally resuscitated the third mate and he strove to rise, that he had both legs broken between knee and thigh.

How that had happened and at what moment, Jedidah Mayhew could not tell, and it made little difference. But stretched out in his berth below, his broken legs rudely splinted with barrel staves, he was of no further use to us as an officer.

With but thirteen men all told left on their feet, the *Beaver* could no longer man even two boats; with our demoralized crew and without a navigator left aboard, it was madness to continue the cruise even had we been able. So with a "clean" ship, the *Beaver*, only three weeks out of port and without a barrel of oil in her hold, was prudently headed back for home.

How to get there, however, apparently puzzled Owen Swain. We were out on the broad Atlantic, according to Captain Coffin's last position on the chart, about two hundred miles southwest of the island of Sao Thiago in the Cape Verde group off the African coast. That position was good enough for a point of departure for our homeward voyage, but how to figure the longitude for our further positions as we sailed homeward was beyond our new skipper. The latitude, computed with relative ease from a daily meridian altitude of the sun taken with the quadrant and some computation from the tables of its declinations, he might perhaps approximate.

In that dilemma, he attempted to solve his problem as had Columbus—he resolved to sail due west keeping a constant latitude till he sighted land in America, which as we were then about 12° N. should raise the island of Barbados, the most easterly of the Windward Islands in the West Indies. After that, with Barbados as a new point of departure, he had only to steer a course due north on the meridian of Barbados, 60° W., keeping our longitude thus constant, till he had made northing enough to reach the latitude of Nantucket. Then by turning west again, he could run down that parallel of latitude till we raised our island. And there he could turn the empty *Beaver* and the shaken remnants of her crew back to the owners.

To the reverberations of those death-dealing flukes astern of us, the *Beaver* squared away before the wind and headed westward. But not till the thunder of that tail had died away at last in our wake did I breathe freely again.

Once again the *Beaver* was like a great bird skimming the seas with all sails set and even our stu'n'sails rigged out that we might take full advantage of a fair wind westward. Then there came to me a surprise.

Captain Swain mustered all hands including the cook, about the mainmast. We stood before him silently, still numbed by our encounter with the great whale, not overmuch interested in anything the new skipper had to say, for nothing he could say might ease the terror we had faced.

"We are homeward bound, men," announced Owen Swain simply, confirming thus only what all hands intuitively knew. "To help me work the ship back, since I am now the only officer left fit for duty, I have chosen as first mate Obed Hussey and as second, Zenas Joy. They will be the watch officers. You will obey them as such, and they will move immediately aft to the cabin. And while we need not a third mate, for we no longer have the boat crews to lower for whales, I have none the less decided to choose one to help me with the navigation."

Meditatively he looked us over, as if still pondering his

[71]

choice, then announced abruptly,

"Thomas Folger, move thy dunnage aft to the cabin. Thou shalt be the new third mate. That is all, men; man now thy stations. And thou, Mister Hussey, take the watch. Keep her steady as she goes, full and by, course, due west." The skipper turned on his heel, vanished down the hatchway to the cabin, leaving his open-mouthed crew gaping at me with one accord.

But if my shipmates were astonished, I at first was thunderstruck. Third mate? I, Tom Folger, the youngest man on board and scarce three weeks at sea on my first cruise?

However, ere I had time to assay what that meant, Obed Hussey at least, fully comprehending his new dignity, took charge.

"All hands!" he ordered. "Stow whaling gear! Clear that larboard boat, and strike all gear on deck below! Shake a leg!"

With alacrity the crew broke up to obey that order. Except for Red Jerry perhaps, there was no man in that demoralized group with any stomach to face a whale again that cruise.

In a daze, I stumbled forward with the others to begin stowing away the spare whaling gear ere I recollected that "All hands!" no longer encompassed me. I was third mate, an officer myself. A little dubiously, I paused, then turned slowly aft to the quarterdeck, where save as helmsman I had not before dared set a foot. Leaning against the rail on those sacred planks abaft the mizzenmast which Hezekiah Coffin had been wont to tread in solitary state the while I had labored through endless dreary watches forward swabbing down the deck, I watched almost unbelievingly my former shipmates striking down into the fore hold every implement of whaling, half expecting each second the swing of a rope end and Jared Macy's harsh voice ordering me to turn to with them.

Neither came, of course. Obed Hussey, the new mate, apparently did not believe in rope ends, and Jared Macy was dead. And gradually it sank in on me besides, that with but

[72]

a word our new Captain, like a King of old, had ennobled me, unworthy though I was. And the reason for his strange action probably was he had no other choice. What he sorely needed in a third mate was some mathematical help in his computations rather than practical seamanship and all others left on the *Beaver* were even less worthy in that respect than I. Better seamen, better whalers, that they certainly were. But none aboard the *Beaver*, not even including the new Captain himself, had half the facility with figures my mother's careful schooling in preparation for my career as a printer had given me, nor one-tenth the chance of making any sense out of the mysteries of finding longitude hidden in such books on navigation as Hezekiah Coffin might have left behind him on his cabin shelves.

10

WITH fair winds to speed us on, we sailed doggedly westward by compass along the twelfth parallel of north latitude, logging a steady six knots in our empty vessel.

I saw little again of my shipmates from the forecastle. Never called on to stand a watch on deck, as never before I spent my daylight hours in the cabin absorbed in figures and in books. That I found this infinitely preferable to my previous toil as a seaman hardly needs mention, and my new glory as an officer kept me treading on air.

The Captain was perfectly frank with me. I had hardly descended into the cabin, once Obed Hussey had turned my old mates to on deck, than Captain Swain beckoned me to him. I ducked my head to clear the heavy beams framing the low deck above and, half-hunched over, sidled to the cabin table at which he sat. Before him, spread flat on the table, was an admiralty chart, about it were scattered Hezekiah Coffin's books.

"Look thee, Tom," said the Captain, pointing to a penciled circle on the opened chart. "There off Sao Thiago is our position of yesternoon, as our late Captain plotted it, and on this line towards the West Indies which I have just laid down, we are sailing westward. I tell thee plainly that though I am Captain now, I know as little of navigation as thou or any man before the mast, and though I have some skill with a lance, I have but slight knowledge of figures and little practice with them. Had I but time and some instructor to teach me, I might indeed master the art, as may any sailor with some schooling. But now I have neither. Instead, with two indifferent mates who do not know their own duties, I have upon me the responsibility of continuously keeping an eye out on deck to see that they dismast not the ship and leave us helpless even to find our way home wholly by dead reckoning. Seest thou that?"

"Aye, Captain," I answered soberly, full well aware of the difficulties of his situation.

" 'Tis well, then." Owen Swain leaned forward, looked hopelessly at the chart. "I have chosen thee as most likely amongst the crew to find some meaning in these treatises here on navigation. I leave it to thee to master at least the means of obtaining the latitude, which had I more time, I could myself take care of, and if beyond that, thou makest anything of longitude, so much the better, lad. But heed thy task on latitude. Within the week, if thou hast not that well in hand, consider that as I have made thee third mate, I can as quickly disrate thee again to seaman and send thee for'd to the fo'c'sle. Understandest thou that also?"

"Aye, Captain," I repeated.

"There is the quadrant, then," pointed out Swain, indicating atop a locker the square mahogany box in which rested Hezekiah Coffin's precious instrument. "Make thyself free with these books as thou wilt, and may the Lord aid thee," he concluded piously, rising to leave me. "I must attend on deck." He went up the ladder, leaving me alone in the cabin.

I slid into the chair he had vacated. Here, indeed, was luxury. Instead of the stuffy forecastle, smelling strongly of soaked clothing, unaired bedding, and of the oily fumes of a swinging lantern, though the cabin was small and its ceiling low, down through the open skylight to the quarterdeck above me swept the ocean breezes. Light in abundance streamed in and through the wide square windows in the stern I could look out upon our foaming wake. Instead of crude bunks lining its sides, to larboard and starboard were staterooms, tiny perhaps, but with built in berths and ports which might be opened in fair weather. And one of those rooms would now be mine, luxurious privacy indeed, after the communal promiscuity of the forecastle.

But all hinged on my aptitude in figures. Here unexpectedly was my longed for chance to learn navigation, with all the impedimenta of the art strewn helter-skelter under my nose, and with no alternative save of quickly acquiring enough smattering of that science to work out latitude or of going ignominiously forward to man a holystone again.

Normally I might have been hesitant about undertaking the study without a teacher. As matters stood, however, I plunged into it boldly enough. I had little desire to go back to the forecastle.

Suffice it here to say that some examination of Hezekiah Coffin's navigational work book plus a close perusal of the earlier chapters of his well-thumbed navigation treatises and an inspection of his quadrant, gave me confidence that I need have no worries about my ability to cope with latitude. The quadrant, I found, was a simple instrument. After a few hours' practice that afternoon in taking altitudes of the sun, I discovered myself competent to operate it. And as for the mathematics of determining latitude from a meridional altitude of the sun, it took but an afternoon's application to the text to comprehend it fully. It was merely a problem in addition and subtraction of angles to apply to the sun's declination and the observed altitude as taken by the quadrant, what corrections were necessary as shown by the nautical almanac. Any lad with a keen eye to bring the sun's lower limb down to the horizon as he viewed it through the quadrant, and to keep sun and horizon line in contact as the sun reached his highest altitude at noon, needed but ordinary intelligence thereafter in selecting figures from the nautical almanac for the sun's declination on that day, to combine properly his corrected altitude and his corrected declination and obtain the latitude therefrom.

If I had any doubts about the matter, there to resolve them for me were the formulae in Hezekiah Coffin's work book day after day since we had left Nantucket, filled out to serve me as examples.

So behold me then, next day, it being June first of the year 1773, shortly before noon in all the cocksureness of my sixteen years standing with legs spread far apart to brace myself, looking due north off our starboard gunwale, squinting through Hezekiah Coffin's quadrant at the sharp line of the far sea horizon, slowly turning the tangent screw on the quadrant to keep the reflected image of the lower rim of the sun's disk as it rose toward meridian, mirrored in constant contact with that line where sea and sky met in the horizon.

Beneath my feet, the *Beaver*, driving before the wind, heaved gently to the following seas, swaying me slightly as I strove to keep the little telescope of my quadrant steady on the horizon. From forward, I well knew my former shipmates were furtively pausing in their tasks to eye me in my new dignity as navigator. Abreast the mizzen, Captain Swain, not so furtively, was also, I knew, keeping an eye on me to observe for himself with what skill I took my observation.

Despite the knowledge that every eye on deck was fixed on me, my own eye, wholly absorbed in what I saw in that combination of lenses and mirrors which made up the quadrant, remained fixed on the image of the sun riding high in the heavens to the northward of us. More and more slowly as the minutes drifted by and the sun approached the meridian, did that image in my telescope lift from the horizon, and more and more slowly did I have to twist the tangent screw to hold it there in contact.

Finally the sun came to a stand on the horizon line, rising no more. Breathlessly I waited, moving nothing on my instrument, till unmistakably the sun began to dip, then lowering the quadrant, I turned inboard toward the mizzen and reported,

"Twelve o'clock here, Cap'n." And Captain Swain gruffly ordered,

"Make it so."

Eight bells rang out over the *Beaver*, I read the altitude on my quadrant—80° 01′ 30″. Subtracting that immediately from the formula figures I had previously worked out, I announced proudly to him the result,

"Latitude at noon today, Cap'n, is 12° 03′ North."

[77]

"Well done, Mr. Folger," smiled the Captain. "I see thou'rt getting along famously."

I blushed with pride, noting that to the Captain I was no longer either "lad" or "Tom" but "Mr. Folger," and I felt quite a man at last, justified in my position as third mate and solidly secure in it.

Day after day we sailed on westward, sometimes by my observations finding ourselves to the northward, sometimes to the southward of our dead reckoning course as the currents, our steering, and our uncorrected compass errors drifted us. Of our latitudes as we drove across the western ocean I felt surer with each day's observations, but our longitudes I could only estimate daily by whatever the hourly readings of our chip log heaved over the stern showed us for our day's run.

For with longitude by dead reckoning I found I would have to be content. So far as I was concerned, the problem of a longitude by lunar distances was as undecipherable to me as those Egyptian hieroglyphics decorating the temples of the Nile. In utter incomprehension I scanned the cabalistic symbols in the maze of formulae involving logarithms, of which I knew nothing, and the tables of the moon's positions and properties of which I soon saw I knew even less. To me the moon had been previously only a luminary in the night heavens over our island of Nantucket, beneath whose lovely light as it waxed and waned I had ocasionally shyly strolled home beside my cousin Delight, noting only how attractively her brown eyes sparkled in those silvery beams.

But when it came now to taking an observation of the moon for navigation, I found it had besides that silvery glow, table after table of formidable figures in the nautical almanac setting out its declination, its right ascension, its semi-diameter, its augmentation, its parallax, its refraction, its dip, its contraction—all changing rapidly in the weirdest manners and all of which, wound up with algebraic signs and incomprehensible logarithms of still more incomprehensible trigonometric functions, made the moon to me an object fearsome to contemplate from the deck of the *Beaver*, let alone to train a quadrant on to any useful end. Till all these mysteries could be illuminated to me by some competent instructor in the higher mathematics, I gave up both the moon and longitude together, content to rest on what the chip log told me of our daily westings.

So for two weeks in the hot tropics beneath burning sun in the day, beneath the even more burning stars at night, we pushed westward homeward bound in the lumbering *Beaver* toward the Windward Isles in the West Indies. But unlike the usual homeward bound spouter, we were a funereal ship if ever there was one, mournful in the knowledge that our return would spread a pall over Nantucket the like of which had not been seen in many a year. And even of those of us who were returning to our families and friends still safe in life and limb, none could blink the fact that our cruise of several months would bring us home with not a penny to anyone to show his kin for all his time and labor on the *Beaver*.

For all of us from Captain down were in that regard in the same boat—whether the lay set against one's name on the shipping articles were the sixteenth for the skipper or the two-hundredth for the seaman, made no difference now. With no oil in the hold to divide, whether one's lay were large or small, the gain was the same for each—any fraction of zero was still exactly nothing. I smiled a little bitterly at that as I thought of my mother's needs and my present position. Here I was at last by the flukes of the whale I had raised, in my long dreamed of position as an officer, entitled now to a lay of one fifty-fifth, practically four times what I had shipped for. But all my dignity and all my lay when once we had landed, would not buy my mother a solitary dab of butter in any market in Nantucket. And that golden guinea I had split my lungs to gain when I first raised the spout of that whale—how prudently had Hezekiah Coffin hedged about the payment thereof! Never could I lay claim even to that!

As I paced the quarterdeck between my labors over navigation, I cursed malevolently that cunning whale as the author of my profitless promotion. And many an hour I spent imagining how, had I been mate in one of those boats, I might have outmaneuvered him to churn a lance deep into his vitals till geysers of red blood had spouted from that spiracle of his. But I always came back to reality with a sigh—he, not I, had been the victor and while somewhere near the Equator he spouted vapor as he pleased, the *Beaver*, empty of his oil or of any, was bearing me homeward penniless, bemoaning the evil hour that ever I saw him.

11

THROUGH two long weeks we drove to the westward over the heaving seas. Uncertain as to our longitude, watch after watch, even during the night, the Captain now kept the fore masthead manned, expecting any moment a landfall and fearful that we might strand ourselves in the darkness. But not till early dawn of the sixteenth day did the hoarse cry of "Land ho!" bring me tumbling up on deck, there to see a vague peak rising in the distance on our larboard bow.

Since our latitude by my account the noon before had been 11° 45′ N., I judged it to be the island of Tobago and advised Captain Swain that if he wished to make Barbados first, we must immediately turn to the north and run close hauled some ninety miles in that direction.

But so set was our skipper, after five weeks at sea, on actually landing to verify our position, being uncertain as to whether what we saw was Tobago or Grenada, that he would hear nothing of my proposal, and instead we veered to the southward, dead for our landfall.

A few hours more and we had the island close aboard, where from the southwesterly trend of the coast and its melon-shaped volcanic mountain rising some two thousand feet above the sea, I was certain it was Tobago.

"Aye, Mr. Folger," agreed the skipper now, "Tobago it certainly is, and thy navigation is thus proved, though by dead reckoning we be some hundred miles wrong in our longitude. But now that we are here, this island serves my purpose as well as any, and here we may cast anchor to pick up a few fresh vegetables and some fowl, all of which are cheaply obtained in these islands. There will thus be no need as we work north to stop at Barbados for any reason, provision or position."

Therefore skirting the southerly shore a few miles farther, we then hauled close by the wind and tacked into Rockley Bay to cast anchor off the little town of Scarborough, the seat of the government of that island.

While we moved into the harbor under reduced canvas, I looked with pleasure, after some five weeks of viewing nothing but the sea, at the verdant slopes of mountainous Tobago so different from the low-lying barren sand hills on our own island of Nantucket. Indeed this was the first foreign shore that ever I looked upon. Against the vivid green of the plantations, the white mansions of the planters with their wide-spread verandahs dotting the slopes of the mountain above the town and looking out over the blue Caribbean, gave me an impression of affluence and of ease of life nowhere to be matched by anything I knew at home.

But Captain Swain found something of much greater interest to him than tropic scenery. Moving slowly through the bay toward our intended anchorage, we were closing on another vessel already moored off the town and on that ship, rather than on the surrounding mountains, Owen Swain fixed his eyes. For from the Captain of that ship, the only craft besides ourselves within the bay, he could most quickly obtain what information he desired about the port of Scarborough.

As we approached her, I read casually the name lettered on her stern—the *Betsey* of London, obviously enough a large ship-rigged merchantman that had been moored there in Tobago some weeks at least from the look of her furled sails and the seaweed encrusting her cable.

A few ship lengths beyond her, we let go our anchor, and as rapidly as might be with our reduced crew, clewed up our canvas, coming gently to rest against our cable with sails loosely furled. The first leg of our voyage homeward was completed.

Our anchor was hardly down when the Captain ordered our whaleboat lowered. Eagerly I looked off toward the wharf jutting out from the waterside at Scarborough, like any youth immediately aflame to set foot upon a foreign shore. But the skipper quickly dashed my ardor.

"Mr. Folger," he said, "while I go ashore with the cook to see what provision this place affords, I shall land thee on yon ship to see perchance whether her master, if he will, can enlighten thee somewhat with respect to lunar distances and longitude, and whatever else thou canst learn from him. On my return, I'll stop alongside her to pick thee up again."

"Aye, aye, sir," I answered, crestfallen indeed that here in broad daylight the moon and her diabolic attributes should thus inauspiciously rise to block my chances of setting foot ashore. But as best I could, I concealed my chagrin, climbed down the ladder into the waiting boat, and we shoved off.

I eyed the *Betsey* curiously as we approached her. Unlike the *Beaver*, she had a high poop, but otherwise in her broad beam and bluff bows she was just such an old tub as we were, being built also solely for carrying bulk and not with any regard to speed.

Our whaleboat danced swiftly across the quiet waters of the harbor, propelled by four oarsmen with Red Jerry stroking, to round to alongside the starboard quarter against an empty wherry tied up there beneath her gangway.

Captain Swain, acting as coxswain of our boat, skilfully laid us close aboard the wherry. Looking up her towering side then expectantly to the deck for some quartermaster but seeing none, he loudly hailed,

"*Betsey* ahoy!"

Still no man appeared at the head of the gangway, nor were any to be seen on deck. Impatient, however, to be off on his way ashore, the Captain gave up awaiting any reply and spoke to me,

"Lay thyself aboard, Mr. Folger, make my compliments to the master of the *Betsey*, and as I have instructed thee, learn what thou canst."

"Aye, aye, sir." I leaped lightly from the bow of our

[83]

whaleboat into the rocking wherry and proceeded, as befitted my dignity, slowly to scale the steep gangway. The whaleboat sheered off smartly and headed for the wharf, leaving me alone with what diplomacy I might muster to face the British Captain with my strange request.

I reached the deck, looked about, surprised by lack of any evidence of activity there. For with every hatch in that West Indiaman open to her holds, forward, amidships, and aft, it appeared that in the middle of the forenoon I might well expect to see the sweating seamen under the driving mates busily engaged in breaking out from the holds the cargo she had brought from London or in stowing below the bags of sugar and coffee or the hogsheads of tobacco they had traded it for with the planters of Tobago.

I paused uncertainly. Through a closed window in the poop bulkhead aft I could see someone seated before a table in the cabin busily engaged in writing who might well be either master or supercargo. I wanted before I thrust myself upon him, to find an opportunity at least to learn from some seaman what his name might be were he the Captain.

I strode forward therefore, trusting I might at least get that bit of information in the forecastle, but when I started down the *Betsey's* forecastle hatch, I swiftly changed my mind. Whatever might be the occasion thereof, there could be no doubt that a violent altercation was in full swing amongst the crew below, with foul oaths and angered threats bidding fair to turn the argument there any moment into blows and broken heads.

Not wishing to be involved on a foreign ship in any brawl amongst a crew drunk perhaps on the rum which that island no doubt plentifully provided, I hastily withdrew. I must face the strange Captain wholly ignorant even of his name.

Avoiding the opened cargo hatches, I made my way aft again down the larboard side, noting only that the holds seemed well filled with fragrantly odorous bags and casks which might indicate that the *Betsey* was due to weigh anchor shortly for her homeward voyage. Abreast the mainmast, I paused a moment, scanned more closely the poop bulkhead, and noted that the solitary door to the cabin lay directly abaft the opened hatchway to the after hold. Skirting that coaming with some care lest I go tumbling below on my head to fetch up there on an unyielding hogshead of tobacco, I stopped before the closed door, listened a moment to the scratching inside of a quill pen over some bill of lading perhaps, and then rapped vigorously.

Immediately the scratching stopped and a resonant voice from within called out,

"Come."

I pulled open the door, entered.

The writer seated at the cabin table looked up casually, but seeing that I was no member of the crew, he rose immediately and looked inquiringly at me. Observing that he was but a young man, probably around twenty-five, and hardly old enough to be master of such a ship, I assumed that I had before me only the supercargo.

"Your pardon, sir," I said, "but I am looking for your Captain. Is he aboard?"

"Aye, and you have him e'en before you. I am Captain Paul, master of the *Betsey*," he replied in a deep voice in which I noted some slight traces of a Scottish brogue. "And you, sir?"

In much confusion at my mistake, doubly unfortunate considering the queer nature of my mission, I gazed speechless into the firm grey eyes confronting me. Then noting no sign of offense there but only friendliness, I found my tongue and mumbled apologetically,

"My humblest regrets for mistaking you, sir. I am Thomas Folger, third mate of the American whaler *Beaver* which has just cast anchor astern of you. My Captain's compliments to you, sir, and he has sent me aboard to ask of you a favor, an' you have time to grant it."

"Indeed? And what may it be? We rarely see a whaler in these West Indian ports as the whales frequent not this part of the ocean. However, pray be seated." Casually he reached out, and with an arm longer than I had ever seen on any man, he gripped a heavy chair on the far side of the

[85]

cabin. As if it had been a feather, he dropped it lightly before the table, which as I had suspected, was covered with bills of lading on which he had been working. "I shall gladly do what I can for your Captain, though in good truth, you catch me at an unfortunate time," he continued. "My second mate is ill below, my first mate has been but lately advanced to that station for the first time in his life and is poorly acquainted with his duties. And my crew, I fear, is being led into rebellion by a vicious scoundrel newly shipped in this port. In this, if I mistake not, the mate encourages him rather than supports me. You saw not the mate on deck when you came aboard?"

"No, sir." I slid into the chair which Captain Paul was courteously holding back for me with those unbelievably long arms of his. "There was neither officer nor man on deck to greet me when I came up the gangway."

Captain Paul sank wearily into the chair beside me and with a gesture of irritation pushed back the sandy locks tumbling over his forehead.

"The worthless rogue!" he muttered. "Then he must be fraternizing again with the men below in the fo'c'sle. Where this will end unless I shortly get to sea, who can tell? For in this port, seamen are not easily come by and if I lose even one man now, can I safely sail so short-handed?" For a moment he looked off into space as if trying to supply the answer to his question, the while I gazed into his resolute face, wondering what was up. Who the mate was that had so roused his ire, I had, of course, no knowledge. But as I noted the symmetry of shoulders that marked Captain Paul's figure to go with his unusual arms, a pair of shoulders and a firm chest that for strength I doubt Red Jerry himself could excel, I had no doubt that it would go hard with the derelict mate should Captain Paul lay hands upon him to guide him back to rectitude.

"Enough of that!" Abruptly Captain Paul came out of his reverie, looked me up and down. "Your Captain craves a favor of me, so you say? What may it be?"

"Some of your time, sir," I answered eagerly. "We are

in much distress on the *Beaver* with our original Captain and our mate, who alone knew anything of navigation, both slain by a whale. Our new Captain has placed that duty on me who never took a sight before this voyage, nor indeed was ever at sea, though I am now rated third mate in this emergency. Latitude I can cope with in some fashion, but longitude is wholly beyond me, and my Captain begs of you to instruct me, an' it be possible, at least in the rudiments of longitude that we may with greater safety make passage homeward to Nantucket whither now we are bound."

"A strange request, that I should teach you in a few hours what has taken me months to learn." He scanned me incredulously, then muttered with a half sigh, "But I see your Captain proves his utter ignorance of navigation in his supposition that I can instruct you in it to any purpose in a few brief hours, even if I had them wholly free. However, I shall gladly do what I may, since you seem a likely youth and eager to learn. Know you anything of logarithms or of trigonometry?"

"No, sir; my schooling in Nantucket ere I shipped went not so far," I responded unhappily.

" 'Tis unfortunate then, for that must come first." He arose, beckoned me to accompany him, moved across the low cabin. Stooping my tall shoulders awkwardly lest I bump the deck beams overhead, I moved at his side, impressed by the lithe grace with which he, who was but of medium height and as a consequence not bothered by the timbers above, strode across that room.

"Here," he ordered, pulling a much worn book off a shelf and giving it to me, "seat yourself on this transom in the stern and cast an eye over these principles of mathematics, that is, the geometry, the trigonometry, and the elucidation of logarithms which a seaman should know, while I complete my manifest on yonder table. I will expound it to you later, but you catch me at a bad moment to help you overmuch, since tomorrow we sail and I can trust no one on this ship

[87]

save myself with these accounts of my cargo." He examined me keenly.

"You are by accident third mate, you say, though on your first voyage? And what may be your age?"

"Sixteen, sir," I confessed, blushing for my youth.

"Sixteen, eh? 'Tis somewhat old to start going to sea, though there's nothing for it now save for you to make the best of it. For a sailorman, a lad should leap practically from his cradle to the forecastle, with no dilly-dallyings ashore between to spoil him. At twelve I was myself shipped on a merchantman bound out of Scotland for the Virginias. At fourteen, I was Mr. Midshipman Paul of His Majesty's Navy. And at sixteen, God help me, I was third mate on an African slaver plying the ocean between the coast of Guinea and these West Indies, with the seas between and the vile ways of many who trade thereon already an old story to me. Well, so be it. Sit down here, Mr. Folger, and make what you can of that book intended to instruct the young gentlemen of the Royal Navy in something else than the use of influence at Court in getting themselves promoted. Though," he concluded bitterly, "well I learned that to that end, family connections far outweigh all seamanlike knowledge or ability."

With that cryptic comment, he left me to examine the book while he went back to the invoices of his cargo.

I opened the book, where inscribed on the flyleaf I saw written in a boyish flourish, "John Paul, Midshipman, Royal Navy, 1761." So this merchant captain of the lumbering *Betsey* had once indeed, as he said, been an officer in the King's Navy. Though it was only too evident from his caustic reference that he must have parted therefrom with a rankling of soul still festering after ten or twelve years. But on that, I had little time to dwell. I plunged immediately into the "Rules and Principles of Mathematics of Use in the Solution of Problems in Navigation."

How long I had been buried in the diagrams illustrative of trigonometric functions I know not, when I was aroused therefrom by a loud commotion on deck. The outer door was flung unceremoniously open and from a mob of sailors clustered outside, a drunken seaman, naked to the waist, without so much as a knock lurched through into the cabin.

"Damme, Cap'n!" he burst out, crashing a horny fist down on the table, "we've had a bellyful o' Scotch stinginess an' we're all shoving off! Fourteen months and not a rag to our backs nor a shilling in pay and the lads for'd have elected me to tell ye plain we'll stand no more of it!"

Startled, I closed my book. So this was what had been brewing in the turbulent forecastle when I stepped aboard. I looked at Captain Paul, half expecting him to leap up and fell the man. But still seated the young Scotch Captain gazed imperturbably at the swaying seaman before him, looking him over carefully from the calloused bared feet and the filthy canvas trousers to the luridly tattooed chest and the bewhiskered face leering drunkenly down at him.

"Inform yourself better, man, ere you speak again to your Captain," he said at last with unbelievable mildness. "The *Betsey* has been but three months out of London and you yourself but a fortnight ago shipped here in this port. Wherein then come those fourteen months you complain of? And till we return to London, no man's pay is due. So what you say is wholly false."

Clearly taken aback by both the logic and the unexpected restraint of this reply, the seaman hesitated, but only for a moment.

"Two weeks or fourteen months, it's all the same to Jack Fry! I've had enough o' the *Betsey*. I'm an Englishman, I am, and I sail with no Scotch skinflints! Look at these bloody rags ye have your seamen wearing!"

Critically the seated skipper again examined Jack Fry's trousers, the only garment that he wore, then coolly remarked,

"Aye, Jack, I see now beneath the two weeks added filth, they are the very rags you shipped in. Had you laid out your advance in pay on clothes instead of that rum which was your choice, not mine, you might now somewhat resemble the decent English sailorman I would prefer aboard

[89]

my ship. However, I see that truly you want clothes. Go about your duty and I'll have frocks and trousers issued you at once." And wholly unperturbed, the Captain rose, drew some keys from his pocket and went forward toward the storeroom abreast the after hold, at which unexpected event the crew clustered outside scattered immediately to start ostentatiously battening down the fore hold hatch.

A look of stupid amazement covered Jack Fry's bleary countenance. That his mutinous slanders on his Captain should have brought this result, as if they had been the most respectful of reasonable requests of a needy seaman, was utterly beyond him. But there was nothing he could do. Outmaneuvered, he followed his Captain on deck, where abreast the mainmast a few moments later, I saw Captain Paul deposit in his arms the promised clothing, the while some others of the crew gathered round requesting the same.

I lost all interest in my book on mathematics. That Captain Paul had so calmly stomached the gross insults of a drunken sailor seemed unlike him or any master, explainable only on the ground that seamen were wholly unobtainable in the island of Tobago, and that, about to sail for London, he dared lose no one of those he had already shipped, mutinous though he might be.

Apparently desirous of appeasing all, the youthful skipper disappeared once again into the storeroom, upon which I saw that Jack Fry, instead of taking his new clothing forward to the forecastle, promptly made for the gangway, down which, clothing and all, he sneaked, evidently bent on immediate desertion.

Soon back on deck, Captain Paul distributed to the others the clothes they had asked, whereupon all hands turned to battening down forward. Their Captain stood by the mainmast for a moment watching them, to note with what will they, together with the mate who had showed up from forward, now went about their duty. Then observing doubtless that Jack Fry was not among them, he sauntered casually to the gangway and peered down into the wherry there.

Immediately he stiffened. But saying not a word, he remained with his glance fixed below till Jack Fry, busy casting loose the boat, looked up to see that his Captain had an eye upon his doings.

"Leave not so hastily, Jack," advised the skipper. "I release you from your agreement willingly enough, provided first I find a man to serve in your room, and otherwise, not at all. But consider well, if you attempt to desert the *Betsey*, after I've had you flogged for it what the magistrates here in Tobago will—"

"I'll magistrate you!" blurted out Jack, leaping up the gangway. "Flog me, will ye? Stay in your cabin and don't show your prying nose on deck again till I'm well clear o' you and your stinking *Betsey* or ye'll die swift!" And like a charging bull, head down with tarred pigtail flying straight out behind, he swept through the gangway opening to send the master sprawling unceremoniously full length out on the deck planks.

"You'll flog me, eh, you Scotch bastard?"

Contemptuously he regarded a moment the prostrate officer, then with an obscene gesture too indecent to be mentioned, he vanished again down the side.

Captain Paul regained his feet badly shaken. With blazing eyes he gazed round for his assailant, but not seeing him, rushed immediately into the cabin. Ignoring my presence, he looked wildly round the room, apparently seeking something which might serve him for a club. Had he wanted weapons, there in plain sight on the table amongst his papers lay by some chance his sword, and I have little doubt that in his desk lay some loaded pistols also.

However, disregarding desk and table, he fumbled frantically through his clothes locker for some stick, but not finding any, he swept up at last from the table his bared sword and sprang again out on deck, brandishing it. Not wishing to lose even the few seconds it would take him to get to the gangway opening in the waist of the *Betsey*, he darted immediately athwartships abaft the opened after hatchway to lean far outboard over the starboard gunwale

[91]

where he could look down on the foot of the gangway.

"Back to your duty, Jack!" ordered the master grimly. "No man deserts my ship!"

Below Jack Fry was on the last step of the ladder, about to drop into the wherry and shove clear. It was as evident to him as it was to Captain Paul that his elopement could now be prevented by no human force. Only if he could intimidate the fleeing seaman, could the master avoid losing him.

But Captain Paul counted not on the effect the sight of his sword actually had on the rum-soaked brain of burly Jack. One glance at that gleaming blade flashing over the bulwarks far above his head and Jack went berserk. Disdaining escape, he withdrew his foot from the wherry and came bounding belligerently back up the gangway.

"To hell with floggings, magistrates, and swords!" he roared, leaping nimbly back on deck before his Captain could get forward to the gangway. "Toss that sword overboard and crawl into your cabin, or I'll ram it down your bloody throat!" Nothing daunted by the master striding forward with that threatening blade, he turned his back upon it insolently, dashed inboard to the fife rail at the base of the mainmast, seized there a belaying pin, and whirling about, rushed headlong upon Captain Paul, wholly heedless of his sword, intent only on crushing in his skull with one deadly smash of that upraised bludgeon.

What ensued, startled me. With his extraordinarily long arm, Captain Paul swept his sword expertly up over his head to the parry, in a shower of sparks squarely caught the descending iron pin close to his hilt, stopped the blow short. Immediately, the drunken seaman, fatally blind to his own danger, threw back his arm for another swing, leaving his bared chest wide open to the lightning thrust which confidently I expected next instant to see run him through and through, ending all.

But no thrust came. Instead, Captain Paul dropped back on guard, point extended to keep his opponent off. And from then on, with the master very evidently intent only on defending himself, the battle was a dizzying succession of smashing blows and hairbreadth parries which left me as dumbfounded as was the silent crew clustered in the waist watching breathlessly that deadly combat. For should but one of those crazed blows slide by that whirling sword, the Captain's brains would instantly be spattered over the deck.

It was beyond me why young Captain Paul in such mortal peril withheld his hand when a dozen times he had good opportunity to get in a decisive thrust on his murderous assailant. But coolly relying on his swordmanship, parrying always, attacking never, slowly Captain Paul retreated backward toward the quarterdeck, intending apparently simply to save himself by withdrawing through the opened cabin door behind, regardless alike of frenzied blows and vile oaths showered upon him by the infuriated mutineer.

If he had only remembered the opened after hatchway in the path behind between him and that cabin door, he might well have succeeded in his design. But wholly engrossed in his defense, not till he stumbled backward against the coaming framing that yawning opening to the after hold, did he recall it and then it was too late. Suddenly thrown off balance when his left heel collided unexpectedly with the high coaming, he hovered a moment on the verge of plunging backward headfirst into the hold. In that fatal instant, I watched horror-stricken as with a fiendish yell of triumph, Jack Fry leaped in with uplifted bludgeon to crush his helpless victim's skull.

Captain Paul could retreat no longer, nor, teetering uncertainly over that open hold, had he even fair opportunity to parry again. But in that terrifying moment, twisting agilely like a falling cat, for the first and last time he lunged fiercely forward, point lowered, driving his sword to the hilt hard up on Fry's naked chest to drop him like a pole-axed ox, pierced through the heart!

Lifted clean off his heels by the savage force of that blow, with the sword protruding horribly from between his shoulders and the belaying pin clattering down from his nerveless arm, Jack Fry crashed heavily backward to the deck

[93]

where with bulging eyes, contorted face, and fingers clawing convulsively at empty air, he sprawled limply out.

In the moment of silence that followed this sudden cessation of the uproar of battle, a chorus of sullen oaths burst from amidships, then from the mate came a hoarse cry,

"He's killed poor Jack in cold blood! Come on, my lads! Down with him! We'll have no murderer for Captain!"

Slowly Captain Paul stooped over the twitching body before him, with an effort dragged from between its heaving ribs his bloody sword. Without even so much as a glance at the threatening mob in the waist of the *Betsey*, he swung unsteadily about toward the cabin door, leaving his crew to rush the bleeding body of their late leader forward.

Never, as Captain Paul turned his countenance aft upon me, have I seen such horror on a human face. He staggered with uncertain feet and blanched cheeks down the quarter-deck into the cabin like a man bewitched, his dilated eyes fixed only on that blade reddened now with human blood. There he dropped heavily onto the stern transom, a picture of abject despair, groaning hopelessly,

"Of all the ports on the seven seas, in Tobago again! In Tobago, where Mungo Maxwell died! Will even my friends here now believe me?"

His head rested in his hands, his staring grey eyes were riveted on that stained steel from which the red blood dripped to gather in tiny puddles on the cabin planking at his feet. In an agony of remorse his fingers swept across his forehead as if futilely endeavoring to blot out the sight of the sword as well perhaps as wipe away some anguished vision of the past.

I stood and watched him uncertainly. I had already seen enough violent death on the *Beaver* so that the richly-deserved end of a mutineer bent on murder upset me not. Why it should so completely unhinge the self-possessed young Captain of the *Betsey* I could make nothing of, for certainly he had but defended himself. Nor could I see wherein his mutterings concerning the mysterious Mungo Maxwell and his death, whether in Tobago or elsewhere,

[94]

were anything to the point in this matter.

While I still cogitated what, if anything, I might do to help, Captain Paul pulled himself suddenly together, rose, addressed me.

"Come," he ordered. "It is bootless to stay here longer. I am going ashore to surrender myself before a magistrate while yet I have that chance. My friends there will see justice done. And you perchance may help me as a witness to the facts. You heard, mayhap, how swift the mate when Jack Fry fell, showed himself thirsting after my command? Between my mate and those rascally followers of Fry, rest assured the truth will not escape the grossest perversions from their lips."

I nodded acquiescence mutely. Captain Paul dragged a hat from his locker, with a firm step though still pale of countenance, moved toward the cabin door. Without a word, I followed out on deck to find it wholly deserted, which was perhaps a stroke of luck for me. For had that mutinous crew, whose hoarse threats of vengeance we heard issuing from the forecastle, or any of them been there to observe, I doubt not but that they would have rushed their unarmed Captain and in good conscience, I could have done naught save aid him, so that weaponless as we both were, it would have gone hard with us.

Down the gangway into the wherry we dropped. I cast loose hurriedly, seized the oars, pushed off, and as silently as I might, began to row away from the *Betsey*, thankful indeed that she had no other boats in the water in which we could quickly be pursued.

Once well clear, I lay back heartily on my pair of oars, which after the massive sweeps I had pulled in the *Beaver's* whaleboats, seemed but feathers to me. In the sternsheets sat Captain Paul moodily facing me, wrapped up completely in his thoughts about the seaman he had slain and what might follow. Only once while I tugged shoreward on the oars did he come out of his lethargy.

"Look you, Mr. Folger, beneath that thwart on which you sit," he ordered.

I rested on my oars, bent forward, looked as he had bid. There, neatly folded up, were a pair of new canvas trousers and a blue frock. I resumed my rowing.

"Those are the very clothes I gave Jack Fry," continued John Paul, "and their presence in this wherry good evidence of his intent to desert the ship. Please to remember that, Mr. Folger, when before the court. It may well be decisive."

"Aye, aye, sir," I agreed, for here indeed had the keen-witted Captain put his finger on the solitary material fact confirming that his action had resulted only from his lawful steps to prevent an actual desertion, which next to outright mutiny, was the worst crime on the seaman's calendar.

We were approaching the dock. I twisted about, scanned it for the landing steps. Well inshore, I glimpsed our whale-boat heaving idly to the harbor swell with Captain Swain already at the tiller, the cockpit piled high with vegetables and melons, and the oarsmen about to shove off for their return to the *Beaver*, via the *Betsey* to pick me up.

I bent my back to the oars, drove hurriedly in astern the whaleboat. Captain Paul leaped ashore with the painter, made it fast to a ring in the dock. In some surprise, Captain Swain looked from my companion to me, then very sourly observed,

"Get thee into the whaleboat, Mr. Folger, and next time observe more closely the orders that I give thee. I like not thy wasting what little time thou hadst for improving thy head in navigation in wearing out thy back in a task any stout seaman of the *Betsey* might have done as well or better."

I flushed instantly red, considering the circumstances in which I had manned those oars, but prudently refrained from argument. Instead, as calmly as I could, I hurriedly explained,

"Captain, this is Captain John Paul of the *Betsey*. There has been mutiny and sudden death on his ship while I was aboard her, and I have come ashore with Captain Paul who is sadly involved therein, to go before a magistrate and there make affidavit respecting what I saw, should he be charged unjustly with murder in this case."

"Murder?" Owen Swain's eyes opened wide. "Is the *Beaver* to be plagued with nothing but murder and sudden death this cruise? Murder, indeed? Then I want no officer of mine involved in it! Get thee instantly into this boat, Mr. Folger! Thou'lt set no foot ashore here to make affidavits that will entangle thee and the *Beaver* here in Tobago with sea lawyers and subpoenas!"

"But, Captain," I pleaded, looking helplessly from Captain Paul, dismal and silent there on the dock, to my own skipper. "It is desperately important to Captain Paul that—"

"Argue not with me," exclaimed Owen Swain coldly. "Dost wish to find thyself a seaman ere thou set foot again on deck the *Beaver?* Let the master of the *Betsey* get what affidavits he desires from his own mates, not from mine. Dost think I dare let the solitary navigator I have, poor though thou art, fall into the jaws of these admiralty sharks while they wrangle interminably over thee and thy affidavits? And for want of thee, the *Beaver* rots idly in this harbor, wasting her owner's substance, instead of dropping out with the ebb tide at dawn tomorrow as I intend? When we are safely anchored in Nantucket, thou canst there swear to whatever affidavits thy conscience allows, but not before. Into this boat, I say, and not another word or it shall go hard with thee!"

In anguish I looked up to Captain Paul for decision, uncertain whether I should obey or no, for of a surety I knew what affidavit he might expect from his disloyal mate. And as for those other brutes on the *Betsey*, thirsting only for vengeance, with what perjuries they might swear his life away I could well guess. And well John Paul there on the dock, in deathly silence seeing his only witness ordered away from him, knew it too. It needed but a word from him and I should leap ashore to make that affidavit, be the consequences to me what they might.

With a melancholy smile, John Paul looked down upon me, gave me my answer.

[97]

"Get into the whaleboat, Mr. Folger. Obey your Captain gladly, for he is right. Your duty, as well as his, is wholly to your ship and not to me. I shall make out in these circumstances as best I may. But, an' it still please you, when you return to Nantucket send to me your attested statement via the *Betsey's* owners in London. It still may be not too late to save me. And fare you well!" With a grim wave and his thin lips tightly set together, Captain Paul turned abruptly on his heel, set off down the wharf.

I scrambled silently over the bow of the wherry into the whaleboat, disregarding Owen Swain's glaring eyes fixed on me as I passed him, for well he sensed that it was Captain Paul's orders and not his I had obeyed. But as the whaleboat shoved clear of the dock and behind Red Jerry the oarsmen swayed rhythmically into the stroke, he looked astern to where, a solitary tragic figure, the master of the *Betsey* strode resolutely off to give himself up to the dubious mercies of a pack of perjurers, and grudgingly observed,

"That Captain Paul of thine hath something to commend him. 'Tis not every Captain knows that as between *his* life and a ship, be it whose it may, the ship comes always first."

12

IN the moonless night, I hung restlessly over the bulwark of the *Beaver*, unable to sleep from the turmoil raging in my mind over what had happened that day. A cable's length away, a dark blotch on the darker water, the *Betsey* swung idly to her hawser, and across the rippling waters of Rockley Bay, the lights of Scarborough glimmered, faint yellow points piercing the blackness.

The *Beaver* was to drift out of the harbor homeward bound with the outgoing tide at the first streaks of dawn. How, I wondered, would Captain Paul, left thus alone among his enemies, make out there in Tobago? And what nameless dangers in addition to those I knew of, did he fear from the nebulous Mungo Maxwell, who had died in Tobago? And why?

Four bells struck, loud and clear in the quiet night. I glanced forward, vaguely made out Red Jerry, save for myself the only man on deck, just releasing the lanyard of the bell. Forward in the forecastle, enjoying their first all night in since we had left Nantucket, slumbered the others of the crew. Aft, unless for any reason they be called by the watch on deck, as soundly asleep lay Captain Swain and both the other mates. This luxury I myself would probably be sharing with them if I could only get that vision of John Paul gazing in horror at his bloody sword out of my mind.

As the echoes of the bell died away I caught a phosphorescent flash in the water lapping the ship's side as of a fish nearby and then to my astonishment I saw a long arm reach from the waves, grasp the lowest step of the gangway, and a dripping swimmer haul himself up on the ladder and start stealthily to climb aboard.

With a sudden premonition as to who it might be, I strolled quietly to the gangway lest I alarm Red Jerry, and went swiftly down it to meet the intruder halfway. Sure enough, it was Captain Paul!

"S-sh!" I whispered, lest he leap overboard again or make some struggle that would alarm the watch on deck. " 'Tis I, Tom Folger! Quiet!"

"Thank Heaven!" breathed the panting swimmer. "I had thought to get aboard unseen, but you at least who know my case will certainly not hinder my design." He clung to the ladder a moment, gasping for breath, then in an anguished whisper added, "I must get out of Tobago tonight! Tonight, before any formal complaint is made, so my friends the magistrate and the governor have advised me! I returned aboard the *Betsey* to get a little money and some belongings, intending to row south with them in the wherry when darkness came, to the Spanish isle of Trinidad but twelve miles off. But that devilish mate of mine, who now calls himself the Captain, forestalled me in that by hoisting in the boat and posting a watch before my cabin. As my last hope I slipped overboard out my stern window to take my chances among the sharks and swim here to stow myself away on board the *Beaver*, remembering your Captain to say you were to sail at dawn. As you love God, Tom Folger, hinder me not in this! My mate and all my men are joined to swear I leaped upon unoffending Jack Fry when he demanded clothing and slew him in cold blood. Return on deck and turn your back. You'll see me not again till the *Beaver's* far at sea and it will get you in no trouble with your Captain!"

I clasped his wet hand reassuringly. I would do what I might willingly enough to save him from a felon's death, but I saw a better plan than that. If but a boat was wanting to take him to Trinidad, the whaleboat streaming idly at our stern would serve his purpose better than any wherry. And if he had gold enough to pay them, I could purchase for him the oarsmen needed and their silence afterwards.

"Have you four guineas?" I breathed.

"Yes, and three pounds besides in silver, for I had little

gold with me on the *Betsey*. 'Twas all the coin I dared load myself with when I swam away, but every shilling's yours, an' you but turn your back now," he pleaded, mistaking the import of my query.

" 'Tis not for myself I want the gold, Captain Paul, but mayhap for others. An' you prefer it, with four guineas I may get you a whaleboat's crew that in three hours time will land you on the shores of Trinidad where among the Spaniards you'll be safer far just now than under the British flag on the *Beaver*, even at sea. What say you to it?"

"A boat to Trinidad?" gasped John Paul in relief. "Nothing better! But can you manage it without endangering yourself?"

"With your four guineas, yes," I affirmed. What the seamen on the *Beaver* returning penniless to Nantucket might do for a guinea each I could easily imagine. I knew well what they had lately faced in whaling for far less than that. "Give me the gold."

He fumbled briefly in a waterlogged bag at his waist, produced the four coins.

"Wait here a moment," I said. Quietly I returned up the ladder, looked round. Red Jerry, forward of the try-pots leaning idly against the foremast, had heard nothing. Going up to him in the darkness, I ordered,

"Jerry, I need the whaleboat immediately for a private trip. Get four good oarsmen quietly up from the fo'c'sle for me, but say naught to them and rouse not the others. Swiftly now!"

Red Jerry grunted that he understood, and went below. What he may have thought about my queer idea of rousing up a boat's crew for no apparent purpose at ten o'clock at night, I could well guess, but at least he showed no surprise. Meanwhile, back aft I loosed the painter of our whaleboat astern, dragged it carefully up the starboard side to the ladder, and silently motioned Captain Paul below to get into the sternsheets.

By then Red Jerry and his four seamen were straggling in their bare feet aft toward the gangway, the newcomers on deck cursing none too silently at losing the only unbroken night's rest of their whole cruise. But the deck of the *Beaver* was no place for explanations.

"Into the boat and pipe down!" I ordered, "and quietly, that you disturb not Cap'n Swain's sleep or he'll take your hides off! Not a word from any of you till I lay below with you!"

I turned to Red Jerry.

"I'll be gone a few hours, Jerry. Keep the watch on deck yourself, don't call your relief at eight bells. And don't call the skipper or either of the mates for anything till I get back unless you desperately have to. That's important if you would keep me out of trouble with the Captain."

Red Jerry eyed me dubiously, suspicious of what a young lad was about in a foreign port. But after all, I was an officer, and orders, crazy though they might seem, were still orders.

"Aye, Red Jerry no call him relief. But you look out. The women in these ports bad even for sailors. No good boys play with them."

"Don't worry over me, Jerry. I'll see no women tonight, good or bad for me!" Hurriedly I slipped down the gangway. "Just let everybody aboard keep on sleeping till I get back!"

Below in the boat I found my oarsmen gaping open mouthed at the soaked figure in the stern, but without any explanations, I shipped the rudder and ordered softly,

"No noise, now. Shove off!"

A gentle push and we drifted clear, favored slightly by the last of the ebbing tide, and just as five bells were struck on the *Beaver*, I called out in a low tone,

"Give way!"

Out went the oars, the men settled back to their task, we drew well clear. Sharply I swung the boat about, to the audible consternation of my crew pointing it not for the twinkling lights of Scarborough as they had expected, but dead for the darkness of the open sea to the southward. Some half a dozen ship lengths off, I deemed the time for ex-

[102]

planations had come, if I wished for good results.

"Oars!" I called sharply. With each man, eyes fixed on me in the darkness, resting on his blade I faced my boat's crew.

"This gentleman beside me, who by misadventure dropped overside ere boarding the *Beaver*, has most pressing need to be in Trinidad tonight. And I need hardly tell you we have to be back aboard the *Beaver* before she sails at dawn. It's about twelve miles each way from here to Trinidad. A guinea in gold for each of you if we're back aboard the *Beaver* six hours from now, by one bell in the morning watch, and each man keeps his mouth shut thereafter!" And ostentatiously I spread the four coins wide before them, where even in the night the gleam of the yellow gold was faintly visible against my palm. Sliding the money back into my pocket, I concluded grimly,

"But should we fail to get back by one bell, you row for naught! And rest assured, if ever one of you blabs about this trip, I'll have him flogged! Give way, all!"

They gave way like men possessed, and the whaleboat drove swiftly forward. Not Jared Macy with all his profane urgings in chase of a spermaceti ever got more speed out of a whaleboat's crew than I with those tantalizing guineas flashed under each man's nose. We shot out of Rockley Bay, met the long ocean swells, and steering by the Pole Star low on the night horizon astern of me, I laid my course, south by west, for the isle of Trinidad.

Only then did I address John Paul, who was seated in the cockpit beside me.

"Who was this Mungo Maxwell," I asked curiously, "and what has his death in Tobago to do with you?"

Startled at the question, Captain Paul stiffened perceptibly, hesitated, then replied quietly,

"I suppose you may well ask that. Mungo was carpenter on the ship *John* of Kirkcudbright, of which I was master three years ago. He was lazy, worthless, and disrespectful in the last degree to me as master, and finally here in Tobago I was compelled to have him flogged, after the which I straight discharged him, only to have the idling scoundrel go before the magistrate here, Judge Simpson, to make complaint against me of the stripes he had received aboard the *John*."

He paused, even in the darkness I saw him clench his fists wrathfully at the recollection, then continued sternly,

"It did that villainous carpenter little good. The judge, having personally examined his bared back to find his stripes of little consequence, and his chastisement fully merited by his derelictions, dismissed his complaint as wholly frivolous. With that, I thought I was well rid of the wretch, but, alas, to what grief it brought me! Some weeks later, Mungo Maxwell, in perfect health, shipped out of Tobago aboard the Barcelona packet bound for the Leeward Islands, on which vessel a few days later he died of a tropic fever contracted aboard the packet." A melancholy sigh, long drawn out, interrupted his narration.

"But, surely," I burst in, "that was in no wise at your door! What matters it now?"

"Sufficiently!" he countered. "Of Mungo Maxwell's death I was totally unaware when several months later, having concluded my trading in these islands, I returned with the *John* to Kirkcudbright. Imagine then my distress on making port in Scotland, to learn from my neighbors there that by various foul means I had murdered the man! One story had it I had flogged him to death. And another (of what vileness is rumor capable!) that as he slept on deck in the sun, I had plentifully anointed his garments with spirits of turpentine, laid a train of powder to his breast, and then ignited the train! So that, a flaming human torch, Mungo Maxwell in agony had leaped overboard and thus perished!" His voice broke, he stopped abruptly.

My fingers closed convulsively on the tiller. I gazed sympathetically at tortured Captain Paul, while for the next few minutes he sat there mutely beneath the stars, with only the steady thumping of the oars against the tholepins to break the silence in the boat. The lights of Scarborough had disappeared, we were well out at sea, and save for the black mass of Tobago looming against the dark sky astern, alone in the night in a world of water. I began to get some insight into the agony of soul of my companion. But twenty-six years old, and the murders of two men already laid at his door! With those rumors of Mungo Maxwell in the background it began to be explainable why, with quick death beating about his head, he had at great peril held back his sword against Jack Fry to the last.

"There you have it, my friend," continued Captain Paul. "Armed with affidavits obtained from Judge Simpson in Tobago and from the master of the Barcelona packet as to the true facts of Mungo Maxwell's death, next voyage I returned to Kirkcudbright to confront his relatives, who were breathing all manner of dire vengeance on me for his passing. But when I demanded of them that they bring the matter into court that I might clear myself on trial, they dared not. Instead my name has been defamed with slanderous rumors, still believed by many both in my home at Kirkcudbright and even here in Tobago where Mungo Maxwell got the flogging he richly deserved. And against rumor, how can one defend himself? So now you see in what state I find myself in Tobago. How can my unsupported word justify the violent killing of Jack Fry against the machinations of my own mate and my disaffected crew, all prepared to swear away my life?"

"Aye, sir, that I do!" In hot anger at the injustice of the web of lies entangling this engaging young Captain to whom I was beginning to find myself being strangely drawn, I burst out, "Why flee? We may between us yet confound these perjurers! Let me put the boat about and head back for the *Beaver*. I'll go ashore secretly tonight with you, and the *Beaver* will be well at sea before my absence from her is discovered. Then I may appear before the magistrate in your defense, however long the case may drag."

John Paul shook his head, with a wan smile full in my face, replied,

"I thank you for that loyalty to a stranger, but even if I could accept it at such cost to you, it would not help me. You would stand then before the court a self-confessed deserter from your duty and your ship, and in that light what weight would your oath carry in this case? No, it cannot be. Both Judge Simpson and the honorable governor of the island, William Young, whom I may call my friends, have soberly advised me to leave Tobago ere dawn and to return not till months hence when a regular admiralty court sits on the island. Then with these hotheads on my ship cooled off, I can confront such few of them as may come into court with what evidence I can gather meantime. There will be a reasonable chance of seeing justice done later, whereas now there is none at all. And that, with your aid, I shall do. Meanwhile, I have no choice tonight save to flee and abandon all I have given years of toil to gain—my ship, my share in her and her cargo (of both of which I am part owner) and my interests in these islands, leaving all to fare as best they may in the hands of my partner in Tobago, Archibald Stuart, who promises to have his manager look after them for me. More than this, I cannot do, and less, I dare not."

Against this cogent reasoning, I had no arguments. Captain Paul lapsed into moody silence and in that silence I was content to let the matter rest, the while to the rhythm of the oars the heaving whaleboat drove monotonously southwards through the night over the dark seas toward Trinidad and the dubious safety it might afford under the Spanish flag to the fugitive young Scotchman.

13

AGAINST head winds, we beat our way northward in the *Beaver* from Tobago. Such a dismal passage I never again hope to make. Short-handed, improperly officered, poorly navigated, in long tacks we fought our way homeward over stormy seas. Our empty vessel made more leeway than headway. We were uncertain always of our true position and sunk in constant gloom over the futility of our profitless voyage and the harrowing deaths of our shipmates.

Five weeks out of Tobago, running westward down the 41st parallel of north latitude from far out in the Atlantic whither the gales and our last tack northward had carried us, we finally picked up Sankaty Head on Nantucket. We beat our way into Nantucket Sound close hauled on the starboard tack, rounded Great Point, and with the wind fair for the first time for our last brief leg, we drove southwesterly for the harbor. With no difficulty at all nor any need to wait for the high tide, the sadly light *Beaver*, riding higher out of the water even than when we had first crossed the bar outward bound, skimmed over the shallows under shortened sail to cast anchor near Brant Point a few lengths clear of the pier heads.

It was evident enough from the crowds fringing the wharves that our return after an absence of but three months had set the town in turmoil. No doubt from the moment the loom of our topsails had been picked up on the horizon from Mill Hill and our identity made certain by the huge black beaver painted on our foretopsail as a recognition mark, Nantucket had been buzzing with rumor. To every Nantucketer, there could be only two explanations for such an extraordinarily swift return of a spouter fitted out for a three year cruise—the greasiest luck for three months ever heard of, or disaster. And even to the veriest tyro in Nantucket, whether man or woman, one glimpse of the *Beaver's* bluff-bowed hull riding high out of water carried the tale that greasy luck had not brought her so unexpectedly back home.

There was no need for our ensign floating at half-mast from the mizzen to carry ashore the news of disaster. The silent crowds on Straight Wharf and along the waterfront had sensed that long before our ensign was visible to them. They stood mournfully, women mostly, with every woman, American or Portuguese, whose husband or son had sailed on the *Beaver* waiting with such fortitude as she could muster in her anguish to learn whether it was to her that crunching jaws or sweeping flukes had brought bereavement.

I strained my eyes across the water to the dock, striving to pick from the rows of motionless figures there the face of my mother, that I might perchance attract her attention by my frantic waving and put an end to her agonies over my safety. But no face there could I identify as hers and finally I gave up, convinced that she had not dared repeat the trial she had gone through on the dock when the *Dartmouth* had returned without my father. This time she would wait the news, be it good or ill, in the isolation of our home.

Our anchor had hardly splashed overboard and our canvas been loosely furled than the whaleboat from the larboard quarter was dropped into the water, manned, and on its way ashore bearing Captain Swain. He scrambled up the dock. The women there fell away to make room for him, then suddenly he was lost to our view in a cloud of skirts and bonnets closing about him as if he had been a messenger from some battlefield. How he broke the news of our disastrous loss I can only guess, but a moment later, across the water to us on the *Beaver's* deck came unmistakably the sobs of many weeping women and the hysterical shrieks of one at least.

I got ashore myself soon, ferried in by the wherry of a ship chandler who had laid alongside us in the hope (vain, of course) that we might with some provisioning quickly sail again. There was naught left aboard for me to do, Obed Hussey having the task of securing all for port. Eagerly, as the shore boat laid me alongside the wharf, I scrambled up the steps, looking swiftly about to see if by some chance I had missed sight of my mother.

By now the crowd had broken up into little knots surrounding the new made widows and wailing orphans, endeavoring awkwardly to comfort them. Just at the end of the dock I could see Owen Swain between Keziah Coffin and Captain Rotch, the two principal owners of the *Beaver*, vanishing in the direction of the latter's counting house to justify, no doubt, his conduct in bringing the *Beaver* back a "clean" ship. What Captain Rotch, himself an old ex-whaler, might think of such uncommercial conduct in a spouter skipper I could only surmise, but if I knew Keziah Coffin, I had little doubt that when her gimlet eyes and rasping voice had finished giving Owen Swain a proper going over for returning home without even one barrel of oil to help cover outfitting expenses, he might well wish it had been his luck to have vanished in the maw of that whale I had sighted, leaving Jared Macy instead to have come home with the explanations.

I stared uncertainly about me on the wharf. Surely my mother was not there, and convinced at last of that, I was just turning my steps shoreward toward Orange Street and home, when from the group surrounding a woman in wild hysteria (whom I soon saw to be Manuel's Portuguese wife) my cousin Delight came running toward me.

My heart began to thump oddly, for aside from my mother, the only person on our island of Nantucket to whom I had given two thoughts during my cruise was this same Quaker minx, as maddening to me perhaps as that contrary moon with which to no more purpose I had struggled in my navigation. It made my pulses leap that at sight of me Delight should instantly leave the comforting of Manuel Sylvia's widow to her friends, and come flying toward me. But I was hardly prepared nevertheless for the abandon with which she flung both her arms about my neck and clung to

[109]

me, for surely I had never before dared more than shyly to press her hand in some frolic at sheep shearing time.

"Oh, Tom, Tom! I thank the Lord who hath brought thee safely back to us from all thy perils!" Sobbing, she looked with tear-stained face up into mine. Queer, I thought, peering into those brown eyes, what three scant months had wrought in Delight, and in me also perhaps, for surely she was a woman now. With a feeling wholly new to me, I caressed the lovely head pressed tightly to my shoulder. "I have seen little but grief," she continued, "since the *Beaver* sailed with thee!"

"Grief?" I asked, puzzled. "What has brought you grief in my doing no more than every man here in Nantucket has done for generations?"

"It was thy mother, Thomas. I did all a daughter might have done to ease her mind, but to—" A fresh outburst of sobbing choked her off, she buried her head in my shoulder.

"My mother?" Gripped by sudden fear, I seized her head with both my hands, savagely turned it upward again that I might look into her face. "What of my mother? Is she ill? No lies now!" I demanded roughly.

"She is dead." With infinite compassion in her tearful eyes, Delight looked up at me. "I had thought to break it to thee more gently, Thomas, hadst thou but given me fair opportunity."

Dead? My mother dead? In a daze, I looked incredulously down on Delight Coffin. It could not be. I had left my mother still shocked, it is true, by the blow of my father's end, but otherwise in as good health as any woman on Nantucket. How could she now be dead?

"Aye, it is true, Thomas," said Delight brokenly, reading in my eyes my evident disbelief. "She was a woman in a trance from the hour the *Beaver* sailed, certain each day that in some horrible encounter a whale had killed thee as he slew thy father. Nothing I could tell her to the contrary affected her belief. She cared not to live. I could not make her eat, though daily I came to see her and tried tempting her with the best my poor skill in the kitchen might afford.

And a month ago, weakened in mind and body by her fast, in a vision more vivid than any before of thy death, she gave a sudden shriek and fell senseless at my feet. Despite all we could do for her, a week later she died. Oh, Thomas, how I pity thee!" Unrestrainedly Delight wept afresh on my shoulder.

With such a lump rising in my throat that I could scarce breathe, I stood motionless, hardly aware of the maid weeping in my arms. I was now alone in the world. First my father, now my mother gone. So this was what whaling had brought all of us! With burning eyes and parched throat, I looked about at the other mourners on Straight Wharf, stricken as I had been by the leviathans of the deep. In bitter anguish I cursed the day I had gone awhaling against my mother's desire that I forswear that calling. I had killed her as truly as if I had struck her down with my own hand. My head sagged down almost unconsciously against my cousin's cheek, like a little boy I mingled my tears with hers, till in a sudden burst of remorse, I tore myself rudely away and went stumbling blindly out West Chester Street to Old North Cemetery to fling myself in anguish before a newly planted marker upon the fresh turned sod covering my mother's grave.

14

IN the weeks that followed, I went about Nantucket more lonely than ever I have been before or since. Even the slight comfort I drew from visiting my old shipmates of the *Beaver* soon vanished, for laden with a cargo of oil taken aboard in Nantucket, she sailed within the week under a new master for London, there to trade the sperm oil from Keziah Coffin's warehouses for a return shipload of China tea destined for Boston. I might have gone with her, though, of course, not as third mate. Owen Swain who went out with her in his old position of second mate spoke so highly of me to Captain Rotch that that weather-beaten worthy offered to ship me on her as an able seaman. I cared not, however, to go to sea so soon again even on a trading voyage to London, for slight though they were, I had the affairs of my mother to settle up, included in the which I found to my chagrin were all her debts to Keziah Coffin going back even to my father's ill-fated voyage on the *Dartmouth*.

Henry Gardner went in my place on the *Beaver*, thus adding further to my distress, for Henry was my boyhood crony and the only man left in Nantucket to whom I might pour out my overburdened heart. Henry earnestly pleaded with me to go, that we might see London together, but I turned a deaf ear, for I dared not till I had sold enough of my belongings to clear off at least some of my obligations to my Aunt Keziah.

The solitary pleasure left me now in life was an occasional visit to the Coffin mansion on Centre Street to see Delight whose sympathetic smiles, not to mention the custards and the pies with which she stuffed me to repletion, did much to lift the burden which obsessed me for my mother's death.

But if my Aunt Keziah passed through the room in which we sat a fresh pall of gloom descended on me, for in her cold glance I had little difficulty in reading no sign of welcome to her home but instead the very commercial, if unspoken, question,

"Well, young man, hast brought me yet that eighty pounds thou owest?"

How to clear that debt, that I might as of yore look defiantly again at my Aunt Keziah, pressed me hard down. That Delight cared not for my debts but only for me was evident enough from the glowing smiles and the gentle pressure of my hand with which, after each such encounter with her mother, she sought to ease my distress. For somehow in that whole-souled gesture of understanding with which she had flung herself upon my shoulder there on Straight Wharf, every trace of youthful shyness had vanished from me and I was desperately in love with Delight in every fiber of my lanky frame. But with that eighty pounds sterling owing her mother (which by look or glance the latter never allowed me for an instant to forget while in her presence) between us like a fence, I was tongue-tied.

When Aunt Keziah had passed from the room, would I sit dumbly alongside Delight, aching to crush her again to me and to feel her arms again about my neck as I had once. And demurely would she sit there, wishing, I swear, the same, till the silence became oppressive, and she might break it mockingly,

"Wouldst have another custard, Cousin Thomas?"

Another custard? Delight's kisses, not her cookery, were what my throbbing body ached for, but lest I be forbidden the house altogether, till I had somehow, somewhere, garnered eighty pounds to pay off Aunt Keziah, I dared not be aught but circumspect.

In my lonely house on Orange Street, I looked about me, room by room, and considered desperate measures. The house, unfortunately, did not belong to me. It was rented, else I should have sold it out of hand to redeem myself from bondage. I gazed speculatively at the furniture and the

[113]

linen. With some shrewdness in its sale and a little luck, it might bring fifteen pounds, and that together with the ten pounds turned over to me in coin from my mother's meager hoard, would cancel a third of my debt. But the other two-thirds?

However, aside from that I dismissed the idea of selling the furniture as utterly foolish. If I wished to marry Delight, what figure could I cut before my Aunt Keziah without a chair, without even a bed in the house to which I sought to bring a wife? That would be complete folly.

Dismally I considered my situation. Keziah Coffin was by far the wealthiest woman on Nantucket, her house the grandest, and as Fate would have it, her daughter by all odds the loveliest and sought by many swains beside myself. And I was perhaps of all the young men on Nantucket in Aunt Keziah's eyes the least desirable, an orphan with no family prospects, practically penniless, and heavily in debt, worst of all, to her.

As the summer drifted away into early autumn I pondered all this morosely but to no account. If I cared to enter Captain Rotch's counting house as a clerk, I might with some ease make enough to support myself, and even mayhap in genteel poverty to support a wife, but there I could never hope to rise far in the world. And Delight, a whaler's daughter, would marry no man whose ambitions soared no higher than a clerkship. There was but one out—I must go back awhaling.

Close aboard I had already looked down the livid throat of the largest spermaceti that I might ever meet, and even from a stove boat, I had not flinched to man an oar again and row back to face once more that fighting whale's flukes and jaws. That, I knew now, I could stand as well as any man. But if I wished to whale it to some profit, I must ship next time for no such trifling lay as the two-hundredth. A harpooner or a third mate's lay at least was imperatively required by my necessities. Persuading some Captain to ship me as harpooner was quite out of question since I had never flung an iron, but could I only acquire what I still lacked in navigation, there was some slight chance I might find a hard-pressed owner who might sign me on as third mate.

With some trepidation at my rashness, I parted with ten per cent of all my liquid capital to acquire from the ship chandler's shelves a copy of the "Rules and Principles of Mathematics of Use in the Solution of Problems in Navigation." This calf-bound tome, as ponderous as its weighty title, I had first glimpsed, though briefly, in the cabin of the *Betsey*. And with it I set resolutely to work to master as a foundation the intricacies of Napier's logarithms and the rudiments of geometry and trigonometry, that I might drag the moon from out the realms of romance and make her serve me in my sordid ends of finding my way over the oceans in pursuit of sperm oil.

If aught were required to complete my utter gloom, my struggles far into the night with that text in the lonely parlor of my deserted house on Orange Street were unexcelled in accomplishing that purpose. Granting the monumental intellects of Euclid, Ptolemy, Pythagoras and Lord Napier, who had from thin air, so to speak, plucked the principles laid down to guide me plainly amidst a maze of lines, angles, and uncouth mathematical symbols, still in the presence of their genius I was a groping pigmy slow to comprehend. But doggedly I hunched myself over the table beneath my lamp, striving to make some rhyme and reason of what I read, with the very certain knowledge that if ever I wished to know Delight as more than an abstract theorem in womanhood, I must make soon some concrete sense of Euclid's propositions in curves and angles.

It was my misfortune that in August when I plunged into this matter, our harbor of Nantucket was deserted of spouters, for otherwise I might well have received some instruction from one or another master or mate disposed to help a former shipmate's orphaned son. But with the *Beaver* had departed also the *Dartmouth* and the *Eleanor*, the last two ships in our harbor, all laden with oil to be exchanged for tea in London, and such were the uncertainties of whale catching that not another spouter had since on any ocean completed her cargo of sperm oil and come home.

So sans instructor, I floundered in Napier and Euclid, making but heavy weather of my text. My sole compensation came September first on my seventeenth birthday. I walked the beach at Brant Point in the lee of the lighthouse and Delight, who in honor of the occasion had accompanied me there, took an unexpected interest in the geometric figures I drew in the sand while I was expounding to her what I had learned.

Somehow, to see her with bonnet tossed aside and her fair hair waving in the breeze, while she sat, skirts modestly spread wide over the sands, gazing absorbed upon the relations between hypotenuse, perpendicular, and included angle in my figures, took the curse off my labors and gave me odd palpitations about my heart in nowise connected to trigonometry. One such demonstration that afternoon was however as far as ever I got, for once Delight turned her enquiring brown eyes upward from my figures in the sand upon me for elucidation, sine, cosine, and tangent were immediately forgot. Down upon the sands I dropped to look enslaved into Delight's soft eyes, engrossed in mysteries older far than Euclid as my arm haltingly encompassed her slim waist and her head sank gently down upon my shoulder.

What magic has the sparkling azure sea laving the warm sands beneath the deep blue summer sky thus to bewitch the hearts of youth? At seventeen, who cares? In a sudden wave of madness, I cast discretion to the winds, awkwardly with both my hands turned Delight's face a little upward, pressed my lips feverishly down on hers, and with a surge of wild elation, felt no struggle to escape but instead her lips yield fervently to mine.

"Delight, Delight! My darling! How I love you!" I murmured at last, releasing her a trifle.

"And I love thee, Thomas, too, with all my heart! My dear, my dear, but thou art so slow! I had thought indeed thou wouldst never get beyond thy propositions in geometry!" With lips slightly opened, she looked alluringly up at me, her flushed cheek brushing mine, her arms about my

[116]

neck. "Hold me tightly now, Thomas, lest Euclid overwhelm thee once aga—"

I seized her roughly with both arms, buried my lips again in hers, cut her short. Euclid indeed! And endlessly we sat there on the warm sands, arm in arm, cheek to cheek, unutterably happy, gazing out over the blue waters of Nantucket Sound, silently adoring each other, too blissfully entranced in our caresses to speak again.

How long we sat there, unaware of time, I do not know, but it might well have been some hours, for suddenly right before us on an ocean which when first I had kissed Delight had been wholly free of sails to the far horizon, there loomed up a ship not a cable off slipping calmly by us into the harbor. And to my great embarrassment and Delight's furious blushes, on her quarterdeck, plainly to be seen surveying us with much interest through his telescope, was her Captain!

Instantly we separated, I in a pretense of scanning the strange ship with a professional eye, while Delight began demurely to draw circles in the sand, to the intense amusement evidently of the observant skipper, for immediately he dropped his telescope from his eye, with ostentatious elaboration closed it up, and then with a friendly wave to us across the water, stowed it beneath his arm.

"Ah, Thomas, thou must keep a better watch," sighed Delight. "Yon Captain seems cordial enough in his gestures, but should he tell my mother what doubtless he saw through that glass—were you still kissing me, darling?"

"Aye, dear. I was wasting not my opportunities." And I kissed her again furiously, hugging her close to me in spite of her struggles to escape. "But fear not for that Captain. His ship is neither a Nantucketer nor even a spouter, and to him we are both perfect strangers, for never has such a vessel before made port here. Look you, Delight, at her rig. Saw you ever that ere now?"

Delight looked, immediately ceased struggling, and nestled again affectionately against my shoulder to watch as that black-hulled ship, a lovely sight with her white canvas hauled flat aft, slid by us.

[117]

"Truly thou'rt right, dear Thomas. That fore and aft rig and that rakish hull do not belong to any ship that ever sailed from here. She is built for speed, not for cargo. What does such a vessel want of our island, thinkest thou?"

I scanned the strange ship curiously before replying. By now she was well past us and over the bar, luffing smartly up into the wind with sheets close hauled to deaden headway before dropping anchor. Fore and aft rigs were a novelty in our harbor; all our spouters were square riggers. And such a hull I never saw before, its trim lines and well raked masts bespeaking speed, especially to windward, to the sacrifice of every other quality. But what was queerest in that black-hulled vessel that had slipped like a ghost so silently upon us, was that upon her stern, now plainly visible to me as she luffed, was painted neither name nor port of entry, nor did she fly from mast or gaff any colors whatever to denote her nationality.

"If she carried George's flag, with that long tom I see upon her forecastle and the two guns in her waist, I should say she was one of the King's men-o'-war," I hazarded at last. "Though what a man-o'-warsman might wish on our peaceful island, I know not. However, that she isn't. Do you think she might be a cutter in the customs service?" I asked with a sudden fear for what that might mean in Delight's home, for it was widely rumored on our island that Keziah Coffin, in spite of her stout adherence to King George, saw nothing inconsistent with her Tory loyalty in cheating him on a grand scale by smuggling. In this nocturnal business her summer house on the waterfront at Quaise figured in many a tale of boats plying on moonless nights between vessels offshore and the shrub-shrouded strip of beach before Aunt Keziah's summer cottage.

"Mayhap!" Delight's fingers closed in alarm about my right hand, and she started to rise. No more than I, was she unaware of the rumors surrounding that house at Quaise. "We had best go now. I must warn my mother of this ship."

"Aye, dearest." Tenderly I helped her up, started to brush the clinging sand from off her skirts, but Delight

[118]

would brook of no delay for that. She seized my arm. "Come, Thomas! Mother would know of this immediately!" Hand in hand, we set off down the beach past the lighthouse, bound for the town, the eyes of both of us fixed on that ship which had so rudely interrupted our caresses.

15

I LEFT Delight at the edge of the town, or rather say, she left me, for had it been my option, lost in the clouds as I was, nothing of my own volition, least of all a ship, could have brought me down to earth or parted me from her lips. However that was, Delight in much agitation over what that odd vessel might portend, broke from my arms as I sought one last kiss in the lee of a convenient hedge and went flying homeward toward Centre Street, leaving me nevertheless still treading on air and deliriously intoxicated.

I neither knew nor cared whither my feet led me; an unreal aura of soft hair, clinging lips, and tender fingers stroking my cheeks, enveloped me completely. Seeing nothing, feeling nothing, I made my passage through the town. That I was not knocked down by a yoke of plodding oxen or suddenly submerged by walking off some pierhead, was merely due to the kind Providence which doubtless watches over lovers and of a surety to no prudent observance of whither I was bound on my part.

So it was that it came a sudden shock when I walked all unconsciously into the figure of a man who, instead of stepping aside that I might pass, had stopped squarely before me in the street fringing the market square at the head of the wharves. Abruptly was I brought up short by the collision, to feel myself seized by the shoulder and hear a vaguely familiar voice cutting incisively into my dreams.

"So, Tom Folger, we meet again! And still so bewitched by ardent kisses you recognize not the man you once befriended at your peril?"

Between confusion and the sharp shock of the encounter, I stared some seconds in a daze ere I came to.

"Why, Captain Paul!" Unbelievingly I looked down into

those firm grey eyes which I had last seen on the beach at Trinidad. "You here?"

"Nay, not Captain Paul!" He looked sharply about to see that no one heard, then added softly, "As you love me, Captain *Jones!* So long as we are beneath the British flag, John Paul has vanished from this life and Paul Jones stands now in his shoes."

"Aye, Captain—Jones," I repeated haltingly, "I understand." A moment I stood looking into his engaging face, then with a blush I continued, "So it must have been you behind that telescope as yon ship"—I flicked a thumb over my shoulder at the cutter riding now at anchor off Straight Wharf—"rounded Brant Point."

"Aye, so it was," he laughed. With a friendly pat, he took my arm in his. "You may have gone late in life to sea to make a seaman, as I told you in Tobago, though if I can believe my eyes when first I picked you up in my glass, you are repeating not that mistake when it comes to love. But I blame you not, for the lady I saw in your arms was lovely in all truth. I envy you. And had I dreamed you both would suddenly become so prim at sight of me, I should have steered farther offshore, for never before might it be said that a sailor was parted from his love on my account. Come," he finished banteringly, "what may I do to reunite you? Perhaps she will e'en bestow one of her dazzling smiles on me an' I do you that favor. Where is the lady?"

"You may well do more that way than you think." Remembering why it was that Delight had so unceremoniously parted from me, I looked a little questioningly from the man who now by way of incognito called himself Paul Jones, to his vessel in the harbor. Certainly no ship captained by him could be in the King's service, and the bearer of that news to Keziah Coffin, perturbed over the prospect of imminent search of her cottage at Quaise for what might well be hidden there without benefit of the King's customs seals, might for once be welcomed by her even though it be Tom Folger. Here was luck indeed! I steered Captain Jones about for Centre Street. "Follow me, and I will take you directly to her. Only," I looked pleadingly at him, "do not mention in her home what you saw on Brant Point, nor indeed, that ever you set eyes on her before, nor on me until this moment."

"Fear not, friend Tom," he laughed. "Why should I send storms, when save for me, your bark of love sails such smooth seas as I have witnessed?"

"Not so smooth as you imagine, Captain," I countered sadly. "You'll see soon enough some lurking rocks and reefs ahead waiting only to dash it to pieces ere it gets fairly launched. But you may well help there to clear a channel." Arm in arm we strode along, my heart gladdened to see Captain Paul, for the time at least, safely clear of his troubles in Tobago and, so startlingly soon, once more in command of a ship. "By the way," I continued, "your ship there? I saw no name upon her, nor any colors, and so strange a craft I've never seen in our waters hereabout. What's your mission in Nantucket?"

"Peaceful enough, though, as you may think so usual with me by now, it has again to do with battle, murder, and sudden death. The less said of it, the better." Grimly Captain Jones clutched my arm. "I came in here to bury an officer, and my specific mission ashore is first to find someone who can make his coffin. Know you where best I should go for that?"

I halted in shocked surprise. Another killing at this young Captain's hands?

"Nay, 'tis not what you think," explained Jones hastily, shaking his head at the unasked question in my eyes. "My ship there, the *Santissima Trinidad* (though at such blasphemy I swear the angels themselves must shudder) for sundry very good reasons bears not her name anywhere upon her, but flies, when she floats any colors at all, the Spanish flag. To put it plainly, as between you and me who have no secrets where I am concerned, she's an out and out pirate!"

"What?" I asked, shocked now indeed. "You Captain of a pirate ship?"

"Well, if the term annoys you," he explained with a queer

smile on his thin lips, "shall we call her a 'special privateer' instead? After all, I sail under what may pass as a letter of marque from the Spanish governor of Puerto Rico to make war on the King of Spain's enemies. But he has none just now, being unfortunately at peace with all the world, so our estimable governor back in San Juan cares not whom we make prize of so long as we come back laden with loot of which he takes the lion's share. If that's not piracy, I know not the meaning of the word."

"But how came you on her and what brings you here?" Amazed at the cool effrontery with which he confessed to an occupation which might well bring him summarily to the gallows if caught, I stopped dead in my tracks, dubious as to whether after all I should proceed with him to my Aunt Keziah's. No doubt that hardened smuggler would be glad to hear that Captain Jones commanded no revenue cutter, but did I bring an outright pirate to her home, who could tell what line that inconsistent old Quakeress might draw as between smuggling and piracy?

But the decision did not rest with me. Captain Jones gripped me firmly by the arm, carried me along.

"We were, I think, bound for your charming lady's home, and I mean to see her where I need not a telescope to watch her smile on you. So lead on, Tom; we pause not here. As for your questions and your puritanic horror of my present occupation? How much choice do you think I had in shipping hurriedly out of Trindad lest I be sought there? With little money, a name hastily snatched out of empty air as an incognito, and no officer's certificate at all under that name, do you think I could pick and choose? The first vessel making sail from Trinidad which would have me in any capacity at all gladly got my services and no questions asked on either side till we were well at sea. Then they learned I was Paul Jones, which meant nothing at all to the skipper of the *Santissima Trinidad*, who cared not whether I was Paul Jones or John Smith, though once he assured himself I could speak a little Spanish, man a gun, stand a watch, and navigate, he promptly enough rated me as second mate. And I learned to

[123]

my sorrow that the *Santissima Trinidad,* outward bound on a cruise, was, in spite of her letter of marque, by her conduct a pirate, and much good the knowledge did me when I gained it. What would you have done then, amidst a shipload of forty Spanish and Portuguese desperadoes, had you been I, my friend?"

"Nothing," I responded, perplexed over such a dilemma.

"Exactly!" agreed Paul Jones. "And neither did I. We took but one prize on our cruise, an Englishman, hardly worth the looting, bound for Jamaica, which at the first shot across her bows, surrendered at discretion so at least we murdered no one in the taking. After that we stood northward for New York, our Captain hoping to pick up a packet laden with specie for the Paymaster of the Forces there, of which vessel he had word in some manner. But unfortunately we fell in instead with the British frigate *Milford* off Montauk. Our skipper, fearing the British Captain's Spanish might not be up to all the niceties involved in our letter of marque and might well solve his difficulties by hanging us from his yardarms out of hand as pirates, sought to flee, instead of rounding to for search when hailed. And the result was we immediately caught a broadside from the frigate which mortally wounded our Captain and killed three men. That might well have resulted in our immediate capture had I not promptly seized command over the head of our panic-stricken Portuguese mate who already was bawling like a calf for quarter, hauled by the wind, and beaten the *Milford* so badly clawing to windward that we soon escaped and lost her in Block Island Sound.

"That was yesterday. Our three dead seamen promptly enough went overside, each with a round shot at his feet. But our expiring Captain, frightened evidently at his nearing approach to the flames of hell, made me, because I had succeeded by common consent of all hands to his command, promise before he died to bury him ashore with benefit of clergy. So here I be, by grace of the devil, Captain of the corsair *Santissima Trinidad,* ashore on Nantucket seeking a coffin for my late commanding officer, and if possible a priest to bury him. What think you of my chances on your Quaker island, Tom?"

"The coffin will be easy enough, sir. Any shipwright here, and of such we have many, will swiftly make you one to what degree of elegance you think the dignity of your slain officer requires and you care to pay for. But a priest his departed soul will have to do without. I doubt you could find one in all New England, let alone on this island where my Quaker neighbors have not even ministers in their meeting houses, performing that duty for themselves as the spirit moves them. Even our declining Presbyterian congregation here has at the moment no dominie. So you must make shift to act as priest yourself. But should we see about the coffin now?" I asked, halting again ere we drew too far from the waterfront where the ship carpenters labored at their craft.

"Nay, it can wait." Once again, Paul Jones urged me on with a prod from his long arm. "You seize so many opportunities to delay the call you set out in such haste to make with me, I begin to think you hesitate to show your lady to me. Is that so?" he asked bluntly.

"Gladly would I have you meet her, Captain," I replied in all sincerity. " 'Tis not her; 'tis her mother I have my doubts about. My Aunt Keziah is a demon, believe me, sir, and will not hesitate to manifest her ire should your profession rouse it, though truth to tell, she is engaged herself in smuggling amongst her other interests at sea."

Captain Jones laughed outright at that.

"Well, keel haul me then if this female demon of yours and I be not two birds of a feather who should get along famously together. Trust a Scot to appeal to any woman with such an eye as she must have to turning an honest shilling. I doubt not that ere I leave her, she will be entreating me to persuade his Magnificence, the Governor of Puerto Rico, to sell her some large share in my ship should she be convinced the business offers chance enough for quick profit. So underway at once, and no more delays. I am as much intrigued now to meet your doughty Aunt Keziah as I am her daughter!"

[125]

16

THE funeral next afternoon drew, by Captain Jones' invitation, a motley assemblage of the curious amongst my fellow townsmen. Two boatloads of the *Santissima Trinidad's* crew, well justifying Paul Jones' characterization of them as a pack of desperadoes, lined the sides of the hastily dug grave just above high water mark beyond Brant Point. The desolate location of the grave overlooking the sea and the fierce aspect of the swarthy be-earringed crew in flaming 'kerchiefs and swashbuckling boots, went well enough together.

A little in the rear of the crowd, Delight and I, hands tightly clasped, stood with bowed heads while over the coffin draped in the gaudy yellow and red of the Spanish flag, Jones himself reverently intoned the burial service in a deep, resonant voice ringing clear beneath the open sky. Incongruously though, seeing that the object of it was undoubtedly a Papist, he read from the Episcopalian prayer book which I had procured for him for the occasion.

With the last solemn words, some half dozen of the seamen, first piously crossing themselves, began furiously shovelling in the sand, and the brief ceremony was over. In twos and threes, the Nantucketers, sober in the face of death, began slowly drifting back to town, to be left far behind immediately by the sailors of the *Santissima Trinidad*. They were restrained by no such inhibition once the business of burying their late Captain was concluded, and made merrily off toward the town to discover what in the way of rum and, no doubt, women godly Nantucket might afford them.

Quietly closing the prayer book, Paul Jones, no whit startled by the celerity and gaiety with which his crew had departed, strolled from beside the rude grave to join us. I marvelled at the versatility of that odd young Captain. No minister could have conducted a religious service more feelingly; that he was a competent mariner I would have taken oath on; and the easy manner in which but yesterday he had unbent dour old Aunt Keziah, amazed me.

What he had said about interesting her had come true. The magic that man had with women I could not fathom. I could well believe that his fascinating profile with its finely chiselled nose, aristocratic thin lips, firm brow, strong chin, curiously moulded ears protruding beneath his sandy hair, and most of all, his compelling bluish-grey eyes, should instantly engage the warm attention of any young woman on whom he chose to smile. But it took much more than merely masculine attractiveness to make Aunt Keziah smile on him or on anyone. Some vital inner fire, the which I had not the eye to see, must burn in that man to make Keziah Coffin hang on his every word, wholly disregarding Delight and me, who sat as silent spectators to what each of us thought a miracle. Never before had I seen Aunt Keziah fail to dominate any man she talked to, listening scarce at all to him.

Yet before engaging Captain Paul Jones, under which name I had introduced him, she had sat an attentive listener, relieved, of course, to learn from him she had no concern over searches by the King's revenue officers. But far from being outraged as I had feared over his "privateering," she had manifested an evident faith in his abilities as a skipper. Indeed so keen an interest had she in hearing his tales of it that I verily believe, as he had prophesied in jest, had he so desired he might well have procured out of hand from Aunt Keziah the financing of such a "privateer" to go cruising on his own account (and hers).

Tucking the prayer book under his elbow, there beside that fresh-made grave, Paul Jones bowed formally to Delight, to which she responded with a curtsey. Then gracefully offering her his arm, leaving me to tag somewhat awkwardly along on the other side, he started slowly in the wake

[127]

of the scattering spectators down the beach back toward the town.

"My mother bade me tell thee, Captain Jones, it would give her much pleasure couldst thou dine with us today," said Delight shyly. "She would hear more of thy experiences in the West Indies trade, feeling that here in Nantucket in our pursuit of oil we overlook too much that opportunity."

"My compliments to your kind mother, and nothing would please me more than further opportunity to bask in the light of her conversation," replied Jones very gallantly, "but is friend Tom here included in the invitation?"

"She mentioned him not, unfortunately," sighed Delight. "I doubt indeed that thought of Thomas entered her mind."

" 'Tis high time then that it did. Has she no eyes in her head? Surely that tender glow I observe in your countenance hath a cause that cannot have escaped her notice. And who else but Tom should she then think of?"

Delight blushed and dropped her long lashes demurely as she answered,

"She hath not the advantage of thy telescope in gaining knowledge as to the direction in which her thoughts should turn, Captain Jones. Wherefore she does not attach the same importance to a maidenly smile on Cousin Thomas that thou dost. I fear that when she notices him at all, her mind dwells only on the eighty pounds he owes her and on naught beside."

"So stands it?" Captain Paul looked keenly over Delight's bonnet at me, towering head and shoulders above her on the other side. "So much in debt, in addition to your other troubles in this suit?"

"Aye, Captain," I answered unhappily, "and with no prospect either of paying it off shortly, unless by some stroke of fortune I can obtain a berth as mate for which position, as when I met you first aboard the *Betsey*, I am still with no great luck striving to master navigation."

"Hm-m-m." Paul Jones pursed his thin lips and looked thoughtfully from Delight to me. "I see now the rocks and reefs you mentioned in this matter. Eighty pounds, eh? Do

I judge your Aunt Keziah rightly, she will ne'er see much merit in any suitor for her daughter who cannot pay his debts. If I had that sum or any part of it, I would willingly advance it myself, seeing under what obligation I am to you, Tom. But the profits of my piracy this cruise have been so meager (and from what I purpose doing will not increase) that I can hardly help you with a shilling. However, I have another thought. You came to me on the *Betsey* for help in navigation. I need now a mate on the *Trinidad*. Come with me to the West Indies, and I warrant you ere we make Puerto Rico you'll be a navigator the equal of any of your spouter skippers here in Nantucket, and well fit to sail as such immediately. So much I can do now to repay the help you gave me, and gladly shall I do it."

"Nay!" Abruptly Delight dropped Jones' arm and in alarm clutched mine. "Tom sail on a pirate ship to be hanged by the British merely to help pay off his mother's debts to mine? Never! I had thought better of thee, Captain Jones, than to suggest such a thing!" With flashing eyes, clinging tightly to me as if to save me from the imminent peril of noose and yardarm, Delight looked scornfully into Jones' startled features. "Thou'rt no friend of mine for that, Captain. I'll flout mother's wishes first to marry Tom, though we both live forever afterwards in a debtor's prison for it, should my mother not relent!"

Gravely Jones nodded in agreement, then gently gave her his arm again.

"Your sentiments do you much honor, my dear. I had not thought to find such fiery affection for a youth in any Quaker maid. If I had the authority, as I might on my ship, I should marry you for it to Tom, here and now while you are still in that mood, seeing that fortunately I have the prayer book with the marriage service yet beneath my arm. And we might then see how, for good or ill, my dear friend Aunt Keziah takes it. But I had not meant to offend you nor hazard your beloved in my offer. Fear not for Tom in my hands. I mean only to sail straight southward to Puerto Rico when I leave here, there to turn the *Trinidad* back to

[129]

her owners, molesting no ship on the way. And as for the British and their gibbets, aside from his giving them no cause upon this cruise I propose to him, they must first catch Tom ere they assay to hang him. And if I cannot elude any British cruiser that may by ill-luck sight us, then I am not a sailor. So what say you to it now, my lovely vixen?"

What Delight, still firmly gripping my arm, might have said to that, I know not, for I forestalled her in the answer.

"Aye, Captain; gladly do I accept your generous offer." I turned to gaze reassuringly down into Delight's dubious eyes. "Concern yourself not over my safety. 'Tis a chance will not soon come again to perfect myself in navigation, and were the ocean full of British frigates, I have faith not one is captained by a seaman good enough to lay Paul Jones alongside an' he wish it not. As you love me, thank the good Captain, darling, for what he does for both our sakes."

17

AMIDST much growling from his crew at such an order, at first sight of any masts or topsails looming up over the horizon, the *Santissima Trinidad* tacked or wore away as the occasion demanded to put the stranger's sticks immediately well down again below the rim of the sea. As a result, so many were our changes of course, we made but a slow passage southward, but regardless of what the crew thought (and often enough, in voluble and profane Spanish, said) I minded it not.

Our crew, villainous enough in appearance and, I have no doubt, even more evil in their souls, grumbled enough as their imaginations painted beneath the thin line of the royal masts of each vessel sighted from our mastheads, a rich prize easily to be taken in one murderous rush over her bulwarks by our band of cutthroats. But under Jones' management we never saw a single hull, and despite the oaths which accompanied the disappearance beneath the horizon of each sail sighted, no man, gazing on Paul Jones' stern face and the brace of pistols stuck in his belt as he trod the corsair's quarterdeck on such occasions, dared to question his orders to his face.

With regard to me, Jones, as I now without the necessity of conscious thought came to know him, was better even than his word. A more accomplished scholar in the lore of seamanship I doubt existed, and his knack of instructing those beneath him in that which he wished them to know, was uncanny. Logarithms, which to me had been a Chinese puzzle, he made plain as day by his elucidation of how his fellow Scotsman, Lord Napier, had chanced on them from his observations on the properties of exponents. Understanding thus their whys and wherefores, I handled them thereafter with much ease simply as problems in addition and subtraction. And such geometry and trigonometry as I needed to know, he likewise illuminated with such skill and apt illustration that I doubt Euclid or Pythagoras could have excelled him.

Moving from these foundations to the matter in point, that of longitude by lunar distances, he pointed out to me with many a sketch the advantages and shortcomings of the moon's rapid motion in the heavens for that purpose and the methods of determining it.

If my feeble powers of explanation leave this matter still somewhat unclear, suffice it to say that the problem is of such intricacy that I marvel Captain Jones succeeded in drumming an understanding of it into my dizzy brain at all. And the difficulty of the multitudinous computations and corrections required to put it in practise far exceeds even the complications of the theory, so that I well comprehended why the average shipmaster was content to figure longitude by dead reckoning. He would prefer to risk the chances of stranding his vessel by the errors therein, rather than undergo the greater errors which lack of understanding of the theory and the thick-headed clumsiness of most seamen with figures might entail.

At any rate, under Jones' careful tutelage I at last mastered the theory of lunars, helped greatly by my natural affinity for figuring, so that two weeks out of Nantucket, I deemed myself competent to assay my first set of sights of the moon. However, when I computed them, to my mortification they placed us in longitude high and dry well inland in North Carolina. Had we actually been there our cutwater would have been ploughing up the tobacco fields, instead of the water some miles to the eastward of Cape Hatteras where Paul Jones' observations, as well as a casual glimpse at the waves washing our lee rail, indicated we more probably were.

This fiasco in correct computation chastened me decidedly, though Jones, laughing at my result, pointed out I had merely applied my correction for the moon's semi-diameter in the wrong direction and completely neglected its parallax.

"However, be not discouraged, Tom," he added. "Somewhat more practise, and the moon will be as much your friend in navigation as it has, I doubt not, been in love. But you may not much longer need her save for the latter purpose, for but recently the Admiralty has awarded its prize of £10,000 (for many years outstanding and unclaimed) to John Harrison of Yorkshire for his ingenious chronometer. That remarkable clock keeps account of Greenwich time so well even under the motion of a ship at sea, that by test on a voyage recently to Barbados and return, it enabled the longitude to be determined at all times within ten miles with slight labor, which degree of accuracy is quite impossible from lunar distances. Once let the cost of such chronometers be brought within reach of ordinary shipmasters and none but lovers will ever again regard the moon."

"My blessings on John Harrison and his clocks if that be so!" I agreed fervently. "What costs one of these marvels?"

"So far, £400, and I doubt there be yet two dozen in existence, but bide the time and they will come. Meanwhile, let us back to the moon, and your mistakes in handling her. Another set of sights immediately; I know no better way of mastering this nor anything, than constant drill."

As we worked south from Hatteras I shot lunar distances endlessly and worked them out till I could not look at the moon without seeing her fringed in a halo of trigonometric corrections and practically eclipsed by column on column of logarithmic tables. But under Jones' watchful eyes, practise made me more nearly perfect so that no longer did my positions plot the ship in some farmer's pasture land, but instead came closer and closer to agreeing with my Captain's. After some three days of such close coincidence, Jones gave me full charge of the navigation, though he scrutinized my work book daily. So that during the last week of our voyage it was by my positions plotted on the chart, we laid our course for San Juan de Bautista in Puerto Rico.

[133]

It may be imagined with what pride I made my landfall
to find that with scarce any change of course at all as we
came in from the northward, we were pointed fair for the
harbor channel off Morro Castle. Not Columbus himself,
first sighting land in America, felt more elation than I at
thus having successfully navigated the *Santissima Trinidad*
in from the trackless seas to her home port.

Paul Jones might well have taken similar pride in the
accomplishment of his pupil I well believe, if he had not
been so perturbed over his probable reception as to forget
all else. For in good truth, he faced far more danger of
hanging at the governor's hands in San Juan for bringing
home a nearly empty corsair than he ever faced from the
possibilities of being caught by the British while filling it.

With the Spanish colors floating from our gaff, we
rounded to under the guns of Morro Castle and from the
two brass pieces which adorned our waist, fired a salute to
the governor's flag over the castle and dropped anchor.

This was scarcely done when we lowered a boat, which
manned by six flamingly 'kerchiefed seamen, took both master and mate immediately ashore to report, leaving me, a
helpless lamb among the wolves forming the ship's company,
theoretically in command, but daring not to open my mouth
to give any order lest my unruly crew unceremoniously
heave me overboard.

All discipline was gone. From shore boats swarming about
us, in some manner a flood of rum flowed aboard to convert
the seamen swiftly into drunken beasts. So that it was a
dismal three hours I spent fearing the worst, locked in the
cabin aft, till I saw my seniors shove off from the stone quay
and head back to us.

Jones was in vile temper when he entered the cabin where
I awaited him.

"Get your sea chest ready to go overside at once," he
ordered curtly. "I'm no longer Captain, you're no longer
second mate. Off we go immediately. And if we linger overlong, we may be heaved over by our good friend, the former
mate, now Captain in my place, who has enraged the gover-

nor against me for my shortcomings as a pirate Captain.
If I had not at least been able to convince the avaricious
governor that save for my skill as a seaman, his ship would
long since have been in the hands of the British and the
mate there accusing me, long since been carrion hanging
from some gibbet, I should myself this moment be clapped
in double irons in the deepest dungeon of yonder Spanish
castle awaiting God knows what! Come, Tom! Over the side
we go, ere the new Captain gets as drunk as his crew and
sets about excelling the governor in the villainy that befits
those whole-heartedly engaged in piracy!"

I hurried to comply. It took but a moment to toss the few
belongings in my cabin into my small chest, slam down and
lock the cover. With the chest then heaved up on my shoulder, I made my way cautiously under the low deck beams
and up the ladder to the quarterdeck. There, fast as I had
been, I found Jones whose possessions, even scantier than
mine, had been jammed into a sea bag, already awaiting me.

Like mariners discharged in disgrace, lugging our own
baggage we went hastily over the side into the waiting boat.
From the quarterdeck, without even a wave in farewell, the
swarthy Portuguese mate, skipper now, watched us depart
in evident satisfaction. He broke his silence only to lean over
the bulwarks and in Spanish order the stroke oar to take
us where we would but on pain of nameless punishment to
return aboard without either of us and that speedily.

"Whither now?" I asked in some dismay of my companion
as the boat shoved clear, for I was not yet used to being
thus unceremoniously dumped penniless ashore in a strange
port where not only did I not know anyone but where even
the language of the country was none too familiar to me.

"To that ship three cables off on our starboard bow,"
answered Jones grimly, heading the boat for a brig anchored close inshore, to which I had previously paid little
attention. "I thought I recognized that vessel by her odor
as we came in. She's the *Two Friends*, an African slaver in
which I was once third mate, commanded now, so I learned
ashore, by James Smith of Edenton who was her mate when

I was in her. So if Smith has not forgotten me after these years, we shall be not wholly friendless here, I think. He has traded his slaves here for a cargo of molasses with which he sails soon for Medford in Massachusetts, where the molasses will be distilled into rum, and with the rum he goes back to the coast of Guinea to trade that for more slaves. So round and round on that ocean triangle from Guinea to the West Indies, to Medford, to Guinea he sails, with slaves, molasses, and rum at its three corners awaiting him, each to be traded for the next and all at a goodly profit provided only that too many slaves do not die on his hands between Guinea and here. With a little luck, I can perhaps prevail on Captain Smith to take us northward along with his molasses as passengers. And if he takes us, we can thank our fortune that on this leg of his voyage he travels not laden with slaves, though the foul stink of that human cargo never wholly leaves a slaver's hull."

So next aboard a slaver! I looked with a sinking heart at the high sides of the brig looming up before us, and truth to tell, had not the gesture been an offense to my companion, I would gladly have held my nose. Our boat, coming up from leeward toward her stern, caught the full benefit of the odors from the human dung which no amount of washing down of the 'tween deck spaces in which the slaves were carried chained to the planking, could ever clear them of.

"You note it, eh?" observed Jones, catching my involuntary grimace. "Well I know that stench! But to get the full flavor of it, Tom, you should be becalmed beneath the burning sun on the Equator with two hundred thirsting blacks below in the stifling heat clanking their iron fetters and screaming pitifully, *'Agua! Por dios, agua!'* and the whole ship reeking with the vilest smells imaginable outside of hell itself! Neither in body nor soul could I stomach it, and I left the ship finally in Jamaica, swearing to starve first ere I had further part in that business! And starve I nearly did too, for only as an actor with a company of roving English players in Jamaica could I earn anything at all for months, and that not much. Imagine me as young Bevil in

'The Conscious Lovers' striding before the footlights for the delectation of all and sundry in Jamaica that I might somehow scrimp together a few pounds to pay my passage back to Scotland! So much I endured to get out of the slavers. But still my bones shake occasionally from the tropic fevers I contracted from the disease-laden vapors of those infernal slave ships. Now it is ironic that I seek one out voluntarily as an escape from something worse. For as compared to piracy, the slave trade is in the eyes of man at least legal, though whether in the eyes of God it be worse to steal white men's goods or black men's bodies, I know not."

Jones sheered the boat in under the high poop of the vessel before us to make her starboard gangway and looked upward speculatively toward her quarterdeck, seeking some sign of her skipper there, then added,

"We have at least the luck that on this voyage to Medford, the *Two Friends* is sweetened somewhat by the fragrance of the cargo of molasses in her holds. That may save me from a recurrence of my fevers. Ah! There stands my friend, the Captain. Pray, Tom, that he take us, for otherwise I know not how we penniless mariners may escape this port!"

Six months before, I never would have believed that I should ever pray to God to be taken aboard a ship engaged in what amongst the good Quakers on our island of Nantucket was considered the most despicable business afloat. But earnestly now I did pray inwardly for exactly that. And whether it happened in answer to my entreaties or due to some *camaraderie* of the sea, the Captain of the *Two Friends*, standing in his gangway scanning the approaching boat, at that moment recognized his old shipmate and in the most friendly manner imaginable, started down his ladder to greet us, exclaiming,

"John Paul, as I live! Welcome to your old ship!"

We scraped alongside the foot of the ladder, where Captain Paul, here in no wise embarrassed at being hailed by his real name, leaped from the sternsheets of the boat to

[137]

the gangway platform. Immediately he was seized by the hand, and I noted the exchange of some mystic grip, which little as I knew of Masonic lore, took on more significance in explaining the warmth of our welcome to the *Two Friends* when later I learned that it was this very James Smith who had stood sponsor for John Paul upon his admittance to the Masonic fraternity at a lodge in Kirkcudbright.

But at the moment nothing máttered save that our welcome was obviously assured, for after a few crisp sentences from Jones and a significant inclination of his head toward the *Santissima Trinidad* astern of us, Captain Smith nodded understandingly and roared out to a motley group of seamen leaning curiously over the bulwarks regarding us,

"On deck, there, bosun! Two hands below here to lay Captain Paul's dunnage up on deck!" He started up the ladder, followed by Jones and me, leaving our baggage to be lightered aboard by the pig-tailed seamen of the *Two Friends*, so that we came aboard her in much grander style than we had slunk from the *Trinidad*.

Late that afternoon on the outgoing tide, to the clanking of capstan bars we weighed anchor and sailed out of San Juan, dropping both Morro Castle and the *Santissima Trinidad* from sight astern. There were no regrets on my part and much audible thankfulness on Captain Paul's that his days of piracy were over and that he had come clear of the corsair and the Spanish grandee who was her owner with no closer acquaintanceship with the dripping dungeons beneath the gun-studded ramparts of that gloomy fort.

There was a further advantage in being again at sea, for with the *Two Friends* going full and by before a fresh southerly breeze, it was possible on deck by keeping well aft on the weather quarter, to escape in large measure the odors permeating that vessel, and even in the great cabin in her poop, with all the stern windows open and the wind sweeping constantly through, breathing became at least bearable.

One other stroke of luck, for my companion at least, appeared from our fortunate falling in with Captain Smith and his vessel. That the *Two Friends* was bound for Medford on Boston Harbor, had for me seemed good enough, for I could, all else failing, at least tramp it from Boston to New Bedford, where I could easily get passage on some of the numerous small craft constantly plying with supplies between that port and our island. And once back in Nantucket, I might try what chance and my new-found skill in navigation would do for me in getting me a berth as third mate on some whaler and start me on the road to fortune and the good graces of my Aunt Keziah, which it was imperative for me to enjoy ere I dared hope for Delight's hand.

But Jones, it seemed, was in no wise anxious to go to Boston whither he had never before been in his voyaging and where he was in no degree acquainted. He was desirous instead of getting to Virginia where I now learned he had a much older brother in Fredericksburg from whom he had great hopes of assistance in his present distress.

We were scarcely well clear of Puerto Rico and had stowed our slender belongings in the tiny cabin allotted us by Captain Smith, with Jones taking the lower berth and me the upper, than we hastily bade it farewell and laid up on deck where on the lofty poop, we might enjoy less scented air. Then Jones explained his plans to me.

"On this voyage, so my friend Captain Smith informs me, he touches briefly at Edenton in the Carolinas to render his accounts to his owner's firm there. They are his brother Robert Smith and his brother's partner Joseph Hewes, though in this venture of the *Two Friends*, he tells me Hewes has no interest, since he is a Quaker and shares the abhorrence of that sect for the trade. But however that may be, at least in Edenton the *Two Friends* will first cast anchor, and there I mean to leave her. It will be no great journey overland, though I must travel it afoot, from Edenton to Fredericksburg. There my older brother William Paul, who migrated to America ere first I went to sea, is prosperously settled as a tailor in the community. Though he is far older than I and was never very close to me (for indeed he was a man grown while I was yet playing with toy boats at St.

Mary's Isle on Solway Firth), still he may aid me till I can get some remittance indirectly from the agent with whom I left my affairs when I fled Tobago. What say you, Tom, to accompanying me to Virginia? Should I get my funds, which may indeed well reach a thousand pounds if they but deal fairly with me in Tobago, I shall be in some position to buy interest in another vessel in which we may both sail again. You'll lose nothing if I make out so, for I can well assure you, Tom, there is far more to be made now in trade with these West Indies than ever you will make in whaling."

"Aye, Captain," I agreed ruefully, recalling only too vividly what my gains had been in the voyage of the *Beaver*. "Well can I believe that. To Virginia it is!" for it was plain to me that this young Scot, could he but get a merchantman again, had an uncanny scent for trade and if I in some measure shared his gains, it might not be long till my accounts with Aunt Keziah were duly settled.

18

WE made swift passage in the *Two Friends* from San Juan to Edenton on Albemarle Sound, favored all the way by following winds before which our brig sped northward. Still, none too soon for me did we enter the beautiful semicircular bay forming the harbor and our straining hawsers warp us alongside the dock on the waterfront of busy Edenton. I hustled ashore there, over the side immediately a gangplank was aboard. And for the first time in over a week, I ate a meal in Hornblower's Tavern without having my stomach revolt from the all-pervading stench of the slaver's 'tween decks.

My hunger sated, I strolled back to the wharf to get my sea chest and learn what arrangements Jones had made to store our baggage in Edenton, while, as lightly laden as possible, we two trudged afoot towards Fredericksburg.

A busier scene than the shorefront beside that wharf of *Hewes & Smith* I had not before glimpsed. There a sight that I had never seen on Nantucket where we had no lumber for such purposes, rose before my eyes. The gaunt ribs of a ship under construction reached toward the skies with the clatter of shipwrights' mauls and adzes ringing cheerfully out as the toiling carpenters fitted and secured the stout planking for her sides.

Amongst the odorous pine beams and timbers destined for that ship I picked my way gingerly toward the outer end of the long wharf where the *Two Friends* lay moored, to find there on the pierhead two strange gentlemen in earnest conversation with my friend and the Captain of the brig.

Feeling my own lack of importance in such company, I

shrank back amongst the piles of timber to await the outcome of the discussion, though I was near enough from
occasional phrases which reached my ears, to judge soon
that the two strangers were that Joseph Hewes and Robert
Smith whose partnership had been mentioned and on whose
wharf I stood.

Smith, who was obviously a slow spoken Carolina gentleman, interested me no great amount as he seemed mainly
engaged in questioning his brother on his success in keeping
alive his cargo of slaves on his late voyage in the *Two
Friends*. But Hewes, who was chiefly addressing himself to
Captain Jones, caught my eye at once.

I had grown up amongst the Quakers on Nantucket and
thought I knew all types, but here plainly enough was a
Quaker the like of whom I had not met. He did not affect
the Quaker garb in his dress, and his forceful speech as he
animatedly questioned Paul Jones, seemed to be free of the
"thees" and "thous" to which I was so accustomed. Apparently Jones and he were on a mutually interesting topic in
their discussion of the conditions of the West Indies trade,
and Hewes' countenance, which was rather long and narrow, giving him a serious mien, lighted frequently up at
Jones' pointed comments on the relative opportunities
offered by the Windward Isles as compared to Jamaica and
the Greater Antilles for such cargoes as our colonies
afforded.

By his self-possession and his evident unusual mental
endowment, I judged this Joseph Hewes must be a person
of much importance in Edenton. It did not surprise me to
learn a little later from the nearby shipwrights that he had
indeed been a member of the General Assembly for his
colony and was even then a leading spirit in the local Committee of Correspondence in opposing Britain's tyrannies.
That Captain Jones had caught his eye was plain enough,
when arm in arm, the two strolled off toward the counting
house of *Hewes & Smith* which stood on the inshore end of
the wharf. This left me, with no interest at all in the conversation still going on between Robert Smith and his sea-

[142]

faring brother, wholly free to mingle with the shipwrights and the riggers who were hoisting up the massive deck beams for the unfinished vessel on the stocks nearby.

I was fascinated by the skill with which the laboring mechanics matched up the timbers. And the speed amazed me by which with augers, bolts, and mauls, timber after timber was securely bolted through and through to the curiously shaped oaken knees joining rib and deck beam that the joint might hold firmly even with the ship racked in a full gale. I lost all track of time and perhaps an hour had thus fled when I found Captain Jones once more alongside me.

"Aye, Tom; we are indeed in Fortune's graces once again!" he greeted me. "This Joseph Hewes is so understanding a spirit and was so keenly interested in my trading experiences, albeit a little puzzled as to why I be now Captain Jones when once I was John Paul, mate on the *Two Friends*, that though I never saw the man before this day, relying fully on his discretion I confided to him my troubles over Mungo Maxwell and that later misfortune of my life in slaying Jack Fry on the *Betsey*, all of which I had meant to tell no man till I was tried and cleared in Tobago. And what think you resulted?"

I shook my head. How could I judge what the reaction of an odd Quaker like Joseph Hewes might be, though well I knew with what revulsion the ordinary Quaker, schooled in non-resistance, would regard Jones after this tale of violent death and sudden flight from consequences.

"Hewes was so struck with my disasters, that with no security at all save my word, he has advanced me five pounds against the day when I may recover something from Tobago and repay him. And now instead of proceeding completely destitute on our way, we have the wherewithal at least to pay for board and lodging on our journey." In high spirits, Jones clapped me on the back, continued, "Shake a leg now, Tom, and get your sea chest overside and into this warehouse where we will leave it, that we miss not this fine day to start and see how well our sea legs navigate these southern roads."

I looked incredulously at Jones, feeling that he was making game of me. Five pounds? That a shrewd merchant should loan such a sum to a casual stranger who had just crossed his path, and moreover to one who was a self-confessed fugitive whom he might never see again, seemed beyond belief. But it was evident from his cheerful manner my friend was speaking truth. However it came about, some responsive chord in this emancipated Quaker had been struck by Paul Jones' vivid character and now we were in funds enough to relieve all immediate worries. With a light heart, I clambered hastily aboard the *Two Friends* for my chest, meditating on the strange manner in which this nameless Scotsman had charmed such decided opposites in all things as my Tory Aunt Keziah and this patriotic Joseph Hewes.

Two stout seamen carried our baggage down into the warehouse. After bidding farewell with heartfelt thanks to Captain Smith for rescuing us from San Juan, we tramped from the wharves to the tavern to get some directions regarding the post road we were to traverse. Then unburdened save for the clothes we wore upon our backs, we set out northward for Fredericksburg, two hundred miles away.

On that journey and the ten days we spent along the dusty roads of North Carolina and Virginia I will not dwell long. Fortunately we were both young, I but seventeen and Jones not ten years older, or I doubt our legs would have stood the weary miles day after day through forest and swamp, up hill by some perversity it seemed mostly, where every milestone passed became an event. Footsore and tired, each night as we lay down in the inns along the way to rest our fagged bodies and in some measure to wash clear our dust-clogged nostrils, we fervently thanked anew kindly Joseph Hewes and the money he had so providentially presented that we had food in our stomachs and decent beds instead of the chill Virginia fields on which to stretch our weary bones.

I got to know Jones better on that hegira. Naturally

communicative, he whiled away the miles along the road by regaling me with stories of his childhood in Scotland, when I got new light on what had molded his strange character. A lonely child, he was seventh born and fifth and youngest of the surviving children of a Scotch Lowlander, John Paul, and of his Highland wife, Jeannie MacDuff. Neglected by his older brothers and sisters and scarce regarded by his father, young John Paul had grown up upon the estate of the Earl of Selkirk on Solway Firth where his uncle was gardener. Adjoining this estate his father was himself gardener to a country squire, Robert Craik.

Alone on St. Mary's Isle, as the Earl's estate upon a promontory jutting into the firth was known, young John Paul grew up beside the sea, sailing toy boats upon the tide which swirled up toward Whitehaven on the English side. He was watched over by his uncle, George Paul, ignored by his father, caressed occasionally by the Earl of Selkirk in the latter's strolls about the shores of his estate.

He was driven into himself by the queer diffidence with which his much older brother and his three older sisters regarded him, and stung to the quick by the avoidance with which the other children in the neighborhood shunned him. Young John Paul began to believe something of truth lay behind the epithet "bastard," with which those who should have been his playmates, with the heartless cruelty of childhood, taunted him openly to his face and chanted loudly behind his back. At the age of six he came to some realization of what shame the carelessly flung taunt implied, and as he grew older he drew still further aloof from his father, regarding him indeed with revulsion.

His only relief was a fierce interest in his toy boats. Longingly he eyed the ships with widespread sails standing before the wind down Solway Firth bound for strange lands beyond the seas, dreaming of the day when he might be borne on one of them to pleasanter scenes beyond the reach of childish taunts and searing ostracism.

But if John Paul were not his father, who was then? The servants thereabouts, noting the affectionate interest with which the lord of the manor caressed the engaging little boy roaming unrestrained through castle and park, found a ready answer, which by their heedless gossip reached his ears. Jeannie MacDuff, his mother, still young, vivid and handsome, full of the Highland fire and abandon with which the clan MacDuff, her ancestors, had scorched their names deep into Scottish history, tiring of her workaday Lowland husband, had caught the eye and fancy of the then heir, now the Earl himself. So in a secret tryst amongst the ferns and mosses of some lonely glen upon St. Mary's Isle, the blood of the lordly Selkirks had mingled with that of fiery Jeannie, to flow now in the veins of him who was born young John Paul, a swan amongst the geese of his stodgy brothers and sisters who were but Pauls.

Could this be true? Trudging the dusty hills of Virginia, I eyed my companion striding over the deep ruts, pouring out to me his childhood memories and griefs of far off Scotland. There was no doubt but that John Paul, swinging now along by my side, firmly believed it as explaining the attention he had received from the Earl, the influence (unfortunately not followed through) which had procured his entrance into the Royal Navy as Midshipman, the unpaternal lack of interest in him the elder John Paul, long since dead, had always shown, and most of all, the utter absence of resemblance in character and physique between himself and the older children of his family. For his mother he had the deepest affection; for his father, none at all. And for the boys and girls about the Solway Firth, now grown into the neighbors surrounding his old home, he had only the deepest antipathy for the cruelty with which they had seared his boyish soul.

In silence, scarce knowing what to say, I received this tale of Scottish lord and Scottish lass, so different from anything I knew on prosaic Nantucket where we had not even squires amongst us. But the tortured heart of youthful John Paul, burning to achieve distinction that he might somehow atone for his double namelessness now, I could fully understand, and what part those memories played in forming the

[146]

strange Captain who strode along beside me, was plain to see.

So day after day we plodded on through Virginia, relieving the endless miles by regaling each other with our memories. Captain Paul dwelt much on his naval days and his months in the slave trade, with occasional bitter cogitations on Mungo Maxwell and Jack Fry, which recollections I saw were constantly gnawing at his heart like a canker. And I on my part, dwelt for his edification at some length on my encounter with the great whale which had wrecked the cruise of the *Beaver*, and on my own childhood amongst the Quakers on Nantucket, unlike his youth, for me a pleasant memory. In this he took keen interest, especially since much of it was tangled with my shy recollections of Delight almost from infancy to the moment he had spotted her through his glass with her lips affectionately pressed to mine.

As the days passed and along the never ending road the miles stretched out behind us, the five pounds sterling in Jones' purse shrank correspondingly. So we dined frugally at each inn, husbanding our capital that it might last for bed and board till journey's end, with some still left for the purchase then of fresh linen that Captain Paul, at least, might present himself before his brother William not wholly in the guise of a beggar. For our constant immersion in the clouds of dust from coaches rolling by and the droves of cattle we encountered, was rapidly reducing us to this appearance.

One topic was never far distant from our tongues. We speculated endlessly on what reception John Paul might expect from his brother William, and how substantial his aid might be. Nightly, when tossing restlessly in one strange hard bed after another, I dreamed strange dreams of William Paul, sometimes visioning him receiving us like a good Samaritan with open arms, enfolding us in deep feather beds that we might cushion well our weary legs, and with hot tubs of water all about to relieve our swollen feet. And other nights I saw him standing stonily in his doorway, flourishing an enormous pair of tailor's shears threateningly

[147]

in our faces, exclaiming harshly, "Begone, John, together with this ragamuffin at thy side! Why come you here? Thou'rt no true brother of mine, and long have I known it!"

So sleeping or waking, the enigmatic figure of William Paul was ever in my thoughts, growing in importance as the miles lengthened out behind us and, nearer and nearer penury, we approached Fredericksburg and the succor that from William Paul alone we could expect.

At last on the tenth day of our journey, with but a scant pound left in Jones' purse, we drew in to Fredericksburg in the late afternoon. I noted a freshening animation on John Paul's face as from the road approaching the town we caught occasional glimpses of the Rappahannock and of the community nestling on its shores at the head of navigation.

For this indeed, he informed me, was the country of his fond predilection since his earliest boyhood. Here he had come on his first voyage to America in the *Friendship* of Whitehaven as a boy of twelve, when at last he had managed to get away on one of the ships of his dreams. And here he had first landed in America to be enchanted by the rolling hills and the placid rivers of Virginia and the gracious plantations fringing their banks.

As we two footsore travelers strode at last into Fredericksburg and our journey neared its end, Jones became more serious.

"I must indeed approach my brother with some circumspection so that he will not give away my incognito here where I mean to stay by openly acknowledging our relationship and my identity as John Paul. For while he may feel no inclination to help me at all, still I have little desire that he do me harm thus. I must be careful to seek him out in privacy."

But on that score, it turned out he had small cause to worry. We were hardly settled in a room at the Rising Sun Tavern, which was the best the place afforded and the rendezvous of all the gentry roundabout, and I ensconced before the fire in the public hall below warming my frame after our chilly journey (for it was now November) than John Paul, bravely arrayed in fresh linen that took all but a few shillings of his last pound, set forth to seek out his brother. He was gone but a scant half hour and it was obvious from his dejected mien upon returning that his errand had been fruitless, though I was shocked nevertheless by the reason thereof.

"My brother is dead," he announced simply. "I get no help here in Fredericksburg."

19

WHAT to do next was a problem. William Paul was dead and buried for some weeks, his little estate tied up in the legal envolvements of courts and executors. Captain Paul, who might otherwise himself have stepped forward as next of kin in America and possibly an heir, dared not to make his identity known to the King's officers lest out of hand he be seized and sent back to Tobago. We could expect no manner of aid in Fredericksburg.

Wholly unknown and friendless in the town to which he had confidently looked as a haven, once more my friend was cast into utter dejection. And I, to speak truth, was in little better frame of mind for had I stuck to the *Two Friends*, I might indeed have been landed by now in Boston harbor not so far from home instead of finding myself stranded several hundred leagues therefrom, utterly fagged out by a long journey, penniless myself and with a nearly penniless companion, and with no prospects at all.

Thus we two sat gloomily sprawled out in chairs before the fire, two mariners marooned far from the sea, pictures of abject despair, while mine host of the Rising Sun bustled about the room taking orders for supper. Jones, sipping a glass of Madeira, shook his head moodily when questioned on his wants, and even I, whose appetite rarely failed, felt it the part of prudence in view of our slender resources, to signify that I too wanted nothing.

Somewhat astonished at our lack of interest in the savory smells coming from his kitchen, the landlord moved on to his only remaining guest, a gentleman in travel-stained riding clothes who had arrived alone shortly before. Obsequiously the stout landlord bowed before him,

[150]

"And what, Dr. Read, of the meats on my spit will you have, sir? I swear the roast of which you catch the odor, will cure you of your fatigues more surely than any of your own medicines. I trust your journey from The Grove hath not robbed you of your appetite the way travelling has these two strangers who shun our Virginia bounty." Somewhat scornfully, with a flirt of his apron in our direction, he indicated us.

The gentleman who before had seemed as wholly engrossed in his own thoughts as we, turned a moment to regard us. Immediately thereafter he, to whom riding in the chill Virginia air seemed to have imparted a sharp hunger, dismissed us wholly from his mind while he ordered such a supper as showed him a keen student of Virginia's products and literally made me doubly famished.

"Aye, the roast, a thick slice of the rare, with one of your golden sweet potatoes swimming deep in butter. And a roasting ear of corn if it be tender. Some Yorkshire pudding with the meat, and a bottle of your excellent port. My ride has indeed worn me out, and that, I think, will suffice to remedy my bodily ills, though for those of the mind I fear I need other specifics."

Rubbing his hands in evident satisfaction at this order, off bustled the landlord toward the kitchen, leaving once more the low-ceiled room to us three silent travelers, Jones and I on one side, the doctor on the other, each staring fixedly into the huge fireplace and its leaping flames.

As I sat, I eyed our companion covertly. In spite of his interest in food, heedless of his appearance he sat as dejectedly as we in his dusty clothes and dustier boots, absorbed in his thoughts, his gaze riveted on the fire. Dr. Read? That stirred some vague recollections in my mind. If he was Dr. Read, as the landlord had addressed him, he must indeed be a connection of mine after some fashion. For I recalled my mother, who was ever the one to keep track of our famous relatives, saying that Deborah Read, who was now wife to my cousin Ben Franklin, had a nephew in Virginia, a doctor and a most important personage in the affairs of

Hanover County which lay just to the south of Fredericksburg where now, sunk in gloom, we all sat.

It may well be true that misery loves company, for if this stranger had not apparently been as disconsolate as I, I never would have mustered up the courage to address him, nor is it probable that he would have done aught but dismiss me brusquely for my impertinence. But as it was, it turned out differently when timidly breaking the silence of that room, I spoke to him,

"Be you, sir, that Doctor Read who is nephew to my cousin, Doctor Franklin?"

A little startled at being addressed at all, the stranger came suddenly out of his reverie to straighten up in his chair and regard me somberly.

"Aye, young man. Ben Franklin is my uncle. His cousin you say you are? And who, then, may you be?"

"Thomas Folger, sir, of Nantucket, and thus related to that Abiah Folger who was Doctor Franklin's mother. I trust you think it not too forward of me thus to claim some relationship to you but in my loneliness here as a stranger in Fredericksburg, when I heard the landlord call your name, I could not resist the impulse."

Immediately Dr. Read rose, a somewhat stout and well fed young man, came over to where I was, and as I stood to greet him, genially clasped my hand.

"By no means. It is a pleasure, especially here so far from Philadelphia, to meet a cousin of Ben Franklin, to whom I owe so much. And especially well can I, who so lately have suffered the keenest bereavement a man may know, appreciate now the pangs of loneliness which prompted you to address me. You are a sailor, I judge by your dress, as are, so I've heard, all the Folgers. What brings you here to Fredericksburg so far from the sea, and apparently in trouble, as I guess from your demeanor? And your friend? What so distresses him?" he concluded, indicating courteously my companion, who was so deeply sunk in his own despair that he had continued to sit apparently unaware either of me or Dr. Read.

[152]

I prodded John Paul to recall him to reality. His clear grey eyes looked up vacantly from the fire at me. Then seeing I was not alone, he jumped up immediately.

"Dr. Read, this is my friend, Captain Paul Jones, who is indeed in real distress as you have surmised. Captain, this is good Doctor Read, nephew to Benjamin Franklin, who as the latter is my cousin, is thus in some respect related to me also."

A moment the two stood keenly surveying each other, then graciously Dr. Read extended his hand and as Jones clasped it, I noted again, as I had on the gangway of the *Two Friends* in San Juan, a sharp start on Dr. Read's part as their hands met, the significance of which I immediately grasped as the emblem dangling from the heavy watchchain across the doctor's waistcoat caught my eye. Apparently Jones had met another brother in the Masonic fraternity, but more than that, it was evident that instantly these two found also some sympathetic understanding as Read's dark eyes gazed into Jones' melancholy greys. They stood a long moment thus, hands still clasped, frankly searching each other out. Then with a bow, Jones released his grip, and in a soft, gentle voice, so different from his powerful tone when on the quarterdeck, he said,

"Your humble servant, sir. I am honored to meet so close a relative of the famous Dr. Franklin."

"Mention it not," replied Dr. Read ruefully. "I fear I bask too much in his reflected glory for my own good." He reached across for his chair, dragged it over toward ours. "Pray be seated again, gentlemen. You are both tired from travel, and perhaps," he added observantly, "in some mental anguish besides. Stand not on ceremony with me."

But at that instant, the landlord entered bearing aloft a tray on which was the doctor's supper, to find his three guests whom he had left strangers to one another, gathered now in a close knot. In some bewilderment, he pushed up a table before Dr. Read on which he set out his plate and lifted the silver cover from the platter, but the latter, interrupting him, ordered,

[153]

"Two plates more for my friends, mine host, who shall also be my guests at dinner! In my professional capacity, I prescribe for them the same medicine I take myself, save that I see the Captain here drinks Madeira rather than port, so bring for him a bottle of that. And the roast, gentlemen? Do you prefer it rare as I do?"

I looked upon the thick slice of rare roast beef floating appetizingly in gravy disclosed now by the lifted cover. Immediately, feeling no longer wholly friendless in that town and needful not to be concerned at the cost in view of the doctor's invitation, with watering mouth I hurriedly nodded acquiescence as did Jones. The landlord, hastily replacing the cover on the platter lest the doctor's supper cool, scurried off with apron flying to carve again his joint of beef.

Soon then about that table before the fire, with Dr. Read at its head, Captain Jones on his right, and me on his left, we three, in somewhat different mood from the silence with which before we had all sat staring at the glowing logs, heartily attacked our supper. The conversation, skilfully directed by Dr. Read, centered mostly on illuminating what it was that individually had sunk each of us in such gloom, hoping no doubt that by airing our distresses, we might in some measure alleviate our worries.

To this end, the doctor quite frankly confessed he was growing somewhat morbid from loneliness on his estate, The Grove, since his wife had died some months back leaving him childless and thus doubly alone in the world. At last in desperation he had resolved to abandon his estate for the winter in the hope that in Fredericksburg among his friends he might regain a more normal outlook.

His own difficulties disclosed, the doctor looked enquiringly towards me,

"You are but young, Tom Folger, to have that hopeless look you wore when you first spoke to me. What weighs you down?"

"Enough in all truth, sir," I replied candidly. "Some months ago I learned I had been reft of my father by the jaws of a whale. Then, disregarding my mother's antipathy

[154]

to that hazardous calling, I went thereafter awhaling that I might support her. Such were her worries over me and her grief for her slain husband, that when from a short and profitless cruise after whales I returned this summer to Nantucket, I found she had died in my absence, killed without doubt by my action. Now I am an orphan and much in debt and, I may add, hopelessly in love where it will do me no good till my debts be cleared. I have followed Captain Jones, who truly has been the victim of ill chance, to Fredericksburg. But here where he hoped for some assistance that might mend his fortunes and mine too, Fate has forestalled us, leaving us perhaps worse off than before."

"You had indeed some cause for gloom, Cousin Tom," nodded the doctor gravely, then turning to Jones who was delicately sipping a second glass of Madeira. "And you, Captain, who I judge be more of my own age, what has the sea done to you or to your ship that you too be so down in the mouth?"

" 'Tis not the sea, good doctor. She has ever been a friendly mistress to me who has done me no ill, nor I her. My distresses spring from some of the rogues who pass as seamen nowadays. 'Twas thus," and to my great astonishment, for the second time in less than a fortnight, I listened to Captain Paul pouring out his soul to another who not an hour before had been a total stranger to him, revealing the secret of his incognito, dwelling again on "that misfortune of my life" in Tobago, and ending up with the last blow of all, his arrival in Fredericksburg to find his brother William dead and all his hopes of aid in America thus dissipated into thin air.

Silently the doctor listened, his heart evidently enough warming as to a kindred spirit as John Paul stood revealed in the recital till at last it was finished. "And now," concluded Captain Paul, "you see, sir, still friendless and still in want, with my last hope of aid gone, under an assumed name I can only wander till the day comes when I may return to Tobago and clear myself, if that be possible."

"Not friendless at any rate, brother Paul," answered the

doctor, leaning over the table to place a reassuring arm about his drooping shoulders. "Somehow I think kind fortune has brought you here to me in Fredericksburg that we may mutually aid each other. Come with me, Captain, to The Grove, where otherwise I can no longer live alone, and you shall have what solitude you please till your affairs mend, and I shall have a friend to commune with. And you, Tom, as a cousin are welcome also, for a little youth will lighten the atmosphere at The Grove and you may well learn something of husbandry on the plantations round about you'll never discover on your Nantucket, that may well help you later in your trading. No arguments now!" he warned, catching a questioning glance I directed towards Captain Paul to see what was his desire. " 'Tis done!" He filled his glass with port, poured out a glass for me. "Come!" He lifted high his glass, in which gesture under his compelling gaze both of his guests joined,

"To a new life at The Grove, and better luck for all of us!"

20

IT was indeed a new life into which I found myself plunged
at The Grove, and amongst people so utterly different in
their way of living and manner of speech from what I had
known amongst our whalers and their staid Quaker families
in our seafaring community of Nantucket, that I might well
have thought myself in a foreign land.

The Grove itself, a pleasant two storied red brick mansion
in the Georgian style, though by no means so pretentious a
residence as those on many of the plantations thereabouts
in Hanover County, still far outshone in magnificence my
Aunt Keziah's home which was the best Nantucket could
boast, and in its gracious hall, lovely winding staircase,
beautiful furniture of English craftsmanship, and brocaded
draperies, breathed a hospitality well exemplified by our
gregarious host.

I could well see how, alone in that spreading house, with
each piece of Sheraton and Chippendale chosen by her hand
bringing back memories of his lost wife, with no neighbors
closer than two miles, and (save for an overseer not on his
social level) with only the negro servants and field hands for
daily companions, so sentimental a gentleman as Dr. Read
would quickly grow morose. But now with the intriguing
Captain Jones constantly at his side, he blossomed in a new
radiance and it fascinated me to watch how the black faces
of the negro servants of that house, sullen and depressed
when we came, glowed into friendly cheerfulness reflecting
the new mood of their master.

As for me, I spent most of my time with the overseer and
the toiling slaves in the fields, engrossed in the problems of
tobacco planting. With youthful curiosity I was absorbed in

the primitive life of the negroes in the whitewashed cabins behind The Grove, for of blacks I had seen none at all on Nantucket. I left Dr. Read and Paul Jones to their own pursuits, which at first interested me little, and which I casually noted now consisted mostly of endless visiting and receiving visits from the surrounding gentry and their wives and of riding with them to the hounds, a sport which seemed almost their major aim in life.

That Captain Paul, a sailor who never before had been astride a horse, took so avidly to this diversion surprised me, the more so that he swiftly picked up both an equine vocabulary and a graceful seat in the saddle that made him practically indistinguishable from his companions who seemed to have been born with riding crops in their hands. But I came soon to see that it was those (and one in particular) whom this accomplishment gave him opportunity to ride with that gave point to Jones' whole-hearted concentration on horsemanship.

My youthful eyes bulged out to learn into what company my chance accosting of Dr. Read in the Rising Sun Tavern had led us. Around Fredericksburg centered the life of those Virginians whose fame had even in far Nantucket come to my young ears, and one and all, Dr. Read, a personage of much importance in that neighborhood, attracted them to The Grove to meet his unusual newfound friend.

First and nearest of all, came Patrick Henry who with his wife and his six children inhabited Scotchtown, a large mansion closely adjoining The Grove. What a figure I had before conjured up in my mind of him who spoke those daring words of a few years before in the House of Burgesses in opposition to the Stamp Act—"Caesar had his Brutus, Charles the First his Cromwell, and George the Third may profit by their example. If that be treason, make the most of it!" It was a shock therefore to me to see riding over to greet Dr. Read's guest the day after our arrival, a tall, thin, stoop-shouldered, awkward man in middle age with an ill-fitting rusty red wig and watery eyes looking as little like a heroic champion of human rights as might be imagined.

But if Patrick Henry suited not my immature ideas of what a defender of liberty should resemble, Thomas Jefferson, Colonel Washington, Captain Dandridge, Richard Henry Lee, and his young kinsman just out of college, Harry Lee, all Freemasons and all constant guests at The Grove, made up the lack.

Young Thomas Jefferson, tall, commanding, handsome in person, the very picture of a Virginia gentleman, with his fiery red hair epitomizing that inner fire which was even then flaming out for liberty; Colonel George Washington, with the laurels of his Indian campaigns resting lightly upon him, quiet and slow-spoken, a big man in every way, whose rugged face bespoke the qualities of leadership and innate honesty of purpose in which all about him had implicit faith and confidence; dashing young Harry Lee, a horseman whose like I have never seen; and staid and bewigged pompous old Captain Dandridge, late of the Royal Navy, settled now far from the sea, but still the self-assured commanding figure that years of ruling the quarterdeck aboard a British seventy-four had made him—all these and many more I saw time and again with Dr. Read and Paul Jones. Astride their flying mounts they galloped by behind the hounds regardless of fences in full cry of some luckless fox, while I plodded along with the doctor's overseer studying the state of the fields against next spring's tobacco planting.

But more often I saw them, one or more, gathered about the dinner table in The Grove, in burning ardor discussing the sad state of the harassed colonies. Never before had I come so close to the heart of the resistance to the tyrannies of George III, his Ministers, and their subservient Parliament.

I listened oftenest to Patrick Henry as, on many a night with himself the only guest, and Dr. Read and Captain Jones gathered beside him with a decanter of Madeira close at hand, I sat myself an inconspicuous auditor. Then, expounding the best means of resistance to George and his pig-headed Ministers, his face lighted up, his hesitancy of speech vanished into a deeply sonorous voice, his drawling Virginian accent blazed into fiery eloquence and I lost all remembrance of his gangling awkwardness. The hated tax on tea, lately laid and universally opposed in the colonies, was now the burning issue, an insidious attempt on our liberties by levying on us without the consent of our assemblies a substitute for the abortive Stamp Act which Patrick Henry with his violent resistance in America and my cousin Ben Franklin with his less obvious but equally effective shrewd persuasion of the practical merchants in London, had managed to get repealed.

Boycotts of British goods now, non-importation agreements, above all abstention from the drinking of tea till the vicious tax was removed and the forcible compliance with this abstinence of those whose love of tea overrode their love of liberty—these were Patrick Henry's remedies. And he did not hold back in that little circle from urging the force necessary, even unto bloodshed, to make them effective. It heartened me to see Paul Jones as the discussions waxed warm, as much as either outspoken Dr. Read or eloquent Patrick Henry, take full part on ways and means, his ardent soul fired by the spectacle of free men struggling to maintain their freedom. I doubt not but some of this harked back to the rebellious spirit of his Highland ancestors, fiercely battling down the centuries among their Scottish mountains against domination by these same overbearing English lords and their Kings. Some of it was gratitude in espousing the cause of his host and benefactor, but mostly was it due to the natural revulsion of his free spirit against tyranny in any form.

So, while I took small part myself, as the weeks rolled into months at The Grove, in the company of Henry and of Jefferson mainly, I saw a new Paul Jones gradually emerging from the outgrown chrysalis of that Captain Paul whose material existence had ended in Tobago. Here was a man whose body, slimmed by hard riding, took on a new gracefulness while his manners and speech acquired the culture and refinements of the most elegant society in America, and his mind blossomed out in expounding to his associates what men of action like himself might do to make effective the oratorical demands for freedom of Patrick Henry and the democratic ideals of the equality of all men which Thomas Jefferson at The Grove and at the Rising Sun so frequently expounded to us.

There was one other influence which worked more change in the young sailorman who had been Captain Paul than either the eloquence of Patrick Henry or the dispassionate logic of Thomas Jefferson: I mean the dark eyes of that ravishing young beauty, Dorothea Spottswood Dandridge, our near neighbor. I have mentioned earlier Captain Nathaniel Dandridge, her father, late commander of a British ship-of-the-line, lord now of a wide-spread plantation hard by The Grove. Quite early after our arrival, on a stalwart mount matching his massive figure came bluff old Captain Dandridge, retired now to his family acres, to meet the newcomers at The Grove, and shortly thereafter at his invitation went my host, Paul Jones, and I (who rode as little as was possible) to his home to join a hunting party.

I had lamented somewhat the necessity of my taking part. The pursuit of foxes did not appeal at all to me and the pains of horsemanship far outweighed in my mind the benefits my lanky youthful body might derive therefrom, but I did not regret my coming from what followed. For we had hardly gathered in the yard amidst a bedlam of baying from the eager hounds and the prancing of the horses than down the steps to join us came slender Dorothea Dandridge. I had not seen her before, and I thought her bewitching in all truth in her riding habit with her exquisite small hands, her soft white skin, her nose slightly uptilted, her red lips and lovely teeth set strongly off by her unusual black eyes and her dark hair. When with a curtsey she favored us all with a dazzling smile ere she mounted her horse, I did not wonder that my young sea captain found without delay the need of so maneuvering his restless steed amongst the other riders as to be close aboard her when we set forth.

Never before had I found Paul Jones overly much interested in women, save as he had bantered me on my suit with

Delight Coffin, but there was little doubt from that moment as side by side they galloped off, his heart had been instantly captured by that first smile and that Dorothea Dandridge's attention too had been caught by a handsome profile and an intriguing personality wholly new to her.

I blamed Jones not at all that from then on he fell in his impetuous way completely under the sway of those flashing eyes. And in my own heartaches over Delight, I sympathized the more with him in his desire for Dorothea, because I saw the difficulties in his path as clearly as he had visualized those confronting me. For Dorothea Spottswood Dandridge was a prize not easily to be got by a nameless fugitive. Granddaughter of the late Governor Spottswood of Virginia, daughter of a Captain in the Royal Navy, first cousin to Martha Washington—behind Dorothea Dandridge, eighteen years old, lay all this joining her to the first families of Virginia, in whom pride of name rose paramount to all else. Wealthy, beautiful, young, she had suitors from all the best families in Virginia dancing before her flame. What chance had unknown Paul Jones, born John Paul, and not certain himself that even that was his name?

But of all this just then Paul Jones made no moment. As Dr. Read's close friend and guest, the doors of Captain Dandridge's mansion were wide open to him, and if my knowledge gained from Delight's tender smiles on me fails me not, the glowing light in Dorothea's eyes with which he was welcomed there each time he came to ride or dine was fired by more than just her gracious hospitality.

At every hunt, Paul Jones rode always by her side. In her father's hall, amongst the young Virginia bucks with their everlasting talk of racing, cocking-mains, and gaming, Paul Jones, to whom all this was Greek, with his engaging smile and his graceful manner more than held his own before a seaman's daughter with his wild tales of the sea which were all Greek to them. Had I but had one-tenth the manner with the ladies which Paul Jones, hard pressed by his numerous rivals, exhibited in fencing with the scions of Virginia for Dorothea's smiles, I have no doubt but I would long since have enchanted my Aunt Keziah and, debts or no debts, with her blessings taken Delight to my arms.

But wildly in love as he was, and warmly as this black-eyed daughter of the Dandridges favored him, still Paul Jones was a Scot not unaware of hard facts and their importance. As friend to Dr. Read, guest of Captain Dandridge, companion on the hunt to Dorothea, that he was Paul Jones was enough. But he well realized that the moment he dared to step forth formally as suitor to Miss Dandridge's hand, in that strict Virginian society where family was all, he must make clear to proud old Captain Dandridge just who Paul Jones was and what was his family. And then—?

He was John Paul, fugitive sea captain from trial for murder of one of his seamen in Tobago; the rumored murderer of another of his seamen; ex-pirate; ex-slaver in a society where, while slavery was approved, those who trafficked in slaves were looked on much askance; brother to the late William Paul, deceased tailor of Fredericksburg, who doubtless had made the clothes which many of the gentry thereabouts were then wearing; son of the gardener John Paul of Kirkcudbright of no family pretensions at all, but somewhat uncertain on the matter of paternity. How would all this sound to Captain Nathaniel West Dandridge, steeped in the traditions of Virginia topped off by a lifetime of rigid regard in the Royal Navy for rank and position, as the qualifications of a suitor for her who was descendant of the Spottswoods and cousin to the Washingtons?

No, it could not be done without immediately forfeiting all chance of gaining Dorothea and even the possibility of seeing her again, for paternal authority throughout Virginia was strong and family ties not lightly disregarded. Dorothea Dandridge, languishing as were her tender smiles upon Paul Jones, would in such matters bow to her father's will, and what that will would be in these circumstances, no one could entertain any doubts who had observed stout old Captain Dandridge in his ancestral home, proud of his family, self-assured that amongst the suitors thronging his hall

[163]

his daughter would make a match suitable to her lineage.

There was but one chance. If Dorothea, though eighteen already and much sought in immediate marriage, could be persuaded to give herself to no one else and wait a few years, somehow, some way, penniless, unknown Paul Jones might acquire the fame and perhaps the fortune which would in her father's eyes somewhat gloss over his family shortcomings as a son-in-law and make the old sea dog amenable to his daughter's wishes.

A difficult situation, but under my eyes Paul Jones undertook assiduously to meet it. First, and for him perhaps easiest, came the persuasion of Dorothea. What he told her and what means he used there as they rode together over the hills of Virginia, I have no way of knowing. But with a girl just blossoming into womanhood and tingling in the love of the graceful, handsome, and gallant figure that was young Paul Jones, it was swiftly done. Of that there could be no doubt, for as the months rolled by with no other suitor making any headway at all and Paul Jones himself staying only on the most formal of terms with her father, it was evident to me and probably also to the much interested Dr. Read, that both our friend and Dorothea were set on waiting yet a while for fairer weather.

As regards fortune, now that his mind was set upon the need of it, those characteristics of the vanished Captain Paul came to the fore which, in three brief years as a shipmaster ere he was twenty-six, had enabled him in trading in the West Indies to acquire a half interest in the *Betsey* and several thousand pounds beside.

It was a wild time, that year of 1774. Normal trade with England was disrupted. The colonists in Virginia were seething with unrest under Governor Dunmore's violent efforts to enforce George's decrees. Farmers were moving in droves from the Tidewater regions westward to escape the ruinous taxes and quit-rents levied on their lands. The times were ripe for speculators, and Paul Jones, practical Scot though he was, was in his soul a canny speculator ready ever to hazard all on a shrewd cast.

Upon his hasty vanishing from Tobago, Paul Jones had left his unsettled affairs there in the hands of Alexander Ferguson, overseer for his partner. Now to get the where-withal to make a fresh start in life, Jones bombarded the distant Ferguson with demands for a remittance of what was owing him as his share of the *Betsey* and her cargo. But since he was of course under the necessity of maintaining the secrecy of his assumed name and whereabouts, Jones requested the funds from Tobago be forwarded clandestinely through a friend of Dr. Read's in Philadelphia, the banker Robert Morris, who would undertake to transmit them to him in Fredericksburg.

But whether Jones was more thunderstruck or enraged on receiving finally a reply through these channels, I could not estimate. Ferguson, sending no cash, blandly informed him instead that nothing was due him. For this astonishing intelligence he offered the far-fetched explanation that a commercial house in Cork (which to Jones' knowledge had by mistake shipped with him nine pieces of coarse camblets over and above what was expressed in their bill of lading and on discovering their error had written him to claim them) laid claim to ownership of the entire cargo of the *Betsey*, leaving nothing therefore available for him to forward to the fugitive Captain Paul.

Jones replied in white heat, setting out the obvious fact that Ferguson was magnifying a demand for a trifling part of the cargo into a claim to ownership of the whole. But to all his further letters he received no replies. The overseer in Tobago was apparently bent on swindling him, taking advantage of his inability to appear in Tobago or even publicly anywhere to demand an accounting.

And there, perforce, the matter had to rest. Jones was helpless to do anything openly either in Tobago, London, or Cork to refute Ferguson's statements or loosen his dishonest grip upon all his assets. So, as philosophically as possible, he closed the door upon that avenue of aid and looked elsewhere. There was but one way he could look—to our host.

Dr. Read now regarded him with more affection than a

brother and would, if asked, gladly have given him his right arm should he need it. Though not himself any too well off in ready funds, the doctor managed to raise for him a hundred pounds for his ventures.

With that borrowed hundred pounds, Jones looked about him. To the westward were virgin lands towards which the displaced husbandmen trekking slowly in their ox-carts through Fredericksburg, were ever heading. To the eastward were the Rappahannock and the James, broad streams on which the tobacco and the produce of the great valley of Virginia flowed down to Tidewater, and along their banks grew the timber, the pitch and the tar much needed for the building of ships.

Paul Jones was twenty-seven now and so wildly in love that from his conversation, which was always larded with poetic allusions, I might judge the sun rose only to shine upon Dorothea Dandridge. That in this state he did not lose the last shilling of his borrowed capital in his speculations was a miracle. But such were his luck and his shrewdness that instead of losing all, ere the year 1775 dawned, between some amazing ventures in western lands, three short trading voyages with tobacco he himself made down the Rappahannock to Norfolk, and another to Edenton with ship supplies, he had run his hundred pounds up to some two thousand sterling. Thus it was that after repaying Dr. Read and sending with many thanks to Joseph Hewes in Edenton the five pounds loaned him there, he found himself once again the possessor of a modest fortune and well on the way to a greater one.

The immediate effect of this was that my friend gave up all thought of ever going back to sea, and with eyes bent always on Dorothea, considered sentimentally becoming himself a landed proprietor in Virginia.

"I tell you, Tom," he confided to me, looking from the green fields to the spreading hills beyond, "here is settled my future place of retirement. As my countryman James Thomson has so exquisitely phrased it in his poem, 'The Seasons'—

'Oh, knew he but his happiness, of men
The happiest he! who far from public rage
Deep in the vale, with a choice few retired,
Drinks the pure pleasures of the rural life
In calm contemplation and poetic ease.
Let others brave the flood in quest of gain,
And beat, for joyless months, the gloomy wave.'

Aye, Tom, there you have it, as only a Scotch poet could express it! 'In calm contemplation and poetic ease' hereabouts I settle, leaving to others 'the gloomy wave.' "

As he spoke the love-sick Paul Jones gazed dreamily off over the Virginia hills, visioning himself no doubt as master of some such mansion as The Grove with lovely Dorothea close beside him as its mistress, while together in ecstatic contemplation of each other, they took their ease poetically amongst the pleasures of their rural life and the choice spirits gathered plentifully about Fredericksburg.

I could see Paul Jones' vision coming true if given a little time yet, though had Dorothea not entered the picture, I could hardly have imagined his forsaking so lightheartedly that mistress of his, the sea.

But so it was, and in his newly regained affluence, as a first step towards the position of a Virginia gentleman, he purchased for himself two negro slave boys, which twain became body-servants to him and to his beloved horse, he having as yet no need of field hands.

21

WHAT might have eventuated from these dreams of "calm contemplation and poetic ease" on the part of my sentimental sailor had not George III so obstinately persisted in intruding himself into our affairs, I can only guess. But like thunder claps, from the north came upon us in Virginia the repercussions of the tax on tea to shatter contemplation, calm or otherwise, and replace it with vigorous and violent demands for that action in which my Captain, in his moments other than poetic, revelled.

To start with, some several months after our adoption of the life of the landed gentry, strange news came on us at The Grove, where Dr. Read as member of the Virginia Committee of Correspondence first got the word by courier direct from Samuel Adams in Boston.

My old ship the *Beaver*, after her disastrous cruise with me, had sailed with the *Dartmouth* and the *Eleanor* from Nantucket laden with whale oil for the London market from the warehouses of my Aunt Keziah and some of her associates. And of all cargoes available to them on the London wharves, through the machinations of that mercenary Tory relative of mine who foresaw much profit in the venture, they had come back to Boston with holds chock-a-block with those chests of tea which no true Yankee shipmaster would now carry regardless of the high freights offered by the East India Company as a bribe.

There these three ships were in Boston. To make their cargoes of tea palatable to New Englanders, the British Ministry, wholly mistaking the causes of American opposition, had through some knavish connivance remitted to the East India Company the English export duties. So that, still carrying the newly laid colonial tax on tea, that commodity could now be sold in America more cheaply even than before the imposition of the protested levy. As my cousin Ben Franklin put it regarding this blindness of the Ministry—

"They have no idea that any people can act from any other principle than that of interest; and they believe that threepence in a pound of tea, of which one does not perhaps drink ten in a year, is sufficient to overcome all the patriotism of an American."

On the arrival of the *Beaver* and her two consorts there had promptly been trouble in staid old Boston town. The angered citizenry, male and female alike, were resolutely determined not to have this tea forced down their throats regardless of its low price while it mingled its aroma with the stench of George's abhorred tax.

Led by Sam Adams, they "persuaded" by such means as they found suitable the three ship Captains to take their vessels, in spite of their charter parties, back to London with cargo holds unbroached. And even in far off Virginia, I could well imagine what type of persuasion it would take to bring about such flouting of her orders by any skipper who sailed for my doughty Aunt Keziah.

So far, so good for my patriotic Yankee neighbors. But at this point unfortunately Thomas Hutchinson, the royal governor, stepped in. His sons as agents of the East India Company were the consignees and as such refused to release the ships from their charter parties.

Using this as a pretext, Governor Hutchinson saw to it that clearance papers for the return voyage to London were refused the ships, and then informed them that if they sought to sail without such papers they would be fired on by Castle William, in addition to which he assigned two warships to prevent their clandestine escape.

Now my old shipmates and my Quaker neighbors, masters and crews of the three tea ships, were truly in a dilemma and wishing doubtless they were again off the coast of Brazil with nothing more than the flukes and jaws of whales to con-

[169]

cern themselves over. For confronting them ashore were the infuriated citizens of Boston threatening all manner of dire reprisals should they land their tea, and before them afloat the equally enraged Governor Hutchinson with his guns of Castle William and his ships-of-war to make good his promise to sink them without mercy, one and all, should they sail without landing it.

So much I knew already from a letter forwarded me from Nantucket from my friend Henry Gardner, who had sailed without me on the *Beaver*. He did not hesitate to state in plain terms the mortal fear in which hourly he and his shipmates lived, eyeing alternately the ominous mob ashore and the frowning guns of the men-of-war trained on them. And to complete the picture, there shortly after came to me a letter from Delight, dolorously stating she doubted much that I could ever set foot in her home again, such was her mother's rising anger at any and all, including me, who by word or action had not whole-heartedly favored our King.

In this impasse, the ships clung idly to their moorings through December of 1773. Not daring to discharge, not daring to sail, thus they lay to the intense anguish of my Aunt Keziah who was unable to collect her freights unless the cargoes were landed and unable to get rid of her now unwelcome tea that her ships might at least get back into whaling. She helplessly watched her losses mount, her rage at Sam Adams and his fellow patriots mounting even faster.

And now as the last post from Sam Adams informed us, the citizens of Boston did my Aunt Keziah a favor though they had not that in mind, by flouting openly both King and Governor. Crudely disguised as Indians and armed only with tomahawks, some scores of patriotic Yankees boarded the *Beaver* and her consorts. There under the noses of the Quaker shipmasters (who true to their principles made no resistance), they broached all the hatches, hove up on deck the odorous chests of tea, and with fierce blows of the tomahawks staved in their sides. Then amidst the wild cries of the cheering populace on the docks, they steeped the waters of Boston harbor with the hated tea in such a vast brew as never had been dreamed of before!

There was a hasty gathering before the roaring fire of The Grove that January night in 1774 to hear this astounding news from Dr. Read's correspondence. Patrick Henry, Paul Jones, Tom Jefferson, our host and I lifted high our glasses brimming with old port and Madeira to toast enthusiastically the Boston Tea Party, the first forcible defiance to King George and his despotic principle of taxation without representation.

"To Sam Adams!" proposed our bubbling host. "There's salt enough in his brew to turn the stomachs of the tyrants who must quaff it!"

"Aye," agreed Paul Jones heartily, half emptying his glass. "Lord North will indeed make a wry face swallowing that. But now," he added ominously, "we had best begin looking to our stocks of saltpeter. Force, not conciliation, will be my Lord North's reaction, and that we can only answer at the cannon's mouth." He raised his half-filled glass, looked from ruddy Dr. Read to the tall figures of Henry and of Jefferson, concluded significantly,

"The time for men of words alone is going by. To gunpowder and men of action, on which our liberties soon will depend!"

"Well and truly put, good neighbor!" In one gulp, Henry drained his glass to that. "I shall send a messenger post haste to warn Colonel Washington at Mount Vernon of this, that he may consider what action is necessary to prepare the train bands. And as for powder, in all secrecy, I shall see my friends hoard safely away from our Governor Dunmore's prying eyes all they may lay hands on here in Virginia and advise Sam Adams that through the Committees of Correspondence we see that in every colony from Massachusetts to Georgia they do the same. Aye, to gunpowder, friend Paul, and many hogsheads of it! That is the one commodity, in spite of our non-importation agreements, we should in full measure import from England while we may. We'll make the

[171]

King remember what are the rights of English freemen!"

"If I know bull-headed Lord North, Sam Adams and his bellicose friends in Boston have truly loosed the hurricane by this spilling of the East India Company's tea," agreed Tom Jefferson thoughtfully, leaning against the mantel where the reflection of the flames gave added fire to his thick red hair as he stared at the glow in his refilled wine glass. "Resist now by force we must, but whether in that resistance we shall very long continue to look on ourselves as Englishmen I strongly doubt. Freemen, yes, but if I read aright the doctrines these last years flowing across the seas from Voltaire and from Rousseau, our natural rights rest only on ourselves and not on what as Englishmen may temporarily be conceded us by princes and by noble lords under duress of our resistance." Towering above stubby Dr. Read and broad-shouldered Paul Jones, the tall Virginian lowered his glass somewhat to clink it against theirs, then lifted it again. "To the only things which will make us free, my friends. To equality and the rights of man! Away with all princes, hereditary nobles, and their feudal courts and trappings which enslave us!"

Heartily was that sentiment drunk down by all, and then while Dr. Read and Mr. Henry withdrew to the former's desk together to frame a letter to Sam Adams stoutly assuring him of Virginia's support of his position, Paul Jones inquisitively engaged Tom Jefferson in earnest colloquy as to what changes in society he thought necessary to insure these rights.

" 'Tis simple, Captain Jones. First, of course, I postulate we must gain our freedom by fighting for it, for in no other way have men ever wrested liberty from tyrants. But once it be gained, lest we repeat only the errors of Athens and of Rome where it was soon usurped again, power must rest only in the hands of free men born equally before the law—no hereditary titles, no primogeniture, no entailed estates, no distinctions of property in the right to vote for those they choose to carry on their government. If our hearts now be true and our arms be stout, this blaze that Sam Adams has lighted with his Boston Tea Party, may yet result in that in America."

For some months after, life with us moved along again more normally. Paul Jones, absorbed mainly in his trading ventures and his pursuit of Dorothea, had little mind or time for aught else. I, as spring came on in a loveliness of blossoming magnolias I had never witnessed in Nantucket, bestirred myself in working beside the overseer with the stolid mules and the almost equally stolid blacks in preparing the fields for the new crop of tobacco.

Dr. Read was never by nature much enamoured of business affairs. The grief of his wife's death was already somewhat assuaged by time and more by the companionship of Paul Jones who had brought him back to a vivid interest in life again. He began in the intervals between his duties as member of the Committee of Correspondence and his desultory medical practise amongst his too healthy hard-riding neighbors, to look with some favor on comely Mrs. Frances Payne, a young widow from nearby Goochland County, who rode frequently to the hounds with the gentry about The Grove.

Mrs. Payne, favored by Nature in her person and by her late husband in the large estate he had left her in Goochland County, seemed not overly anxious to continue long in her single state. As a consequence, she made no great difficulty, once Dr. Read's mind had been cleared of its morbidity, of attracting to herself his close attention. On both sides of me, between Dorothea Dandridge and Frances Payne, I soon saw ardent courtship in full flower beneath the benignant spring sun. All of this did little, however, to cheer my youthful heart, since physically my own Delight was beyond the reach of anything but occasional circumspect letters which her mother might read and without doubt, did.

So we came serenely to May, with the three bachelors inhabiting The Grove immersed mainly in thoughts of how we might soonest take unto ourselves the ladies of our dreams;

with the House of Burgesses in Williamsburg gallantly passing resolutions of welcome to Lady Dunmore, but lately come from England with her children to join the Governor; and with the colonial gentry in the Tidewater regions thereabout completely occupied in gay preparations for a grand ball at the end of the month in honor of her Ladyship and the Governor.

Then like a blow in the face came down from the north, by couriers fagged from furious riding, the news of the Boston Port Bill. White-faced, Dr. Read read out his dispatches to us while with his thin nostrils dilated wide, eagerly sniffing action, Paul Jones listened. The Port of Boston was to be closed! Commencing June 1, now almost at hand, no vessel might enter or clear that harbor till the citizens of Boston should show their repentance of the Tea Party by reimbursing the East India Company for its tea, £15,000 worth!

Here was reprisal from Lord North with a vengeance! With her harbor closed to shipping, Boston would be prostrated, her means of livelihood, even the means of obtaining the wherewithal to buy food, wiped out. And to make enforcement of the decree sure, General Gage, late Commander-in-Chief of His Majesty's forces in America, was now made Governor of Massachusetts, with Boston so full of redcoats there was one to every five citizens, all to be fed and housed by the inhabitants about to be deprived of the trade on which alone they lived themselves!

"And how take they that in Boston?" asked Jones anxiously. "Under this barbarous blockade, do they submit?"

"No," replied Dr. Read, scanning further the despatches. "Sam Adams and his compatriots say here they are firmly determined to resist though they starve, and ask what aid Virginia will extend in this extremity. Here is something for the House of Burgesses to cogitate immediately. Now must we stand together in resistance, lest having strangled Massachusetts in her trade, we next be throttled by outrageous impositions on our husbandry! Brutus!" he shouted to his body-servant, who came instantly running. "Saddle my horse and put these papers in my saddle-bags! I'm off at

[174]

once for Williamsburg to see what action Patrick Henry can persuade the Burgesses to take on this!"

What action the Burgesses took, as the news drifted back to Jones and me at The Grove, made Paul Jones smile grimly.

"These Virginians!" he muttered. "They are beyond all understanding! In the morning they vote to make June 1, the day the Port of Boston is sealed up, a day of mourning and of prayer throughout Virginia, to send money and nine thousand barrels of flour to Boston that they may hold out there against the King, and to urge all the other colonies to join with Virginia in a general Congress to consider what other steps can be taken to foil King George. And in the same evening they gather, garbed in silks and satins, to bow loyally at the gay ball in honor of his Lady before Lord Dunmore, who is the willing instrument here amongst us to carry out all the King's villainies and God knows what others on his own account! Can you reconcile all that, Tom?"

I shook my head. Not in New England among the stern Puritans of Massachusetts whom I knew could such a thing occur. But truly in Virginia, as well I had learned by now, was life and those who lived it there, very different from New England, let alone from our sober island of Nantucket where there were never any balls.

"Well, now comes it! This Congress will lead to more force from England, and that will lead soon to blows. Tom, there will be civil war in these colonies ere a twelve-month! I must reconsider what I lately said about abandoning the sea. Though Britain hath the most powerful navy in the world, only by what we may do afloat to strike her mortally in that commerce by which she lives, can we hope for any success. Our train bands and our militia, led even by valiant Colonel Washington, can never hold out long before the British regulars flowing across the ocean unless we can choke off the troopships and the merchantmen laden with supplies for their sustenance so far from home. Seamen, Tom! I tell you, lad, if Britain draws the sword, 'tis our opportunity as seamen to strike it from her hand!" His face lighted up, he quivered with excitement, his grey eyes gleamed as he glimpsed a new future. "Ah, Dorothea!" he breathed passionately, wholly ignoring me. "On the sea! There's my chance to gain the fame we've dreamed about to make your father forget all else about your Captain Paul and bring you to my aching arms! On the sea!"

22

FROM then on, life and events moved swiftly, with couriers constantly coming and going from The Grove to keep us in close touch.

The First Continental Congress, called by Virginia, met in Philadelphia in September to petition the Crown for a redress of grievances. Their respectfully phrased document was received in London with a contempt matched only by that accorded the attempts of my cousin, Ben Franklin, as agent there for Massachusetts, to bring about a reasonable understanding of the American position.

Now new causes for dissension rose both in the angered colonies and in a subservient Parliament, bribed to do the will of an even more angered King and his Ministers. From the colonies, knit together by the Committees of Correspondence, came fresh boycotts of British goods, well-observed, and riots of the citizens against the quartering of redcoats upon them. From Parliament came fresh reprisals in more stringent enforcement of the Navigation Acts, which already were distressing American commerce. New decrees cut off all New England from foreign trade and from the Newfoundland fisheries. Further regiments of redcoats were sent to be quartered on the rebellious colonists. Sudden descents for visit and search were made on suspected patriots. Further exports from Britain of powder and military supplies to America were prohibited.

This last, definite notice to the colonies of what was shortly impending as 1774 drew to a close and the fateful year of 1775 approached, brought matters to a head. From north to south the colonies seethed with excitement. Pretence of concealment in arming was now abandoned while everywhere went round the word for the militia companies to hold themselves in readiness. Where they were at hand the military stores of the Crown, powder and guns alike, were seized by the local bands of patriots and carried off to places of safety.

Fearful that what was soon to come might drag him away from Virginia, Dr. Read hastily made up his mind to delay no longer in asking the hand of Mrs. Payne in immediate marriage, so that in December The Grove acquired a new mistress and the days of our bachelor rule there ended abruptly.

The wedding, in view of the turmoil about us, was a simple one, with Paul Jones as best man and Miss Dandridge as maid of honor looking longingly at each other as they stood behind the happy bride and groom, each hopeful that the impending cataclysm which had brought about this union, might, when it came, lay the basis for their own.

I could see that our long stay at The Grove would not continue much longer, now that our host had taken unto himself a wife, for though we were made to feel as much welcome as before by the new Mistress Read, still there was much talk of the Reads abandoning The Grove as their residence to move to Goochland County upon the much larger estate of the former Mrs. Payne. In this desire, I believe, as much as anything she was motivated by a wish not to have before her daily remembrances in the gracious furnishings of The Grove of its former mistress, her predecessor in the affections of Dr. Read. But however that might be, it was obvious to both my companion and to me, that we could not accompany the Reads with good grace to Goochland County, where after all the residence did not belong to our friend, regardless of how pressing his invitation or even that of its owner might be.

But that did not worry Paul Jones. He was no longer in any want, and furthermore, regardless of all else, it was plain to me that in the strained state of colonial relations, my friend could not be kept much longer so far from the sea on which he was now staking all his hopes should there be resort to arms.

Matters were moving toward action. In March the Second Revolutionary Convention of Virginia was called to meet in Richmond, to consider the question of further conciliatory steps or of arming for resistance to the measures of the King. The Convention met, oddly enough, in St. John's Church.

I rode to Richmond with Dr. Read and Paul Jones where my friend hoped for some action which might perchance give him the opportunity to enter service at once should Virginia vote for the arming of any vessels to protect her shores. But once there, we listened from the gallery of St. John's Church in amazed dismay to the unexpected opposition offered to the resolution of our neighbor, Patrick Henry, to prepare Virginia for defense and to raise immediately the forces for that purpose.

The older Tidewater leaders backed by Lord Dunmore's influence were vehemently opposed to any such action. One by one they rose before the delegates to denounce the seditious resolution, urging instead moderation to maintain peace, negotiation to obtain redress, no imitation of the hot-headed Yankees of Massachusetts, and above all, submission of the weak colonies to the King's will lest worse happen. Their arguments seemed to affect the delegates profoundly.

I watched Paul Jones gripping his seat in despair as they spoke. The veins in his wide temples stood out strongly in revolt at this prospect of supine submission, while Dr. Read, in utter disgust at such sentiments, slouched back hopelessly in his pew.

On the floor below us rose our gangling, rusty-headed neighbor to speak against the rising tide. Disdainfully looking upon the dignified gentlemen who had preceded him, he swung his eyes over the assembly a moment while he poised himself. Then fanned to white heat by the fire that was in him, as his voice rose his unimpressive form became by some miraculous transformation before my eyes the very incarnation of all heroic souls struggling against tyranny in every age since time began. Forgotten as I listened were his awkward figure and my knowledge of him as a country squire, while I looked upon that tense face, those burning eyes, and Patrick Henry's quivering lips passionately pouring out his soul in scornful invective and in such a fighting speech as never have men heard before.

"If we wish to be free, we must fight! . . . An appeal to arms and to the God of Hosts is all that is left us! . . . They tell us, sir, that we are weak. But when will we be stronger? Will it be when we are totally disarmed, and when a British guard shall be stationed in every home? . . . The war is inevitable. And let it come! . . . Gentlemen may cry Peace! Peace! but there is no peace. The next gale that sweeps from the north will bring to our ears the clash of resounding arms. Our brethren are already in the field! Why stand we idle here? . . . Is life so dear or peace so sweet as to be purchased at the price of chains and slavery? Forbid it, Almighty God! I know not what course others may take; but as for me, give me liberty, or give me death!"

As that mighty voice closed on its daring challenge to America, I leaned back breathless in the sudden silence that ensued to see Paul Jones, his face enraptured in a fierce glow for liberty, twitching the fingers of his long right arm about the seat of his pew as if clutching for his sword to leap immediately from that gallery amongst the Tories on the floor below.

We left the church, Paul Jones literally treading on air. When those searing words of our neighbor had spread throughout Virginia and from thence over the continent, there could no longer be any doubt that Virginia would stand by Massachusetts in armed resistance and that every colony would join it. And inevitably that meant action on the deep, with its chance for this man by my side who understood ships and the sea far better than he knew his own strange self, to strike a decisive blow for freedom and therein gain his longed-for happiness.

But I could not share his rapture unmitigated by gnawing fears. For ever present in my mind as I contemplated a war on the ocean was my recollection that my Nantucket was a small island, distant from the mainland. In such a situation, it was incapable of defending itself against Britain's Navy and sure of having its wide-spread whaling fleet a prey to British cruisers. With the British bent ruthlessly on suppressing sedition, my friends and neighbors, Quakers and non-combatants though they were, would be cut off from the continent. They would be wholly unable on our barren little island to raise the food for their bare subsistence or even to obtain firewood there to keep themselves from freezing. And how in that plight, come next winter, would Delight fare? I shuddered to think on it.

Colonel Washington and his frontier militiamen, left now wholly to their own ideas and fighting Indian fashion as they would have fought at Fort Duquesne had not obstinate Braddock overruled them there, might hold their own on the continent against the British regulars led by some General as imbued with European ideas of warfare as Braddock had been. But how could we, without a single vessel of war, make any headway on an ocean which I visioned swarming with British frigates preying on our commerce? What could we do against the invincible fleets of British seventy-fours before whose crashing broadsides the powerful navies of Spain, of Holland, and of France had in succession in the two centuries past gone down to bloody defeat? It was inconceivable, and my heart, unlike that of Paul Jones, was of lead as I contemplated the prospects of war on the sea and what that war inevitably meant in suffering and death to the women and children with whom helpless Nantucket was mainly peopled while her men were away pursuing whales.

Both at home and abroad, it became quite obvious to all observing events with any discernment, from the feverish efforts of the Ministry to bolster up its forces in America and from the firmness with which Massachusetts and New England stood their ground, that now all awaited only some spark to touch off actual hostilities.

Losing hope that either the Earl of Chatham or Edmund

Burke, leaders of the minority forces for conciliation in the Lords and in the Commons, could ever accomplish anything in that direction in the face of the venal Parliamentary majority fawning on the King, my disillusioned cousin, Ben Franklin, gave up his post as colonial agent in London after ten fruitless years of struggle there against disruption of the Empire. He was fully convinced that resort to arms alone could remedy America's grievances and preserve any semblance of freedom, so he set sail for America in late March of 1775. During the voyage, like the scientist he was, he seized the opportunity to study with thermometers over the side the course of the Gulf Stream whose influence on aiding or retarding a vessel making the Atlantic passage my late father had some years before called to his attention. While he was still at sea came that fateful spark.

In mid April, a detachment of redcoats sent out by General Gage set forth from Boston to Concord to seize and destroy a hoard of powder stored there by the minutemen. They dispersed with a volley a small detachment of militia they encountered on Lexington green, and proceeded thence to Concord where, after some resistance, they destroyed the powder and in triumph began their return.

But now came reprisal from the despised colonials. The embattled farmers thereabouts hastily gathered for resistance behind stone walls and fences lining the roads back. On the marching redcoats they poured so hot a rain of lead from their long rifles that the return swiftly became a hurried retreat and then a rout pell-mell back to Boston.

The harassed redcoats ran so fast in their race to escape the fire of those blazing rifles that, encumbered though they were with their muskets and accoutrements, they covered the twenty miles to Charlestown Neck and safety in a scant three hours. My sturdy neighbors were left literally with tongues hanging out in their attempts, by cutting across fields, to keep close enough up with the fleeing infantrymen to get in further fire on them.

And when it was over, along the country roads from Concord to Charlestown Neck lay bathed in their blood clotting in the dust fifty of my New England countrymen and seventy-three British redcoats.

That news, borne post haste south, spread like wildfire over Virginia. I need hardly state what effect it had on us at The Grove. But in Virginia, as in every colony, all were not of one mind with us regarding what to do. Dissension arose immediately between conservatives and patriots, between those who supported the King in suppressing sedition or hoped for success through further attempts at conciliation, and those who saw all chance for negotiation had been forever swallowed up in the smoke of the rattling volleys of British musketry and the ragged fire of the minutemen answering them at Lexington.

23

WE stayed but a few days longer at The Grove.

The immediate effects of Lexington and of Patrick Henry's ringing cry for liberty or death were electric. In New England, to General Gage's astonishment, thousands of armed farmers suddenly gathered from nowhere to encircle him and his redcoats in Boston with their deadly rifles. From Virginia, volunteers all, other companies of riflemen set out on foot to join them. Through Fredericksburg daily passed in buckskin hunting shirts or homespun jackets other hundreds, singly and in motley squads, of backwoodsmen and of grim farmers from the Carolinas and from Georgia, all with hunting rifles and powder horns slung from their shoulders, bound for beleaguered Boston. Truly America was spontaneously on the march in defense of liberty.

With Patrick Henry, now a Colonel of militia, raising troops; with excited meetings led by Tom Jefferson and Richard Henry Lee day and night at the Rising Sun to consider ways and means of arming; with proclamations nailed to every court house door calling the patriots to action; with fox-hunting completely forgotten; with even the women forsaking all gaiety for sewing parties to make uniforms, I might well have found myself swiftly with rifle and powder horn from Dr. Read's hunting collection marching off with the enthusiastic youth of our neighborhood had not Paul Jones held me back.

"That's not for you, Tom Folger. America can provide a hundred farmers and frontiersmen, fitter far for soldiering than you or I, for every seaman she can muster now. Let the others go. We sailors will do far more yet for her than a

[184]

hundredfold our number on the land. Wait!"

That young Paul Jones, burning himself for action, should prudently counsel me to wait seemed passing strange in him, especially since nowhere in America were there any ships-of-war in which we might fight nor indeed any signs of there ever being any. On the other hand all about us companies of soldiers were forming in which Jones and I might easily have obtained commissions, seeing that unmilitary Patrick Henry, who knew nothing of the warrior's life, was now a Colonel.

But impatient as I was, I waited beneath Jones' impelling eye, though it left me uncomfortable under the questioning gaze of every woman on every plantation thereabout. They knew me well for a Yankee, and looked with lifted eyebrows on my continued presence about Fredericksburg while their sons, their brothers, their husbands, and even their fathers were rushing to arms in defense of my native Massachusetts.

We had not, however, much longer to wait. On May 10, 1775, in Philadelphia the Second Continental Congress was to meet. Scanning the list of delegates to that body, which came at once to Dr. Read's hand, Paul Jones found amongst those from North Carolina the name of that Quaker shipbuilder and ocean trader, his friend in need, Joseph Hewes.

"There," exclaimed my friend impetuously pointing it out to me, "is our chance, Tom! Hewes, Quaker though he be, is a member of a Congress which has no choice now but to wage a war. And no man knows better than Joseph Hewes, whose interests lie all at sea, where we may strike our most telling blow. My good friend Hewes, together with some New England members I note here like John Adams, will be for a Navy. I must be at hand then to see he puts me in it. Come, pack your saddle bags, my lad! Our days of waiting are over. We're off for Philadelphia and a berth aboard some ship-of-war in the Continental Navy that soon must be!"

With Paul Jones, when wrong was to be righted, there was never any such dilly-dallying and uncertainty of purpose amongst possible courses as afflicted the too-thoughtful

[185]

Prince of Denmark. With my youthful sea captain, to think was to act. Within a few minutes of his discovering that Joseph Hewes was a member of the new Congress, he left to pack our belongings. Booted and spurred he galloped off across the fields regardless of fences toward Captain Dandridge's to acquaint Dorothea of his sudden resolve, and to say farewell.

An hour later he was back, his expressive features a mixture of beatific exaltation, engendered I doubt not by the tenderness of her farewell kisses, and of depression at the thought of leaving her—for how long, he knew not.

Shortly thereafter we twain stood upon the spreading steps of The Grove, our saddle bags packed, our mounts held ready by the eager negro grooms, with the master and the mistress of that gracious mansion which had been a Heaven-sent haven of refuge to us in the hour of our deep distress, at our sides.

Affectionate was the parting of Paul Jones and Dr. Read. The long embrace with which they silently clasped each other fully bespoke the deep regard binding their hearts together. As they separated, Jones bowed deeply to the mistress of The Grove on the step above, saying gallantly to Dr. Read,

"I leave you now, good friend, to arms far more tender and fitter to comfort a man than mine. So fare you well together, my brother, and you, lovely lady, till in peace we meet again!"

He swung about abruptly and flung himself upon his horse lest the tears showing in his eyes become too obvious. I mounted likewise, and as we galloped off amid the waving of kind Dr. Read and of his lady, we caught his last shout,

"Forget not, friend Paul, in Philadelphia to make my duty to my father and my mother there!"

Jones waved in acknowledgment, and in another moment, rounding a bend in the drive, we lost sight of them amongst the trees, and with them, of The Grove, from whose halls and his contacts with the friendly Virginians who thronged them,

Paul Jones had emerged a new man from the plain sea captain he had been.

We made good progress on our journey via Alexandria and Baltimore, being in a few days in Philadelphia, to find that city in a turmoil such as I have never witnessed anywhere. The day preceding our arrival, the delegates to the Congress from North Carolina, Virginia, Maryland, and Delaware, riding up from the south, had been met some six miles out of town by half a thousand mounted Philadelphians, to be joined some miles nearer by companies of riflemen and of foot soldiers, so that they had been conducted to their taverns with blaring military bands and church bells ringing everywhere.

On the day we came, the delegates from Massachusetts, New York, and Connecticut were welcomed with the same military escort and under the eyes of at least a score of thousands of watching Philadelphians. So we found the city full of marching men in all sorts of uniforms and in no uniforms at all, with a wild blaze for resistance to preserve the threatened liberties of America flaming everywhere on the faces of soldiers and citizens alike.

In the midst of this sudden inundation of Philadelphia with delegates, with volunteer soldiery, and with others like ourselves come to be close to the scene of deliberation, every inn and tavern was swamped and we were hard put to it to find accommodation, the public houses having none at all. At this juncture, Jones took matters into his own hands, and choosing Spruce Street as being suitable from its general pleasing appearance, wagered me one pound against a shilling that within the first three private houses at which he should try the knocker, he should persuade the mistress of one of them to accept us as lodgers.

I took the wager gladly, judging from their exteriors that the owners of these houses were in such circumstances as normally to be much affronted at such inquiries. But it cost me my shilling. At the very first house, its mistress who came to the door in answer to Paul Jones' vigorous knocking was so

[187]

charmed by the infectious smile he gave her and the gallant manner in which this handsome young gentleman phrased our predicament as patriotic but homeless wayfarers come to aid in fighting redcoats, that we found ourselves soon installed in a most comfortable front chamber with the solicitous Mrs. Stevenson putting out her best guest sheets and linen for this engaging would-be defender of America's liberties.

Thus we were fortunately housed in a city where accommodations were not to be had at all for money and with difficulty, I doubt not, even for love. Jones took himself immediately off to lay siege to Joseph Hewes with his request, while I wandered about gaping at the wonders of Philadelphia, the largest city by far in which I had yet found myself.

But now Jones' tribulations began. He, judging all from his own habit of speedy decision, had no doubt been under the impression that the new Congress, composed of those most eminent in the public eye, and confronted with a situation clear as crystal to himself, would take prompt steps to meet it. Never was a man more completely disillusioned.

The days passed into weeks and the weeks into months while Jones chafed away his eager heart, without the Congress as a whole showing the slightest inkling of comprehending what America might do at sea and no inclination at all to found a Navy. It rankled deeply in Jones' soul that men of such eminence in colonial affairs should be so blind to this obvious necessity. Indeed what went on in that Hall of the Pennsylvania State House where the Congress met was a trial to many of more importance.

Each delegate was so impressed with his own omniscience that action was lost in floods of oratory. Bitter wrangling with much pounding of tables, wild accusations of self-interest, and acrimonious argument of motives took the place of that prompt decision which the dangerous state of our affairs demanded.

That a Navy got no consideration under these circumstances as the months drifted by, may be clearer when I mention that even the needs of the Army, vividly high-

lighted in the final fierce charge of the British regulars up
Bunker's Hill in June to bayonet the helpless patriots whose
powder had given out, received no attention save further
oratory to which no one listened but the speaker. Colonel
Washington, indeed, was made a General and sent in hot
haste after that debacle as Commander-in-Chief to take
charge of our troops besieging Boston. But Congress took
no effective steps to provide him with the powder and the
siege guns he so badly needed. Nor did they provide him
with soldiery regularly enlisted for some sufficient term of
service rather than the volunteers free to come (and mainly
to go) when it suited best their private affairs. Even Washington perforce had to wear out his energies in endless ap-
peals to Congress for the means with which to fight rather
than address himself wholeheartedly to the task of conquer-
ing Gage.

Our talkative Congress was bringing our affairs on land
to sorry straits. There were a few, mostly from the New
England colonies, who perceived the answer to our problems
lay on the sea, whence alone we might import the sadly
needed ammunition or indeed seize it from the British. Privately they began to grow sarcastic about the futile debates
over ships-of-war. For those orators who were doing nothing
about the war on land concerning which they might have
some knowledge, still presumed to argue endlessly over warfare on the sea of which they knew nothing at all.

John Adams, major advocate of ships-of-war, with his
Massachusetts background giving him uncommon insight
into this problem, finally wrote in disgust,

"There is in Congress a collection of the greatest men
upon this continent, in point of abilities, virtue and fortune.
Every man in it is a great man, an orator, a critic and a
statesman and therefore every man upon every question
must show his oratory, his criticism and his political abilities."

But Stephen Hopkins of Rhode Island, whose knowledge
of shipping was even greater, went further in condemnation
of his disputatious but inactive associates,

"When we draw aside the veil of words and professions— when we attend to what is done and what is said—we shall find that Liberty is a cant term of faction and freedom of speaking and acting, used only to serve the private interests of a party. What else can be the cause of our unhappy disputes? What other reason for the continual struggle for superiority and office? What other motive for the flood of calumny and reproach cast upon one another? Behold the leading men meeting in cabals and from thence dispersing themselves to several quarters to delude the people."

As the weary summer months of '75 dragged into autumn Paul Jones listened in anguish from the gallery to furious debates over buying and outfitting men-of-war. He heard it denominated "the maddest idea in the world" and one that would "mortgage the whole continent" by men who knew naught of ships and less of how to prevent the arms and soldiery that had slaughtered our countrymen at Bunker's Hill from reaching our shores in ever-increasing quantity till General Washington and his ill-equipped troops were conquered by sheer force of numbers and weight of enemy metal.

Jones now saw Joseph Hewes daily, to advise him on the question and to furnish suggestions as to how this or that merchantman which he had examined in the harbor might be converted into an improvised man-of-war to obtain arms for our troops by raiding enemy supply ships. Hewes was, I think, the only person who managed to keep Jones from complete despair. He was older than Jones, completely unemotional, and by long experience with politicians undeceived by their pretensions. It was his firm belief that the orators, declaiming for the benefit of posterity, would ultimately talk themselves out and that then those few like himself who relied more on work than on words would have opportunity to accomplish what needs must be done.

How long this process might have taken had Nature been left free to run her course, I know not. General Washington was convinced at last that Congress would provide nothing for him in the way of ammunition save the voluminous reports of its debates which his soldiers might use as wadding for their rifles provided only that he could obtain the powder and the ball to go with them. He determined of necessity to fend for himself. He observed that the British supply ships for Gage's army, though practically unarmed, were coming unmolested and unescorted from Halifax to Boston through Massachusetts Bay. So he presumed upon his authority as Commander-in-Chief to issue commissions to a few small ships to cruise about the waters of Massachusetts to see what they might capture for him.

With commendable industry, Captain John Manly in the *Lee*, one of these tiny cruisers, shortly made prize of an ammunition ship and of three of Gage's provision ships and got them safely into port to Washington's great joy.

The news of this exploit put a period to the six-month debate in Philadelphia. This was concrete evidence of what even a trifling schooner like the *Lee* could accomplish despite Britain's huge Navy in providing arms for an army destitute of them. Those favoring a Navy finally carried the day in Congress. A Naval Committee, presided over by Stephen Hopkins, for long Governor of Rhode Island, and containing among others John Adams, Robert Morris, and Joseph Hewes, was appointed. The purchase and arming of four ships was authorized and at last in early December the Continental Navy became a reality.

Jones, for long months a prey to despair, was now suddenly overflowing with enthusiasm. Four ships were ordered, his friend Hewes was on the all-important Naval Committee. Already he could see himself an officer aboard one of those ships, at sea again exchanging broadsides with the British. Exuberantly he confided his joy to Mistress Stevenson, explaining to that lady, who had with reason begun to fear in her generosity she had acquired two permanent additions to her household, that shortly we were leaving for berths afloat.

But his joy was short-lived. The new Naval Committee, its members having finished their day in Congress, met that evening at a tavern in its first session, the all-important business at hand being the selection of the officers for the new fleet. The committee went to work, presided over by the venerable Stephen Hopkins, above seventy years of age, who provided for his fellow members lest they thirst unduly while they meditated, a plentiful supply of Jamaica rum lightened somewhat by water.

We waited in the taproom anxiously drinking Madeira the while the committee labored over the personnel of the infant Navy. As we walked home together near midnight beneath the moon in the dimly lighted street, Joseph Hewes reported to us in much gloom what had happened.

"I have sad news for you, friend Paul. Four members of the committee, Hopkins, Adams, Langdon, and Deane, comprising the chairman and the most influential persons in our little body, are from New England. And they insist (and by their numbers are fully able) on naming none but New Englanders to posts in the new Navy."

"What?" Stock-still, Paul Jones stopped dead in the middle of the broad flagging there on Chestnut Street, gripped Hewes in his powerful hand, stared incredulously at him. "You permit that? What boots it to the sea whether a man comes from Massachusetts or the Carolinas so he be a seaman?"

"It matters naught to the sea, my friend, but you show your gross ignorance of politics if you think it matters not to politicians seeking places for their friends. I stand out against it, and no final decision is yet reached, but I fear the worst. Unfortunately for me, Hopkins and Adams in this demand have much reason on their side. They point out most of the seamen and the ships must come from New England, which stands far above all the other colonies together in shipping. As their clinching argument, they have thrown into my teeth and those of Richard Henry Lee who supports me, that they have stood mutely by while we of the south have filled all the important commands in the Army with our Washington, our Lees, and many other southerners, and therefore—"

"Aye!" broke in the excited Paul Jones, "but what of that? Who in all these colonies, other than Washington who has been a soldier from his early youth, is better fitted to command?"

"It might startle you, my impatient young friend, if you knew all the flaming orators, made now into amateur Generals by their colonial assemblies, who think they are! Moreever they are scheming secretly to oust him that they may show their genius in the field rather than on the rostrum which they know better. 'Tis fortunate for us there are so many that they cannot agree upon any one of their number, or else within a week Washington would command no longer, and then indeed we would have to rely on God alone. But you miss the point in your excitement. Hopkins and Adams insist that so long as they have conceded to the south the Army commands, admitted at least by them to be in the hands of those best fitted therefor, it is plain as day that we must concede to New England alone, which above all sections has made a business of the sea, the Navy commands to be placed by them in the hands of fellow New Englanders. Against that logic, what can I say as a southerner? And, logic or no logic, backed up by the influence of John Adams who more than any man on the floor of Congress has labored to provide a Navy, what can I do in opposition if I would?"

Hewes looked into the face of Paul Jones, in the moonlight there as pale and chalky as if he had just heard sentence of death, and sympathetically placed a comforting arm about his shoulder. "Much as it grieves me to say it, friend Paul, there will be no place for you in this new fleet. But look not so stricken, man! Perhaps with the aid of Richard Henry Lee and of General Washington, both of whom know you well and esteem you, we may make a place for you in the Army."

Broken-hearted, my young Captain relaxed his fierce grip on Hewes and allowed us to resume our homeward way. Now indeed were all his dreams of glory shattered and he took it hard.

"Nay, good friend Hewes. I am no soldier and would only be the death of better men should I presume to lead them on the land. The sea I know, and I dare say I may well hold up my head amongst even these Captains of seafaring New England should you but provide me opportunity." His mobile features looked mournfully into Hewes' lean face, seeking there some comfort. But it was not in Hewes' character to deceive any man with false hopes.

"I see no chance at all of that, much as myself I desire it, and sure as I am from my knowledge of you and our many discussions on this subject that you know your profession well. New England will have her way in this, and many are the good seamen available there for these few posts. Against their pretensions to command, what chance have I in urging the name of John P. Jones, in their eyes an unknown southerner, of whom no seafaring man or merchant in these colonies has ever heard? I might be a trifle better off if I could bring you forth as Captain Paul, experienced British shipmaster, but that, as we both know, is quite impossible. So it stands, friend. Bear up as best you may, and may God be with you in your distress of mind. Good night." And coming to the door of his own domicile, with that benediction, Joseph Hewes parted sadly from us.

Through the night we wended our way silently over the snow-covered flagging toward Spruce Street. Jones said not another word but his anguish was only too evident. He was a sensitive man, always responsive to mood, and for long months now he had lived in the dream that America would provide the ships behind whose guns he would gain the fame his soul thirsted for, doubly necessary to him in achieving that domestic bliss embodied in alluring Dorothea. Now he was truly stabbed to the heart, for less than ever could he approach aristocratic Captain Dandridge with lame explanations. Nothing could gloss over what would appear the obvious fact. After the Congress had at last provided ships-of-war, it had passed over as unworthy of its consideration his claims to a berth aboard one of them. Now was his house of cards tumbled about his ears, and he helpless to do anything to rectify matters.

We came to our house, cautiously climbed the stairs to our chamber lest at that unseemly hour we rouse the owners, were soon in bed. But as Paul Jones tossed and twisted endlessly beside me through that night till dawn, I had clear notice what bitter torment in his mind the collapse of his fond hopes had engendered.

Both of us rose in the chill dawn, unrefreshed at all by any rest. I wandered to the State House to listen to a scheduled debate on reprisals for the atrocious act of the British in burning Falmouth. But that day Jones never left our chamber, pacing it like a baffled tiger unexpectedly caged at the instant it was poised to spring upon its long-awaited prey.

From my seat in the balcony at the State House I looked down upon the delegates. The debate was as usual—from one speaker after another a denunciation of the fiendish act of the British in descending upon defenseless Falmouth on Casco Bay with their ships-of-war, there to strike terror into the King's rebellious subjects by burning the town over the heads of the helpless inhabitants, leaving them all, men, women and children alike, to face the rigors of approaching winter on the distant Maine coast, homeless and destitute.

This fiendish destruction to no military object of the town of Falmouth was worthy only of savages. To me it was especially heartrending as presaging a similar attack upon my even more helpless Nantucket. Still the debate on it soon made me yawn. In fiery language it was denounced by brilliant orators, but the futility of debating it after the event by these men who so long had closed their eyes to the necessary ounce of prevention, reminded me comically enough of that fable of the convention of mice debating the advisability of belling the cat. And to some members on the floor it must have seemed likewise, for I soon saw those who had work to do slipping out of the chamber one by one.

Thus Joseph Hewes rose shortly. To my knowledge he had never yet spoken on the floor, being content simply to work unostentatiously to provide as well as might be the implements of war. Then in the rear of the room I saw him in earnest conversation with Robert Morris, a person of vast influence in that assemblage. Upon him more than upon any man rested the herculean problem of finding such funds (mainly from his private fortune) as could be had for the empty Continental coffers. The two apparently came to some agreement and went back upon the floor. There Morris took John Adams by the arm and Hewes likewise beckoned Stephen Hopkins from his chair. The quartet left the debate to the debaters while they went upstairs, apparently for a confidential discussion.

Had I aught else to do, I should have left myself, for the debate and the high-flown oratory bored me. But I had no desire to go home to look upon the wreck which the news of the night before had made of my impetuous friend, and the sharp chill of that December day made wandering about the streets of Philadelphia no inviting diversion. So willy-nilly, since the balcony of the State House chamber was at least warm, there I stayed, doing penance for my bodily comfort in having my ears assailed by a thunderous cataract of words devoid of all promise of effective action.

An hour perhaps dragged away thus, when I noted John Adams, his sharp face flushed with anger, come stamping down the aisle to drop heavily into his seat facing the Speaker. A moment later, entering with somewhat more deliberation, occasioned doubtless by the infirmities of his threescore years and ten, came Stephen Hopkins, more deliberately, yes, but from the purpling of his aged face, quite as enraged.

What had occurred to upset these two self-possessed Yankee statesmen so was beyond me, till arm in arm after them Robert Morris and Joseph Hewes entered to beam benignantly upon their ruffled colleagues. Then Hewes, noting me in the balcony, beckoned me to meet him in the hall outside.

From Hewes' smile on me, I knew immediately something was up.

"Where is our friend this morning?" he questioned. "He is not often absent from our sessions."

"He cares not again to show his anguished face in public, I fear, sir. What the Congress does now no longer interests him. He has remained at home today, and I am afraid will so continue till he leaves Philadelphia. Truly is he like one slain, though his body still lives."

Hewes nodded sympathetically.

"Knowing how his soul has been wholly wrapped up in serving on our new ships, I understand. But I regret his absence for I would not have him suffer another moment. I have good news for him, though my conscience pains me at the means I used to get it. Listen closely, lad, then hasten home to friend Jones with this.

"This morning when our session opened, Hopkins immediately communicated to me the list of officers which he and his associates had chosen to officer our Navy, and which later today they purposed to present to the Congress. While the debate proceeded, I studied it to find, as I had anticipated, that all were from New England. To this, I was already fully resigned as I told you last night.

"But as I pondered the individual names upon that naval roster, a strange thing struck me, considering the two, Adams and Hopkins, who had made it up. Often have they in public and in private denounced members seeking offices for their friends and have laid strictures upon their colleagues for not rising above personal considerations in their public actions. Despite all this their slate showed that when *they* had offices at their disposal, so pure were they in motive that even their friends were not worthy of consideration—none but their relatives were named to the important commands!

"That was too much for me. For the sake of American unity, I could stomach officering our Navy only from New England, which has many fine seamen, to the disregard of my own friend of whose competence I have no doubt. But to swallow a list which purported to proclaim that a monopoly of seamanlike ability, even in New England, lay only in those related to Hopkins and to Adams, was beyond me. Consider—of those named on this startling naval list comprising at the top a Commodore and four Captains, the new Commander-in-Chief is Stephen Hopkins' brother, one

Captain is his nephew, another is his brother-in-law, while yet a third Captain of the four is closely related to John Adams! If only I knew New England genealogy somewhat better, I doubt not but I could show the fourth Captain and probably all the Lieutenants on their list related to them also!

"But what I knew sufficed. I called aside Robert Morris, who like myself had unavailingly been urging the appointment of a Philadelphian whom he knows to be well qualified, and pointed out to him what that list meant. Immediately he sided with me and put the weight of his influence at my disposal. Together then we summoned Hopkins and Adams to a conference at which we presented our ultimatums. Either Morris should have the appointing of one Captain and I of the senior First Lieutenant, or their own list (while it still might be made up of New Englanders) should contain the name of no one even distantly related to either of them. And should they not concede this, Morris threatened to lift not a finger to obtain the funds for any ship, without which there could be no Navy for their relatives to officer. On my part, though I have never before spoken before the Congress, I promised to rise in my place when their slate was presented and denounce it from the floor as a most brazen piece of nepotism, especially despicable as coming whence it did.

"In the face of this, both Adams and Hopkins fumed and protested violently till I had thought they both might suddenly have apoplexy, but we were firm in our position. So finally, rather than consent to the elimination of their relatives in favor of others from New England, they conceded us our two appointments—with what grace perhaps you may judge if you observed their countenances upon their return here. Morris promptly named Nicholas Biddle, well and favorably known here in Philadelphia, to the fourth Captaincy. I on my part, to the great astonishment of all my colleagues who lifted their eyebrows in puzzlement that I should make such a great to-do over one whose name none of them had ever heard, nominated as senior First Lieu-

tenant in our new Navy, him whom you alone would guess—
John Paul Jones! Hasten, now, lad, and inform him that
he is North Carolina's representative in our new fleet. And
may he bring honor to the colony he represents, for it will
take much to ease my conscience of such political chicanery
as I have never before been guilty of, to gain it for him.
May God help him in a Navy so much officered by Hop-
kinses and Adamses whose appointments I must now accept
in silence that he may have his! What keeps you, lad? Be
off now, that friend Jones suffer not another moment!"

Indeed kindly Mr. Hewes had need of his last sharp ad-
monition, for so overwhelmed with joy was I at this sudden
sharp reversal of fortune's wheel, that I stood gaping at
him motionless till the prod which accompanied his final
words startled me into action.

24

NEED I say how Paul Jones, still distractedly pacing our chamber, received the news I bore? Ere I had half finished, I found myself gripped suddenly in those powerful arms of his, clutched to his breast while, emotional as any woman, he literally wept for joy on my shoulder and I in youthful embarrassment, suffered it perforce in silence.

Then as unceremoniously as he had seized me I was released and rudely thrust from him to be totally ignored in his anxiety now to fly to thank good Joseph Hewes.

"Where's my hat?" he asked, wildly looking from wardrobe to lowboy without avail while in his excitement he wrapped his cloak about him.

"There," I pointed, "far under the bed where you heedlessly tossed it last night as if you would never again have need of it. Shall I get a stick and retrieve it for you?"

"Nay, bother not." Instantly, as if afraid I might not display proper dispatch in the task, he dropped agilely to the floor, thrust one of his unnaturally long arms full outstretched beneath the cords sustaining the mattress on our bed, and in one wide sweep dragged forth the missing hat, its tri-cornered brim now fuzzy with dust and lint.

Clambering again to his feet, he regarded it ruefully. Then dusting it meticulously with his left sleeve, he muttered,

"Mistress Stevenson should attend more to how her maid performs her duties in this chamber. If I got such slovenly cleaning on my ship, I'd have the culprit flogged!" and jamming the hat hard down over his sandy locks, he was off precipitantly.

Later that afternoon of December 22, 1775, after I had

[200]

dined alone, I sat again in the balcony beside the now radiant Paul Jones to hear Stephen Hopkins present to the Congress the recommended naval roster. With keen interest I listened as the resolution was read.

"Resolved, that the following naval officers be appointed:
Ezek Hopkins, Commander-in-Chief.
Dudley Saltonstall, Captain the *Alfred*, flagship.
Abraham Whipple, Captain the *Columbus*.
Nicholas Biddle, Captain the *Andrea Doria*.
John B. Hopkins, Captain the *Cabot*.

First Lieutenants: John Paul Jones, Rhodes Arnold, Eli Stansbury, Hoysted Hacker, Jonathan Pitcher.

Second Lieutenants: Benj. Seabury, Joseph Olney, Elisha Warner, Thos. Weaver, James McDougal.

Third Lieutenants: John Fanning, Ezekiel Burroughs, Daniel Vaughan."

There was no dissent from any member so it was shortly adopted.

Overflowing with the joy and enthusiasm limned clearly in his facile countenance, Paul Jones I do not doubt heard no name save his own, as Stephen Hopkins read it off slowly, still chafing with resentment at the bitter pill he was swallowing in two names upon that list. But the other names interested me more.

Ezek Hopkins, the new Commodore, was Stephen Hopkins' brother. John B. Hopkins, Captain of the *Cabot*, was his nephew. Abraham Whipple, Captain of the *Columbus*, was his brother-in-law. Dudley Saltonstall, for whom John Adams had obtained the prize of captaining the flagship *Alfred*, was that patriot's relative. Looking down on John Adams who was grimly silent as Hopkins read the roster, I wondered whether perchance, the intended Captain of the *Andrea Doria*, displaced now in favor of Nicholas Biddle, had been his relative or another of the Hopkins clan. But then I saw John Adams gazing up at the entranced Paul Jones who had been indicated to him. It was probable from the malevolence with which he scanned this unknown emigrant and foreigner from the south, that it must have been another of his family whom Joseph Hewes had thrust aside to make a place for Jones.

However all that might have been, once the Congress had adopted the resolution by vote, all was settled. Captain Paul, fugitive British shipmaster from Tobago where first his face had burned itself into my memory as horror-stricken he stood, sword in hand, over the bleeding body of a slain mutineer, was now by virtue of this Act of Congress, First Lieutenant John Paul Jones of the Continental Navy, solemnly burdened thereby with the task of upholding the liberties of America in the tiny fleet being outfitted against countless British men-of-war. As I gazed upon him at my side in that balcony, I saw him (strange mixture of poetic fervor, almost womanly emotion, and iron will) bursting with energy, eagerness, and gratitude at the opportunity his adopted country had given him. I felt assured that however the Hopkins-Adams appointees might make out in their encounters with the enemy, here was one seaman at least the Congress would never regret having named.

Gone now were the seemingly endless months of weary waiting—the time for action had come. And he acted swiftly. Out of that balcony and down to the assembly chamber below shot lithe Paul Jones the moment the final vote was announced, to pause there only a moment to thank Joseph Hewes fervently.

"You are the angel of my happiness! To your friendship alone I owe this present enjoyment as well as all my future prospects!" he exclaimed, embracing that staid Quaker exuberantly. But delayed only an instant by that, he dashed from the hall of Congress through the wide-spread entry beneath the cupola with its strangely inscribed iron bell, and as if the liberties of our country depended solely on it, made haste through the snowy streets for the docks.

Long-legged though I was, I had much difficulty keeping up as he flew down Walnut Street, off the foot of which lay moored the flagship *Alfred*, on which by virtue of his seniority, he was now First Lieutenant.

Perhaps a cable's length out in the stream swung the *Alfred* and beyond her, tugging at single hawsers in the outgoing tide, her three consorts lay at anchor in the icy waters of the Delaware.

"There, Tom, lies opportunity for such glory that posterity shall never forget us!" exclaimed my companion exultantly, while he motioned a nearby shoreboat at the wharf to take us out.

I was not so intoxicated as my friend at the prospect of glory and in no wise interested in what posterity might think of me. So I looked more critically than he at the unmanned vessels swinging forlornly to their anchors amidst the floating ice of the frigid Delaware. My ignorance of naval matters was vast, but I could see that they were but merchantmen of no great size, much inferior in displacement to the average British frigate, and of course not to be compared to the towering ships-of-the-line on which rested Britain's might at sea.

The *Alfred* and the *Columbus*, the two largest, though ship-rigged with high forecastles and poops, did not seem to me even to equal in size my late ship, the *Beaver*, while the other two, the *Andrea Doria* and the *Cabot*, were but brigs and even smaller. How, save by some miracle, sufficient guns of heavy enough metal could ever be mounted on any of these awkward tubs to menace Britain's men-of-war I could not see.

It was in my mind as I gazed unhappily upon them that instead of gaining glory, more likely their crews, such as escaped death in battle, were sailing straight for English prisons, if not English gibbets, as pirates caught red-handed, if ever they brought these clumsy merchantmen hastily converted into makeshift armed vessels, within sight of any British ship-of-force.

But there I saw not eye to eye with my exuberant companion.

[203]

"Come, Tom, you waste time!" he cried to me as he leaped from the dock into the wherry answering his hail. "I ache for the feel of the solid planking of a ship beneath my feet again!"

I followed him obediently into the boat and sank down upon the bow thwart while Jones, muffled in his cloak, rested in the sternsheets and the oarsman shoved clear into the stream. And thus, I morosely and Paul Jones deliriously as if the dominion of the seas were his already, did we two leap from the tossing wherry when it finally made the *Alfred's* side ladder, to set foot upon our first American man-of-war.

The cold December wind swept dismally through the slack rigging of that deserted ship, rattling shrouds, stays, and blocks most mournfully. No crew and of course no officers, met our glance as we gained the snow-covered deck. It was littered with scraps of cordage tossed away by the freezing riggers working on the spars above us, and with all manner of shavings, chips, and lumber left in the wake of the ship-wrights laboring on the new gun ports.

I saw the *Alfred* as she was, the ex-merchantman *Black Prince*, a lumbering bluff-bowed hulk with no pretensions to speed or handiness under canvas. She was even less pre-possessing than usual now to the eyes, reft of any crew, and in the hands of shipwrights who were tearing like harpies at her sides, her forecastle, and her poop with augers and chisels for beaks, cutting through the ports which should convert (so well as it might be possible) that waddling argosy of commerce into a counterfeit of something her designers had never intended her to be.

But obviously enough, Jones saw her as something else. His breast swelled with pride and his nostrils dilated wide in exhilaration sniffing again the odor of tarred seams and hempen rigging, as his keen grey eyes swept over that deck and turned aloft to scan masts and spars. In his soaring imagination he visioned her as flagship of Commodore Ezek Hopkins, Commander-in-Chief of the Continental Navy, trim and taut, afloat on the blue defiantly flaunting the colonial flag from her masthead. And most important of all, under the charge of Paul Jones, First Lieutenant, her sides bristling with the guns which should give him his opportunity for glory!

25

THE ensuing week was the most hectic of my life.

Captain Saltonstall, commander of the *Alfred*, ignorant as yet of his formal appointment, was in distant Boston. Our new Commodore, Ezek Hopkins, equally unaware that the Congress had raised him to Commander-in-Chief at sea, a position comparable to that of General Washington on land, was almost as far removed from us in Rhode Island where he was a Brigadier General of the militia of that tiny colony.

Thus it was that Paul Jones, senior officer in Philadelphia of the *Alfred*, had thrust upon him the sole duty of fitting out the flagship, mounting her ordnance, enlisting her crew, and preparing her for sea.

Jones promptly rated me a Midshipman on the *Alfred* and set me the task of finding seamen, while he with boundless energy undertook personally to supervise all else on board.

Never did a man work harder. He was determined that when the Commodore, notified immediately by his brother of his selection, should arrive on board, he should find his flagship in all things shipshape and ready to sail against the enemy.

From dawn till winter dusk made work impossible, he was all over the ship. Not a ringbolt went into the gun deck that he did not personally test for the security of its fastening, that no gun might ever come adrift in a storm for want of soundness in the anchoring of its tackles. Not a gun port was finally passed till he had assured himself that it gave maximum arc of train for the gun there emplaced. And aloft, in spite of icy shrouds and the biting December winds, from deck to topgallant crosstrees, he checked the stepping

of each mast, the slings in which the yards hung, the taut-
ness of the lashings in each deadeye on which depended the
security of stays and shrouds. Line by line, through the infinite maze of halliards, braces, sheets, and tacks, he went
over the running rigging to see that no chafed or rotten
cordage existed there to let go in action and broach to the
ship under an enemy's guns. And with the same care each
sail was gone over from courses to topgallants, from flying
jib to spanker, to insure that cringles, clews and canvas
were sound and seaworthy.

Paul Jones was gunner, carpenter, boatswain, and sailmaker that week as well as acting Captain. And such was
his ardor in bringing order out of chaos on that ship, the
burning zeal within him was communicated to the mechanics
toiling under his eye and all alike, through Christmas Day
and New Year's, forgetting they were holidays, labored
patriotically to complete the *Alfred's* conversion.

My own task of recruiting I found not so difficult. Britain
had blocked all her ports as well as her West Indian possessions to colonial trade, declaring all American ports closed.
And the Congress had not yet entered into any treaties with
foreign nations that would permit us to trade with them.
We were still simply colonies in armed resistance to the
Crown's oppression though still acknowledging allegiance.
As a consequence, all colonial shipping was prostrated and
the waterfront inns and lodging houses of Philadelphia were
thronged with destitute seamen, a condition which might
have been even worse for them had not many, despairing
of any employment at sea, gone north to join Washington's
Army as soldiers.

I posted hastily printed handbills advertising the attractions of service on the *Alfred* in every public house and in
every waterfront haunt of sailors, including many dives and
brothels where the scenes of drunken debauchery going on
in staid Philadelphia shocked my youthful eyes. These, written by Jones himself, in burning phrases called on all true
Yankee sea dogs to defy Britain's tyranny behind the batteries of the mighty *Alfred*. From his glowing encomiums,

[207]

one might have thought this vessel a four-decker at least, officered only by Drakes, Hawkinses, and Raleighs. And to top off all, he did not omit to intertwine with this appeal in extravagant terms the lure of prize money plentifully to be gained in the performance of this patriotic duty on the *Alfred*.

Between the effect of Jones' artfully worded handbills and the sad plight of the penniless seamen, the *Alfred*, to which all desirous of immediate service were directed to apply the day after Christmas, was soon swarming with eager sailors clambering up her larboard gangway to pass in critical review under her First Lieutenant's eye. That day Jones might easily have obtained men enough to man a seventy-four, an unprecedented situation for any Navy. Very soon and many times later in his career he had occasion to look back on it with much heart-burning. As it was, in this plethora of seamen rudely jostling one another for a chance to ship aboard the *Alfred*, I wrote down the names and ratings of the hundred-odd whom Jones' seagoing eye chose as showing most ability to hand, reef, and steer, and directed them below to the gun deck. The unfortunates rejected were advised by him to try the other vessels of the squadron when they began recruiting.

In one day we had our crew. Once their bags and hammocks were stowed below, Paul Jones promptly turned to his eager crew in cleaning up the *Alfred* from keel to forecastle deck. She was sadly in need of it, having been out of commission for some time and in the hands only of ship-keepers and laborers.

Next day on barges and floats our ordnance came alongside, the heavy pieces and their carriages to be swayed carefully up on deck under Jones' watchful eye lest even one of those priceless cannon, of which America had but few, slip from its slings to be lost in the Delaware.

Paul Jones personally directed the reeving off of the top burtons to brace up the main yard to withstand the heavy loads, and the rigging of the special tackles and slings to hoist aboard the guns. As a final precaution, to each gun

[208]

ere it left the barge a stout hawser was secured, well buoyed off, that we might have opportunity to retrieve it from the bottom should it by some mischance go overside.

Then with our entire crew stretched aft along the falls and Jones directing at the gunwale, to his hoarse shouts of "Stamp and go, lads! Sway her up, my hearties!" our men laid back rhythmically, in steady heaves to hoist the heavy guns one by one clear of the rail, swing them in, and then cautiously walk back the falls along the icy deck while they lowered them down the hatch to the gun deck. Finally there each was mounted on its waiting carriage and rolled to its designated port.

Most of that day, with their freezing breath rising in clouds as they heaved, all hands put their backs into that job. Not till our twenty-fourth and final gun had safely been swung aboard did Paul Jones leave the gunwale to partake with all his men of the double ration of rum which, to the cheers of his chilled seamen, he ordered served out.

Now indeed we began somewhat to resemble a man-of-war, with twenty nine-pounders lining our gun deck starboard and larboard, and four more mounted in forecastle and poop. And more than ever did Jones now have need to exhibit his miraculous quality of seeming ubiquity, for he alone of all those aboard had ever served on a ship-of-war and knew the handling of her guns.

Wherever I happened to look on that ship amidst the turmoil of fitting out and hoisting in stores, there was her energetic First Lieutenant. In the new magazines, he was directing the stowage of powder and shot. On the gun deck he was showing the impromptu men-o'-warsmen how to secure the gun carriages for sea, with tackles well set up and gun ports sealed with oakum. In the newly-fired galley with the ship's cooks, he was tasting critically of the contents of the kettles destined for the crew's mess. Aloft with the riggers he was putting the finishing touches to the top-hamper. Down in the well, he was personally sounding the bilges. In the Commodore's cabin in the poop, he was running a white-gloved finger everywhere to make sure its inexperienced steward had it shipshape and with brightwork glistening as befitted the quarters of the Commander-in-Chief of the Navy. Even down in the gloomy cockpit on the orlop deck below the waterline where the surgeon was to hold forth in action, I observed him meticulously checking off against the inventory list a harrowing array of saws, of scalpels, of probes, of other instruments of queer shapes intended to assist the surgeon in his bloody business of sawing away and binding up the mangled limbs and torn bodies of the victims of enemy shot, of flying splinters, or of cutlass and boarding pike.

Here I may say that in my long life I have sailed in war and peace with many Captains on ships-of-force and on merchantmen, but with only one Paul Jones. Never was there another seaman like him—no detail on his ship was beneath his notice, no sailor in his view too unimportant for his interest.

And well he showed that on the makeshift *Alfred* with an entire ship's company of merchant seamen bewildered in the midst of ordnance none save him had ever handled before. By New Year's Day, he had them well shaken down, responding smartly to their stations in the watch and quarter bill at the beat of the drum, organized already into gun crews drilling constantly at the batteries. Now he also had some assistants, for after one day's shrewd observance of his seamen, he selected from among them a boatswain, a carpenter, a sailmaker, and a gunner, rating them as warrant officers, together with some other prime seamen designated as petty officers to serve as their mates, as quartermasters, and as masters-at-arms.

On the new gunner and his mates he concentrated to impart his knowledge of ordnance and of practise with the great guns. On the bosun and the other warrants he had little need to spend much time as they knew their duties well, these differing not materially from what they had long since learned in the merchant service.

Not once had Paul Jones set foot ashore save only on the afternoon of his appointment after his first inspection.

On that occasion we had both returned to Mistress Stevenson's to get our belongings and give up our chamber. This news no doubt much gladdened that good lady who had too long suffered our presence to disturb the privacy of her home.

While I packed for both of us, Jones in the front parlor below had remained engaged in earnest conversation with Mistress Stevenson, the which I had supposed related to the settling of his accounts for our protracted stay. But except for that one brief excursion to settle his affairs ashore, he had done naught since, whether awake or asleep, save work and dream of how best and most speedily to make a fighting vessel of the *Alfred*.

Now was it January 2, 1776. On board the *Alfred* life truly moved in martial rhythm. With all the workmen gone at last, the watches were set and smartly changed to the shrilling of the bosun's pipes each eight bells. Side boys attended the gangways always should any dignitaries of the Congress or any officers entitled to such honors approach our side. Quartermasters with their glasses beneath their arms, alert to scan and hail any boat nearing us, manned both gangways. And below from the gun deck came the constant rumble of gun carriages running in and out the ports to the hoarse orders of the quarter gunners and the gun captains drilling their crews.

This day our new commanding officer, Captain Dudley Saltonstall, was expected aboard and on the next, the Commander-in-Chief, Commodore Ezek Hopkins. In the poop their cabins were ready for them, brightwork gleaming like the sun at noonday, the nine-pounders protruding into their staterooms from each quarter glistening in their coats of unsullied black paint.

On the starboard side of the quarterdeck, sacred precinct reserved now only for the commanding officer, stood Lieutenant Paul Jones in a new red and blue naval uniform, a while yet lord of the *Alfred* and all in her. With justifiable pride he scanned his freshly holystoned deck, carefully freed of all trace of ice and snow, with each gleaming plank startlingly outlined by the black ribbons of tar filling the newly caulked seams; his orderly rigging singing in the frosty January breeze; his sails neatly furled on the yards. A few moments he inclined his head to listen to the rumbling of the guns below at their never-ending drill, till, content evidently with the improved speed with which they now ran in and out again after each sharp order, "Fire!", his restless eyes began surveying the topside again.

No First Lieutenant, even with years of service behind him in the British Navy, could have done better in shaking down a newly commissioned ship, none would have done it so swiftly, and Paul Jones, never overly modest in assessing his own achievements, knew that and well showed it in his mien. But still from his restless manner, it was evident that something on which he had not yet placed a finger, was missing to complete his full satisfaction. On the larboard side of the quarterdeck, I lingered as midshipman of the watch with the side boys in the lee of the gunwale, endeavoring to avoid freezing. Covertly I followed his roving eye as it travelled inquisitively over our deck and aloft through the swaying rigging, wondering what it was we lacked to please him, but so far as I could judge, all was in place and in order.

"Quartermaster!" sharply ordered the First Lieutenant, our shortcoming having apparently suddenly come to mind. "Tell Mr. Midshipman Folger to report to me!"

Since I stood then not thirty feet away from him across the narrow deck as Jones very well knew, I started to answer immediately, in some surprise at this roundabout summons, but then prudently thought better of it. This now was the Navy, and Jones had already shown himself a stickler for naval etiquette.

"Aye, aye, sir!" Respectfully the quartermaster saluted him, crossed the deck to me, saluted again but, though for the life of me I could not say wherein in his gesture it lay, with considerably more familiarity and less awe.

"Cap'n wants to see ye, Mr. Folger," he informed me gravely. "He's on the quarterdeck, sir."

"Aye, aye," I answered, and being now officially made aware of my Captain's wishes, I walked smartly across to him, saluted him very stiffly and in such a respectful voice that no one would ever have dreamt that for the six months preceding we had been constant bedfellows, asked,

"You wish to see me, Captain?"

"Aye, Mr. Folger." As disinterestedly as if I had been a total stranger to him, he continued to gaze beyond me at the mizzen rigging singing in the wind. "Up to this moment I had forgot an important item in my outfitting. Have the bosun's mate call away immediately the first cutter, go you ashore in her and keep the boat waiting at the wharf the while you proceed to Mistress Stevenson's on Spruce Street where lately I dwelt. Get from her that parcel she promised to have ready for me yesterday, and return straight aboard with it. And mind you lose it not, sir," he admonished sternly, "for there is not now time to replace it. You may go!"

Thus formally dismissed, in my most nautical manner I saluted again, walked off to larboard, again leaving my Captain in solitary possession of the sacrosanct quarter-deck. Motioning the bosun's mate of the watch, I ordered the first cutter manned, and immediately his silver pipe started shrilling, to be followed by his hoarse voice crying down the hatch through the roar of the rumbling gun carriages,

"Away the first cutter! On deck all the first cutter's crew! Shake a leg below there, sailors!"

The speed with which the coxswain and the eight seamen composing the crew came tumbling up on deck to swarm like monkeys out the boom and slide down into the first cutter swinging from its end, evidently satisfied our Captain. Apparently ignoring all this, he continued seemingly only to study the rigging. But I have no doubt that if the call had not been answered to his fancy, both myself and the bosun would swiftly enough have found out his absorption in that rigging was hardly as wholehearted as it seemed.

In another moment, the boat had dropped down to the

[213]

gangway, where in officer-like dignity I boarded it. Bravely arrayed in my own bob-tailed midshipman's jacket, I took the seat of honor in the sternsheets and in the best imitation of my Captain's manner my scant years could muster, ordered the grizzled and pig-tailed coxswain beside me at the tiller to shove off for the Walnut Street slip. This he proceeded to do in some style, for the coxswain well knew his Captain had an eye upon the progress of that boat and were it not properly nautical, he would find himself disrated to seaman on his return. He gruffly admonished his oarsmen to mind their stroke and catch no crabs, while he sheered the boat dextrously in and out amongst the floating ice-cakes with which the Delaware abounded.

Once alongside the slip, with a stout seaman at my back to carry the Captain's parcel, for now that was beneath my dignity, I set out for Spruce Street, pausing only long enough to warn the coxswain sternly that no other man should leave the boat till my return. My recruiting had acquainted me only too well with the perils of the grog-shops thereabouts, and I had little desire to return aboard the *Alfred* to face her stern Captain with a boatload of drunken seamen at the oars.

Up Walnut Street we went then, I a little self-conscious as soon I noted head after head beneath the broad-brimmed Quaker hats filling the walk, turn sedately to stare at me. But head erect and eyes forward, I swung along, not wholly displeased to attract so much attention, which I knew was directed not so much at me as at my naval uniform, new then to Philadelphia and indeed to all the world.

Philadelphia was well accustomed by now to soldiers and militiamen in wild variety of uniforms, and gave them not a second glance. But the new uniform of the Continental Navy, brave in blue and red, had quite a different effect. So many seemingly sober Philadelphians stopped me to shake my hand or clap me on the back to acclaim me a bold defender of our liberties at sea, that my face was soon rosy as the trimmings on my jacket. I did not regret it when at last I hammered on the knocker of our late domicile on

Spruce Street, resolved firmly to make my way back to the boat by less frequented thoroughfares.

But to my confusion, made complete by the fact that the seaman following saw it all, hardly had Mistress Stevenson who opened the door, set eye upon my jacket than she drew me to her with a maternal kiss!

"Ah, brave Thomas, it gladdens my heart to see thee thus arrayed at last in thy country's uniform! Come in, lad, and let me scan thee all about!"

Then I must blushingly pivot about to please her amidst her admiring Ohs! and Ahs! at my naval clothing before I could say anything at all of the mission on which I had been sent.

"Ah, yes!" she exclaimed, thrusting into my hands a moderate sized parcel, which promptly I passed along to my grinning seaman to distract his attention. "Tell Lieutenant Jones I trust he finds this to his full satisfaction, for the silk is of the best and much love went into the making!"

I was even more humiliated at this, from which I could only deduce that Jones, ever a lover of fine body linen, had sent me to collect for him some newly made shirts! But I marvelled at his brazenness, not so much in his using me, a Midshipman, as messenger instead of sending his steward, as in his asking Mistress Stevenson, certainly no seamstress, to sew them for him.

Now the fat was in the fire of a certainty. From that bewhiskered seaman leering up at me, the story would be all over the ship ere hammocks were piped down, with what embellishments regarding Jones and his amours, God knows! Silk of the best, and much love in the making, indeed! I could well guess what, in crude language, our sailors gathered about the scuttled butt would make of that. And I, brave lad, kissed by the lady in the bargain!

To her evident amazement, I slammed the door abruptly in Mistress Stevenson's face and mortified beyond expression, shot down the steps lest worse occur.

So still a fiery red, I was rowed back to the *Alfred*. On her quarterdeck I took the parcel from the seaman and, choking back my fury, silently presented it to Paul Jones. He received it noncommittally, sent for his steward, and ordering it stowed below in his stateroom, went back to his absorbed study of masts and yards.

Captain Saltonstall failed to arrive that day, being apparently still detained in Boston on his own affairs, but late in the afternoon we had word from shore that the new Commodore had reached Philadelphia and would come aboard next morning as scheduled. Jones promptly made signal to the other three ships, anchored farther out than we, to prepare to dress ship in his honor.

But the coming arrival of the Commodore in the absence of our regular Captain, put Jones immediately in a quandary. Not to every Lieutenant comes the opportunity to receive aboard his first flagship the Commander-in-Chief of a newly-born Navy, and to Paul Jones' glory-loving heart this was an unexpected thrill. Still it left him with a problem he had expected Captain Saltonstall to resolve—with what honors should he receive Ezek Hopkins? For the Congress in its act appointing him had, whether with reason or no, failed to assign him any rank whatever. He was officially simply Commander-in-Chief—not Commodore, not Rear-Admiral, not Vice-Admiral, not Admiral. Washington, Commander-in-Chief of the Army, was also formally designated by the Congress as General, with Major Generals and Brigadier Generals galore below him in command of the motley and ill organized colonial troops. But of the Navy, Ezek Hopkins, aside from being Commander-in-Chief, was nothing at all.

Much puzzled, Paul Jones pondered over that, eager that everything should be done in strictest naval order. Unofficially he considered Hopkins a Commodore. Some others, he well knew, referred to him as Admiral, though most in excessive zeal for equality, regarded that title as smacking too much of royalty and its abominated symbols. The Congress, which alone had authority to say, had kept discreetly silent in its fear of offending American prejudices or in its ignorance of naval matters. What did Ezek Hopkins consider himself? Nobody knew, least of all Paul Jones. But full well Jones realized that should he, upon whom the responsibility now devolved, on this day of all days salute the new Commander-in-Chief with one less gun, a smaller array of side boys, or fewer ruffles of the band than that ex-Brigadier General and unknown worthy felt himself entitled to, the luckless Lieutenant would have cause to regret it to the last day of his naval career.

Jones hastily sent me ashore once more, to get from the Clerk of the Naval Committee of Congress a copy of the Regulations of the new Continental Navy. I returned aboard shortly to report to him ruefully that there were no copies yet available for distribution nor in the single copy on which the Clerk was working, was there anything touching on the point. Neither the Congress nor its Committee had attended to that detail.

Thus thrown back wholly on his own judgment, Jones prudently decided that it was better to risk a reprimand for excessive zeal in imitating the obsequious English in saluting their rulers, which would certainly be only perfunctorily administered by the over-honored Commodore, than to obtain the lasting animosity of a ruffled Commander-in-Chief who thought his merits insufficiently recognized by a subordinate. So sending for the gunner, Jones directed that warrant officer to prepare to salute Ezek Hopkins next morning with all the guns given a British Admiral—thirteen.

Next morning, cold and blustery in a raw January wind blowing up the Delaware, all vessels dressed ship promptly at eight bells. From jibboom to taffrail, in a long line smartly run up to the mastheads, our signal flags started to snap in the breeze as the last stroke of the bell died away, and in gala array did the flagship await her flag-officer.

Farther out in the stream toward the New Jersey side, similarly decorated, the rest of the fleet swung to their anchors, the *Columbus,* the *Andrea Doria,* and the *Cabot* together with four smaller ships recently joined—the *Providence,* a sloop of twelve guns fitted out in New England, the *Hornet,* a ten gun sloop, and the *Wasp,* an eight gun

[217]

schooner, both of which had recently arrived from Baltimore, and the little *Fly*, an unarmed despatch vessel.

On our gun deck, Paul Jones himself saw to the loading of the guns, somewhat fearful lest his inexperienced gunners in their excitement inadvertently ram home a solid shot atop some powder charge, to lay low the honest Philadelphians and turn our celebration into a day of mourning and recriminations. And to insure against seeming lack of civility, should any charge misfire and thus leave his salute short, he ordered two extra pieces loaded, primed, and held ready against that direful contingency.

All was now ready. The coxswain and crew of the first cutter in freshly washed white duck trousers and carefully tarred pigtails (personally inspected, of course, by Paul Jones) lingered abreast the mainmast awaiting the calling away of their boat. The first cutter itself, the Commodore's barge now, with thwarts, bottom boards, and sides scrubbed till they shone, tossed in the stream at the end of its painter, decked out with a wide blue cloth spread in the sternsheets where the Commodore would rest his august figure.

Down on the gun deck, standing to the designated guns, were the gunner, his mates, and the crews of the loaded guns. Except for them our entire ship's company dressed in their best—wide duck trousers, blue jackets, and tarpaulin hats—was clustered in the lee of the bulwarks forward of the mainmast to keep themselves as well as might be from freezing.

Ashore we could see flags of all descriptions hung out in the streets. And on the slip at the foot of Walnut Street, as well as on all the nearby wharves, throngs of eager Philadelphians were gathered. Well aware of the importance of the occasion, they were braving the chill blasts of the river that they might witness the formal birth of their infant Navy.

Self-possessed in the assurance that all was in order, in solitary state Lieutenant Paul Jones slowly trod the quarterdeck of the *Alfred*. I looked admiringly upon his handsome figure, his clear-cut profile and deepset grey eyes well set off by a dark blue tricorne with a device in gold lace upon its turned up brim. Most striking perhaps were his unusual shoulders and his arms, with an epaulette of gold and the red and gold trimmings of the cuffs upon his coat sleeves to delineate a set of arms and shoulders of which any man might well be proud.

About his neck a new white stock was wound with much care, outlining clearly his firm chin. His breast gleamed bravely beneath the red facings of his coat glistening with gold buttons running down to his trim waist. From his left side hung a newly acquired sword rubbing against the silk knee breeches and the white silk stockings covering his slender thighs and firm calves.

All in all, as my speculative eye ran over that costume wondering what silken part of it Mistress Stevenson had contributed, I concluded the whole had cost him a pretty penny, more especially as the tailors must have labored night and day to finish that gorgeous dress coat. But it was worth it, for surely no naval officer treading the quarterdeck of British ship-of-the-line or huge French four-decker ever presented a finer picture, or looked more to the manner born than did Paul Jones.

But one thing I thought was lacking, and from what I knew now of Jones, never unaware of his own excellences, I have little question he thought so too. If only Dorothea Spottswood Dandridge could have been there to gaze upon this youthful Lieutenant treading his quarterdeck, graceful beyond expression in naval uniform with all the self-assurance his position gave his naturally commanding features, his cup of happiness would have brimmed over. And before nightfall, Captain Nathaniel Dandridge with Virginia and all its traditions to the contrary notwithstanding, she would have been Mistress Jones. For what fluttering maidenly heart, looking in war time upon our attractive First Lieutenant, gay in the red and blue and gold of his country's uniform, could have resisted the entrancing smile of Paul Jones did he but choose to exercise it on her? Surely not Dorothea, who had fallen ardently in love with him when he wore only the sober garb of a country gentleman!

A sudden burst of cheering ashore and the sharp cry of the quartermaster scanning the slip through his glass, interrupted my thoughts.

"Coach an' four making the wharf, Cap'n!" he shouted.

"Away the barge!" ordered Jones, and then, "Officer of the deck! All hands to quarters!"

I was officer of the deck in the absence yet of our complement of junior Lieutenants. Immediately was I bawling out orders—to man the barge, to stand by below at the saluting guns, to fall in at quarters.

Our barge was speedily manned and shoved off. The ship's company was drawn smartly up by divisions in the waist between poop and forecastle facing the starboard gangway, and eight side boys, the most seagoing and well set up seamen in our crew, were arrayed at the head of the gangway with the bosun's mate to pipe our Commander-in-Chief over the side. Behind them stood the band, bravely clutching their instruments, ready despite frozen fingers and chattering teeth to blare forth the ruffles and the march befitting an Admiral.

I took one last glance down the hatch to the gun deck where the gunner stood blowing on a spare slow-match. He assured me by a nod that all was well with him. I strode past the mainmast to the quarterdeck, and shivering more from excitement than from cold, reported,

"All hands at quarters, sir. Gunner reports guns ready below."

"Aye, aye," acknowledged Jones casually, as if all this were but the usual day's work. "Stand by the midship hatch to the gun deck, Mr. Folger, to pass me the word instantly should anything go amiss there during the firing, and check you the number of guns fired that the gunner make no mistake in his count. After that," and here he relaxed some trifle in his stern manner, his eyes smiling mischievously on me, "you may take post three paces aft me on the quarterdeck while I receive the Commodore. And should need arise (provided you have lost some of that fury you so poorly

[220]

suppressed yesterday on returning aboard) you may assist me if you will in displaying to him Mistress Stevenson's gift to me."

In much confusion at being thus reminded of my mortification, I bungled my salute badly as I retreated from him to my post at the hatchway, the more so since I did not understand his cryptic invitation. All the silk upon him was sufficiently well displayed for any perfumed dandy, let alone for a seagoing naval officer. But I had little time to cogitate that. Amidst the shouts of the cheering mob on the deck, the barge had just shoved clear bearing the new Commander-in-Chief and was in the stream, maneuvering as best it could to dodge the floating ice while the coxswain strove to hold his course against the incoming tide for our starboard gangway.

I peered down on the gun deck to see the gunner in the twilight gloom there nervously eyeing me. He was mumbling to himself the phrase Jones had taught him to time the intervals between shots, like a schoolboy conning by rote the lesson of which he is none too certain. Assured that he was watching me, I straightened up to stare across the bulwark at the oncoming barge.

About a shiplength off, as Jones had directed the coxswain, it rounded to, parallel to the *Alfred* and gruffly I heard the coxswain order his oarsmen.

"Way enough!" and then, "Toss oars!"

Up into the air, stiffly vertical, went the eight oars of the barge, and the coxswain rose to salute as his boat lay to under our starboard broadside.

I looked at Paul Jones. Curtly he nodded to me, and instantly thrusting my head down the hatchway, I sang out,

"Commence firing!"

Immediately a glowing match was applied to the touch hole of the forward gun. With a thunderous roar, that nine-pounder shot back in its breechings, belching from its iron muzzle a dense cloud of black smoke acrid with the odor of sulphur and saltpeter, which drifted slowly from our side toward the barge.

[221]

Then below me, while the first gun crew as if in action were hastily sponging out their smoking gun, I saw the gunner pacing across the deck to larboard, in singsong cadence repeating, aloud now, to time his discharges the ancient ritual of the gunner since the custom of saluting with guns at sea began,

"If I wasn't a gunner, I wouldn't be here! Larboard! Fire!"

Another clap of thunder as the forward gun in the larboard battery was touched off, and now came a cloud of biting powder smoke drifting in the wind directly over our deck, while from below again came that monotonous singsong of the plodding gunner, directing his tread now to starboard,

"If I wasn't a gunner, I wouldn't be here! Starboard! Fire!"

The third gun roared out, once more to starboard.

Leaving the gunner in his rhythmic drone to continue bemoaning his fate below while he fired his remaining guns, I straightened up again, to enjoy myself the spectacle as mentally I tallied off the discharges. Off to starboard in the barge which was drifting slowly with the tide toward our stern, wreathed in clouds of smoke sat our Commodore stiffly erect in the sternsheets. Beyond him across the ice-flecked Delaware on the docks was a huge crowd, silent now as the salute thundered out from our nine-pounders. Rigidly at attention, hands raised in salute facing the barge to starboard, stood every man on deck the *Alfred* from Lieutenant Paul Jones down to the powder monkeys. Aloft above us in the breeze whipped out our halo of signal flags, and off to larboard, gaily dressed also, lay our consorts with such crews as yet they had, mustered on deck facing us.

My youthful heart was pounding hard with pride at even my small part as gun after gun thundered forth to acquaint the world that a new naval power was that day emerging to challenge tyranny in its mightiest stronghold, the sea. Carefully I counted till at last the thirteenth and final discharge crashed out from our starboard side. Nothing had gone wrong with our novice gun crews. There had been no misfires. No mistake had been made in the number of guns fired. Come of it what might, our new Commander-in-Chief had received thirteen guns, the same as if he had been lord of Britain's vast Navy. I turned with relief from the hatchway, sang sharply out across our smoke wreathed deck,

"Thirteen guns fired, sir!"

"Aye, aye, Mr. Folger! Order the gunner to secure the battery!" crisply replied the First Lieutenant, his eye fixed now only on the barge, vaguely to be seen off our quarter through the dense smoke surrounding it.

The thump of the oars on the gunwales of the barge came to us audible but scarcely visible as the coxswain let fall the tossed oars and got underway for our side ladder. With considerable celerity I passed the word to the gunner to secure below and took post as directed three paces aft of Lieutenant Jones.

All was silent now on our quarterdeck. At the head of the gangway, ranged inboard from the bulwark in two stiff lines stood the side boys, four on each side, bronzed faces fringed with whiskers impassive as they waited to carry out the centuries' old ritual of helping their flag-officer over the side should the state of the sea (or his state) require it.

Behind them at the gunwale, nervously fingering the small silver pipe to which he was little accustomed, stood the bosun's mate, prepared to pipe him over the side with such trills as he could extort from that queer whistle. A little inboard of the passage between the side boys, waited Paul Jones, the brightest splotch of color on our quarterdeck.

With oars bending under the sturdy backs of the rowers, the barge swept up to the foot of the gangway, made fast there. Immediately the bosun's pipe began to quaver shrilly in long drawn out notes embellished by odd trills, the side boys lifted their arms in salute, and a moment later in the opening in our bulwark at the head of our gangway appeared Ezek Hopkins. Automatically I saluted with Jones as he stepped on deck, and the band blared forth in a fan-

[223]

fare of four high pitched ruffles which drowned out completely the continuing efforts of the bosun's mate, to be followed by six bars of a march none too melodiously emitted by the frozen musicians. During all this, while the rest of us remained stock-still at salute, the Commodore, to my surprise, gawked curiously about like any country bumpkin.

As the march ended in one last note, abruptly cut short, Paul Jones stepped forward, in a soft voice greeted our new Commander-in-Chief.

"Welcome aboard your flagship, sir," then before any answer was possible, turned sharply about, and in very different tones sang out,

"Quartermaster!"

Immediately the quartermaster to whom I had before paid scant attention stepped forth, bearing a neatly folded silken flag.

"Mr. Folger!" ordered Jones sharply. "Clear away the signal halliards to the main truck!"

I sprang swiftly to the foot of the mainmast, loosed from the belaying pins there the signal halliards. While I held them Paul Jones expertly bent to the halliards the still folded flag, and then removing his hat which he handed to the quartermaster, he stepped back, and himself manned the halliards.

For an instant this nameless emigrant, American for scarce a year, stood with head reverently bared in the cold wind, then with a quick jerk of the halliards he unfolded the flag and with his own hands rapidly ran it up to the masthead. With abashed eyes I gazed on it. This then, and not any finery for Jones himself, must have been what I had been sent for to Mistress Stevenson's, this banner of the finest silk into the making of which had gone much love!

Spread wide by the wind, swiftly it soared aloft as Paul Jones heaved. A moment later it whipped bravely in the breeze at our masthead—a broad yellow silk ensign bearing on its field a lively representation of a rattlesnake with vivid red fangs protruding, coiled ready to strike, and flaunting to all the world its daring motto, "Don't Tread on Me"—

[224]

the first flag ever to fly from a vessel of the new Continental Navy.

In exaltation Paul Jones gazed aloft at it, as it whipped stiffly out from our masthead. To the last day of his life was it the proudest boast of his sea career,

"My hand first hoisted the American flag!"

26

WHEN the signal halliards were once more belayed, Paul Jones replaced his hat and with eyes still flaming in emotion from the sight of that new ensign, which like his new name, he was resolved to make respected and feared on the seas, he turned again to the Commodore, proudly announced,

"Your flagship is ready for action, sir. Would you deign to inspect her?"

"Aye, Lieutenant; immediately."

While the Commodore with Jones at his left elbow moved across the quarterdeck to inspect the afterguard, drawn up at attention before the larboard gangway, I had good opportunity myself to inspect our Commodore. I eyed him in some disappointment. Awed already by the fire, the seamanlike skill, and the martial bearing of Paul Jones, who was but a Lieutenant, Heaven only knows what I had expected in a Commodore, but whatever it was, I found it not in Ezek Hopkins.

Elderly, somewhat stoop-shouldered, in nowise military in look or bearing, he struck me simply as some workaday merchant Captain who had been plucked at random from a trader's quarterdeck—an utterly uninspired skipper, who by grace of his brother's influence in the Congress had been made head of our infant Navy.

Ezek Hopkins, an antiquated figure very ill at ease in his faded uniform, which looked as if it might be his Brigadier General's costume somewhat altered to more nautical trim, was a sorry sight beside Paul Jones. I compared the evident lack of authority in the Commodore's stodgy face and the absence there of any semblance of leadership, to what the Army had been blessed with in George Washington whose rugged and inspiring countenance I had worshipped many a time in youthful silence at The Grove or in the Rising Sun Tavern. I could only conclude that we in the Navy had fared but ill in the Commander-in-Chief the Congress had bestowed on us.

But it was obvious enough Ezek Hopkins was pleased. A self-satisfied glow was evident on his broad features as he stepped aboard. Apparently our salute of thirteen guns had fully accorded with his ideas of propriety. And now as he proceeded down the lines of rigid seamen, and then on the gun deck passed along the long rows of nine-pounders ominously protruding from the opened gun ports, with tackles rigged, pyramids of shot piled by each piece, crews standing by each breech, needing only the powder charges from the magazines below to loose a flaming broadside, he expanded genially. When he was informed of his appointment only ten days before he knew this ship to be an unmanned, an unarmed, and an only partially converted merchantman. Now he found her most unexpectedly a vessel of war, ready to sail immediately to engage the enemy.

At last when inspection below was finished and the crew piped down from quarters, Paul Jones escorted him from the quarterdeck into his cabin. For neatness I doubt he had ever seen the like of it on any ship he had ever captained. He beamed cordially upon the First Lieutenant.

"Is everything aboard such as your experience approves of, sir?" asked Jones perfunctorily as Hopkins stepped to the starboard quarter gallery to gaze out the huge window in his cabin there at the crowds still cheering on the dock. "If not, I'll have it changed immediately."

If Ezek Hopkins, swelling with importance at all the homage done him ashore and afloat, had answered with a negative, surely Paul Jones, proud of his judgment and execution, would then and there have wholly disbelieved his own ears. But he got his expected answer.

"Aye, Lieutenant. You have done well. But one thing is wanting, and that beyond your power to remedy. When does Captain Saltonstall expect to join his ship?"

"I regret I have no word yet, sir. But till he reports aboard, rest assured I shall do my poor best to carry out your orders in his stead, and I trust the ship suffers not too much the lack."

"Captain Saltonstall is an officer of much sea experience, equaling nearly my own, and we shall be sadly handicapped if he does not appear before we sail, which should be shortly," commented Hopkins. He was eyeing now for the first time with some care the Lieutenant standing deferentially, hat in hand, before him in the great cabin. "You seem to be not so far along in years to be named eldest Lieutenant in our Service, young man. What knowledge have you of ships?" he finished bluntly.

"I have for six years been master of as large vessels as ply the western ocean in the West Indies trade, sir," answered Jones proudly, "and for five years before that have I been mate in other trades. In all have I spent sixteen years at sea, and may lay claim to some close acquaintance with it, despite my lack of years."

" 'Tis a fair record," admitted the Commodore. Then recalling the ceremony with which he had been received, he added handsomely, "And you seem well to realize the customs of the sea. Should Captain Saltonstall not report aboard ere we sail, since you are eldest Lieutenant in the fleet and next in line, you shall be Captain in recognition of your services in fitting out. You may go, sir."

Overwhelmed by this prospect of promotion, Jones thanked him profusely, and coming again on the quarterdeck from the poop, he seemed literally to be treading on air. All had gone well. He, who dearly loved pomp and ceremony, had by kind Fate been leading figure in a ceremony unique upon the continent. And now should luck favor him, this chance! But in his joy, he cannily did not lose the opportunity to bind his new crew to him by giving his shivering seamen some cause to rejoice also.

Hardly had he set foot again on the quarterdeck than he sang out,

"Bosun's mate! Pass the word, 'All hands! Splice the main brace!'"

And soon on the frigid deck below amongst the guns, it was evident from the hoarse cheers of the chilled seamen smacking their lips over brimming pannikins of fiery Jamaica rum, that well Paul Jones knew the surest way to a sailor's heart.

27

MEANTIME events were moving in Virginia, which soon had effect on us.

Throughout the summer and the autumn Dr. Read had kept us closely informed by post of the rebellion there, with Governor Dunmore striving to suppress it and Patrick Henry vigorously blowing into flame the embers of discontent.

But Paul Jones, ordinarily fond of exhibiting his skill in correspondence, was for once so sunk in gloom during those months over the dilatory course of the Congress in providing a Navy that he answered his friend not at all. Then late in the fall came a letter the final sentences of which roused him somewhat from his lethargy.

"Two letters have passed from me to you, and no return. What can you say for such neglect? Shall I beg of you to wait on my father and tell him of the method I have fallen on for a more convenient correspondence? It is long, very long since I have heard from you. What can you urge in extenuation? I wrote you by Colonel Jefferson, requesting you to purchase me a *Cullau au Chasse*, provided you staid in Philadelphia till Christmas, as I am become a military man. Make my duty to my father and family. Tell mother her little namesake is the finest girl in this government. Had it been a boy, there would have been no bearing with me."

"So!" mused Jones in his discouragement. "Thank God someone at least is joyous! A girl, eh? I can see my good friend, the doctor, glowing like the noonday sun in pride of fatherhood over her. Go you, Tom, and see what you can find in the shops suitable to present such a marvelous baby. I shall myself, when I go out, select some feminine trifle for the happy mother."

He glanced again at the letter.

"A *Cullau au Chasse*, provided I stay in Philadelphia till Christmas, as he is become a military man. Sensible fellow, good Dr. Read, that he waits not till he die of old age to join a Navy that a squabbling Congress bids fair never to organize! He'll get his *Cullau au Chasse* all right, and a dozen of them if I but purchase for him one each Christmas I am here waiting on this Congress to act. Would I were back in Virginia with him, where Patrick Henry, hesitating not to seize Lord Dunmore's stores of powder from under his nose, shows how to act as well as to talk! Well, speed you, Tom, and let us see what you know of babies."

But save for that affectionate letter, while the autumn dragged away to winter, Dr. Read's epistles to Paul Jones were full of dire tidings about Virginia as Lord Dunmore, driven from his capital at Williamsburg, retreated to the lower Chesapeake to board the British fleet lying there and wreak vengeance on the unruly Virginians.

And now, the day following the formal commissioning of our fleet, Philadelphia was again in a fever of excitement, not so pleasant this time. From Virginia had just arrived the news that Lord Dunmore, after bombarding Norfolk from his fleet, had landed redcoats there and burned much of the town. From the remnants of that town as a base, covered by the guns of the formidable *Fowey* the vengeful Governor was proceeding to ravage all the Tidewater plantations on the lower James. He was even going so far as to attempt to start a counter-rebellion freeing the slaves by proclamation and arming them to rise against masters who had dared to rise against *their* master, good King George!

In Philadelphia indignation was at white heat over all this. But whereas the burning of Falmouth in Maine some months before could be answered only by flights of oratory, now the Congress was in possession of a fleet of eight warships plainly visible to all the members. And promptly messengers came flying down Walnut Street from the State House where it was meeting, with orders for Commodore

[231]

Ezek Hopkins to get to sea immediately with his fleet and drive the ravaging British from the Chesapeake.

But if the Congress fondly expected this order to be soon followed by the rattle of capstans weighing anchor and the unfurling of sails from the spreading yards of the assembled ships, it knew neither its fleet nor Commodore Hopkins.

Save for the *Alfred*, 24, and three insignificant vessels, the *Providence*, 12, the *Hornet*, 10, and the *Wasp*, 8 (which three had come from elsewhere to join), the ships of the fleet were not ready to sail. And as day after day drifted by in January with no movement, Commodore Hopkins showed more and more by his inept orders and his lack of force, his total inability to comprehend what was necessary to get ships ready as vessels-of-war and then to maneuver them out as a fleet.

Not till early February were all the ships of our squadron finally equipped. By then, weeks after we should have sailed, Captain Dudley Saltonstall had reported, and with his arrival from Boston went by the board our ambitious Lieutenant's hopes of taking out the *Alfred* as commander.

Our frantic Commodore was at last spurred to some action by the caustic criticisms of the Congress, and especially of the Virginia members, who fain would have his ships in the Chesapeake rather than in the Delaware. Now that he had a Captain for his flagship, he sought to help matters somewhat by getting his embryonic fleet beyond the reach of that constant flow of messengers from the Congress. So early in February, though well knowing he could not get into the Atlantic, he made signal to sail, and helped by the outgoing tide, all ships managed to drop well down the bay towards Cape Henlopen. But while we might easily have got to sea in January, so late in the winter had our sailing been delayed that we were caught in the ice blocking the lower bay and our further progress for the time being was effectually stopped.

Even this brief cruise in land-locked Delaware Bay, with most of it a drift with the tide, produced some dissatisfaction in the Commodore's mind over his handling of his vessels. Casting about for means of improvement, it occurred to him apparently that an officer who could interpret signals, if properly placed midway of his squadron, might expedite the maneuvering of his eight ships. Therefore, he sent for the *Alfred's* First Lieutenant, and said,

"I have in mind some change in the commands, Mr. Jones. How should you like to leave the *Alfred* to go as Captain of the *Providence?*"

"The *Providence*, sir?" Through the cabin windows of the *Alfred*, Jones could see the insignificant *Providence* jammed in the ice astern, a small sloop mounting but twelve four-pounders, so small indeed that she was steered by a tiller instead of a wheel. And compared to the battery of twenty-four nine-pounders which the *Alfred* mounted, which he had sweated over so much already, her battery of four-pounders was nothing. Immediately Jones' face fell.

"I am sorry, sir, but I confess I find myself yet imperfect even in the duties of a Lieutenant. I would prefer, an' it please you, Commodore, to remain here on the flagship where I hope yet to gain much useful knowledge from men of more experience than myself."

Normally I judged Ezek Hopkins would have been much nettled at this refusal of his offer. But mollified by the subtle diplomacy of Jones' last remark, he let it pass. Jones stayed on the *Alfred*.

We had finally gained our full complement of officers. Benjamin Seabury joined as Second Lieutenant and John Fanning as Third, together with three other midshipmen whom Captain Saltonstall had appointed immediately on his arrival. This somewhat lightened the burden on Lieutenant Jones and on me, who had ourselves borne fully the chaos of fitting out. More particularly there were now others to share the watches and, in our First Lieutenant's case, to look after the topsides the while he concentrated on gunnery exercises.

Now almost from reveille to taps life on the *Alfred's* gun deck under Paul Jones, who commanded the battery there, was one long drill at the great guns. From morn till night

[233]

the crews exercised endlessly at the battery, till starboard and larboard, our nine-pounders on each side (though no two matched exactly in length, they having been gathered from all over the Continent) went through the motions of broadsides and rounds as exactly as a company of soldiers performing the manual of arms. From gun captains down to powder monkeys our men by example and constant repetition were trained letter-perfect in their duties of loading, aiming, and firing with precision and celerity.

I could well see what natural flair Paul Jones had for the Navy. What knowledge he now showed respecting exercises at the guns he could have acquired only during a scant two years service long before as Midshipman in the Royal Navy. But twenty years of being a Lieutenant could not have taught him better, and I had little fear that the *Alfred* would hold her own in gunnery at least if we had the luck to fall in with nothing of heavier metal than ourselves.

So for two weeks more, except when huddled in our hammocks at night, we lived amidst the Delaware ice in the clamor of rolling gun-carriages and thudding rammers. This, if nothing else, served to keep us from freezing in the chilly 'tween decks of the *Alfred*.

At last on February 17, the ice was sufficiently in motion to release us. The Commodore made signal to weigh anchor, and like a flock of straggling geese, our scattered vessels went out with the tide into the open Atlantic. There we were freed of the infernal ice which had been our bane since I joined the *Alfred*. We managed to gain some semblance of formation and stood out to the southward in line ahead on the starboard tack before a fresh breeze, the flagship *Alfred* leading and the little *Fly* bringing up the rear.

Our squadron was in no way homogeneous. No two vessels were alike in size, and their rigs varied from full-rigged ships through brigs, schooners, and sloops down to the cutter rig of the tiny *Fly*. So it may easily be seen that the sailing qualities of that nondescript collection of square riggers and fore and afters hardly coincided. Even a better Commodore than Ezek Hopkins would have been hard put to

[234]

it to keep them in line of battle and reasonably well spaced.

But to our Commodore, who never in his life had handled more than a single ship and had not the faintest idea of what spread of sail the varying vessels of his fleet required to keep station in formation, it was impossible. After an hour's futile shouting to the signal quartermaster, and, even through a trumpet, to the *Columbus* next astern of us, Ezek Hopkins, face blue from impotent rage and exertion, gave it up and retired to his cabin. After that, we proceeded simply as a flock of scattered vessels in no formation at all, each Captain content apparently only to keep the flagship in sight from whatever position, whether to windward or leeward, that suited his fancy.

Where were we bound? It was well known about every scuttled butt in the fleet, from the uproar in Congress preceding our departure, that our orders were to proceed to the Chesapeake and there attack Lord Dunmore's fleet. Lord Dunmore and the British Admiral commanding his squadron undoubtedly knew it as well as we, seeing that Philadelphia was plentifully supplied with Tories and time enough had elapsed for them to have informed Lord Dunmore of it a dozen times over.

I looked with no great pleasure now to the coming battle, for the *Fowey* alone, the British flagship, far overmatched any ship in our squadron. Only if we in close formation could catch her by surprise and alone, was there any hope for such of us as survived the *Fowey's* broadsides to escape hanging as pirates, which fate was promised by His Majesty's Admirals to all rebels taken in arms at sea. But certainly all chance of surprising her away from her consorts was gone long since. And as for the possibility of engaging with all broadsides in our squadron concentrated on her more powerful battery, it needed but a glance at our ships scattered helter-skelter over the ocean to see the folly of that.

I had found out how general was the fear of hanging among the officers of our squadron, from the furtive scraps of conversation I caught on deck between some of our Lieutenants and those of other vessels who came aboard to visit us while we lay in the ice before sailing. Among our seamen there seemed, however, to be no such corresponding terror. Their worst fate, if captured, was obviously enough impressment on His Majesty's ships which were always shorthanded, for those who might choose that as alternative to a British prison.

There was no telling how I, as a Midshipman, coming between officer and seaman, might fare if caught, but such was the uncertainty of my situation, I took a lively interest in what course our Commodore was steering as bearing directly upon my chances of longevity.

My fellow Midshipmen knew my close acquaintanceship with the First Lieutenant and egged me on to gain some information to allay our uncertainties in the steerage, so that night as Jones paced the deck, trumpet in hand, in charge of the first watch, I took my courage in both hands, sauntered over the quarterdeck to his side, and broached the subject.

"Whither, sir, is the squadron bound?" I asked nervously. "Go we, as rumor has it on the gun deck, to the Chesapeake?"

"I know no more about it than the lamp-lighter," answered Paul Jones gloomily, "and perhaps less, since I note the Commodore takes more interest in talking with the bosun nowadays than with the Lieutenants."

"But the Captain, sir?" I persisted. "Has he let fall no hints on our destination?"

"Not to me, Tom!" Bitterly did Paul Jones snap that forth, pouring out his heart to me as of old, forgetting apparently for the moment it was the heaving quarterdeck of the *Alfred* we trod, not the dusty road from Edenton to Fredericksburg. "Captain Saltonstall's rude, ungentle treatment tries my soul! Men of liberal minds who have long been accustomed to command, can ill brook being thus set at naught by others who claim a monopoly of sense. Confide in me, his First Lieutenant? I doubt that irascible old tyrant confides in God! And he behaves toward his inferiors indiscriminately, as though they were of a lower species. Such conduct will damp the spirits of any man! His behavior may be the fashion in his Boston, but I observed it not in Virginia where I associated with gentlemen and men of strong and well connected sense. Whither go we, Tom? We steer south. 'Tis all I know!"

Not for weeks had Paul Jones relapsed thus into our old intimacy, so swallowed up had he been in his labors. There was no question from that intense outburst, however, that the aloof treatment accorded by our stocky, short-necked, and unquestionably irascible skipper to his sensitive First Lieutenant who had so whole-heartedly labored to fit out his ship, irked the latter almost to madness. And Jones was hardly one to bear his slights in silence, be the consequences what they might. I trembled lest, if somewhat further tried, he tell the Captain directly what he thought of him.

"I'm sorry, sir, I touched so sore a point in my question. I had not thought so much involved."

"Mistake me not, Tom. My distress is not wholly personal that I am ignored; it relates more to the success of this first sortie of the fleet on which our impoverished Continent has expended its all in treasure and heart's blood. Success is vital to our infant fleet! Should we lose our ships to no good purpose, between the despair of our friends and the contempt of our enemies never on our shores will there rise another Navy! And then, may God help this Continent in the struggle in which I have stept forth as a free citizen of the world in defense of the violated rights of mankind, and not in search of riches whereof, I thank God, I inherit a sufficiency!

"The fleet must in this, our first cruise, succeed! And to ensure success, no bit of knowledge, whatever be its source, touching on our mission may safely be disdained. Understand you then, Tom, my chagrin? When I inform my Captain I have sailed with many British officers of note and know their weaknesses and that of the Service we sail to attack should our destination be the Chesapeake; that from my long trading in those waters, I know every island in the

West Indies should our course south lead us there; and that
mayhap my knowledge may be useful to him and to the
Commodore in effecting the proposed plan of action, I receive from Captain Saltonstall only such a stare of aloof
suspicion at my offer I can but conclude he thinks I ask to
know our plan of action that I may at my convenience convey it to the enemy!"

Abruptly he cut short his relation, and leaning against
the weather rail, stared moodily up through the swaying
shrouds at the dark heavens above, burning in indignation
that he should be suspected of such baseness.

Finally with a melancholy sigh, he resumed his endless
pacing of the quarterdeck.

" 'Tis that which irks me in this treatment, Tom. The
Continent will suffer from such rude conduct of its officers.
As for your question, go back to the steerage to tell your
shipmates there that as all Philadelphia knows, the Commodore's orders are to proceed to the Chesapeake and engage
Dunmore's fleet. Should he try that, then our neighbors are
right who regard us as frantic rather than wise men that we
step forth in ships so altogether unfit for war to meet a
trained squadron of the British Navy. But to ease your
minds somewhat, you may inform them also of what is not
so generally known—that by the last article of his orders
Commodore Hopkins is authorized to use his own judgment
as to the direction of his cruises. When you have told them
that, the young gentlemen of the steerage will know as much
as do the Lieutenants in the wardroom. But on your life, tell
them naught else of what I have confided to you as a friend!"
he concluded, grimly shipping again, so to speak, his quarterdeck face.

28

By next nightfall we still continued due south out of sight of land and had certainly dropped below the latitude of the Virginia Capes. It was plainly evident to all in the fleet our Commodore did not mean to engage the British forces in the Chesapeake. Whither we were bound was, however, still much of a mystery, though no longer of such deep concern to us. There were no British fleets to be encountered south of Virginia.

I noted that several of our officers and even many of our seamen now went about their duties with heads more erect and shoulders not hunched up as before about their chins as if unconsciously striving to preserve their necks. From the more cheery countenances of all hands and their remarks, rough though the language of the sailors was as always, it was evident that the Commodore had risen much in the estimation of the fleet for his prudent judgment.

We stood on with wind abeam for Hatteras, off which stormy cape we arrived on the evening of February 19 with the wind freshening considerably and hauling to the northward, so that as darkness fell we were running dead before a fresh gale. We found now the *Alfred* to be a "crank" ship, rolling heavily to the high-placed weight of her battery and yawing so to the following seas that two helmsmen, struggling with the wheel, had much difficulty in holding her steady before the wind.

Except for this, we, being a square rigger, made no difficulty of managing our canvas before a fair wind nor did the *Columbus*, the *Andrea Doria*, and the *Cabot*, square-rigged also. But with the four smaller vessels of our fleet matters went not so well. For them, all with fore and aft canvas,

[239]

running dead before the wind in that gale involved grave danger of jibing should they yaw unexpectedly, and thereby taking out their sticks when their booms swung violently athwartships.

Having sailed with Jones in the *Santissima Trinidad*, also schooner-rigged, I well understood the danger and appreciated his concern as he stood there on our poop gazing anxiously aft at the bobbing lights of our small consorts.

In the gathering dusk, across the rising sea with white caps running everywhere and cold spray whipping sharply off the tumbling crests to come streaming aboard biting into our faces, it was no pleasant task to face that gale studying the plight of our four small vessels. Truly were they making heavy weather of it. They rolled with their booms, far out over their gunwales, one instant buried in the sea, the next high in air.

Captain Saltonstall, swathed in oil skins, came on the poop a moment, gazed aloft at our canvas well squared before the wind, looked briefly about, started again below down the hatch abaft the straining helmsmen. Lieutenant Jones, expecting some order perhaps, waited respectfully in silence nearby the while, but seeing our Commander intended going again below, he stepped swiftly to the hatchway, stopped him.

"The *Alfred* goes well thus free before this gale, sir, but I fear the sloops and schooners astern are in some danger with the wind dead aft as it is on this course the Commodore has set for us," said Paul Jones, pointing to the *Providence* yawing wildly off our weather quarter. "May I suggest, sir, you intimate to the Commodore that, if it please him to change course a little easterly to bring the gale a point or so upon our larboard quarters, the smaller ships would sail with more assurance?"

Masked in the gloom and shrouded by his dripping sou'-wester, there was no telling from his countenance how Captain Saltonstall took this deferential suggestion, but there was no mistaking the icy coldness of his voice.

"The Commodore has been long enough afloat not to need

lessons in seamanship from young Lieutenants. Nor do I. Good night, sir." Abruptly he flung aside the canvas hatch screen, vanished down the ladder, leaving his abashed First Lieutenant to take it as best he might.

There was no change of course. Night fell, in stronger gusts the wind sang through our groaning shrouds. Astern of us in the darkness, all sight of hulls and spars of our consorts was lost. Only the gleam of their running lights, intermittently visible as they rolled and yawed, came fitfully to us on the heaving *Alfred.* Farther and farther toward the east and west horizons swung the lights of the smaller vessels, apparently tacking down wind to do for themselves what the flagship failed to achieve by changing course— that is, running out toward one horizon with the wind well on one quarter, then coming about and sailing for the opposite horizon with the wind on the other quarter, so to reduce the hazard of jibing unexpectedly.

But in this, as we drove straight before the gale and they perforce zigzagged diagonally down it, they constantly lost distance. And at midnight before I went off watch, chilled and soaked to tumble into my hammock in the steerage, so faint had their lights grown that I was left uncertain whether my straining eyes saw them bobbing far astern in the darkness or merely imagined it.

When dawn broke on February 20 over an ocean streaming with foam, the matter was cleared up. Widely dispersed in our wake but five others of our squadron staggered along before the wind—the tiny *Fly* and the *Hornet,* 10, had parted company during the night and we did not see more of them again on that cruise.

What Paul Jones thought of this, he kept to himself. Formally and without comment, he saluted his Captain when the latter came on the quarterdeck, yielding it to him and retreating to the larboard side. Then long and earnestly through a glass our flag-captain scanned the tumbling seas for the missing vessels. He even sent a quartermaster armed with the best glass aboard to the main masthead, there to search a wider horizon for their topmasts, but all without avail.

Finally in ill-concealed temper, he motioned his First Lieutenant,

"No exercises at the guns today, Mr. Jones. I fear some one of them, should you cast them loose, may get away from you in this rolling and wreck the ship." And with this scarcely veiled slight on his subordinate's skill, he vanished into the poop, there, no doubt, to inform the Commodore that due to unavoidable stress of weather, two of our little fleet had been unable to maintain touch and were lost to sight on a stormy ocean.

With six vessels only we continued on, setting our course after passing Hatteras to the south-southwest. The *Alfred's* gun deck was again alive with galley rumors at this, the favorite one being that, as our new course pointed us for the coasts of southern Florida and western Cuba, we were bound for those Spanish possessions to pick up an army which the King of Spain, inveterate enemy of the British, was there secretly gathering to assist General Washington in chastising his ancient foes. And indeed I heard bare-footed seamen, as they pushed their heavy holystones back and forth over our wet decks, gravely informing their mates swashing similarly about in the water and sand, of the exact size of this army, the numbers in its regiment of horse, and even the name of its Commander—brother to the King of Spain, no less!

It astonished me that anyone, save only the company of marines under Captain Nichols which we carried, should believe this nonsense. But it passed solemnly from mouth to mouth, losing nothing in each retelling, in the absence of anything authentic to the contrary, gaining general credence on the lower decks.

Another week we stood on, with fairer weather and warmer breezes to cheer us as we increased our southing and dropped winter astern of us. Somewhat to the southward of Cape Canaveral, we stood over toward the Bahama side of the Florida Straits, whether to avoid the Gulf Stream

[242]

flowing north or in conformity to a prearranged plan, I know not.

But at any rate, off Great Bahama Island shortly after dawn we fell in with two schooners from New Providence, capital of the Bahamas. These vessels, bound north to Cape Breton for coal, sailed unsuspectingly into the midst of our scattered fleet. Immediately they were hove to by round shot across their bows and easily made prize of without more ado. Resistance was useless since they were unarmed, and flight impossible. Gratified by this initial success, Commodore Hopkins made signal for the fleet to rendezvous at nearby Great Abaco Island, where at more leisure the prizes could be examined. So there a few hours later, having been over two weeks under way, we cast anchor.

There was at first wild excitement in our ship's company at these first concrete fruits of our enterprise—before us at Great Abaco lay our prizes and many and varied were the ways our seamen proposed to spend the prize money they had gained. But an inspection quickly disclosed that the two schooners were in ballast only and in themselves of no great value. A hasty estimate showed me my share amounted to about four shillings and I came to the conclusion that in a mercenary sense, prize money might be as poor a road to wealth for me as had been my whaling.

Still if the schooners themselves proved no great gain, their Captains did. These two unfortunate Englishmen, much bewildered at what had befallen them on an ocean ruled by Britannia, were brought aboard the *Alfred* for questioning. From them Commodore Hopkins learned that Fort Montague, guarding the harbor of New Providence, while heavily armed with guns and well supplied with powder and military stores, had but an indifferent garrison and was in poor state to defend itself by land, though with its great guns it might well beat off any attack by sea.

Here was a chance for a prize indeed. Heavy ordnance and powder were the crying needs of Washington's army and of our Navy too, if it were ever to grow above our tiny fleet. What better way to get them than to seize them from our enemy and thus doubly injure him?

Whatever may have been Ezek Hopkins' intentions previously, then and there his mind was made up. He had aboard the flagship Captain Nichols, senior officer of the Marine Corps, together with a company of marines. With seamen from his vessels, he could make up a landing force of some three hundred men—surely enough to take unwalled New Providence and even to assault Fort Montague at the harbor mouth with fair prospect of success.

Immediately signal was made to the fleet to weigh again. With the *Alfred* towing one of the captured schooners and the *Columbus* the other, we were soon underway from Great Abaco for New Providence Island and the capital of colonial Bahama.

Meanwhile the landing force was organized. Captain Nichols of the marines was naturally made Commander, with fifty men (aside from the marines) from each of the larger vessels and twenty from each of the smaller ones to go in the storming party.

On the *Alfred*, Lieutenant Jones mustered and armed our boarding party as the shore detail, but to his chagrin, Captain Saltonstall decided to send it in charge of our Second Lieutenant, Mr. Seabury, who was junior to Captain Nichols, which Jones was not. And to my great chagrin, neither was I, though senior among the Midshipmen, permitted to go, that post being given to a Midshipman whom our Captain had brought from Boston with him.

By late afternoon our fleet appeared off New Providence, for what purpose I know not. One glance at the frowning battlements of Fort Montague guarding the harbor indicated that any attempt to pit our wooden sides against those stone walls in bombardment would be suicidal, and without that we could not enter the harbor, the only safe anchorage on the island. On the quarterdeck of the *Alfred*, side by side our Commodore and his flag-captain scanned the fort through their glasses and the town beyond while slowly, with courses clewed up and topgallants furled, we drew in toward the shore.

What first may have been thought in New Providence of this unexpected appearance of ships-of-force before it in broad daylight is uncertain. But no British squadron was expected and since our battle flags were shortly made out, our character was of course discovered and a round shot, falling far short of us, came ricocheting across the water from the aroused fortress.

If it had been our Commodore's purpose to advertise our coming, he could hardly have done better, and fluently did our First Lieutenant curse at that warning shot. If we had lingered at Great Abaco until evening and then come into New Providence under cover of darkness, we might well have passed the unalarmed fort, anchored inside where most of its guns could not bear on us, and then before we were recognized, have taken town, fort, and all supplies before the unsuspecting garrison, far from the scene of any known hostilities, could fire a shot in defense.

But now that was out of question, and apparently it had never been any part of Ezek Hopkins' plans. Having taken a good look at the town and its harbor, which was evidently his purpose in approaching it, he nodded in satisfaction.

"Proceed now, Captain," he ordered.

"Mr. Jones!" sang out Captain Saltonstall.

"Aye, aye, sir!" Immediately the First Lieutenant came running across the deck for orders.

"Haul by the wind on the starboard tack, Mr. Jones, and stand to the westward close aboard the coast three leagues to the western end of this island, where you will disembark the landing party for the assault!"

"To the westward, sir?" In astonishment Jones stared at his Captain. "I know this island well, and no road leads from its western end to the town. Before the marines traverse that broken country to New Providence, it will be morning and the town will have had time to organize a defense. And besides," he threw in desperately, noting the rising choler of his Captain that he should dare to question an order, "there is on that shore no sheltered anchorage whatever for the fleet nor even any holding ground for our anchors. With this

[245]

northerly wind, that coast will be a lee shore for us. If we escape stranding every vessel in the fleet before we have completed the disembarkation, it will be a miracle!"

Ezek Hopkins, a cautious man, stared uncertainly at the presumptuous Lieutenant, startled at the difficulties thus presented, but there was no uncertainty whatever in our irate Captain.

"Indeed?" he sneered at his assistant, the tendons in his bull-neck tautening ominously. "So the Commodore's orders suit you not, eh? What would you have him do then, pray, Lieutenant?" he asked ironically. "Abandon the attack and sail back to Philadelphia empty-handed?"

"By no means, sir!" burst out Paul Jones earnestly. "In spite of the alarm already given, we can still attack soon and take the town at least by nightfall before the Governor can arm the citizens for its defense. Three leagues to the eastward lies a deserted cay with a good anchorage for the fleet. We can lie there, while we load the marines on our captured schooners, transport them to the *eastern* end of this island, and land them at a road only four miles from the town. Over that they can swiftly advance and an hour later New Providence is ours!"

Nonplussed, Captain Saltonstall glared speechless at his daring First Lieutenant, whom a moment before he was ready to break for his temerity then and there on the quarterdeck. This was not the equivocal answer he had expected to his sarcastic inquiry—it was a complete plan of attack, plausible and, assuming Paul Jones knew that island and the surrounding cays, much sounder than the Commodore's. But the Commodore's plan was the Commodore's. Without a word in reply, Captain Saltonstall turned to look inquisitively at that worthy to see which way the wind blew. Should he proceed forthwith to make an example of Paul Jones, or was the matter open to discussion?

Ezek Hopkins, gazing uncertainly from the nearby shore to the protesting Lieutenant, settled it for him. Hesitantly he spoke,

"This cay to the eastward you mention, how good an

anchorage is it, Mr. Jones?"

"I have seen ships larger than the *Alfred* riding safely out a gale there, sir," assured Paul Jones with all the earnestness he could command. "I swear, sir, it is fully adequate to our present need, and it lies as close to New Providence as does the western end of this island where you purpose landing."

"Aye, but have you yourself been in it?"

"Nay; that I have not, sir."

"What boots it then in our present case? You do not know the channel, you say, and I would as lief risk my ships lying off this coast which I can see, as in taking them into an unknown anchorage to encounter unseen reefs you know not of. We waste our time in this discus—"

"That is taken care of, sir!" interrupted Jones desperately. "We have two pilots—the skippers of those captured schooners. I have spoken them on this subject and they know that cay and all the waters hereabouts perfectly. They can pilot us in!"

"Those Englishmen?" Incredulously Ezek Hopkins gazed into Jones' pleading eyes. "If I trust my ships to them, it will be their opportunity to avenge their capture by stranding every keel I have!"

"Give me the chance, sir!" begged Paul Jones. "It is not a difficult channel. Let me take one pilot to the masthead with me to con the *Alfred* in, and I swear we make it safely. If we scrape one rock, then you may immediately shoot the pilot out of hand for his treachery, and me with him for my clumsiness! It's our best plan, and I stake my life on it!"

Swayed by his ardent earnestness, but still dubious, the vacillating Commodore turned from the *Alfred's* First Lieutenant toward her Captain. Taking chances was no part of prudent Ezek Hopkins' character, but here, it seemed, he must either chance it one way or the other, or give up the attack.

But from his flag-captain he got no assistance in decision. Captain Saltonstall was obviously disgusted that the Commodore knew his mind so little as to dally with a Lieutenant and had turned his back on both of them. Through his glass he was ostentatiously studying the narrowing gap of water between us and the fort.

"We must bear up, or shortly we come within range!" he exclaimed, still keeping his back turned as a second shot splashed near our jibboom. "Which way, west or east?"

Ezek Hopkins looked from Saltonstall's unhelpful back to the long line of surf breaking heavily along the western shore. A lee shore, and a dangerous looking one. Perhaps that cay was better. At any rate, it could not be worse.

"Hard astarboard, Captain!" he decided unhappily. "We go to the east! Signal the other ships to follow us."

"Haul by the wind on the larboard tack, Mr. Jones," said our disgruntled skipper. "And now you have taken this matter on your shoulders by your intrusion, God help you if your cay be not as you say!"

"Aye, aye, sir!" exclaimed Jones exuberantly. "Hard astarboard!" he sang out to the helmsman. Then in a deep voice that needed no trumpet to make it heard on deck and aloft, he roared out, "Loose courses and topgallants! Haul aft the starboard sheets and braces!"

Down went our helm. Obediently the *Alfred* swung slowly to larboard. The topmen raced aloft to unfurl the topgallants, while in huge folds the courses, clewlines slacked off, dropped from the yards and billowed out, catching the wind. To the hoarse cries of the bosun, the lee sheets and braces were handed and swiftly hauled aft, swaying over our heavy yards and the sails with them so that we soon lay close hauled, heeled well down to starboard headed to the east with the fort on our lee side still firing futile ranging shots at us.

Under full sail we were clearing the eastern end of New Providence Island in half an hour. In less than an hour more, we were off a low lying cay fringed by reefs to the northward with the ceaseless booming of the surf breaking over them coming plainly to our ears. We shortened sail again, and with leadsmen in the fore chains starboard and larboard, stood slowly in toward the cay before the wind.

At the main shrouds stood Paul Jones and the English Captain he had selected to accompany him—the elder of the two captured skippers.

Ezek Hopkins gazed uneasily from the foam crested reefs ahead to the two men before him. That uncharted channel looked more forbidding than the open coast. But it was too late to draw back now. He had chosen.

"I trust your eye is keen in piercing this broken water from the masthead, Mr. Jones." None too hopefully the Commodore eyed it from the deck. "But make no mistake. A court-martial will hold you strictly to your word. And as for you," blusteringly he turned full upon the unhappy English-man at Jones' side, "no treachery now!" He pointed significantly to the company of marines drawn up in the waist ready for landing. "If we spring even one seam on yon reefs, a volley will bring you tumbling down immediately from the crosstrees!"

"Aye, aye, Commodore!" agreed Jones confidently, springing into the main shrouds. "Captain Watts here has a wife and six children in yonder town. He means us no more harm than we mean him. Aloft now, skipper; cease that shivering! You're as safe with me as in Mrs. Watts' arms. Let's get it over with!" Nimbly he scrambled up the ratlines to the main top, swarmed over the futtock shrouds to continue on his way. Behind him, more cautiously went the elderly Captain Watts to crawl through the lubber's hole and somewhat shakily to assay the loftier rigging.

Another few moments and at the main topgallant crosstrees Paul Jones stood far above us, swaying gracefully with every roll of the ship, while not so gracefully, clinging tightly for support to the topgallant mast at his side, was Captain Watts, nervously pointing out to him the channel.

That so much ado had been made of the matter seemed odd a few minutes later. As we went in with the *Alfred* leading and the other vessels following cautiously in her wake, it is true that there was much white water not far off either beam and the surf there thundered loudly in our ears. But calm and strong in crisp shouts Paul Jones' voice came from aloft, conning the helmsman on our poop, and shortly, with no sharp turns and coming not within a ship's length of any reefs I could make out from the deck, we were through, to cast anchor in the placid water well inside.

So far, so good. Down from aloft came Jones and his companion, the latter's countenance not so pallid now. Our anchor had hardly caught and the *Alfred* been brought up on her cable than our capstan was heaving in the towline to the captured schooner astern of us, warping her alongside.

With ill-disguised regret, Jones watched Captain Nichols and his marines, Lieutenant Seabury and our boarding party, all laden with muskets, pikes, and pistols, swarm over our bulwarks to the deck of the schooner, there shortly to be joined by the boats from the other vessels. Soon the deck of that coal schooner was bristling with armed men. But so great was the bustle and excitement on the *Alfred* in getting our landing force overside, that our disconsolate First Lieutenant perforce could stand only idly by unnoticed and unthanked either by Commodore or Captain. His task was done, and the fighting, in which alone any glory might be gained, was given into the hands of others.

It was three o'clock in the afternoon when we cast loose the laden schooner and she stood out, carrying her late skipper, our ex-pilot, to con her. The other schooner, similarly laden alongside the *Columbus*, followed her. Our two smallest vessels, the *Providence*, 12, and the *Wasp*, 8, both of which were of slight draft and easily handled, went in their wakes to cover the actual landing with their guns should any opposition be offered.

But all went well. While we on the *Alfred* (and doubtless also all those left behind on the *Columbus*, the *Andrea Doria*, and the *Cabot*) chafed impatiently at our enforced inaction, Captain Nichols and his whole force without impediment of any kind, landed on the eastern tip of New Providence Island. On it they beached the two schooners while the *Providence* and the *Wasp* stood by in the offing with their four-pounders cast loose and matches burning to loose their broadsides if any defending force should come

[250]

down the exposed road from the town.

But none came, and swiftly down that road went the marines and our seamen, to swarm into New Providence without resistance in the gathering dusk and take possession. Immediately Captain Nichols proceeded with a squad of marines to the Governor's palace to demand of that worthy that he surrender the entire colony, but he was too late. The Governor had fled to the fort, over which alone the flag of Britain still floated.

In the darkness, Captain Nichols cautiously reconnoitered the fort, which had been built long before to repel by sea or land the attacks of Spain's armadas or of her heavily mailed *conquistadores*. If those thick-walled bastions were properly manned and stoutly defended, Nichols had but a gloomy prospect before him, storming the guns plentifully visible even on the land side in the face of grape and canister.

Still there was nothing for it but to attack, and Nichols bravely disposed his forces for the attempt, with hastily built ladders dragged close up to the walls under cover of night scattered along his front. It seemed evident that he would be warmly received, for till well past midnight the interior of the fort was alive with dull rumblings and the gleam of lanterns in constant motion.

With the first faint glow of the dawn giving barely light enough to make out the walls facing him so that the scaling ladders could be placed with advantage, Captain Nichols signalled the attack. Down upon the land face of the fort swarmed the marines and the sailors dragging their ladders, expecting momentarily the guns above to open on them with grape. But not a cannon was discharged, and only a few muskets. With wild cries, up went the scaling ladders and in a moment the ramparts of Fort Montague were swarming with Nichols' marines and seamen in possession of all her guns!

Captain Nichols, himself atop the parapet, looked about him incredulously. Not a great gun was manned. The few sentries on the walls, having fired their muskets only per-

[251]

functorily, were now surrendering at discretion to his threatening seamen.

The dumbfounded Captain Nichols descended the stone stairs inside a nearby gun embrasure, and reached the court inside where he received the surrender of its commander and of Governor Brown also. Not until then was the cause of this weird capitulation without resistance explained. There was not a pound of gunpowder in the fort! Governor Brown, warned by the sight of our squadron off the port, despaired of successfully defending the place with the slight force at his disposal. Nevertheless he had done what he could to outwit us. Truly guessing that the powder in the magazines was the real lure, he had during the night loaded every last barrel of it aboard two small schooners which had safely escaped from the harbor in the darkness!

Still Nichols had the fort and all its guns. Hastily our flag was run up in place of Britain's and a rocket was fired to notify the *Providence*, standing prudently well off the harbor out of range, that the place was ours. From their anchorage in the nearby cay our vessels were soon underway at this news. We sailed slowly in past the silent guns of the captured fort, wildly cheering Nichols and his companions on the ramparts, to drop anchor in the harbor of New Providence, captured without loss of a single man!

We stayed in possession three days which were occupied day and night by ferrying out the loot of Fort Montague for lading aboard our larger vessels—one hundred guns, large and small, besides many stands of small arms and miscellaneous warlike equipment, but no powder. Still the guns alone were sufficient cause for rejoicing in America. So, laden deeply with them, on March 17 we made sail homeward, taking with us as prisoners the Governor and two British officers captured in the fort.

From the *Alfred* down to the little *Wasp* officers and men looked up with awe toward Commodore Ezek Hopkins who had brought us this glorious success. A hundred British guns taken and not a man even scratched in the taking! Our

future under Ezek Hopkins looked bright indeed! Even
Paul Jones, hastening to write his patron Joseph Hewes of
the success of our first venture, while he modestly omitted
all account of his own part therein, added,

"The Commander-in-Chief is respected thro' the fleet."

29

WE stood northward for New London, our burdened ships making but indifferent speed on the passage, though for compensation, their steadiness in a seaway was much increased with so much artillery as ballast in their holds.

Such irrational elation amongst our ship's company I never saw before. Where they had gone about before as if in imminent danger of hanging, now they were apparently heedless of Britain's vaunted Navy. Had not a massive British fortress armed with a hundred cannon surrendered to us almost at our call?

In this state of mind, our seamen, who had enlisted only for the cruise, took little interest in further gunnery exercises, feeling that now all was over. Though with all his fiery enthusiasm our First Lieutenant strove to keep them at it, he got a lackadaisical response to his efforts, and shortly a disaster came upon us to damp his efforts still further.

From Abraham Whipple, Captain of the *Columbus* and brother-in-law to our Commodore, came signal that smallpox had broken out in his crew! Soon we were hailed from the *Andrea Doria* with news to the same effect, and in a few days, not a ship in our squadron but found itself with its sick-bay unable to accommodate its stricken seamen. Thus did New Providence, unable to defend itself by force, avenge itself on us. There could be no doubt that the dread disease had been contracted while ashore on that tropical island by some members of our landing party, to be rapidly disseminated in the close quarters of our vessels to their shipmates.

We kept on north, with the smallpox spreading till the *Andrea Doria* was practically useless as a vessel of war, and manned her sails with difficulty. To a lesser extent all our other ships were also incapacitated. It was for this reason, I think, that the little *Wasp*, smallest of our remaining fleet, parted company from us off the Maryland coast to make the nearest port and we saw no more of her.

By April 4, we had arrived off Montauk Point, where we met and easily took a small British tender, the *Hawk* schooner of six guns, in charge of a son of Commodore Wallace, commander of the British forces blockading Newport. Standing on, next day we fell in with the British bomb brig *Bolton*, 8, Lieutenant Snead commanding, and added her also to our prize list.

Judging from our encounter with these light vessels that we should soon fall in with Commodore Wallace and some of his ships-of-force, Paul Jones gazed uneasily over the ocean at our dispersed squadron, sailing as always in no formation whatever, for now, if ever, we had need of proper alignment of our broadsides against that contingency. Still no effort was made by our Commodore to sail his ships in line of battle and we stood on northward past Block Island during the night.

At one a.m. I was tumbled out of my hammock by the roll of the drum beating to quarters. Immediately our gun deck resounded to the cry of the bosun's mates,

"Clear for action!"

In the dim light of our battle-lanterns it became for a moment a madhouse of seamen lashing and carrying hammocks to the nettings on the deck above. My station was at the starboard gun deck battery, which Jones commanded, and there for the next few minutes I was busy with my quarter gunner mustering gun crews, opening gun ports, casting loose, loading, and running out the guns. In five minutes from the first beat of the drum, my battery was ready and its gun captains blowing their matches, eyeing the First Lieutenant for orders.

Complete silence now fell on the *Alfred*, deepened seemingly by the darkness of the night. What was the occasion of that call to quarters? Stooping over the muzzle of the forward gun and craning my neck out the port, to starboard

[255]

and some distance away I made out dimly a strange vessel. She was bearing down from the northward over a smooth sea in a light wind upon the *Cabot*, farthest to leeward of our squadron. Shortly the newcomer went about under shortened sail, now steering parallel to us almost before the wind, with the *Cabot* on her larboard quarter and closing rapidly on her.

I could discern the unknown vessel only vaguely through the night. That she was an enemy was practically certain in those waters, and from the loom of her hull and her canvas, I judged her to be of about our rate and certainly far superior to the *Cabot*.

We were not long left in doubt. Across the water, in the stillness of the night we caught the *Cabot's* hail,

"What ship is that?"

Hoarse and strong came the answer,

"His Majesty's frigate *Glasgow*, Captain Tyringham Howe! What ship is that and what ships are with you?"

To this the *Cabot* replied only with a broadside from her four-pounders, smartly delivered. Immediately in answer came the flash of the *Glasgow's* guns, ten livid streaks of flame in the darkness, followed by the thundering crash of her round shot smashing into the *Cabot's* hull.

One broadside from the *Glasgow* was enough for the *Cabot*. Badly cut up alow and aloft, it was evident to that converted brig she had incautiously closed an enemy of far heavier metal than her four-pounders were ever meant to cope with. Immediately she boarded her tacks, hauled by the wind to larboard and sheered out from under her antagonist's counter while she still could, with her sailing master slain and her Captain badly wounded together with many of her people.

Standing on now in the wake of the battered *Cabot*, we ranged up running free with the wind on our larboard quarter to take her place, all our starboard guns trained far forward in their ports, breeches laid horizontal for point-blank range. The *Glasgow* obligingly clewed up her courses to wait for us.

[256]

We stood tensely to our guns, every man at that battery awaiting with what composure he could his baptism of fire. Drawing slowly into the arc of our vision first came the high poop of the *Glasgow*. Then her larboard side loomed up with its row of open gun ports vaguely outlined as dim squares of light aginst her black hull, framing in their centers the ominous muzzles of the guns which had just shattered the *Cabot*, slewed hard aft now to bear on us!

The *Glasgow* was now fair target for my tier of forward guns and I ached to fire before those terrifying guns across the water could fire on me. But Paul Jones, coolly sighting down the muzzle of our aftermost gun, waited motionlessly till it bore, determined to make the most of his first carefully laid broadside. Then—

"Fire!" he roared, and down on the powder trains at the touchholes came the glowing slow matches.

Whether the resulting concussion which heeled the *Alfred* sharply to larboard came from the recoil of our own guns in their breechings or from the impact of the *Glasgow's* broadside which smashed into us simultaneously, I know not, nor did I have time to learn. Amidst the shrieks of the wounded on our spar deck where the enemy broadside apparently struck, we hastily sponged our smouldering guns, swabbed out, rammed home and wadded down a second charge, and with wild yells again ran out the carriages.

Two more broadsides thus we fired in short succession as precisely as if we had been engaged only at drill. Our round shot were delivered point-blank into the enemy's nearby hull, while so far as I could judge from the lack of damage to our battery, the *Glasgow* was concentrating her equally rapid fire on our topsides.

While we were thus hotly engaged the *Providence*, coming slowly up behind us, managed to draw in range astern the *Glasgow*. It appeared she might well do some damage there, but if she did, I noted it not from any slackening of the *Glasgow's* fire. That frigate held steadily on before the wind and a little on our starboard bow, scarce a pistol shot across the calm sea from us. Also the brig *Andrea Doria* got within

[257]

long range, opening in the darkness from some distance off
our larboard bow, but the *Columbus,* our second largest vessel, was so far away in our scattered formation that in the
light wind she was completely out of action and so remained.

If our squadron had been in any semblance of line of
battle, we might well have poured such a fire from four ships
at least into the *Glasgow* frigate from ahead, abeam, and
astern that within a few broadsides she must have struck to
us or been so badly shattered that a boarding party might
easily have swept her decks. But as it was, the *Columbus* was
completely beyond cannon shot, the *Cabot* already disabled,
and the *Andrea Doria* and *Providence* not in line and none
too well placed for any continuous fire without danger of
hitting us. The *Glasgow* was, therefore, left free to devote
her gunnery to us, and well did Captain Tyringham Howe
improve his opportunity. With his fourth broadside, aimed
high as before, a round shot came crashing across our poop
to smash the wheel and carry away both block and wheel-
ropes!

Immediately our stern swung away before the wind, and
the *Alfred,* unable to steer, broached to helplessly with her
stern squarely beneath the *Glasgow's* smoking guns. Meanwhile in dismay we on the gun deck found not a gun we had
could be trained aft in its port enough to bear again on her!

Seizing that Heaven-sent chance, Captain Howe of the
Glasgow deliberately held his fire till every gun he had to
larboard had been slewed round to bear on our exposed
poop. Then he sent crashing into us a full broadside to rake
our gun deck fore and aft!

Now indeed through the gloom of that low ceiled space
came the rending crash of splintering beams and the shrieks
of wounded seamen, torn and gashed by hurtling shot and
flying splinters. With guns loaded and run out, Paul Jones
impotently stood by ready to fire again from either side
when those on deck should by a jury steering rig regain control. But meantime not a broadside gun we had could be discharged on the *Glasgow.* Thus we rolled helpless, a perfect
target to the enemy. God only knows what the *Glasgow*

might have done to us with a few more such raking broadsides poured into our stern! But fortunately for us, so badly had she herself been cut up by our previous steady fire that Captain Howe decided not to wait to deliver them. He was already crippled and feared that further delay might bring him into close action with some one of our undamaged ships hovering in the offing.

Instead, taking advantage of our helplessness, up went the *Glasgow's* helm instantly after that terrible broadside. She sheered off to starboard, bringing all our vessels dead astern of her and crowded on all sail to escape close hauled.

I almost sobbed with relief as I saw through a gun port the bowsprit of the *Glasgow* haul slowly up into the wind and swing away from us so that those murderous guns no longer bore on our defenseless ship. In the heat of battle, running back and forth behind my blazing pieces, I had given little thought to what enemy shot might do to me. But once we lay ourselves with helm disabled unable to fire and I gazed for the first time upon smashed bodies and horribly torn seamen, a sudden ague of terror swept over me. While I awaited hopelessly the *Glasgow's* next broadside to tear me limb from limb and strew me similarly over the deck, I should have flung myself out a port to escape if I had not caught sight of Paul Jones in our shattered poop, coolly running in our after guns to slew them astern that they might at least keep up some fire upon the enemy through our knocked-in transom.

That steadied me somewhat, though how I might have stood a second raking broadside I do not know. At any rate, it never came. Left thus unhindered by the *Glasgow's* slipping away in the darkness, our afterguard on the topside managed shortly with an improvised rig to bring the *Alfred* once more under control of her rudder and lay her on the starboard tack.

By now the *Glasgow* was at long cannon shot, running close hauled easterly through the night for Narragansett Bay. Astern of her, still in a huddled group, lay our disordered fleet, with Ezek Hopkins signalling by lantern for a general chase. As best we could, each vessel hauled by the wind after the fleeing frigate, firing indiscriminately at her with bow chasers. To this the *Glasgow* replied with guns run out her cabin ports.

What might have resulted from this chase had it been pressed, is doubtful. From three a.m. till dawn broke, we pursued the *Glasgow*, our larger vessels sailing dully and making no appreciable gain. If our Commodore had been more daring the *Providence*, a fast sailing sloop, might, I think, have been able to overhaul the frigate and bring her to in action. She would of course have been in much danger herself till our heavier vessels had come up to engage again, when surely we must have taken that frigate.

But if this occurred to the Commander-in-Chief, at least he made no signal to that effect. Captain Hazard of the *Providence*, though ahead of the others of our fleet, was thus left to make his own decisions, and, deciding on prudence rather than daring, kept well to windward of the *Glasgow's* guns and far out of range.

When finally the day broke, our Commodore lost all stomach for further chase. Fearing that the firing now might bring out others of Commodore Wallace's squadron from Narragansett Bay to assist the intrepid *Glasgow*, he made signal to abandon all pursuit, haul by the wind on the larboard tack, and steer for New London. And so with chagrin we came about, to watch the unmolested *Glasgow* outlined against the rising sun continue easterly toward Newport while we stood westward for Long Island Sound.

A sad affair, our encounter with the *Glasgow*, over which Paul Jones, clearing up the wreckage of our gun deck, could ill conceal his disgust. A single frigate under our guns had escaped from an entire American fleet, having inflicted meanwhile on all of us far more damage than she got! For on the battered *Alfred* and the *Cabot* lay twenty-three of our men dead or wounded from the *Glasgow's* raking broadsides. By no conceit could we have inflicted on her an equal injury in the few broadsides we had fired before we broached to. And even the *Columbus* which had not been in the main action had in the chase received some disastrous balls from the *Glasgow's* deadly guns which had torn an arm from one of her seamen and badly mauled her.

By next afternoon our battered fleet made New London, having on the way encountered and taken a third lightly armed tender of the *Glasgow* cruising in that direction. There as our anchors splashed overboard, we thankfully terminated our cruise, in no such fool's Paradise regarding Britain's Navy as had possessed us when we left New Providence.

All our crew was busily engaged in assisting our First Lieutenant in the dismal business of washing down our bloody decks and making what repairs we might aboard. Since our consorts were likewise employed, only our Commodore set foot ashore. Not till next day did I and my chastened shipmates have liberty in New London. But then I received a startling surprise.

On every hand were we hailed as heroes and time after time were dragged from the streets into any nearby tavern by exultant citizens to toast with them our victory! Our victory? In amazement my eyes popped out to learn that Ezek Hopkins had won a glorious victory over Commodore Wallace's squadron. It was spread all over town that we had taken three of Wallace's light vessels of war and compelled a ship-of-force to flee incontinently lest she be taken also!

Of what avail to argue over that? A victory! I groaned to think how anyone could distort the lacing Captain Tyringham Howe in the lone *Glasgow* had given our out-maneuvered squadron into a victory. But such it was, a victory, and in tots of rum and tankards of ale thrust upon us startled mariners, all our shame-faced disclaimers were drowned out as over-modest. Was not our Commodore's report at hand? Willy-nilly we were heroes, and soon our valiant Commodore would sweep Britain's remaining forces from our coast, lifting the blockade which was strangling New London's shipping!

With the agonized shrieks of our dying still ringing fresh in my ears; with the reek of torn bodies and blood-soaked

[261]

planking strong in my nostrils; and with the sight still sharp before my eyes of the *Glasgow* against the rising sun sailing practically scot-free from under the guns of a faint-hearted Commodore too cautious to bring her to action again, all this adulation and these cheers of victory nauseated me. Escaping with what grace I could from the second taproom into which I had been dragged in celebration, I slunk back to the wharf hastily to board again the *Alfred*.

But the misguided citizens of New London did not persist for long in their illusions. By next day, they saw their hospital ashore filled with our wounded. They saw burial parties sadly firing parting volleys over many a new-made grave. From small boats flocking about our ships they eyed their smashed and battered hulls in open-mouthed astonishment. When the knowledge sank in that all this damage to the fleet had been inflicted by a solitary frigate which had then escaped, by no stretch of imagination could the good citizens of New London conceive of our action any longer as a victory.

And then to top off all, we began to land boatload after boatload of seamen desperately ill with the loathsome smallpox. Full two hundred men were ferried ashore to fill to overflowing the schools and churches improvised hastily into hospitals to take them. There came a swift revulsion in the town.

Two days before we had been fawned-on heroes, now we were cowards beneath contempt. An astounded citizenry cried out against the poltroonery we must have shown to let the *Glasgow* escape. Ezek Hopkins and all his Captains were violently denounced for incompetence, but not stopping there, in the general clamor all the Lieutenants of the fleet were indiscriminately included with them as if they had any hand in the maneuvering of the squadron!

This general denunciation went so far that no officer dared show himself in public in New London lest he be openly insulted by the citizens and jeered at by the children. Perhaps it was too much to ask that in such a fevered state of mind, any distinction should be made between subordinate officers

[262]

who had stood bravely by their guns under the *Glasgow's* deadly fire and those commanding in whose hands alone lay the maneuvering of the ships. It was human enough that Ezek Hopkins, no more fit to command a fleet in action than any powder monkey in it, should be blamed for incompetence. The blame, however, lay more at the door of those in Congress who had placed that antiquated Brigadier General on the *Alfred's* quarterdeck. But that those of us who had served our guns manfully were similarly treated went not so well with us, and in particular Paul Jones was cut to the quick by the censures so indiscriminately thrown out for our not having taken the enemy.

For my part, I was disgusted both with the adulation and the contempt I had received in New London, neither of which I had earned in the slightest. And I was thoroughly sick over the prospect of being taken into action again under the inept leadership of Ezek Hopkins. Of what avail were bravery and the long hours spent toiling in exercise at the guns, only to serve under one who knew not how to achieve a victory when he had the means?

Since my appointment as Midshipman on the *Alfred* was for the cruise only, now that I was back in New England I began to consider how I might obtain my discharge and go home to Nantucket. There at least I could hold up my head amongst my neighbors when I showed myself, without being followed by crowds of taunting children and barking dogs. There also I might seek a third mate's berth on some whaler, which was sure to be commanded by a skipper who went not out after whales, hazarding his life and those of his men, without some understanding of the business. And finally there was Delight from whom nigh a six-month I had heard nothing at all. In what plight had the rebellion left her?

My discharge in my pocket, and enriched by five pounds sterling which I had earned as my pay for four months service and some seven pounds odd additional as my share of the prize money on the cruise, I packed my bag and hammock and without regret, save only for Paul Jones, bade farewell to my shipmates on the *Alfred*.

[263]

In the tiny stateroom of the First Lieutenant, fitted in amongst the heavy timbers of our stern with but a small port to light it, I solemnly took leave of Paul Jones.

"I thank you, sir, for the long months you have supported me in Philadelphia, and for the navigation you have made me master of. Now I shall see what I may do with it in whaling to support myself."

Dubiously Paul Jones eyed me.

" 'Tis a chancey business now, Tom, with so many British cruisers on the seas to seize you, ship and oil together, and rob you of your profits. Better stay with me."

"I dare not, lest I disgrace myself. I would rather die facing a spermaceti in a whaleboat which I know at least to be skilfully handled, than slaughtered on a ship commanded by officers for whose naval abilities I can have but deep contempt! You know not how close I was to flinging myself into the sea to escape the *Glasgow's* guns while I still had some respect for Ezek Hopkins. Now I have none whatever, and I fear I should skulk from the guns before a shot was fired if I should have to go into action again beneath his pennant. Nay, while I still do not deserve the epithet of coward flung at me here in New London I shall leave his fleet, lest I soon earn it in full measure under him!"

In melancholy Paul Jones nodded agreement.

"I would not chaffer with you on that point, friend Tom. When I applied for a lieutenancy, I hoped in that work to gain much useful knowledge from men of more experience than myself. For that reason I once declined the command of the *Providence* to stay on the *Alfred*. I was, however, mistaken, for instead of gaining information I was obliged to inform others. Sad as I am to say it, there's not a Captain in our fleet fit to command a ship-of-war, save mayhap Nicholas Biddle. Nor am I now myself. Though to my sorrow I must say I know myself to be fitter to command than some who do. So fare you well, Tom, in Nantucket. Make my regards to your dear aunt, and do not forget to remember me to your Delight. And if you should not find matters amongst the whalers to your liking, seek me out again in the fleet. Mayhap matters here will have mended somewhat, for I have wind there are some courts-martial impending which may well ease our infant Navy in these iron times of those who flaunt broad pennants and others who call themselves Captains when they are hardly fit to be bosun's mates!"

30

I GOT my bags ashore, and being tolerably well supplied with funds, took stagecoach for New Bedford. In two days I was aboard a tiny packet from that town rounding Brant Point into our harbor of Nantucket, there to my joy to see the wharves lined with the hulls of six stout spouters. Unquestionably with all those vessels fitting out at once, I could land a berth on some one of them as third mate at least.

But I did not give too much thought to that. Behind that array of masts and spars lay Centre Street, clearly marked among the trees by the "widow's walks" topping their roofs and looking out over the harbor. I could easily make out from the deck of the packet that of my Aunt Keziah, more impressive than the rest. With palpitating heart, immediately I had set foot on the wharf, I laid course for that. Not for over two years now had I set eyes on Delight, nor even heard from her at great length.

It was Aunt Keziah, sad to say, who met me at the door.

"So, Thomas Folger, thou hast returned to us!" Suspiciously she scanned me head to foot, uncertain whether it was best to slam the door in my face or ask me in. "And how hast thou fared since my daughter last heard from thee? 'Twas then thou wert wasting thy time between the idling Virginians and that pack of rebels in Philadelphia. Hast come here to stir some mischief on our peaceful island for Sam Adams and those other villains who would rob me of my substance and shed our blood in the bargain? If so, begone! I'll have no traitors to the King in my house!"

"Nay, Aunt Keziah; spare your wrath. I have but returned to go awhaling once again, now I am somewhat fitted for a mate. You recall that young Captain Jones I brought

[266]

to see you? I come here to present to you his greetings, and if I may, my own."

"Ah, yes, Captain Jones!" Keziah Coffin's face lighted up immediately. "Verily a proper young man and a stout ship captain who knew his business and feared neither man nor devil in pursuing it." She sighed heavily. "Thou bringst me tidings of him, eh? Come in then."

Aunt Keziah swung her tall frame inward, unblocking the door, at the same time calling out,

"Delight! Come ye down below! Here is Cousin Thomas come back with news of Captain Jones who so impressed thee!"

I smiled inwardly. If my Aunt Keziah only knew the circumstances under which Delight had been so impressed, she would not thus casually be calling her down again to see me and hear more of him. But while I awaited her in excited anticipation, her mother turned her angular features unhappily upon me.

"I have seen much trouble since thou left us, Thomas. Our Captains here are become but a degenerate breed who disgrace their calling and have cost me dear! Would I had had your Captain Jones upon some one of those tea ships in Boston harbor instead of the three faint-hearted cravens who quavered before Sam Adams and his vulgar Boston mob! He would have landed the tea and saved me my freights, I'll warrant you! And since then, I have had naught but losses on every hand. If I do not see some way to mend my fortunes soon, neither Delight nor I shall have a shelter for our heads. Thou hast not perchance brought me what thou owest, Thomas?" she concluded hopefully.

"But a small part," I answered unhappily, passing over to her the ten pound note which constituted practically the whole of my gains on my late cruise and which I had in nowise intended so to part with, though I was now shamed into it by her dolorous manner.

"'Twill do well for a start." Carefully she scanned the note, then fingered its crinkling surface lovingly. "That leaves yet seventy pounds, Thomas. Thou must bestir thyself more, lad, to pay thine honest debts."

I shivered uneasily. Now I must bestir myself in good truth, debts or no debts, for my Aunt Keziah had artfully inveigled nearly my last penny from me, and should I not swiftly land a berth aboard a whaler, it would be I and not good Aunt Keziah who would be lacking shelter for his head.

But now a light tread echoed on the stairs, and I swung about, leaving Keziah Coffin still caressing that note. There was Delight, brown eyes glowing happily on me, grown more lovely even than I had dreamed.

"Ah, Cousin Thomas! It is good to see thee once again!" Demurely she stepped toward me, the soul of primness under her mother's glance. "You have been adventuring with Captain Jones, you say, and bring some message from him? He is in good health, I trust?"

Inwardly I damned Captain Jones. What did I care now of him or his health, with Delight again before me, two years older and truly a woman grown? I longed to seize her, knock down my Aunt Keziah, if she interfered, as the knights of old smote the dragons in their paths, and rush forth with my lady fair to live happily ever afterwards. But on what? Those three shillings Aunt Keziah had left me, rattling loosely in my pocket? I subdued my ardor and answered meekly,

"When I last saw him, yes, Delight."

"Ah, Captain Jones! I had forgot you bore some word from him," interrupted Aunt Keziah. "One moment while I store this note away upstairs, and I would hear then how he is employed, and whether, mayhap, he might come here to take service now with me. I could use a Captain in these troublous times who hath some backbone." Still gripping my note, she started for the stairs.

She had hardly gained the top step when I could restrain myself no longer.

"Ah, Delight, Delight!" I crushed her to me, my lips deliriously on hers, my tingling fingers running through her soft brown hair. And then, tossing all caution and propriety to the winds, I swept her from the floor completely, started

[268]

for the door. "Sh-h-h!" I quieted her startled protest. "We must get out of here before your mother returns! One question only from her on Captain Jones' employment and on mine, and she sends me flying from this Tory household!"

I was at the door, through it. Outside I set Delight swiftly down, closed it behind us.

"Come!" I seized her hand. "You can explain afterwards as you will! But, darling, come now with me or I will never have another chance to see you!"

Down the street we two went flying, to the first corner, round it, then suddenly slacked to a more sober pace that we excite not comment, and set out toward Brant Point.

Breathlessly Delight looked up at me.

"How much two years with Captain Jones hath changed you, Cousin Thomas! I must thank him thus for tutoring you in decision!"

"Cousin me not, Delight, or I shall take you back straightway to your mother and toss you incontinently there upon the floor! Have you no words for me after these two years save 'Cousin' and prattle about Captain Jones? He's safely in New London where I left him to seek you, but if you can find no better word for me than 'Cousin,' back I go to him at once!"

"Indeed! Did I struggle so much when you kissed me a few moments gone?" Quaker though she was, her lashes lifted archly on me. "You have learned little amongst the maidens of the South if you have not yet learned that a woman may say more wordlessly in one kiss than in a thousand honeyed words—darling!" she ended, so softly breathing out that word it seemed a long-drawn-out caress.

In ecstasy over that I literally floated on air out of town beside Delight, to end unconsciously upon that sandy point where amid my geometric diagrams we had first found ourselves in close embrace. There again upon the sands looking out over the empty sea we sat down once more. And in close embrace again did Delight there demonstrate for me her theorem of what might be conveyed in a woman's kiss—the longing of a woman's heart far beyond the power of any

[269]

burning poet even to phrase into speech.

At long last came we to more practical matters—our chances of marriage now. I confessed gloomily that while I had gained much knowledge of the sea and was as competent to navigate a ship as anyone, I sat there beside her as penniless as when over two years before I sailed from Nantucket in the *Santissima Trinidad.*

"Save for seven pounds I left in Captain Rotch's hands when I left, and the belongings of my mother's house stored also by his courtesy amongst the casks of sperm oil in his warehouse, I have naught," I concluded, adding hopefully, "Still, however, I have that furniture and some linen. With that we may furnish out a rented cottage, and you may have the seven pounds to keep you while I go pursuing whales for more."

"Nay, darling Thomas, it cannot be." Tenderly Delight nestled her head on my shoulder, turned her eyes on mine. "Thou hast no idea how frightfully prices have risen on Nantucket. We must wait."

"What? Wait three years more?" I asked, dismayed. "But why, dear heart? Good sperm oil has also risen in price, and I may get credit from the merchant on whose vessel I sail against my lay on her return. Surely you can do as well thus in my absence as ever my mother did!"

Still Delight shook her head.

"You do not understand what hath happened on Nantucket since Bunker's Hill. It is not as it was before that. Thou'lt not go awhaling, Thomas, nor will any merchant—"

"Not go?" I asked, much puzzled. "Why, I saw six spouters lying light against the wharves, and with six at once to be manned here on this island, surely there must be a place for me on one of them. Every oil merchant in this town well knows the Folgers for good whalemen, and now my arm and shoulders can dart an iron as strongly as ever my father did!" And to prove it, my arms pressed her so tightly to me she gasped at last for breath in that embrace.

"Nay, Thomas; I doubted not thy arms might even crush a whale as thou hast nearly me! It is not that. But hadst

[270]

thou not hastened so to Centre Street upon thy landing, thou wouldst have learned upon the wharves not one of those ships you saw is lading stores against her sailing. No oil merchant now sends his vessels to sea for whales, and in our meeting house instead they sit in silent prayer, beseeching the good Lord he may allow the ships they have at sea to return home uncaptured on the way! Credit against your lay on your return? There is no longer credit for anyone on this island, and," here her eyes filled with tears, "ashamed I am to say it, my mother is the most detested person on Nantucket. Aye, even amongst the good Friends of our own faith. Oh, Thomas," she cried, weeping unrestrainedly, "how I long to leave that house!"

"Aye, well I know among the patriots the Tories fare but hard," I tried to comfort her.

"Nay, 'tis not that she is a Tory. There are many others here as loyal to the King as she. It is that food here is now scarce and difficult to obtain from the Continent, what with British cruisers everywhere. And my mother, who hath shrewdly stocked her warehouse, grants credit to no one, and demands in cash or oil prices so outrageous for provision it is truly a sin against the Lord to take such advantage of famished neighbors. Were not the inhabitants of this place mainly Friends and meek in their distresses, I truly believe they would burn our house over our heads and sack our warehouse for my mother's want of common charity! See you, dear Thomas, how impossible it is that anyone should grant me credit in thy absence out of their scant stocks when my mother grants none from her abundance?"

I gnashed my teeth impotently. Keziah Coffin to the life! And that shrewd trader least of any on Nantucket would lift a finger to assist her own daughter should she marry me. Not after my Aunt Keziah learned I had been consorting with the fiercest amongst the patriotic firebrands and had come to her daughter's bed fresh from armed resistance to the King!

Sadly I brushed away the tears on Delight's cheeks.

"Aye. I see it as you say—we must wait yet awhile

[271]

longer." I looked mournfully into the wide brown eyes gazing appealingly at me. Wait? Must we forever keep on waiting who so thirsted for each other?

And why wait, anyway? What might not this war, raging now in venomous fury from Boston to New York, do to either or to both of us to make all our waiting a vain jest? I had seen enough of flying arms and legs and mutilated torsos in those few minutes of exchanging broadsides with the *Glasgow* to know well what war might do to a man. And if a landing party of savage seamen, crazed by long months of cruising off our coasts far from any semblance of women, should ravage Nantucket, I could guess what might happen to the women in their path.

But still I was whole, and Delight there in my arms soft, loving, and desirable. What either of us might be soon if we delayed, who knew? Impetuously I pressed her down upon the sands, my burning lips feverishly on hers, desire flaming in my eyes. Why wait?

Clearly enough she read my meaning and she struggled not. Lovingly, trustingly her soft brown eyes gazed upward into mine.

"I love thee, Thomas, and I long to be thy wife! Forever shall I wait for thee. But not thus, darling, may our love begin. For then it cannot last, and I would not so soon lose thee. Kiss me again, dear, that I may have strength for both of us, and then lift me up."

I did as I was bid. Had she struggled, I am sure I should have overwhelmed all protests with ardent kisses till she could protest no more. But in the soft affection and the utter trust of those deep brown eyes I saw new understanding of a woman's love which I had not grasped before—of love that stopped not with her body but went far beyond in sympathy of soul.

31

I DID not go back to Centre Street with Delight.

Instead, having parted from her at the market square, I went to see Captain Rotch to get from him my seven pounds sterling, the which he paid me without demur.

"Here, lad," advised that sober-faced merchant, "take it and husband thy little hoard with care. It will be long before thee add a shilling to it on this island."

"Are affairs so bad, Captain?" I asked anxiously. "Only this day I have come home after two years' absence, in great hope of getting from you or some other shipmaster here a berth as mate. I am fully qualified to fill it."

Sadly Captain Rotch shook his drawn face.

"Nay, Thomas. For thy father's sake I would gladly help thee, but I shall not send my ships to sea again. Two of my whalers have already been taken by the British, and their crews impressed or imprisoned. Even if I myself cared to venture another after oil, still it would weigh too much on my conscience to expose thus my honest neighbors to danger. I am a peaceful man, as well thou knowest, Thomas, and would have no part in this quarrel. Would to God Nantucket could remain neutral in this strife! I do not believe in shedding blood and would have naught to do with those who take up the sword. Yet for our beliefs we suffer from both sides because we help neither in their breaking of the Lord's commandment. Your patriots on the Continent mistrust us all for Tories, and the King's men all for rebels. Yet like Job, with faith in God must we bear it! We can get little provision as charity from the off-islanders who hate our non-resistance to the King, and the King's cruisers rob us of the sperm oil which alone we could trade for food.

Nantucket is already sore distressed, and should there be no reconciliation before next winter, desperate then will be our plight on this treeless island for want of fuel as well as food! Look not to me or any of my fellow merchants here for aid. Pray to the Lord, lad, as I do daily. He alone can help thee. I cannot."

With this pious counsel my lagging feet sadly carried me from his counting house down to the waterfront. There truly, on casual inspection the appearance of the spouters all bore out his words—deserted, save for shipkeepers, not one showed any sign of fitting out.

Nantucket held nothing more for me except a visit to my mother's grave. With mournful steps I went out West Chester Street, there briefly before her simple wooden marker to meditate as Captain Rotch had bid me on the ways of the Lord. Sharp as my grief had been two years before when she had died, still it had spared her much suffering since, and who knew how much more in the dolorous days to come?

Back again towards Straight Wharf then I went hurriedly to catch once more the little sloop that served as packet to New Bedford. I could not, I was sure, see Delight again save clandestinely, and should my sharp-eyed Aunt Keziah suspect that of her, Delight would pay dearly in the months to come for some few hours of my company. It was best to go at once and stir up no further trouble for her, nor rouse again my unquenched desires.

But when I strode down Straight Wharf to board the sloop, I found a figure vaguely familiar to me on her deck in close converse with her Captain. A second glance, and I hailed him from the dock,

"Henry Gardner, as I live!"

He spun about.

"Tom Folger! Welcome, Tom! But what brings ye back to this non-resistant Quaker island? I'd heard you were a fighting man with Commodore Hopkins."

"I was, Henry. You heard true." I sprang from the stringpiece of the wharf over her low gunwale to the packet's deck to clasp his hand warmly. "But I did not like fighting under him and came back here to fight whales instead."

Henry laughed ruefully.

"Less'n ye take a whaleboat, Tom, and with some other hungry sailors like me for oarsmen and boatheader put out for a few hours offshore hunting, like a century gone Chris Hussey and his neighbors used to do whenever they sighted a spout from Mill Hill, ye'll have to pass it by, I reckon. There ain't a single spouter fitting out."

"Too well I've learned that, Henry, so I'm leaving now. And you?"

"Me too. I was bound fer New London to look ye up, only now ye've saved me the trouble. I heard tell from Delight last month ye were an officer in the fleet. So now it's in New London, I been athinking ye might land me a billet as a bosun or something like that, seeing they don't have need for boatheaders on a man-o'-war. I'd make a fine bosun, Tom; I know every line of a ship's rigging from gunwale to truck."

"I was a Midshipman on the Commodore's flagship, but if you ship in the Navy, you'll find a Midshipman isn't much of an officer, Henry. I couldn't do anything for you myself, even if I still belonged to the *Alfred*. But I know her First Lieutenant well and he might if I spoke up for you."

"That's good enough for me. All I want's a chance to talk to somebody that knows a seaman when he sees one. You'd be surprised, Tom, how I come along since my first cruise on the *Beaver* when Sam Adams dumped our tea into Boston harbor on us. There's the old *Beaver*, now, Tom," he paused to indicate the third ship over, "laid up like all the rest of 'em. Old man Rotch has me slated for third mate on her next cruise. Only when that's going to be, nobody knows. Not till the fighting's over, I reckon. So meanwhile I thought I might as well die fighting the King as starving here."

"Come along, Henry. I've about come to the same conclusion and I'm shoving off too. Only after what I've seen of Ezek Hopkins, how much fighting there'll be, I can't tell

[275]

you. I doubt he'll ever get his ships to sea again, being so short of seamen from wounds, disease and discharges. But if he does, you'll die, all right. He doesn't know any more about fighting ships than peace-abiding Captain Rotch here. As for me, I'm through with him. I'm going to join Washington's Army myself."

So an hour later we sailed together for New Bedford, Henry bound for the fleet at New London, and I for the Army in New York by way of the same town, promising Henry I should there recommend him to Lieutenant Jones.

By midnight we were in New Bedford, where to economize, we slept aboard the night with the permission of the Captain of the packet. There in New Bedford, a whaling port second only to Nantucket, we tarried some days, though originally we had not so intended. But such a dismal picture had I painted of the Navy that Henry thought better of joining it out of hand. Contrariwise, he cast doubts about service in the Army, which he assured me solemnly was much torn by petty politics. The result was that each of us, dissuaded from his purpose by the other, determined it was best we try again for a whaler in New Bedford, where at least no Quaker scruples might discourage the shipmasters from braving British cruisers.

But it was all to no purpose. After a weary week spent in seeking out personally every oil merchant in that town we found there was no prospect of a whaling voyage. Cold mercenary considerations apparently brought the shipmasters of New Bedford to the identical conclusion reached by the Quaker consciences of Nantucket—it was an unpropitious time to go awhaling.

That there may have been another consideration in New Bedford also, I got some inkling of. Congress, so I heard of several merchants, had just decided to issue letters of marque and reprisal to any and all who might care to go privateering. Should we care to wait some weeks till guns might be obtained, it was intimated to us we might then have ample opportunity to ship out on the private vessels of war into which the idle ships we saw in New Bedford were like to be converted.

But at this bait I shook my head. I had listened too long to Patrick Henry. If I fought, like him I wished to fight for liberty, and not for loot alone aboard some privateer bent only on enriching its owners rather than on chastising our tyrannical King. As for Henry Gardner, whatever his reasons were, he had not the funds to wait in idleness, and declined also.

So poorer by a pound sterling, all of which came from my light purse, a week later Henry and I continued our journey. First we headed for Providence by coach, determined, now that we had no option, to stick to our original inclinations—Henry to join the fleet, I the Army.

In Providence we arrived by late afternoon, intending to seek out the least expensive inn the town afforded to house our tough young bodies till the coach left next day, since the tavern at which the coach drew up was very evidently beyond our slender means.

But hardly had the sweating hostlers unhitched the horses from the traces and tossed my bags unceremoniously from out the boot into the dust of the courtyard than I had cause to change my mind. For there in the doorway of the inn, berating mine host in a manner which I recognized very well, stood irascible Captain Saltonstall, exploding in his most furious quarterdeck style!

"What would you have me do, sir?" Apologetically the tavern-keeper shrank before the irate Captain. "Should I ask them to be quiet?"

"Throw the damned dogs out!" demanded Captain Saltonstall. "That'll teach 'em better manners!"

"But, sir, my tavern would be ruined!" The innkeeper threw up both hands in despair. "How can I throw out my guests, the best citizens of Providence, because you imagine they do not look on you with due respect?"

"Imagine? You snivelling villain! Imagine? Don't you think I know when I'm treated with contempt? Damn your eyes! Get rid of that pack of low scoundrels in your tap-

[277]

room cracking jokes about the *Glasgow*, or I leave at once! Your best citizens, forsooth! If it were not for the church spires in between, I'd lay the *Alfred's* guns on your infernal tavern and blow you and your insulting jokesters into the river! So help me, I will yet!" And his short neck bulging wrathfully, Captain Saltonstall flung his stocky figure about and stamped angrily off.

"Well, Henry," I observed philosophically, "there's the Captain you've come to serve under. Apparently he does not like the way the good people of Providence regard his encounter with the *Glasgow*. But by now I had thought he had learned some restraint in that matter. In New London it was worse."

"He sure was mad," agreed Henry. "Is he always like that?"

"That's his idea of commanding respect. I want no more of it! I'll warrant if only he had those loungers in the taproom on the *Alfred*, he'd have 'em all triced up to the gratings with the bosun laying on the cat till there wasn't a shred of flesh on their bared backs! He's like that, Henry." I stooped to pick up my bags.

"But what's he doing in Providence, Tom? Didn't ye say ye'd left the fleet in New London?" asked Gardner, also picking up his dunnage.

"That's so, but now I wonder?" I looked thoughtfully after him. "Did you catch what he said about laying the *Alfred's* guns on this tavern? I'm going to ask." Shouldering my canvas bag and hammock, which were tightly lashed together, I approached the still flustered innkeeper.

"Your pardon, sir, but is Commodore Hopkins' fleet now in the port?" I asked.

"Aye, lad, they came in yesterday, the worse for me! Because my guests say only what's common talk these last weeks all over New England on what they think on a whole fleet which takes not a lone frigate, I must suffer this! 'Snivelling villain,' am I, eh? What's he, in spite o' his sword and that gold-laced coat? No sailor, anyway, I'll wager!" Venomously he looked after Saltonstall's vanishing figure.

[278]

"If they like not in Ezek Hopkins' ships what's said of 'em ashore, let 'em do better on the sea—not go blowing up inoffensive tavern keepers who daren't answer 'em back!"

With that, he came suddenly down to business, rubbed his hands in his apron, and asked obsequiously,

"Be ye two lads seeking bed and board? Ye'll find nothing better in all Providence than what I offer. Come right in!"

Henry shook his head.

"Nay, thank 'ee, friend. We were bound fer New London to join the fleet, but seeing it's here, that saves us the trouble. We got friends aboard the *Alfred*. We'll go right down and swing our hammocks there."

"The *Alfred?* That demon's ship? Heaven help ye then, and your friends too!" exclaimed the landlord, turning to reenter his taproom as we started off, then adding, "If ye think better on it, lads, come back here. Ye'll find friendly company and no tuppenny tyrant to spoil the enjoyment of your dinner!"

"Pleasant prospect, eh, Henry?" I asked as we trudged on under our baggage. "Maybe you'd better come to New York with me and join the Army."

But obstinately Henry shook his head.

"For a fact, Tom, the Army's worse! There's only one Captain on a ship, and with a weather eye out, ye can manage to keep well to leeward o' him and out o' trouble. But between what Congress has appointed and what the colonies 've commissioned to maintain their own dignity, there's almost more Generals in the army 'n there is privates, and there's no getting away from 'em like there is on a ship. I'll take my chance afloat."

So we kept on to the waterfront, where on our arrival, I saw the *Columbus* some little distance out hove well down to starboard with shipwrights busy caulking her newly exposed planking. There also, but not hove down, swung to their cables the *Andrea Doria*, the *Cabot* and the little *Providence*, but I did not glimpse the *Alfred* till scanning the shipping alongside the wharves, I recognized her hauled to a dock some squares off.

Thither then we tramped, congratulating ourselves it would cost us nothing for boat hire to get aboard. My heart quickened as we drew near, for though I liked not her Commander, still much of me had gone into the making of a man-o'-war out of that vessel. I pointed out proudly to Henry the battery of forward guns protruding through her starboard side which I had served in the *Glasgow* action.

But as we came on the wharf at which she lay, starboard side to, I gripped my companion.

"Belay, Henry! Not yet!" I halted him. It was not the moment to go farther. For on the *Alfred's* quarterdeck alongside the gunwale opening stood four side boys rigidly at salute, and the bosun's mate was shrilly piping over the side the still purple Dudley Saltonstall, stamping up the gangway in fierce majesty.

Inboard a trifle from the side boys, armed with a spyglass, stood the *Alfred's* First Lieutenant to receive his Captain.

"That's Paul Jones." I nudged Henry. "You'll like him. There's not a seaman in the fleet his equal. He don't need bluster to command respect."

Eagerly Henry Gardner craned his neck to look at that firm figure, waiting respectfully to greet his returning Commander.

"Aye, Tom. He stands there with that glass tucked under his arm as if he was born to tread a quarterdeck. A sailor-man after my own heart, if ever I saw one!"

The brief ceremony was swiftly over. The piping ceased as Captain Saltonstall's foot hit the deck. Deigning not to say a word, with glowering eyes only did the *Alfred's* skipper return his Lieutenant's salute and vanish aft into his cabin, the one spot where he was not likely to catch any slurring remarks anent the *Glasgow* affair.

Shouldering our burdens again, we trudged up the dock toward the *Alfred's* bow, where unceremoniously, sans side boys, piping, or any notice at all, we two clambered up the crew's gangway to the deck.

Immediately we were on familiar ground. I knew every

[280]

plank on that ship. Tossing our bags into the lee of the larboard fife rail, I looked about for some seaman I knew to keep an eye on them while we laid below. But to my astonishment, save for a few seamen aft near the poop, I saw naught but soldiers in the uniform of Washington's Army about the deck!

"That's queer, Henry," I muttered. "What's happened to the fleet, I wonder? Looks as if I might join the Army and still stay right here in spite of myself! Well, let's go below and find out."

We went down the forecastle hatch to the gun deck. More soldiers lounging there or sprawled out asleep between the gun carriages, and scarce a seaman. After some futile searching for someone I recognized, I gave up, and hunching down my shoulders to clear the low beams overhead, I led Henry down between the rows of guns still housed for sea, to the steerage aft.

There before the spindle-grated door to the First Lieutenant's room, I paused, knocked.

"Come!" came back the answer.

I opened the door, hat in hand, stepped respectfully into the doorway, which was as far as I could get. For there, back to me in the narrow space between berth and desk, up to his elbows in an opened sea chest, bent Paul Jones, coat off, with his belongings strewn over the berth, the desk, and even the deck. He twisted his neck about to see what was wanted, then straightening swiftly up, he spun about.

"Why, Tom! It's a pleasure to see you back again!" He scanned me up and down inquiringly, then with an amused light playing in his grey eyes, asked mischievously,

"So soon tired of Nantucket, eh? Did you find your Delight in the arms of another, as too often happens to the swift-forgot sailor? Or did my dear friend Aunt Keziah bar her door to a penniless seaman?"

"Neither, sir," I answered boldly. "If you fare half so well with Dorothea left amongst the young bucks of Virginia, truly fortune smiles on you. Nantucket is the absent sailor's Paradise—the maids there have long been used to

[281]

wait for them. They have, indeed, no other choice, for if they wait not for one, then must they wait another. It was not that, sir. The greeting I had from Delight well paid me out a two years' parting. And as for my Aunt Keziah, I did not give her the chance to send me packing. My misfortune lies elsewhere. It's that whaling has fled our island. It's deader than a split and salted mackerel!"

"So Delight has not shaken my faith in the constancy of woman? She still waits, eh? Too bad so lovely a maid must wait further on the whales. But what is her loss is my gain. That leaves you free, then, to ship again. You're just in time, Tom. I can use you now as never before."

"Not me. If I had any thought of rejoining the *Alfred*, the glimpse I just got ashore of our fiery Captain would have cured me of it. I'm on my way to join the Army. But I've brought you someone, sir, you well can use." I stepped out of the doorway to the passage beyond, revealing Henry. "This is Henry Gardner, sir, of Nantucket—a fine seaman and well fit as mate of any vessel. I thought you might get him rated bosun here, knowing the *Alfred's* bosun by ill-chance lost an arm to one of the *Glasgow's* round shot, sir."

Swiftly Paul Jones looked Henry up and down.

"So you're from Nantucket too, eh? A good enough recommendation for any seaman. But as you love me, Tom, don't let Gardner out of your sight or someone else will shanghai him before I can get him shipped! Sailors are much sought after now; we've scarce one aboard the *Alfred* for every ten we started with. You saw all those soldiers aboard? If General Washington had not loaned us some hundreds, we could not have worked the fleet from New London to Providence, so short were we of men. Only, worse luck, now all those soldiers must be returned to General Washington, or I'd soon enough make sailors of 'em." He sighed, then turned a persuasive eye on me.

"But I'll not have a good sailor spoiled in you, Tom; you're coming with me. You've not heard what's happened, eh? Captain Hazard of the *Providence* was yesterday tried by court-martial and broke for his part (or rather lack of it) in the *Glasgow* action, and this day I've been made Captain of the *Providence* in his stead. I declined that sloop once at Philadelphia, nor should I now have accepted it, had it not been for the rude unhappy temper of our Commander. This morning my new commission as Captain, signed by our Commodore, has come aboard, and I'm packing to go as you have caught me. So now all's well! I had philosophy sufficient to avoid quarreling with my late skipper, and I have even obtained his blessing at this parting. Now am I myself a Captain in our Navy with my own ship, and henceforth my future's in my own hands!" he exclaimed exuberantly as if now that future was well assured. "Report to me on the *Providence*, Tom, and you too, Gardner, and I'll warrant you'll not regret it, either of you!"

32

WITH alacrity Henry and I possessed ourselves of our bags and make knots for the *Providence*. All my ideas of the Army were forgotten. Here was luck indeed—a chance to serve with someone as Captain in whom I had much faith.

Captain at last of a man-of-war, though but a small one, Jones swiftly justified that faith. On a tiny sloop whose commander had just been broke by court-martial and which was manned by a crew thoroughly dispirited like all the seamen of the fleet for the drubbing they had received from a vastly inferior foe, within a few weeks he had the British commanders up and down the coast anathemizing him profanely and his new crew eyeing him awestruck, wondering whether he be devil or man.

I knew the little *Providence* somewhat, having often watched her bobbing along like a cork in our wake. Her armament was not much—only twelve four-pounders— mounted in the open on poop and main deck. After my experience with the *Alfred's* nine-pounders, the four-pounders the *Providence* carried seemed but insignificant popguns, too small in bore to command respect even from unarmed merchantmen, but there was no help for it—the lightly scantlinged *Providence* could mount nothing heavier, nor would her slight beam permit of it.

In her rig also the *Providence* excited my contempt, accustomed as I was to square-rigged and heavily sparred three masters, such as the *Beaver* and the *Alfred*. The *Providence* bore no such intricate spread of sail. Sloop-rigged, she had but one mast placed well forward, with a huge fore and aft gaff-rigged mainsail, the boom of which protruded somewhat beyond her stern when housed. Above her mainsail, she carried on light yards one square-rigged topsail, and to balance these, running out to her flying jibboom, she flew as headsails an array of staysails and jibs which for the size of her hull was amazing.

I had not been overly happy in the *Alfred* in meeting heavily armed British frigates, though in her at least I had some protection from her stout sides. But when I perceived the lightly built hull of the *Providence,* unable to withstand a round shot of any size, and considered that the weight of metal from all her guns together totalled but forty-eight pounds, I could well see why Paul Jones had not originally leaped at the chance to command her in Philadelphia. But now for better or for worse, she was his, and my life and those of all my shipmates depended only on his skill— neither offensively nor defensively could we count on either the guns or the sides of our fragile sloop to save us in any combat.

In the crew alone, aside from the Captain, was there any ground for hope. My heart leaped when I came alongside the *Providence* with Henry, to see peering down at me over the low gunwale, of all persons—Red Jerry!

There he was, barrel-chested and coppery of countenance as I last remembered him, needing only an uplifted harpoon to make me think I was beside him again in a whaleboat, facing that fighting spermaceti.

Happily I clambered aboard to clasp his outstretched hand.

"You here, Jerry! Welcome, shipmate! But what do you on a ship-of-war?"

Impassively Red Jerry suffered my greeting.

"Whaling all gone, Tom. No one want me now for harpooner. So now I am warrior again like my fathers. I want in my ears the big noise of much battle."

"Well, you'll get it soon now, I warrant you, Jerry. Look, Henry, here's a fellow harpooner of yours, save he's from Gay Head. Too bad you two haven't your irons; if you had, I might persuade our new Captain to lower for whales if luck fails us otherwise in our cruising. Jerry, you take

Henry in tow forward, while I lay aft to the steerage to see who my shipmates are there."

Soon we had our crew, between Jones' sharp eye and the force of circumstance, better than on the *Alfred*. All told, we were only thirty souls aboard the *Providence* to start with, but they were mainly picked men. Not another vessel of the fleet was in any shape to sail, and Ezek Hopkins was under strict compulsion to deliver immediately in New York the soldiers he had borrowed.

Perforce then the Commodore allowed Paul Jones to select from the other ships what men he needed for a bare minimum to man the *Providence*, and well did our new skipper choose. For sailing master he took Sam Stacy of Philadelphia, a rotund, red-faced seaman with a most lurid vocabulary which he did not hesitate to use on all and sundry to inspire them while scrambling up the rigging. For Midshipmen he named little Charley Hill of Barnstable, a mischievous lad of fifteen though scarce big enough to be out of his mother's sight lest he get himself in trouble; Richard Wallingford, from Philadelphia also; Henry Lunt, much older and, I thought, well qualified already for Lieutenant; and myself.

For our bosun, was chosen the hardest seaman on the *Providence*, old Jack Robinson, another Philadelphian, bronzed, broad of chest, with a rolling gait which bespoke long years of balancing his heavy body on a heaving deck. Of him I think it could be truly said he chewed oakum for diversion and picked his teeth afterward with a marlinespike, for to him even salt horse seemed too soft a diet.

Long, lean and taciturn Nathan Sargent of New Hampshire was made gunner, a sandy-haired, blue-eyed Yankee with a square chin and a rugged countenance that much resembled, I imagine, that Great Stone Face of which his state boasts. For he surely seemed carved out of granite and no more talkative as he went about his business of making up the powder charges and overseeing the readiness of round shot, rammers, and guns.

As his assistants, Owen Starbuck, one of our Nantucket

whalers, and my crony Henry Gardner, another whaleman, were made quarter gunners. Jones had much faith that those who were used to the meticulous work of honing and keeping in order harpoons and lances and had learned to launch them truly from a rocking whaleboat, would with the same care devote themselves to touchholes and trunnions and could soonest be taught the care and use of great guns in hurling round shot with the accuracy they had acquired in flinging irons into whales.

And thus next day we went to sea, laden with soldiers as passengers, to run the blockade of Commodore Wallace's forces off Block Island and Lord Howe's off New York. For Paul Jones it was truly a shakedown cruise, in which on every possible point of sailing from close hauled to running free he tried out the *Providence* to learn her qualities.

Well did I note that his experience on my cruise with him in the piratical *Santissima Trinidad* in dodging other vessels stood him in good stead now. We were so jammed with soldiers that any broadside sweeping us would make a slaughterhouse of our deck. We made that passage to New York in thirty-six hours, with no vessel ever getting close enough to sight more than our topgallant mast before we were off on a course to bring her dead astern and keep her there.

In New York we discharged our soldiers, with difficulty shipped a few more seamen, and set out for New London, where we picked up a dozen more discharged from the smallpox hospitals. With these, still short-handed, we returned again to the head of Narragansett Bay, carefully eluding every sail we saw.

Still dissatisfied with the speed his ship had shown, there Jones hove down our little vessel, to find her bottom foul with barnacles and long grasses which she had picked up on her stay in the Bahamas. With much labor, we scraped first one side, then the other, far down toward her keel. To this end our Captain insisted on careening her far more than I had ever seen a vessel heeled before, so far indeed that in alarm our Commodore sent word to him to exercise more caution and ease her back somewhat lest she capsize.

But to that warning Paul Jones paid no attention.

"Tell the Commodore," he said laconically to the frightened Midshipman alongside who dared not to set foot on our careened ship, "that I intend to go where danger is. For that I need a clean, fast ship!" He turned to Robinson, the new bosun, who with Sargent, our gunner, was shifting guns to larboard for careening, "Keep on heaving her down, Jack. I can't see the keel yet."

We got her clean to suit even Paul Jones though I have no doubt it nearly gave Ezek Hopkins heart failure before we finished. Then we were turned to rerigging till all was taut, and the *Providence* was ready to try her skill against the enemy, the only vessel in the fleet fit to go to sea.

Immediately we went out to meet danger. The unarmed *Fly*, Lieutenant Hacker commanding, hull chock-a-block with heavy guns for the defense of New York, was our first concern and hardly were we rerigged than we received from Commodore Hopkins orders to convoy her through the squadron blockading Narragansett Bay till she was safely into Long Island Sound.

We weighed and started, the *Fly*, deeply laden and but a dull sailer now, astern of us. Until clear of Brenton Reef off Newport we met nothing, but as we tacked westward with the wind on our larboard hand, from Block Island Sound danger came on us with a vengeance. There in the southern board, standing toward us before the wind under a huge press of canvas, we made out H.M.S. *Cerberus*, 32, the heaviest British frigate on the coast! To us in the insignificant *Providence* she looked as ferocious indeed as Pluto's three-headed dog guarding the gates of Hell against any lost soul trying escape.

Now we were near lost souls ourselves with the formidable *Cerberus* bearing down on us. If the *Providence*, just cleaned, was fleet enough we might while we still had the chance flee to the northward and perhaps escape ourselves, but for the wallowing *Fly* and her cargo of precious artillery there was no eluding the *Cerberus;* she was gone!

Hopelessly I scanned the distant frigate through a glass over our larboard rail. She was coming up with a bone in her teeth, a more vicious antagonist than that *Glasgow* which had given our whole fleet such a drubbing. Any pair of her thirty-two heavy guns over-matched our whole broadside!

In some trepidation I waited lest Jones delay his flight too long and we be lost along with the *Fly*. But Jones, apparently realizing the hazard as well as anyone, was already hailing Lieutenant Hacker in the *Fly* hovering helplessly close under our stern.

"*Fly* ahoy! Stand on due west! We part company now!"

With a farewell wave to Hacker who was eyeing dismally from his forecastle his fast approaching doom, Jones turned sharply to his helmsman, and sang out,

"Hard down the helm!"

Doubting his own ears, the helmsman made no move.

"Hard down, sir?" he repeated, dumbfounded. That would head us for the *Cerberus*, not away from her.

"Aye! Hard down, I said! Mr. Stacy!" he shouted to the sailing master in the waist. "Come about, and lay me on the starboard tack athwart the hawse of yonder frigate!"

Down went the tiller. With Stacy profanely bawling orders to hand the sheets, we came smartly about, leaving the *Fly* to continue lumbering westward through our foaming wake while like a little terrier we stood down to engage the huge *Cerberus!*

Paul Jones coolly called out to beat to quarters. To the roll of the drum we dazed mariners stood to our guns. There was nothing else we could do. Our fanatic Captain was going to sacrifice the *Providence* in hopeless contest with a heavy frigate, that the *Fly* and Washington's priceless artillery might escape!

On came the *Cerberus*, a magnificent sight had conditions been otherwise, full square-rigged with all canvas spread and in addition stu'n'sails set and drawing full, gun ports flung wide open, and from her forecastle ports her bow chasers trained menacingly on us.

[289]

We closed rapidly, the *Cerberus* coming up free before the wind and we close hauled running into it as nearly as our trimmed in boom would take us. Remembering well what it had meant to lie alongside the *Glasgow* frigate even behind the thick sides of the *Alfred*, I cursed the folly which had led me to join this flimsy sloop. However, even in the face of imminent death I could not but admire in Paul Jones the devotion with which this immigrant American was rushing himself toward destruction that he might save the Army's cannon.

"Stand by there, starboard battery!" shouted Jones.

Mechanically on poop and main deck our gun captains slid back their quoins to give our pieces the maximum elevation their carriages permitted, while with tackle and bar the sweating gun crews slewed them forward so they all bore on the massive frigate—six little four-pounders all told. At that range, over half a mile, our guns would hardly reach. While those of the *Cerberus* might, still she would be well content to wait a little till by yawing she could bring her heavy broadside to bear at closer range and then blow us out of the water.

Now, broad off our starboard bow, had we the three masts of the *Cerberus* fairly in line as we sped athwart her hawse.

"Fire!" roared our Captain.

We fired. If any of our shot reached, save one ball which tore through our enemy's jib and fore course, I failed to see evidence of it. But apparently Jones was satisfied that he had achieved his object, for immediately our helm was put up, and instead of firing again, we bore away before the wind, coming sharply round eight points so that we brought the *Cerberus* on our starboard quarter, while with sheets eased we headed northeast back for Newport.

Now the *Cerberus* was presented with a problem. Heading west from her into Long Island Sound was the *Fly*, an unarmed vessel of no great size. Heading northeast from her was the *Providence*, sloop-of-war. Which should she chase?

Paul Jones smiled grimly as the bow of the *Cerberus* swung to starboard to chase him. He had gauged well the reaction of the enemy skipper. No British Captain would dare face his officers again if he permitted a man-of-war which had loosed a broadside at him to escape scot-free the while he chased an unarmed vessel like the *Fly*.

There was no engagement. After that first broadside, Paul Jones, fully satisfied, sang out to the gunner,

"Sargent, secure the battery! Turn over the gun crews to the sailing master, who will have more need of them than you. We fire not again, as I need waste no more powder on that frigate!"

Running free, with every sheet and tack constantly manned for swift maneuvering, we easily outsailed the heavy *Cerberus*, which never, once she had squared away after us, got within range. Of this Jones, sure of his sloop, very prudently made certain, though with equal prudence he did not draw far enough ahead to discourage pursuit. Two hours later, when even from our crow's nest the *Fly* had been dropped so far below the horizon that it was certain the *Cerberus* could never catch her, he decided to end the chase lest something untoward occur. So hoisting another flying jib and setting the stu'n'sails on our square topsail, we increased speed so much that the *Cerberus* soon gave up in disgust and hauled by the wind to stand south again to seek slower game off Montauk.

With deep relief we witnessed that. The *Fly* with her cargo of artillery was safe, we were untouched. It seemed unbelievable to men who but short hours before had been sailing hopelessly to death under the *Cerberus'* guns. With increased respect our jubilant seamen looked on their Captain placidly pacing his quarterdeck.

Two days later we were again in action off Block Island, once more with the *Cerberus*. From our masthead a brig was sighted coming up over the horizon running westward toward us for the Sound. Immediately we bore down to investigate. We learned, when we came close enough to hail, from her frantic Captain's response that she was the *Hispaniola* from Santo Domingo, bound for New York with military stores and hotly pursued by the *Cerberus*. Of this last we did not need the distressed *Hispaniola* to inform us, for there was the *Cerberus* in plain sight and even then round shot from the frigate's bow chasers were splashing dangerously close under the brig's stern.

With more interest than trepidation this time, we heard the long roll of the drum beating to quarters. Undismayed we stood again to our guns on the little *Providence*, watching the *Cerberus* close hauled on the larboard tack slowly overhauling the burdened *Hispaniola*. Meanwhile on the starboard tack we beat hastily to windward on the frigate's bow, hoping again to draw her off in chase of us.

That the *Cerberus* instantly recognized our little sloop for her antagonist of some days before there could be no doubt, for our rig was distinctive. But whatever may have been the feelings of her baffled Captain toward us, he was determined not to forego again a prize practically in his hands to be led off on any wild goose chases. He stood doggedly on after the *Hispaniola*, which he was outfooting, leaving us to go or come as we pleased.

That suited Paul Jones. Keeping well to windward out of range, we stood on past the *Cerberus'* larboard hand, getting a fine view of that close hauled frigate heeled well down to starboard, with her windward ports flung wide bristling with guns pointing futilely at us. When well on her windward quarter, up went our helm, and swiftly before the wind we ran down toward the stern of our huge enemy, keeping too far aft while we closed for any of her broadside guns to be brought to bear on us. By this maneuver, Jones insured that only with the two stern chasers run out her cabin ports could the *Cerberus* oppose our whole broadside.

But since the *Cerberus* was well heeled to leeward, it was easily visible to us that the straining crews at those stern guns were having great difficulty on their steeply listed deck in training their two fore and aft pieces on our fast moving sloop at all. So it was almost with impunity that Jones suddenly yawed the *Providence* in to close pistol shot to bring the towering poop of the *Cerberus* fairly abeam us as we crossed her wake. At that tense instant we gave her a full broadside aimed somewhat high to send the double-headed chain shot with which our guns were loaded flying through her rigging and canvas, doing there fine execution.

"Blow me, lads, if we ain't shortened sail on her!" sang out our jubilant bosun amidst a chorus of wild yells at our success. We saw her mizzen topsail yard come crashing down to enfold the helmsman in a cloud of billowing canvas, and a huge rent appear in her main course where a pair of our whirling shot, chained together, had gone tearing through that taut sail!

After that broadside, up went our helm smartly and in came our sheets, to bring us close hauled on the larboard tack on the lee quarter of the *Cerberus*. There, some safe distance off, we tacked to come down under her stern from leeward this time and repeat our maneuver with our starboard battery, which was likewise loaded with double-headed shot.

Once again the Captain of the *Cerberus*, while his men strove frantically to clear away the tangle on his poop, found himself in a quandary. If he continued on in pursuit of the *Hispaniola*, we could and would at our leisure tack back and forth across his stern, cutting his sails and rigging to pieces till he could hardly maintain steerageway, let alone overhaul the *Hispaniola* ahead of him.

And if he came about to drive off that troublesome gadfly astern him before it did further damage to his canvas, not only would the *Hispaniola* escape him but he well knew he had not the slightest chance of bringing our fleet sloop to any effective action.

With relish did we seventy cheering Yankees aboard the *Providence* chuckle, as we spun about to come down for a second broadside, at the predicament in which our young Captain had put the mighty *Cerberus* with all her thirty-two guns and her two hundred British tars.

We never fired that second broadside. I could well guess with what inward fury and outward profanity the Captain of the *Cerberus* ordered his helm up to bring his leeward battery to bear on us, and thus gave up the chase. But that

[293]

the alert Paul Jones enjoyed the joke as well as any of his
men, he showed by his jovial order the instant the enemy
frigate started to pay off from the wind,

"Ready about, Mr. Stacy! But don't put too much sail
on her lest you discourage too soon my good friend, the gen-
tlemanly Captain of yon frigate, who seems ready always to
oblige me in my wishes!"

"Aye, aye, sir!" answered our sailing master cheerily.
"Ease the main sheet, lads! We're going to be chased again!
Hard up the helm!"

Long before the crippled *Cerberus* could wear ship, we
were off before the wind with that heavy frigate dead astern
of us busily engaged in sending her topsail yard up again
and in setting every rag of canvas she could spread. Her
infuriated skipper was determined to settle us this time once
and for all. Like a huge bird skimming the waves, the *Cerberus* blossomed out in stu'n'sails, water sails, spritsails, and
jibs galore, while topmen were easily discernible to us heaving up buckets of water with which to souse their sails, hoping thereby to make them hold the wind better.

I viewed in awe that vast press of canvas beneath which
the *Cerberus*, still out of range, staggered along in our wake.
But Paul Jones, well aft on our poop critically watching the
Hispaniola, which was now freed of pursuit and dropping
rapidly hull down below the western horizon toward New
York, eyed her only in derision.

"Here, Mr. Stacy," he called out to the sailing master,
"take my glass. You have the deck now. Call me only if
something untoward occurs. I must go below to write an
account of this to my friend, Mr. Hewes, who will enjoy it
hugely. With two four-pounder broadsides only have we
saved two vessels from a British thirty-two. If you have a
mind to, Mr. Stacy, you might search out with the glass for
your edification what sail a ship can carry in a fresh breeze
should her Captain be sufficiently aroused. I doubt not, if
you look closely enough, you will find the Captain's shirt
flying also from the stu'n'sail booms to help along. I trust
some careless topman on that frigate does not ruin it with

the bilge water they pump up to soak their sails in!"

And confident in his sloop and in his men Paul Jones went below to write the letter as he said, leaving us to enjoy the spectacle. Not till an hour later did he come on deck, to find the *Cerberus* a little nearer, close enough indeed to encourage her Captain to continue the chase. For now an occasional ball fired from the bow guns of the *Cerberus* to test the range, came skipping over the waves to splash not far astern, so that in another hour the frigate might hope to land her shot well on our poop.

No longer was the *Hispaniola* in sight, even from aloft. Assured of that, Jones dropped all pretense of further play.

"Haul by the wind, Mr. Stacy!" he ordered sharply, and swiftly our sheets were trimmed in to lay us as close as our fore and aft mainsail would hold. In this maneuver the *Cerberus* was perforce obliged to follow us if she wished to continue the chase. But close hauled in that breeze she was forced to house her stu'n'sails and all her light canvas. And once those were struck, we rapidly outfooted her to windward so that soon again, hull-down, the baffled *Cerberus* abandoned pursuit, once more outwitted by madcap Paul Jones in a trifling spit-kid scarce fit to be called a man-o'-war, which our ponderous enemy might almost have hoisted aboard as a longboat.

33

FOR some monotonous weeks we cruised Block Island
Sound, after which on orders from our Commodore, we stood
northward for Boston to pick up a convoy of merchantmen
gathering there for Philadelphia.

These we delivered safely at that destination without incident save that they sorely tried our Captain's patience. Such
were the independence and the diversity of opinion amongst
the liberty-loving masters of those trading vessels as to
which courses were best steered, and so little did they seem
to like one another's company, that only by resolute action
could they be kept in position in our lee where we might protect them against attack. We on the *Providence* already
knew what manner of man they had convoying them. But not
till Paul Jones had sent a round shot whistling through the
rigging of a brigantine which twice ignored his signal to
keep station, with a promise roared across the waves next
time to give her a broadside, did the skippers of our charges
appreciate they were dealing with a Captain who meant to
have his orders obeyed. And subsequently they were.

In Philadelphia where we arrived on August 1, 1776, we
found a gala spirit. At last the Congress had abandoned all
pretense of being loyal subjects of the King remonstrating
only against encroachment on their rights as Englishmen,
and declared for independence. After hot debate, with the
matter hanging for days in the balance with that body
evenly divided, our Quaker friend, Joseph Hewes, had settled it.

As John Adams, who had little love for this southerner
who had upset his naval slate, put it,

"Hewes, who had hitherto constantly voted against it,

[296]

stood suddenly upright and lifting both hands to Heaven, cried out, 'It is done and I will abide by it!' I would give more for a perfect painting of the terror and horror upon the face of the old majority at that critical moment, than for the best piece of Raphael."

So it was our Quaker benefactor from Edenton who cast the deciding vote for independence. And on July 4 was our Declaration of it finally approved. Penned by Thomas Jefferson, this document in burning phrases which all Philadelphia was repeating, clearly proclaimed to all the world those fiery doctrines which at The Grove I had often heard its author expounding to our little group.

Paul Jones was in ecstasy. America was to be free! He was fighting now that a new nation might rise, his ardent soul aflame at that vision. We had hardly cast anchor in the Delaware than he was off in our longboat to get from his friend Jefferson a copy of his Declaration to nail to our mainmast that all aboard might read.

But in the midst of these ecstatic transports, Jones did not forget more practical matters. After all, his commission as a Captain as of May 10, 1776, was issued only on the authority of Commodore Ezek Hopkins, of whose every act Jones was beginning to have doubts. Suppose Hopkins, never sure of his own mind, should see fit to cancel it?

Against that contingency, Paul Jones promptly sought out the man whose persistence had put him in the Navy. Accompanied by kindly Joseph Hewes, he then went to John Hancock and got from him, signed with the selfsame flourish that decorated the first name on the Declaration of Independence, a new commission as Captain issued in the name of the Congress—the first ever awarded by independent America.

But Joseph Hewes did not stop with that act of friendship. Confirmed now in his belief in Paul Jones' competence, he was easily convinced by that impetuous Captain that we should never get anywhere in achieving our declared independence as a fact by waiting in passive defence for British attacks. Only by flouting Britain's claims to rule the seas

[297]

and carrying the war into foreign waters and to British territory could we so alarm Britain as to force recognition of our independence. And for an opportunity to accomplish that did Paul Jones plead. Britain's vast fleets of ships-of-the-line and widespread frigates did not daunt him. In the little *Providence* he was ready to set forth to show the way in inflicting such damage on British commerce that the injured merchants of Manchester and the shipmasters of London would soon be more powerful advocates for conceding American independence than even Sam Adams.

As a start, he asked permission to raid off the West African coast which well he knew from his slave-trading days. There he could destroy the rich stream of East Indiamen flowing north and south between England and the Indies. Nothing, he knew, would so touch the raw nerve of the British pocket as to assault the ships of that privileged monopoly. Had it not been the tender solicitude of King and Ministers for that Company which had led them to those acts of reprisal for the Boston Tea Party which had driven the outraged colonies to revolt? How better could England be harmed than by smashing that prized trade?

And there Paul Jones put his finger on the crux of American strategy. To seek one active commerce destroyer in foreign waters Britain would need a dozen cruisers at least. If we carried the war to European waters how then, in the face of destruction to vital British trade, could she maintain off our coasts the fleets of frigates which alone enabled Lord Howe to move his army by water where he would? With all the fire in his spirit Jones stressed that. Draw off the British squadrons from America by foreign raids! Then General Washington would easily dispose of the immobilized hostile armies already in America. But leave those ships there as Ezek Hopkins' futile leadership insured, and soon we would be overwhelmed by the mobile redcoats free to move by sea along our coast to attack where and when they would.

Hewes was convinced by his fiery sea captain, in whose abilities he had implicit faith, but he was unable to convince his cautious associates of the Naval Committee. They were hypnotized too much by dread visions of the invincible fleets of seventy-fours to be encountered abroad to risk a single ship on such an enterprise. Instead, to pacify the urgent Hewes, they offered to his protégé command of the newly converted *Hampden*, 14, that very brigantine lately named the *Hispaniola*, which Jones had saved from the jaws of the *Cerberus*, now purchased by Congress, armed and renamed.

But this tempting offer Jones declined. The *Hampden* was much larger than the *Providence* and carried heavier guns and was a far more impressive command—but she was slow. That had been proved vividly under Jones' very eyes. Since she was no match for a British frigate with only fourteen guns and had not the speed to outrun one, Jones could see little merit in her. He preferred to stay in the *Providence*.

Under Jones' urging, Hewes tried again. If he could get no permission to carry the war abroad, could he not at least get permission for an independent cruise off our coasts, free of the hampering hand of our cautious Commodore?

This, at least, the persistent Hewes achieved. In jubilation our Captain came aboard with orders "to go out on a cruise against the enemy for six weeks or two or three months." Immediately all hands turned to loading stores in preparation. On August 21, having been three weeks in Philadelphia, we sailed—seventy young men on the little *Providence* all in as high spirits as our gay commander at those broad orders. And long did the British commanders on our coast have occasion to remember that cruise!

As a beginning we ran to the southeast and within a week had taken and sent in two prizes, the brigantines *Britannia*, a whaler, and the *Sea Nymph*, a West Indiaman laden with rum for London. Both oil and spirits had grown scarce in the colonies, so we had good cause to rejoice over these rich cargoes, of which we on the *Providence* were entitled to one-third, the Congress taking the other two-thirds for its empty Treasury. But there was much grumbling aboard even over this division, for on the privateers being now fitted out the captors got everything, and the Congress no share at all.

[299]

Continuing eastward, in the forenoon watch of September first, off Bermuda we sighted to leeward on the horizon five scattered sail of merchantmen. Immediately the *Providence* was agog with excitement. Here was a haul which promised to make all us poor seamen rich indeed even though we got but a third of it. We answered with alacrity the rattle of the drum beating to quarters, while in anticipation the boarders were made ready and the prize crews told off to take each vessel in.

As we came down through a heavy sea before a fresh gale to raise the hulls of that fleet above the horizon, it was soon seen that the vessel nearest us was by far the best of the lot. As her hull and spars stood out across the whitecaps between us and the morning sun, she was seemingly a West Indiaman of the largest size.

I feasted my eyes on her in exhilaration. Between that ship herself and the vast cargo of sugar, rum and coffee she must have stowed within her holds, my share of the prize money would go far to pay out what I still owed my Aunt Keziah. And if we took only two more of her smaller consorts all my debts would be paid. If we should take the whole fleet, as well we might, the prospect fairly intoxicated me! I would return a gentleman of some fortune, to bid defiance to my aunt and all her Tory notions and marry Delight with no more ado!

Flying no colors to disclose our character, we steered dead for that West Indiaman as our first venture, to bring her to under our guns before she took fright. In that rough sea our little sloop was making heavy enough weather even going free to leeward. It was easily possible therefore, that if she fled before we got in range, she might, being much larger and better able to carry canvas in a seaway, outfoot us and escape, though with luck we still might take some of the smaller vessels.

But in that we found no cause for worry, for she held on steadily, in nowise alarmed at our approach, which was not surprising to us since no American cruisers had yet been so far to sea. So with boarding party ready at the rail to sweep over her gunwales armed with pistols, cutlasses and pikes, we stood down on her.

But alas for human hopes! From our starboard long tom, taciturn Nathan Sargent at long range had just sent a round shot skipping across her bows to bring her to, when from the poop, Paul Jones, eagerly scanning our prey through his long glass, roared sharply out,

"Hard astarboard! For your life, haul by the wind, Mr. Stacy! That ship's no merchantman; she's a frigate!" And without waiting further, our Captain flung himself madly at the tiller to aid the straining helmsman there in jamming it instantly hard down!

Like a blast from the trump of doom that cry fell on our ears to chill our hot blood thirsting for the fat merchantman under our bows. A frigate? And there we were, practically delivered beneath her hidden guns!

Under the impetus of our skipper's flying body, down went our helm and we spun to larboard into the wind. With furious oaths the sailing master was shouting to the dazed boarding party to drop their useless cutlasses and hand the sheets to trim all close hauled. Never have I seen a vessel so suddenly whipped up into the wind as was the *Providence* that morning. Cutlasses, pikes, and pistols went clattering helter-skelter to the decks. Under the lash of Stacy's tongue our men leaped wildly from the gunwales to seize sheets, tacks, and braces and trim in our main boom, lay flat aft our jibs, and hastily sway over our topsail yards that we might, if it were not already too late, beat instantly to windward out of danger.

We had hardly started to swing away from her into the wind than it was seen on the frigate that further deception would serve them nothing. We could clearly hear from her sides the crash of gun ports flying wide open and the rumble of gun carriages being run out. Before our startled eyes in a few brief seconds as we heaved frenziedly on our taut lines, we saw that tempting merchantman transformed into a frigate cleared for action! There in a deadly row from poop to forecastle came thrusting forth the ugly muzzles of

[301]

her menacing broadside, literally leaping through the ports at us, and we hardly three cables off! And now we made her out, the *Solebay*, 28, a frigate with whose nine-pounders we had not the slightest chance in action behind our tiny battery of twelve puny fours.

"Sloop ahoy! Do you strike?" came across the water to us an expectant hail from the *Solebay*, for obvious it was to all that resistance was impossible and flight seemingly hopeless, so close were we already under those suddenly unmasked guns.

But every man on the *Providence* was engrossed in heaving, including even our Captain who was now busy at the tiller in meeting her as we luffed that we lose not the slightest bit of headway by swinging too far up into the wind. No voice therefore, least of all his, answered that hail.

Another moment passed, in which we could make out the muzzles of the *Solebay's* guns, run full out now, being slewed forward to bear on us.

"Heave to there instantly, or we fire!" came the second hail from the *Solebay's* poop, and to emphasize that imperative command, we could now see plainly the glowing matches like fireflies hovering over the breeches.

Still we were swinging, heeled almost on our beam ends to leeward with every scrap of canvas aboard coming flat aft to hold the wind toward which our jibboom was pointing, and hardly more than our narrow stern was now presented to the enemy. That our Captain, grimly quiet at the tiller, meant not to heave to, every man jack of us aboard the *Providence* well knew, and he answered not.

But the hail did not go unnoticed, for loud and clear over our decks rang out from Nathan Sargent, for once jarred out of his native reticence, the nasal taunt,

"Fire and be damned to ye! There's nary a gunner in the King's Navy good enough to hit a luffing sloop!"

The black side of the *Solebay* erupted suddenly in flame and smoke, and whistling toward us came a hail of round shot. But Nathan Sargent was right—the gunners of that frigate laying their hurriedly run out pieces on a swiftly

[302]

turning target off their bow could not train forward fast enough, and their shot went screaming harmlessly down our larboard hand. Before they could reload, we were steady on our new course heading away into the wind off their larboard bow, and the *Solebay*, swinging herself up into the wind as she braced up her yards to follow us, perforce put her broadside out of action. Now we had only to endure the fire of her bow guns till we drew out of range.

But to our infinite dismay, soon we discovered we were never going to do that. The *Providence*, with her fore and aft rig, should easily have outsailed any square rigger close hauled, but in that sea we swiftly found we could not. Plunging heavily bows on into every oncoming wave, our little sloop with no high forecastle to lift her was continuously awash forward. Over our heeled down lee gunwale came green seas hurtling in endless succession to smash against our poop bulkhead and to check our speed sensibly with each shuddering impact. But the *Solebay* with her higher sides and raised forecastle was in no difficulty and drove ahead more easily, with no such racking from the boarding seas as threatened to pound our staggering sloop to pieces if we held on into wind and sea.

And now came our trial. From the *Solebay's* weather forecastle port (her lee port was too much buried in spray to be of use) she opened on us with solid shot. One after another those heavy missiles came hurtling down about us, ahead, astern, on either beam, for we were never out of range from the beginning. At each flash we watched apprehensively with strained eyes the high curving flight of those balls toward us, our breathing instinctively suspended, till a fountain of water hurled up from some nearby wave assured us we might safely draw breath again till the next flash.

Our predicament was gloomy indeed as the minutes sped by and we did not draw away. If we could not outfoot the *Solebay* in a beat to windward, it was even more hopeless that we could draw away from her on any other point of sailing where her square rig should give her even greater advantage. That we had not yet been hit was due mainly to

[303]

the fact that, pounding heavily into the seas, we were a lively as well as a small target, while the *Solebay* from her own pitching was a most unsteady gun platform, making the fall of each shot wholly a matter of chance.

Still that was little comfort to seventy seamen clinging like monkeys high up on our weather rail to keep from being washed overboard by the seas sweeping our heeled down deck. Given time enough, even by chance some one of those solid shot would come smashing down through our rigging to carry away mast, spar, or stay and bring us to, crippled, fair target for a whole broadside from the frigate ranging alongside us before we could possibly repair damages and fill away again.

For an hour thus we plunged along through head seas, with clenched teeth enduring as best we might the terrifying sight of the foaming bows of that frigate creeping gradually up in our wake, doggedly belching round shot at us in the knowledge that ultimately she would crash one down on us.

More to raise our drooping spirits than in any hope of injuring our pursuer, Paul Jones swung aft one of our own four-pounders mounted on our poop—which battery was in charge of Charley Hill—and bade Nathan Sargent himself lay the piece to see what he could do with it to silence the *Solebay's* bow chaser.

That granite-faced gunner skeptically eyed the distance down our wake to the *Solebay*, then glumly shook his head.

"Can't reach, Cap'n," he announced. "Just wasting good powder."

"If you can't reach now, you will ere long the way that frigate's crawling up," said Jones grimly. "Fire as our stern lifts to the sea; that'll give you more elevation."

With Gardner and Starbuck assisting, Nathan Sargent carefully laid the gun, drew back the quoin to get full elevation of his muzzle, and waited for a favorable wave, which did not take long. At almost the next sea, as we slid down the trough and our poop rode high on its crest, he fired. But as he feared, the shot fell short. The *Solebay's* guns far out-ranged us. Our fire ceased.

Our seamen began mournfully to pass about to the ship-mates who were clinging nearest them such stories as they had heard of English prisons and British prison ships. For it was certain now that soon should we make acquaintance with them. Gone were all our fine hopes. As I listened to some of the tales told of starvation, of prison fever in rat-infested hulks stinking with bilge water, of inhuman gaolers in those vile holes where more men died than were ever released, I began to wonder whether it was not better to let the *Solebay* sink us when she finally ranged alongside rather than to strike to her.

Another hour passed in agony and torture and then a third with the *Solebay* steadily drawing up on us. That we had not been hit so far seemed almost a miracle, till noting some change in the relative alignment of the frigate in our wake with our poop, I sensed it was not so much chance as I had thought. During the first hour of the chase, when the range was longest, the *Solebay* had been a little on our lee quarter because the *Providence* was able to point a trifle closer to the wind than her pursuer. But we had not the speed to draw away, and the only result of that had been to allow the *Solebay* under excellent conditions to fire to wind-ward. Since then, without exciting suspicion astern of his intention, Jones had gradually eased the *Providence* down to leeward, not pointing so high as he might have. Now though closer, we were somewhat on the frigate's lee bow where her weather gun, hampered by her own jibboom and bobstays in the line of fire, could get no fair shot at us, while her lee gun was too much buried in the waves foaming up there under her cutwater even to open the port.

As a consequence Jones had craftily maneuvered his pur-suer into a position where his fire was bound to be ineffective, and where, had her Captain been a better seaman, he would not have suffered himself to remain, easing off likewise to put us dead ahead at least. But evidently deluded by the be-lief that he was outweathering as well as outrunning the Yankee sloop ahead, the British Captain held his bow into

[305]

the wind, in spite of the fact it made his bow chasers wholly futile.

I now saw that this was all that had saved us through a four-hour cannonade, but to what end? It was obvious that ultimately the *Solebay*, a fleet sailer, would draw up so close on our weather quarter that, unless we then instantly struck, by a sudden yaw to leeward she could pour into us at close range her waiting larboard broadside and sink us incontinently.

As disconsolate as any other of the little knot of officers standing with me on the poop of the *Providence*, I looked aft at the *Solebay*, within good musket shot now of our larboard quarter. Not much longer would the chase last, and soon I would be a prisoner in irons in the foul hold of that frigate—or a corpse! Which it should be, depended in nowise on my preference but only on whether silent Paul Jones, nearby alongside the helmsman, thought best to strike his colors or to die fighting.

Covertly I eyed my Captain for the answer to my fate. That he was unafraid of death I knew well from his strange conduct in Tobago with Jack Fry brandishing a belaying pin over his skull. Still, there was now more to live for with Dorothea waiting for him in Virginia. Death might seem more bitter than it had in Tobago, while surely it was no dishonor to strike to overwhelming force to save his life and ours.

But I could read nothing of his intention in his face. Unperturbed, his finely chiseled features were as calm as ever I had seen them, as he stood near the helmsman eyeing at close range that frigate off our weather quarter tearing through the waves. She was close enough so that Nathan Sargent could easily have landed a four-pound shot in her bows. But that would profit us nothing now. Instead, it might perhaps precipitate the final action to end all by the *Solebay*. That vessel, foaming along off our larboard quarter with her lee gun ports all awash and closed lest she flood her gun deck, seemed still content to draw up even closer before she yawed to spring upon her prey.

It was finally not the gunner but our sailing master that Paul Jones beckoned to his side.

"A fine frigate there, Mr. Stacy," commented Paul Jones irrelevantly. "I trust the elegant manner she has outfooted us to windward commands your professional admiration?"

"Admiration? God damn their lubberly souls! Admire 'em for running me down in a little spit-kid beating to windward in a heavy sea? Blow me, no!"

"Perhaps running free you might have done better then, eh?"

"Running free?" Incredulously the rotund sailing master stared at his quizzical skipper. "They'd've been alongside us in an hour before the wind, and well you know it, Cap'n. Close hauled was our only chance, and by God, now that's gone by the board! What ye going to do now? Say the word and we'll fight 'em till we sink! Damn my eyes if I'd not sooner go straight to Davy Jones's locker than rot by inches o' prison fever in one o' their stinking prison ships! But let's end this blasted suspense! Do we strike or fight?"

Reflectively Paul Jones looked aft at the *Solebay*.

"Neither, I think, Mr. Stacy. That's why I called you. The time has come to say good-bye to our pressing friend astern. For some hours now I have been working to get him into proper position and close enough, and now all seems ready to render our farewell safe. Attend carefully now, sailing master."

Close enough? In amazement, I looked from our eccentric Captain, jesting in the face of death, across the water toward the *Solebay*. She was close enough, in all truth! Almost with certainty I could plant a musket ball in her mainmast if I wished! And as for saying farewell to her, how, save by scuttling our own ship, could we of our volition do that? But while I scanned the *Solebay*, Jones had finished his curt instructions to the sailing master.

"Aye, aye, sir! I understand. I'll get the people all placed," and Mr. Stacy sauntered slowly forward off the poop, dropped down the ladder to our main deck, and instantly became all action there. Sheltered by the poop bulkhead from observation by the ship astern, he immediately summoned Jack Robinson, our bosun, and his mates to him, and soon up the hatch from below in our hold rolled-up sails came flying to be cautiously dragged forward, carefully screened from view behind our weather gunwale. And slowly, so as to excite no suspicion astern, a few topmen laid aloft while the rest of the crew gathered here and there in little knots about the fife rails where our straining sheets and braces were belayed.

Apparently with that all was ready for our farewell, since then from the base of our mast Mr. Stacy waved negligently aft.

Paul Jones nodded briefly to him, twisted about for a swift glance at the close-by frigate, then lifted his hat courteously to the skipper who was clearly to be seen standing on the *Solebay's* quarterdeck with spyglass trained on our poop, as if he were really bidding the British Captain farewell.

And with that signal to Mr. Stacy, to my surprise, we did. Without a word of command, hard up went our helm, instantly our main and topsail sheets were let fly to send our after canvas streaming free far out to leeward. Off from the wind swung our bow, casting under the still taut jibs. And spinning round to starboard like a top under straining jibs and hard aweather helm, the little *Providence* in another instant was off dead before the wind, shooting down the lee side of the oncoming *Solebay* toward that frigate's stern, so close aboard her that a pistol shot now might easily have bridged the gap!

It was laughable almost. There we were, so close abeam our formidable enemy, one broadside from her would have swept us to destruction. Yet not a single gun could she fire as we swept by her with impunity, for heeled hard down as she was to starboard, every gun port on the side toward us was buried in the foaming water!

As our poop passed abreast the frigate's quarterdeck, again Paul Jones waved his tricorne in elaborate farewell to the enemy Captain, though the mocking gesture was plainly lost on that frantically gesticulating skipper who was roaring out orders to wear ship.

Meanwhile on our topsail yards nimble seamen already stationed there were running out the stu'n'sail booms while aloft shot those light sails, and over to larboard went our jibs and staysails. So that almost before we had cleared the *Solebay's* stern, we were hauling away from her wing and wing before a fresh gale with every rag of canvas the *Providence* owned spread wide and drawing so full it threatened to leave the bolt-ropes.

The *Solebay*, caught unawares by our audacious maneuver, lost all headway while she clumsily attempted to box about in our wake. Her men, being mainly below at the guns, waiting to blow us out of the water, were in no wise stationed to hand promptly the vast number of lines required to ease out the array of close hauled square sails on fore-, main-, and mizzenmasts. Long before she was half squared away before the wind and moving through the water on her new course, we were far out of range dead to leeward of her, and rapidly increasing our lead. And before she could get her stu'n'sail booms run out and her light sails spread to do her best running free, we had the *Solebay* so far astern that, since it was then well past mid-afternoon, she could never hope to bring us in reach of her bow chasers again before night fell.

"Secure the battery, Mr. Sargent!" sang out our jubilant Captain to the gunner when that was well assured. "And, Jack," he added to the bosun gazing admiringly at the huge spread of canvas our sailing master had out, "belay that gawking at the sails, and pipe down mess gear! I fear the *Solebay's* salutes to us have made us all forget our dinner, but in compensation if our saucy escape does not spoil their supper for them on that mortified frigate, then I'm not Paul Jones!"

34

IN spite of our gay Captain's badinage over the manner of
our hair-breadth escape, my over-wrought nerves and tense
body had little zest for what food was soon served out from
the galley for our delayed dinner. One cannot for hours
look helplessly and hopelessly down the flaming throats of
ever-nearing cannon hurling round shot at him and then casually bid his stomach forget its cramps.

Red Jerry and Jack Robinson, I noticed, piled high their
pannikins with salt horse and potatoes soggy from undue
dalliance in the galley kettles, and stolidly squatting themselves between a pair of gun carriages, soon devoured the
whole. But my own stomach must have been more closely at-
tuned to my mind, for so tightly knotted were my abdominal
muscles at their overlong exposure to the prospect of round
shot tearing through them, that neither sight nor smell of
steaming food enticed me in the least.

With what unabashed awe we all looked on our youthful
skipper calmly pacing his quarterdeck as we made off, I need
hardly state. Now indeed with him we would all without
qualms sail our little sloop straight into the very gates of
Hell itself if he said the word, firm in the faith that he
would sail her out again unharmed! With relish, though with
no comment, our Captain listened to the coarse jests of our
seamen hurled across the waves at the baffled skipper of the
Solebay, which was vanishing in gathering dusk astern. And
surely he would have been more than human if his heart did
not swell at the loud boasts, larded with lurid seagoing oaths
to give them salty emphasis, which floated up from every
knot of seamen gathered about their mess tins that never
had there been another sailor like Paul Jones!

We stood on to the southward through the night with our sloop carefully darkened and steering various courses, so that it was no surprise at dawn to find ourselves alone in an empty ocean, safe from further pursuit. Standing still south across the trade route from Barbados, we cruised the open Atlantic for several days but with no success. On September 6, however, we sighted and after a long chase ran down by evening and took another brigantine, the *Favorite*, laden with rum, which was soon on its way to Philadelphia in charge of a small prize crew.

Despairing of further captures in those waters, our Captain decided to act on his idea that greater fear might be engendered by a descent on the enemy coasts. This was sure to be followed by loud demands for protection there which would have the effect of drawing enemy vessels from our own shores. Accordingly we turned to the northward for an attack on Nova Scotia.

For ten uneventful days, close hauled we beat our way toward higher latitudes with the weather daily growing colder, while watch after watch from our crow's nest the lookouts fruitlessly searched the far horizon for any sign of sail.

But on the 16th of that month somewhere off Cape Sable the monotony was broken by a howling gale which struck us from the northwest. Soon under one storm jib and a close reefed topsail we were hove to on the larboard tack, while over our low deck broke the cold northern seas and through our rigging in increasing fury screamed the chilling wind.

The gale grew worse as night fell. We were rolling so badly in spite of being hove to, that I could hardly stay in my swaying hammock and all about me came such a groaning of strained timbers as to make me wonder whether our racked sloop would sooner capsize or be pounded into basketwork by the boarding seas. Surely it seemed she could not last the night through without foundering.

At six bells of the first watch, while I was pondering whether I might be better off on the topside, down the midships hatch came Jack Robinson's raucous voice to echo through our pitch-black berth deck,

"All hands! On deck, sailors, while ye got a deck over ye! Lively now!"

Fully dressed, I fell out of my hammock, to bump my head violently on the invisible beams while I groped my way over the drunkenly heaving berth deck to the hatchway ladder. Still dazed from those fierce blows, I came on deck to be soaked immediately in solid water swashing from side to side with each breath-taking roll, while to my ears the shriek of the wind through the taut rigging now came in full volume.

About the base of the mast in a huddled knot I made out vaguely in the darkness our skipper, the bosun, the gunner, and the sailing master. I did not like that location for a conference, for so violently were we rolling that each instant our swaying mast threatened to go by the board, and which way it might fall no man could tell. Still I sloshed forward through the surging water for my orders, dragging with me little Charley Hill clinging tightly to my jacket to avoid being washed bodily overboard.

"Dismount your guns, Mr. Folger!" shouted Paul Jones above the screeching of the gale. "Strike everything immediately below into the hold for ballast! But for your life, let no gun carriage break free on you! And the same for you, Mr. Hill!"

I nodded dismally. The starboard main deck battery of four guns was mine, worst of all to dismount in that gale. Hove to as we were on the larboard tack, those guns of mine on our open deck behind the lee gunwale were continuously under water, and half the time on their muzzles hanging almost vertically downward on their lashings.

But there was no help for it. In the darkness I mustered my four gun crews and Henry Gardner, my quarter gunner, and we turned to.

That I should ever have managed it on those leeward guns save for Red Jerry and Henry Gardner, I much doubt. But Red Jerry with his herculean shoulders and Henry with his long body, did what no other two aboard might have done. They were both harpooners accustomed to keep footing on

[312]

the oily carcass of a whale heaving in the sea alongside a rolling spouter while with sharp spades they cut away the thick strips of blubber. So they made no moment of keeping footing on our gyrating deck about those plunging guns till they had secured to them the necessary tackles.

I can never forget the chaos of those next hours, when amidst foaming seas, cold driving spray, and whistling wind we heaved on coarse wet hemp with fingers raw from salt water and eyes wide dilated in the blackness, to haul inboard our submerged guns with one set of tackles, while on an opposed set we strove to hold back on them on our wildly pitching deck. One moment I and half my men with straining backs were struggling like demons to heave uphill and inboard a gun. And the next instant, with the lines in our hands suddenly slack as the ship rolled to windward, we were praying fervently that Henry Gardner and the other half of my little company would not let slip through their wet fingers the preventer tackles on which they were holding back, lest that unseen mass of iron come hurtling downhill to crush us.

So in that mad night we worked our guns one by one inboard, where with a tackle hung from the masthead, Jack Robinson could sling each piece, lift it from its trunnion seats, and with guys running in every direction to stop its devastating pendulum motion, lower it slowly into our holds to stow it atop our keel.

By six bells of the mid watch it was finally done, and at three a.m., half drowned, with bleeding hands stinging from salt, arms numbed from cold, and bloodshot eyes, we knocked off and laid below in our soaked clothes to tumble into our hammocks again. But now, though the gale howled on unabated, the little *Providence*, heavily ballasted below, relieved of the dangerous top weight of her battery, rode the seas more easily. Her topsides were no longer racked by the massive guns tearing at their fastenings and she was no longer in any danger of capsizing.

Two days more the gale blew in full fury, during which, hove to, we drove to leeward, pounded by the seas, cut by the

[313]

cold spray, in wet clothes always, living only on cold scraps, for our cook could keep no fires alight in the galley. Nor indeed, even if he had managed that, could he have kept a kettle atop his crazily inclined range.

On the eighteenth, the gale eased and we made sail northward, meanwhile heaving up again and mounting our guns so that we would not be helpless if we should fall in with anything.

But by now, having been about a month at sea, we were short of water, wood, and even of all food save a little salt horse. As a consequence having made the Isle of Sable on September 19th, somewhat to westward of that spot Paul Jones hove the ship to, the weather being very fair, while at his order the bosun passed the word,

"All hands! Break out your fish lines!"

So alluring was the prospect of fresh cod for dinner instead of salt horse, hooks and lines came forth from every diddy-box immediately. Soon the *Providence* presented a most unwarlike appearance with both gunwales lined with seamen casting overboard hooks baited with everything from salt horse to red flannel. It depended only on each fisherman's influence with the cook and the state of his underwear whether he offered the cod thereabouts the one or the other.

That any fish in his right mind should be so foolish as to bite on either of those unsavory lures might seem beyond belief, but nevertheless our deck was shortly sprinkled with cod flopping goggle-eyed amongst the gun carriages while overboard time and again went the selfsame pieces of flannel or tough salt horse to entice yet more upon our hooks.

While our whole topside was thus a mass of floundering fish and shouting fishermen proudly measuring against each other their various catches, from the crow's nest came a hail, nearly lost in the bedlam below,

"Sail ho!"

Immediately from Paul Jones, a moment before as hilarious as any of his crew over the endless arguments as to whose fish weighed most, came the chilling order,

"Belay all fishing! Clear for action!"

I much doubt that it ever happened before on any man-of-war that the main task involved in clearing ship for action was literally to clear the decks. But now by the hundreds went codfish, hurled by tails, gills, or heads, whichever came first to hand, flying down the hatch almost to hide from view our cook at whom they were flung. And over the side went buckets by the dozen to come back full of sea water to be sloshed hastily about the decks to wash them as well as might be of fish scales and slime, while over all was flung far and wide the usual coating of sand to give firm footing, doubly needed now as our decks were already slippery before they were wet with blood.

What was the sail sighted? We knew soon enough. Agilely Paul Jones swept up the rigging with a glass to look for himself. On deck again in a few minutes, he remarked casually to his anxious officers gathered at the foot of the shrouds,

"It is the English frigate, *Milford*, 32, gentlemen, directly to windward with a ship in convoy. Her Captain is so good-natured as to save me the trouble of chasing him, since from the instant of sighting us, he bears down this way. No hurry with the sails, Mr. Stacy. This frigate we shall lead such a merry chase as may cool his ardor when next he sights a Yankee sloop!"

The *Milford*, 32? That called something to my mind, and I blushed. The *Milford*, eh? She was the British man-of-war that three years before had chased Captain Paul in his piratical days on the *Santissima Trinidad*. And it had been to bury the unfortunate Spanish Captain of that corsair, killed by the *Milford's* broadside, that he had first chanced upon Delight in my arms as he rounded Brant Point into Nantucket. Now as Paul Jones he was once again deliberately enticing that same frigate into another chase.

Our observant skipper caught my blush.

"So, Mr. Folger, my mention of the *Milford* frigate causes you some embarrassment, eh? But save your blushes. They are naught to what mention of my name will cause the

Captain of the *Milford* after this day's work," he promised gaily.

Still hove to, but with all hands stationed, not at the guns, but at our running rigging, we awaited the closing of the *Milford*. If we had had any other Captain, it would have brought on instant mutiny thus to permit so heavily armed a frigate to approach a sloop-of-war without crowding on all sail to escape. After our experiences with the *Cerberus* and the *Solebay*, however, the deep contempt with which each man of our crew looked on the oncoming enemy foaming up over the horizon was easily understandable. No doubt lay in any seaman's mind as to the outcome, save in what manner our madcap skipper would make game of his huge antagonist.

When our enemy was about a mile off, Paul Jones impudently ordered the quartermaster to run up our Continental colors, so that the frigate would make no mistake we were an enemy. But not till he was within long cannon shot dead to windward of us and coming down free, did we make sail to try his speed.

Quartering then, we got underway just as two round shot splashed under our stern, soon to find, as Paul Jones well knew, that in such moderate weather our light sloop had much the advantage of any heavy frigate on any point of sailing.

Accordingly, so cautiously that it should excite no suspicion, Mr. Stacy was ordered to check our speed by changing the trim of the sails so they drew not too well. By this device Paul Jones held the *Providence* just far enough ahead to tempt the *Milford* continually into wasting powder and shot by firing at us.

No gun of ours was even loaded, and once we were settled on our course, the Captain ordered the drummer to beat retreat from quarters, so that such as wished might gather on the poop to enjoy the chase.

For eight long hours that day the *Milford* ploughed eagerly along in our wake, both her bow chasers firing continually, always hopeful that she had closed enough for the next round to carry to our poop.

Occasionally our Captain even hauled slightly by the wind as if striving to escape in that direction, thus opening the *Milford's* weather broadside so it bore somewhat on us. And each time that happened, came a thundering crash of round shot from the *Milford's* whole starboard battery to splash harmlessly in our wake, at which like a frightened bird we would promptly swing clumsily back to our previous course, and stagger along with the wind on our quarter as before.

Consummately like an expert actor well versed in his role, Paul Jones put the *Providence* through all the gestures of a vessel frantically striving to draw clear. We changed our trim, running guns forward, then aft, as if shifting ballast seeking a better balance of our weights. We hoisted various staysails, and then as if dissatisfied, we struck them. Ostentatiously we heaved up endless buckets of water (most of them empty, however) to splash them on our sails that they might draw better. And our Captain even ordered up the carpenter with his saws to go through the motions of that time-honored last desperate resource of a ship striving to increase its speed—sawing through the bulwarks. In this device, however, even had there been the need, our Captain had no faith at all.

So through a long day from morn till night the *Milford* chased us merry seamen in the *Providence*, firing fruitlessly away enough valuable round shot and powder to have carried her through a hot engagement. But never a shot had a chance of striking home. And finally as night fell and the *Milford*, apparently still unaware of the comedy in which she was taking part, rounded to for a final broadside, so much had she excited our Captain's contempt by her continual firing at twice the proper distance that Paul Jones cried out,

"I must return that salute of sixteen guns to me or I stand convicted of grave discourtesy! Corporal of marines! Fire your musket in acknowledgment!"

So with a single musket shot echoing in the darkness we returned her thunderous salute, after which, with sheets

[317]

trimmed flat, we hauled by the wind and swiftly ran her out of sight.

Regretfully Paul Jones watched the *Milford* fade into the night. Waxing somewhat poetic, as I noted he occasionally did when well pleased, he remarked to Nathan Sargent, who had no more poetry in his soul than his native granite hills,

" 'Tis unfortunate that night with her sable curtains hath come to put an end to this famous exploit of English knight-errantry, think you not so, Mr. Sargent? Truly if the day had lasted, I might have cajoled him into firing away the last shot in his locker in this curious mock engagement, after which, even with your four-pounders, we might have made good prize of a British 32."

We stood northward again through the night, coming as dawn broke to the latitude of Halifax, though, of course, well to seaward of it. And there as the rising sun illuminated enough the waves, was the *Milford* again, not five miles off and in plain sight from our deck. Obligingly our Captain shortened sail to let her come up again if she should wish. But apparently the *Milford* had had enough. In sharp contrast with the eagerness with which but yesterday she had rushed down to chase us the instant our topgallant mast was sighted, now she ignored even a fine view of our hull and stood steadily on westward for Halifax, perhaps to replenish the ammunition she had so heedlessly wasted on us.

By nightfall we were off Canso. Next morning we sailed in, destroyed three English schooners we found in that harbor, and having replenished our wood and water under cover of our guns, put out again for the nearby Island of Madame where lay the English fishing fleet soon to sail back for Britain with their season's catch. There we took the entire fleet without firing a shot, twelve sail altogether. Four of these we sent home under prize crews, five, which we could not man, we burned, and three others Jones with great humanity turned back to their former proprietors in order that they might be used to carry home across the western ocean to Britain the unfortunates who had manned that fleet, not short of three hundred men.

[318]

And thus having effectually destroyed the fishery at Canso and Madame, and what was of greater importance, having set the whole north coast of Nova Scotia in such a panic by our sudden raid that the echoes thereof could not fail to be heard in the Admiralty in Whitehall, we hastened southward to convoy our prizes out of harm's way. What risk we ran during our three days' stay while we ravaged the fishery may be judged from the fact that two men-of-war, the *Dawson* and the *Savage* brigs, lay all the time within fifteen leagues of us and each hour daily we expected to be in action with them. But such was the completeness with which Paul Jones seized every craft along that coast, not one vessel got to sea to carry warning till we were safely out.

We ourselves were glad enough when having ridden out another violent gale off Canso, we saw the last of that bleak coast and the destruction we had wrought. Now it was late September and very cold. So Paul Jones thankfully ordered his crew, scarcely able to stand the deck for want of proper clothing, to head southward again for Rhode Island. There, after taking another British whaler on the way, we arrived safely on October 7, some six weeks out of Philadelphia. Yet in that short time our little sloop had captured sixteen vessels, of which eight were sent in as prizes and eight destroyed.

With pride did Paul Jones, making out the long list of his captures and referring hardly at all to his own part, report to Robert Morris and the Marine Committee in Philadelphia,

"It is but justice to add that my officers and men behaved incomparably well on the occasion."

But who it was on that weird cruise that really had behaved incomparably well, no officer or man aboard the tiny *Providence* was in the slightest doubt.

35

BACK once again in Providence on October 7, 1776, I looked forward with high hopes to such an improvement in my fortunes as should permit me to proceed immediately to Nantucket and end the suspense in which I, already nineteen, with all the impatience of youth had ill endured my last separation from Delight.

Many a night watch as we came down from Canso I had spent figuring over and over again the value of the prizes we had taken, ships and cargoes, rum, sperm oil, and fish. At the very least, seeing that the crew of our sloop at the outset was but seventy men, I computed my share of the prize money at over a hundred pounds sterling. With that I could well free myself from debt and with the remainder Delight and I, far away from glowering Aunt Keziah, might easily establish our own home on the Continent. Which prospect dazzled my impressionable mind most, the startling success of our cruise and the glory we had gained under Paul Jones, or the vision of Delight with soft arms once more about me, mine to caress forever, I cannot say, but between glory and love certainly I was fairly intoxicated as our anchor splashed overboard in Providence and we were home at last.

And then one after another came successive shocks to shatter every dream.

First we learned that while we were at sea matters had gone but ill upon the land. Washington had been badly defeated on Long Island and now New York was in possession of the British. And our retreating army, torn by internal dissension, weakened by defeat and scarcity of supplies, bled by private greed, and hampered by the indecision of the Congress, seemed almost on the point of dissolution.

The patriot cause for which I was fighting was in sad state. With the colonies cut in two already by the loss of New York, it was further threatened by the imminence of a descent from Canada by Burgoyne's army, there to cut New England off from all contact with and hope of supply by land from the south.

Meanwhile by sea matters were still more dismal. Lord Howe's fleet now centered on New York, in undisputed command of our central freeboard, and what to me was almost insufferable, Nantucket was cut off from all communication with the Continent and in parlous state for food. That my grasping Aunt Keziah would somehow turn this to her advantage, I doubted not, but my heart bled for my neighbors.

To add insult to that injury, there in Narragansett Bay nearby our little sloop I looked at the larger vessels of our Continental Navy which alone might have done something to mitigate these disasters, swinging idly at their moorings!

Under Ezek Hopkins' bungling management affairs in our fleet had gone from bad to worse. Off Providence lay the ships of our little fleet, unmanned, unequipped, practically unled. Our Commodore, who apparently had had his fill of fighting in the *Glasgow* action, did not set foot again upon a man-of-war unless it was securely moored in some safe harbor.

Disgusted with this inefficiency, Congress the very week we had sailed from Philadelphia in August, had hailed our unseagoing Commander-in-Chief before it for his continued disobedience of its orders to take action. After this it passed a vote of censure on that petty genius, which John Adams, however, to the great hurt of our Service, had persuaded that body to keep secret. To make matters even more desperate for the fleet, privateering was now in full swing, and against the inducements offered by the privateers the vessels of the Navy could ill contend. The privateersmen got the whole of what they captured; the seamen of the Navy but a third.

We who had witnessed in Philadelphia the birth of the Navy as an instrument which might aid to clear our shores of British men-of-war, viewed dismally the results of that short-sighted policy. The privateersmen did not go out to fight the British, nor even to make captives of the seamen on the ships they took that they might be exchanged for Americans in British gaols, but only to enrich themselves by ill-disguised piracy upon the high seas, releasing all their prisoners lest they lose chance for further gain.

The ships, the naval stores, the guns, above all the Yankee seamen by the thousands engaged in this private looting, might, if coordinated in a public purpose and well led, have made life off our coasts impossible to British commanders and have immobilized the army opposing Washington.

But so thoroughly was every American maritime resource soaked up in that mad race to fit out privateersmen, that the new frigates ordered by the Congress there in Providence lay before me unfinished on the stocks. Meanwhile the very men who were delegated to build them were surreptitiously diverting to privateers in which they had interest, the materials, the equipment, the guns, the shipwrights, and crowning infamy, even the seamen who should have manned them! And yet such mercenaries claimed to love their country!

I hang my head with shame when I look back on that dark period to see what the lust for gain did to my countrymen. Aye, many there are now who point with pride to what the privateersmen did in injuring Britain's commerce. But they are wholly blind to what they did to injure America's cause in our desperate struggle.

They nearly strangled our Navy altogether, and much prolonged the war at a vast cost to us in treasure, in blood, and in suffering to all, that far outweighed the filthy gains of those conniving at the destruction of their country's power on the sea that they might privately profit!

The realization that even in the Navy we were not free of such harpies came as the final blow to shatter all my dreams. We returned on the *Providence* expecting little or nothing in the way of pay, for we well knew by now that such was the mismanagement of the Congress that the Continental treasury was bare. But at least there was our prize

[322]

money waiting us, and we had earned it by bringing back to turn into the public coffers twice as much to bolster up the Continental finances.

Imagine then the shock I got when, once ashore, I went to see the prize master at the Customs House, to be informed by that worthy gentleman the prize money due me was not a tenth of what I had anticipated! Not that our prizes had not brought at sale what I had estimated—no. The reason, forsooth, was that we of the *Providence* must share it, by Ezek Hopkins' order, with every ship of that fleet swinging safely at anchor there in the bay while we were at sea braving English broadsides to take the ships! And as a final insult I was told that Ezek Hopkins, our unseagoing Commodore, himself out of harm's way at home with slippers and pipe ensconced before his fireside while we fought gales and faced hurtling round shot, was taking for his own share one-twentieth of every ship we had captured!

With that news my house of cards collapsed. My prize money did not come to ten pounds. And when I might get that the prize master could not tell me, so complicated had become the distribution from the claims of all and sundry ashore. So infuriated was I with that knowledge, that if I had had Ezek Hopkins then and there within my grasp, I might in my unbridled rage have done the Navy good service by ridding it of its Commander-in-Chief, though I soon hanged for it.

But I could do nothing save to return still penniless aboard the *Providence*, with Nantucket and Delight both as far out of my reach as the moon.

In bewildered bafflement, I looked across the water of the harbor at the idle vessels of our fleet—the *Alfred*, the *Columbus*, the *Cabot*, and the *Hampden*—half-manned, ill-equipped, unready, while privateersmen by the score were going to sea with not only all the available seamen seeking berths, but with many sailors of the Continental Navy barefacedly induced to desert their vessels to ship on these corsairs!

Had not the Congress, I wondered, the wit to see that

[323]

common men must be given some proper encouragement? A
Navy might be officered on almost any terms, though those
who bore them might not be equal to their commissions, as
to our sorrow the Congress had already only too well proved
—but the seamen? And of what profit was it to the Continent if some hundreds of mercenary shipowners enriched
themselves by privateering, while on sea and land our forces
fell before the British for want of the men and the resources
thus dissipated in search of loot? And where then would be
the vaunted Liberty for which we were daring King George?
Patriotism, indeed! In agony I went below to hide from my
eyes the sight of those sad-looking ships which, if we had
leadership instead of sectional politics in the Congress,
might now be at sea under a Commander-in-Chief capable
of doing something with them.

Such a comedown did we suffer on the *Providence* on our
return when the word spread among the crew as to their
prize money, that if we had at that moment been nearing an
enemy ship, I doubt that one seaman in ten could have been
induced to stand to his gun—the others would have been
content to see us strike with arms folded. Our Captain was
as enraged at this treatment of his crew as any of his men,
and in a letter to the Marine Committee he violently denounced the folly of such a policy—but to no avail. The
Congress not only did nothing regarding increased encouragement as compared with privateers, but refused also to
interfere in Ezek Hopkins' bare-faced looting of the prizes
we had gained.

The result was natural. Those who had shipped for the
cruise only, refused to sign articles again. Others deserted
to the privateers, whose shipping agents were constantly
amongst us. Within a week of our arrival home we had lost
almost half our crew.

But meanwhile Ezek Hopkins was having troubles of his
own. For the Congress, while it did nothing to rectify the
situation with regard to privateering, still felt it had a fleet,
and in more and more vigorous orders, commanded our Commodore to get to sea with it and harass our enemy. But the

fleet moved not. Ezek Hopkins could not equip his ships, he could not man them, and verily, I believe, he even began himself to suspect he could not lead them.

Two weeks after our return from Canso, imperative orders came to our Commodore that no further evasions would be permitted—at all hazards to take the fleet and get to sea with it!

At that prospect, Ezek Hopkins threw up his hands. Getting ships to sea was entirely beyond him. But something had to be done lest he be broke out of hand, and he did it. Immediately there came to his mind some recollection of his one subordinate who had shown himself capable of getting action, and he hastily boarded the *Providence*.

With all the formality with which Lieutenant Paul Jones had first received him on the *Alfred*, Captain Paul Jones received him now on the *Providence*, though it was plainly evident to me, with none of the pride and faith which had marked the first occasion. And from the sour looks on the faces of the bewhiskered side boys, whom our Commander-in-Chief had but recently sheared of their prize money, I could easily judge they would have been far happier if they had been heaving him bodily down the side rather than ceremoniously assisting him over it.

"A fine cruise you have just completed, Captain Jones," commented the Commodore in returning our skipper's salute. "And in reward for it, I have come to order you to take command of the *Alfred* and all the ships here in the harbor fit for sea and sail immediately against the enemy."

For the first time since ever I met him in Tobago, I saw my Captain completely at a loss. Blankly he eyed Ezek Hopkins. Take command of the whole fleet, and he but six months before only a Lieutenant in it? Was this perhaps our antiquated Commodore's idea of a jest?

But the Commodore, engrossed only in getting out of his own predicament, took no note of his subordinate's reaction. Instead, continuing on towards the poop, he added,

"Come, sir. I have little time for this business, as I must

[325]

get ashore again. In your cabin I will inform you of the details."

Half an hour later, Hopkins emerged again on deck and Paul Jones, escorting him to the gangway to see him off, was bubbling with such enthusiasm as I had not seen in him since the day I had informed him that Joseph Hewes had procured his appointment in the Navy. It was true then!

"Expect me on the *Alfred* late this afternoon, when you may report to me your sailing date," said Hopkins in departing. And as soon as the stooped shoulders of our Commodore had been piped over the side, Jones beckoned me.

"Tom! I have much on my hands now, and so much of writing orders will there be I want your help in it that all may be kept in good order!"

So to the cabin I followed him. With no formalities at all, he plunged in.

"The Commodore hath orders to take the fleet to sea immediately for a raid on Cape Breton, Isle Royale, and the Newfoundland fisheries. But as he is much involved, he says, in the construction of the new frigates as well as in an endeavor to embargo further manning of privateers (in both of which, God knows, I wish him luck), he hath delegated his orders to me! I am to take command of the *Alfred*, the *Hampden*, and the *Providence* (the *Cabot* and the *Columbus* being yet wholly unfit for sea), man them, and sail at once. While I go to inspect the *Alfred*, will you convey my compliments to Captain Hoysted Hacker of the *Hampden* and beg of him to meet me within the hour aboard the flagship with a full report on his readiness to sail. And you come with him to the *Alfred*. Speed you now, Tom!"

I needed no spurring to speed me on that errand. So Paul Jones was going up in the world—not only was he to command the *Alfred*, but a squadron in addition! Soon then, if fortune favored him, I might hope perhaps myself to be Lieutenant, seeing that in fact, if not in name, he now was made Commodore!

In our second cutter I boarded the *Hampden*, scanning the ship for the first time at close range which, as the *His-*

[326]

paniola, Jones had saved from the jaws of the *Cerberus*. Oddly enough it was commanded by that very Lieutenant Hacker whom, in the little *Fly*, he had also saved from that same frigate. Now the *Hampden* was a man-of-war of fourteen guns, much heavier than our *Providence* sloop, and also, I well knew, much slower.

Captain Hacker, whom I had not met before, I eyed with much curiosity on being received in his cabin. Here sat a good sample of what manner of seaman nepotism was putting in command of our ships. I knew he was from Rhode Island, like our Commodore, and I could not but wonder what relation he might be to Ezek Hopkins. For his competence to captain a ship-of-war rested wholly on the fact that he had, before hostilities began, the honor to command the trifling passage boat plying Narragansett Bay between Newport and Providence! Though that salty service had imparted to him naught of navigation and, I soon learned, he did not understand even the first case in plane geometry, still after slight service in the unarmed *Fly* Ezek Hopkins had commissioned him Captain of a considerable man-of-war!

But I had little time to satisfy my curiosity about Captain Hacker for on my entering the cabin, he looked inquiringly up at me with no greeting at all. So with no more ado, I passed on to him my Captain's compliments and his message.

Captain Hacker's face fell.

"What? Get to sea in the *Hampden?* Has your Captain Jones taken leave of his senses? Don't he realize the unready condition of these vessels? My ship wants everything, including a crew!"

In much agitation, Hacker rose and began to pace the narrow confines of his cabin. "It's impossible! Seamen are not to be got these days on any terms! Go back and tell Captain Jones what he asks of me, I can't do!"

So Hacker, like Hopkins, was unequal to his task. Inwardly I groaned that our destinies on the sea were in the hands of such men. But outwardly with all respect I answered simply,

"I am ordered, sir, to direct you to meet Captain Jones on the *Alfred* to make what report to him you will. I cannot bear your message for Captain Jones does not brook such flouting of his orders. Shall I tell him you will not come, sir?"

Hoysted Hacker abruptly stopped at that, his lean face instantly aflame, ready to flay me on the spot. But I did not wait for his outburst, being not responsible to him. Leaving the cabin immediately, I had the officer of the watch call away my boat and set out alone for the *Alfred* lying not far off. But my oarsmen had taken not a dozen strokes when I heard the bosun's pipe shrilling on the *Hampden's* deck, calling away the gig, so I judged Captain Hacker had concluded it was best to obey.

Boarding the *Alfred*, I found Paul Jones on deck gloomily eyeing the dismal wreck of the ship that once had been his pride. For six months since arriving from New London in May, had she swung idly to her moorings there off Providence, and now with slack rigging, unscrubbed decks, and rusting guns she lay neglected and hardly manned.

Jones looked up as I came aboard the untended gangway. Noting my surprise at first glimpsing the unkempt deck, he spoke bitterly,

"This is the state in which our Commodore suffers his flagship! Truly does it reflect our Navy. The situation of America is critical, her affairs cry, and thus like a stranded hulk is left to rot our most powerful ship-of-war! I find aboard but thirty men, not a fifth of what should be her complement. But even thirty men could keep her clean, Tom, if she had one officer aboard with any pride in his profession. Well, this will shortly change! How found you the *Hampden?*" he finished in evident anxiety.

"Captain Hacker is on his way to inform you of it, sir," I replied evasively. "His gig was being called away as I left her."

"Aye, that were best. But I can afford to lose no time

now. Return immediately to the *Providence*, Tom. Direct Mr. Stacy to muster our whole crew there for immediate transfer to the *Alfred*, that I may get this ship in some semblance of her old fighting shape. I have but little time before I must sail, if I am not to miss my chance at Newfoundland. It may be Hacker can send men enough to the *Providence* to man her for the cruise."

I seized the opportunity to depart before Captain Hacker came aboard to tell him there was no chance at all of that. Even with the thirty-odd men left aboard the sloop transferred to her, the *Alfred* would have only half a crew. And from Hacker's statement, the *Hampden* had even less, so the emptied *Providence* would be left with none at all. How then could Paul Jones sail?

What agonies Paul Jones suffered ere that day was out, his mobile face well showed on my return to the flagship. I could well imagine that Hacker's report on his own ship had staggered him. But what really galled his soul was Hacker's stolid acceptance of the situation as one in which nothing could be done. It was bad enough to have to take that incompetent with him on a dangerous cruise. What was insufferable to Paul Jones, as I gathered from the snatches of conversation I overheard as I went in and out of the *Alfred's* great cabin with orders and reports, was Hacker's oxlike attitude—his ship was unready, he had few men, how could anyone expect him to sail?

That the desperate condition of our country required of him that figuratively he *must* make bricks without straw, Hacker could not see any more than his ineffective Commodore. Only one thing he knew—the expedition was impossible.

Finally in disgust Jones dismissed him and sent him back to the *Hampden*. And soon in deep thought our Captain was pacing the *Alfred's* quarterdeck while we of the *Providence* turned to without orders, with buckets, hoses, swabs, and holystones to wash down, starting with the great cabin, empty now, in order that we might reduce the *Alfred* to some shipshape semblance of the vessel she once was.

In the midst of this flood of water and sand Commodore Hopkins came back aboard to check with Jones the day of his departure. He was received formally as always. Immediately he reached the deck, he started for the cabin which once had been his. Jones stopped him.

"I regret, sir, the cabin on this ship is in such filthy state I cannot receive your Excellency in it, though next time you board the *Alfred* it will be ready. Mr. Folger!" he beckoned to me, "bring your notebook here and attend the Commodore's orders!"

So on the quarterdeck of the *Alfred*, the only dry spot on her topside, the conference was held.

"Your sailing date, sir?" Hopkins asked perfunctorily of Jones, ready I could see from his set features to belabor his subordinate instantly when he begged for time.

"In five days, sir," answered Jones firmly. "On October 27 we sail. I cannot go sooner, for it will take that much time to rerig this ship. And I dare not go later, or the expedition will be overset by ice so far north."

At that unexpected reply, Ezek Hopkins stared incredulously at Paul Jones, and truth to tell, knowing the conditions, I was even more astonished than he. If Jones had thought our Commander-in-Chief was indulging in a joke when first he had offered him the squadron, even more did Hopkins believe now he was being made game of.

"I am in no humor for ill-timed jests, sirrah!" exclaimed the Commodore angrily. "When *do* you expect to sail?"

"On October 27, sir," repeated Jones soberly. "Five days is the least time in which I can get ready these neglected ships."

"Never mind the ships! I know all about them!" countered Hopkins testily. "It's the men! Where will you get seamen in five days? I want no promises you do not intend to carry out!"

"In all truth, sir," apologized Jones, "I should have told you I had given up any hope of manning the *Providence* at all, and I mean to go only with the *Alfred* and the *Hampden*. So that sloop's crew is already transferred to the *Alfred* as you see. What more people I need for this ship and the *Hampden* I shall take by searching every privateer in the bay. There are deserters enough on them to fit me out, and it is high time someone took action to return them to their duty and end that damnable abuse!"

"So?" The cautious Ezek Hopkins thoughtfully scanned his exasperated Captain. "You think you can break through the hold our privateersmen have on our eloped seamen, eh? Well, you are welcome to try, though I do not doubt you will find yourself heaved overboard from the first such vessel you try to search! Our privateer Captains are a law unto themselves, Captain Jones, and do not like any interference in their affairs. I have this day failed in my last effort to get our Legislature to embargo their recruiting, and the Congress has steadily refused to take a hand. However, if you wish to try your hand, since the case is urgent you have my orders. If you find any deserters aboard a privateer take them off and as many other seamen on that ship as suits you, so only you leave men enough aboard to work her back to port."

"Aye, that I will! I may take others too, then?"

"If you can," hastily qualified the prudent Hopkins. "The taking is up to you. So you sail then in five days? I shall report immediately to the Marine Committee that their orders are being carried out." In much relief at the prospect, the Commodore turned toward the gangway.

"One thing more you may do for me, sir," broke in Jones. "Captain Hacker, I find, hath little stomach for this enterprise, and makes so many sound objections to its success that I should prefer someone who hath more faith in the project and less logic to prove its impossibility. If it please you, sir, move him from the *Hampden* to the *Cabot*, which stays safely here, that I may put the *Hampden* in command of some one of my late officers of the *Providence*, who will leave the difficulties to me while he cheerfully obeys my orders."

But to that request, Hopkins obstinately shook his head.

"Nay," he answered, "that I will not do. Hoysted Hacker

[331]

is a fine seaman, whom I have myself made Captain. I have full faith he will acquit himself with credit on this venture." And having thus settled everything to his satisfaction, Commodore Hopkins amidst the whistling of the bosun's pipe and the salutes of all hands at the gangway vanished over our side.

Wryly Paul Jones watched him go. So he had to take Hacker, who saw a thousand reasons why he could never start, and nothing but disaster ahead if he did. Well, so be it! With a shrug, our Captain turned inboard, motioned me to him.

"Tom," he said with his old engaging familiarity, taking me by the arm as he started slowly to pace the quarterdeck again, "the Commodore hath generously taken a heavy load off my mind. Between the crew of the *Providence* and what few men I can take off the *Cabot* and the *Columbus*, I have a hundred and twenty men all told to man the *Alfred* and the *Hampden*. I need twenty more at the very least. You heard his Excellency's statement regarding the privateers. I rely on you to get me those men."

I nodded soberly. Once again, as in the first fitting out of the *Alfred*, I was to be recruiting officer for her. But this time, instead of merely posting bills in Philadelphia brothels to have seamen come tumbling aboard by the score pleading for a chance to enlist, I was going to have to fight for them. For I well knew the privateers—as lawless a lot of pirates as that crowd of desperadoes I had cruised with on that other corsair, the *Santissima Trinidad*. And to make matters worse for me, they were backed up by the very best people of the state who owned interest in them and had just squelched Ezek Hopkins' efforts in the Legislature to interfere with their activities. If I got any deserters, it would be only at the pistol's point, and I was far more likely to get a broken head or a boarding pike through my lungs if I were not wary.

"Aye, Captain, I heard him," I answered without enthusiasm. It was one thing to die facing a British man-of-war; quite another to be murdered ingloriously by my own countrymen for a busybody prying into their affairs.

"It is well then," continued my skipper. "He has done me a greater favor than he thinks. I had thought I must search a dozen or two privateers for those twenty deserters, picking mayhap one here, another there, and meanwhile over some days losing the services of valuable seamen here whom I can ill spare now even for an hour. But all is made easy by our Commodore's generous order! There's not a privateer afloat without at least one deserter on her. And since the Commodore has ordered me to take what men I need from any privateer so caught, now you need search but one, Tom. And having first secured on her the eloper from our fleet, you can press the twenty most likely looking seamen aboard her, and our recruiting is complete! See you that?"

"Aye, aye, sir," I responded again, with no more eagerness than before, in some hope that he might perhaps note my lackadaisical manner and send someone else on the business. But I was disappointed.

"Good!" he exclaimed. "All is settled then. I even have the privateer in mind for you to board. This morning, so I have word, there came into Tarpawling Cove nearby, the privateer schooner *Eagle*, which Samuel Aborn and some others of this city had fitted out. She's inward bound from her first cruise, which for their sake I trust proved successful, since she will not soon make another. Tomorrow she moves up to Providence when a berth is cleared for her discharge. She has, I'm told, some thirty men aboard, sufficient for our needs. Tom, take what boats you will, what men you wish, and arm them as you please. Tonight while her crew is still all aboard, she's yours to search!"

I swallowed hard. So I was nominated to take the *Eagle* privateer by boarding, be her resistance what it might. I saluted, went forward.

After some deep consideration, I chose my crew—thirty stout seamen from the *Providence* and ten from the *Alfred*, to go in three boats, with myself heading one, Henry Gardner the second, and Red Jerry the third.

[333]

Just before midnight we shoved off, each man with a loaded pistol in his belt and a cutlass at his side; each boat with grapnels, sea ladders, pikes and half a dozen muskets should we need them.

Silently we headed away in the night, the other two boats following mine. Except for Paul Jones and myself, no one in the party knew our destination nor our purpose till we were off Tarpawling Cove. There we lay on oars the while I brought the other boats alongside to inform them of it.

In the darkness of the cove, her hull a faint blotch only against the shoreline, lay the *Eagle*, a sizeable schooner, swinging to her single anchor. I had hoped to catch her with her unsuspicious crew asleep and with perhaps not even an anchor watch set, but unfortunately for me, alongside her starboard gangway another boat was already lying. There were lights aft in her cabin, and we could vaguely hear voices coming across the water from some men on deck.

Here was a difficulty. I wanted no fight, for aside from any other considerations, I neither wished to lose any seamen in our own scant crew nor kill the seamen that I hoped to press. Yet once we were observed, it was hopeless to expect that we would be permitted to approach at all. And if we then persisted in boarding her the six four-pounders that the *Eagle* carried could cut our fragile boats and all in them to pieces before we got a grappling hook aboard.

That unexpected boat alongside was evidently the cause of so much midnight activity on the *Eagle*. What more likely than that her owner had come down in it from Providence, impatient to see what loot his ship had brought home? But if one boat had come alongside on some such mission, another might be permitted there also.

Softly I called to Henry and to Red Jerry in the other boats, bade them circle the *Eagle* to the inshore side, keeping well clear of her. For this I should give them ample time. When I judged they were in position but well hidden from sight against the dark shore, I would approach the starboard gangway from seaward boldly and openly, engaging the attention of those on deck. Then while I held the watch

[334]

in converse, were they to rush in silently and board from the other side.

"But how'll ye get yerself to that gangway without being swept by grape, Tom?" queried Henry anxiously. "Them privateering pirates're about as trustful as a rattlesnake about letting any boat approach 'em. We'd better all try to creep in close in the darkness and then all rush 'em at once."

"Don't worry over me, Henry," I answered softly. "Just don't you and Jerry give yourselves away by making any noise till you're alongside, that's all."

So for ten minutes my boat lay there while the other two cautiously pulled through the darkness to circle toward the *Eagle's* stern. When I judged they must be in position, I ordered all but four men at the oars to crouch low under the gunwales, that too many men be not sighted, and then got underway.

"All the noise you can make rowing now, lads!" I ordered. "I want them on that schooner to hear us."

Obediently the oarsmen thumped their sweeps against the tholepins in such a racket as could not fail to be heard on the *Eagle*. Immediately it was, for on the schooner's desk I caught sight of dim forms running to the gunwale, the familiar sounds of a gun carriage rolling out, and then came a rough hail from her while still we were a hundred yards off.

"Boat ahoy! Keep clear of us or ye'll git hurt!"

"Is that the *Eagle?*" I sang out, still steering directly for her, while under my breath I muttered to my men to keep on rowing. "I have an important message for Mr. Aborn if he's aboard!"

"Aye, that he is!" A note of uncertainty came into the voice of the mate on watch, for Samuel Aborn was the owner as Paul Jones had informed me, and I had guessed right as to the meaning of the boat alongside. Now I was sure my stratagem would work. "But he ain't left word he's expecting any messengers while he's aboard! Lie to where ye are while I send fer him, or I'll sink ye!" and ominously I saw a slow match glowing in the darkness.

[335]

"Aye, aye!" I replied, and to show compliance, sang loudly out to my oarsmen to cease rowing. Now was the critical time that I must attract all attention to myself. "But for God's sake, man!" I shouted, "don't train any guns on us, and be careful with that slow match! We won't come any closer!" And as if in a panic of fear, I called shrilly to my crew,

"You clumsy fools! Head her out! What do you think I am paying you for? To row me all the way from Providence, just to get me killed running Mr. Aborn's errands? Keep her off, I tell you, or not a shilling will you get in pay! On the *Eagle*, there! Hasten to get Mr. Aborn, for I like not lying thus. Are we far enough off for you?"

"Aye! But belay all that bawling, you lubberly calf, or ye'll wake the whole crew. The anchor watch's gone for Mr. Aborn, and in a minute ye can tell 'im who ye are. If he wants to—"

A blood-curdling war-whoop drowned out the remainder. Red Jerry, I judged, was aboard.

"Give way, all!" I shouted fiercely, crouching low to dodge the hail of grape that I now confidently expected to come swirling about us. "Dead for the gangway! Stand by to board!"

But no gun was fired, and we had, I found moreover, no need of haste. Before we made the *Eagle's* side, I was well assured by the loud cheers I heard that my men were safely in possession, and I tumbled up the gangway at the head of my boat's crew to find the ship was taken already. In one mad rush, once they had made the larboard side, my men had swept over the rail, led by Red Jerry. And that wild Indian had instantly settled all opposition with one cast across the deck of a boarding pike. This impromptu harpoon had pinned to the starboard gunwale the arm of the mate stooping to bring his slow match down on the breech of his loaded four-pounder! And there, moaning in pain, he still was, with Red Jerry working over him to extricate his pike.

On deck, where they had been overwhelmed by rushing

boarders before they could get any weapons to resist, were the four men of the watch, while cutlasses gleamed ominously over every hatch and hoarse voices roared out, warning those below to stay there on pain of instant death!

In the cabin aft where they had been trapped before they could get on deck, I found the Captain cowering before a brace of pistols in Henry Gardner's hands, and a gentleman in a beaver hat who I judged must be Mr. Aborn.

"What damnable outrage is this?" shouted Mr. Aborn, as I, obviously in command, ordered Henry to step back a little while I conducted my inquiry.

"None at all, sir," I answered. "Mr. Aborn, as I told your mate, I have a message for you from Captain Paul Jones of the Continental ship-of-war *Alfred*. I am sent to search this schooner for deserters from the fleet. Had I been permitted to approach your vessel peaceably there would have been no blood shed, but I see some little has been spilled by your foolish orders. Henry," I ordered, drawing my own pistol, "I'll take care of these men. You send that wounded mate below with somebody to bandage him up, and take charge on deck. And meantime send in a couple of men in case I need them."

"Aye, aye, sir." Henry thrust his pistols in his waist and went forward, but immediately his place was taken by several of the men outside.

"Now, sir," I asked Mr. Aborn, "is this your Captain?"

"I am," broke in sullenly the hatless seaman alongside the owner. "An' I tell ye flat ye'll find no deserters aboard my ship. Ye'll suffer fer this, ye impudent young scoundrel, boarding an honest man's ship to murder his crew in their sleep!"

"We'll see, Captain," I replied calmly. "Jerry!" I sang out.

"Aye, Mr. Folger!" Red Jerry, naked to the waist, still fondling his bloody pike, stepped in from the darkness, to the instant dismay of Mr. Aborn, but I bothered not over him.

"Jerry," I ordered, "get the crew of the *Eagle* on deck

[337]

from the forecastle immediately. Have Henry line 'em up at the mast for inspection, and make their bosun break out all the lanterns he has aboard so I get a good look at 'em. And mind, Jerry, they come up one at a time, to cause you no trouble."

"Aye, Mr. Folger," replied Jerry confidently. "Nobody cause me trouble," and out he went.

"Now, Captain," I ordered curtly, "break out your muster roll."

"I haven't got any," growled the skipper. "It went up to Providence this afternoon with all the ship's papers. But I wouldn't give it to ye if I had it, damn you! Ye'll get no help from me! Get off my ship!"

"Take warning, young man!" burst in Mr. Aborn. "Leave at once! I'll have the law on you and your Captain Jones for this! You're worse than the British!"

"Captain Jones didn't send me here to argue about the law or the British either, but to make a search. You've no muster roll, you say? Well then, Captain, how many men in your crew?"

"Find out yourself. I answer nothing," he replied. "But ye'll find no deserters!" and with that he slumped down in his chair at the cabin table, folded his arms, and glared defiantly at me. Evidently I would get no help from the ship's papers and certainly none from her master. I turned to the seamen with drawn cutlasses behind me.

"See these two men stay in the cabin!" I ordered, and went back on deck.

There in the flickering light of half a dozen lanterns ranged on the fife rail the crew was lining up. A fierce looking lot they were who might well have caused us much trouble had they got armed on deck. But now, unarmed and surrounded everywhere by pistols, pikes and cutlasses and considerably outnumbered besides, they were meek enough in obeying orders. I counted them up. There were twenty-five all told, aside from the wounded mate, the Captain, and two other mates whom we had roused out aft.

Hurriedly I went down the line, questioning each man

[338]

as to his previous ships within the last year. Not one of them but answered readily and, so far as I could judge, honestly. And not one of the lot, including the two mates, but claimed to have served only on merchantmen since the war began, or on other privateers.

As a check, I had my own men look them over, for I had with me seamen who had served on every vessel of our fleet, but no one recognized any former shipmates.

Now I was in serious trouble. I had boarded without permission and by force an innocent privateersman and wounded her mate, and could find no deserters aboard to justify my conduct! But worse than that, I had no excuse now to seize from her crew the twenty men Paul Jones so badly needed for our cruise! To no purpose I had stirred up a hornets' nest about my Captain's ears, for there was no mistaking that Mr. Aborn, whom I had so cavalierly handled, meant just what he said.

Still it did not seem possible. With the large number of deserters from the fleet that I had chanced on a privateersman without any seemed beyond belief. Perhaps all the crew was not on deck.

"Anybody else below, Jerry?" I asked hopefully.

Red Jerry shook his head.

"Is this your whole crew?" I asked the second mate standing sullenly at the after end of the line of sailors.

The mate stepped out, looked up the line, slowly counted the men, then answered,

"Aye. Twenty-five, including the cook, aside from the officers."

Was he telling the truth, I wondered? I could soon find out.

"Henry," I said, "go forward and count up the bunks."

While Henry was gone, I looked again at the *Eagle's* crew before me.

"Who's the cook?" I asked.

"Ah is, sah." A negro, scarce visible in the poor light, stepped out.

"Where do you sleep?"

[339]

"In de galley deck-house, sah."

I nodded. That should leave twenty-four bunks occupied in the forecastle, where obviously enough the crew of that schooner must sleep.

Shortly was Henry Gardner back, much excited.

"There's thirty bunks for'ard, Tom, and twenty-eight of 'em has got bedding in 'em that's been slept on tonight! Somebody's missing here!"

Caustically I turned to the second mate.

"Do you hear that, you damned liar! Where's the rest of your crew?"

But the mate had an explanation.

"Maybe some o' the men's using two bunks, sir. The crew's all here."

A sailor using two bunks, eh? I had been at sea long enough to know that there never was a seaman who had two sets of bedding. But there was no use arguing. We must find those men.

"Search the hold, Henry!" I ordered. "There are four men hiding on us, and if they're hiding, they're the men we want. Jerry, you search that fo'c'sle again! And take men enough and lanterns, both of you, to keep at it till you find those men!"

For an hour Henry and Red Jerry, good seamen both who knew ships well, went through that vessel thoroughly at the head of searching parties but nowhere did they run across a hiding seaman. We searched the fo'c'sle, the holds, the galley, the cabin, all the staterooms, even the lazaretto beneath the cabin floor. In despair, I even sent men up to the schooner's crosstrees, and out her jibboom, to see that no one was concealed by darkness in the rigging or clinging to her hawser, but we could find nothing. And each time I passed him the second mate solemnly assured me I was wasting my time—there were no others.

Nonplussed, at last both Henry and Red Jerry reported that every space had been examined without result. They did not know where else to look.

"Somewhere they're aboard, Henry," I argued. "There's

that bedding. And since they weren't on watch when we boarded, they were in the fo'c'sle then. And there's no way out of that fo'c'sle save the hatch on deck that you had guarded till you let these men here up, so the others must still be down that fo'c'sle somewhere. Henry, you guard these men on deck. Jerry, come down into that fo'c'sle again with me!"

For now it struck me that the master of the *Eagle* had been so assured we would find no deserters that he must have prepared himself against search by arranging beforehand some secure place of concealment for them. And that I must find!

Having that in mind, the rest proved absurdly easy. Going first into the forehold, a glance with a lantern showed me the forepeak bulkhead ran solid vertically from keel to main deck, which was what I expected of such a heavy collision bulkhead. Then going into the fo'c'sle from the topside, I found that triangular space lined on all three sides from deck to ceiling with bunks as was natural, with nothing below save the forepeak tank. Lifting the deck scuttle, I lay flat down on the deck to look into that dank space. Except for some few feet of water far down, it was certainly empty, but either in that compartment or in the fo'c'sle with me were four men.

While Jerry held the lantern for me, I sighted aft below and above along the deck on which I lay, at the forepeak bulkhead. And there was the answer. In the fo'c'sle, the collision bulkhead seemed several feet closer to me than it lay in the space below. Dropping back in place the scuttle, I rose.

"Jerry," I said softly, "go on deck and come back here with half a dozen men and some axes. That after bulkhead's not what it seems to be. There's room enough behind it for a small compartment!"

Up went Red Jerry. Carefully I examined the after bulkhead, but so lined with bunks was it, I saw no signs of any joints in the pine sheathing to which the bunks were nailed.

But behind that sheathing I was sure my men lay.

Shortly Jerry returned, followed by a squad of seamen with one axe and some boarding pikes.

"Come out, you skulkers, or you'll get hurt!" I shouted. "That bulkhead's going to be smashed now in a minute!"

But there was no response.

"Lay on, Jerry," I ordered then. "Break it down! Stand back, everybody!"

Red Jerry braced himself, swung viciously waisthigh across an empty bunk into the pine sheathing behind, driving his axe clean through it. And instantly from behind that sheathing came a cry of pain, and then a muffled shout,

"Belay that, mates! We'll come out!"

A moment later the sheathing over the topmost bunk swung downward over the bedding there, and out through that neatly fitted panel, one after another my four men crawled sheepishly! My raid was justified!

In triumph I led them up on deck, where the miserable culprits confessed—one had deserted the *Hampden*, one the *Columbus*, and the other two had deserted from the Rhode Island Brigade, lured from the Army by the wild stories they had heard of the riches to be got in privateers.

I dallied no longer with the *Eagle* then. Hurriedly I went down the line of her seamen, told off three men and the negro cook, who seemed least promising as men-o'-warsmen, and bade them stand aside. And then ignoring the protests of the astonished mates at my proceedings, I hustled the other twenty, plus my four deserters, hurriedly at the points of the pikes down the gangway to be distributed amongst our three boats, and then I was nearly ready to shove off.

"Henry," I said, "it would be only prudence to pour a bucket of water down the muzzle of every gun aboard before we leave. You do that while I say goodbye to the Captain and his owner." And while Henry went about that business I entered the cabin again, where Mr. Aborn and the Captain sat still under guard.

"Ye quit searching yet?" snarled the skipper. "It's getting nigh on morning and I'm damned sick of being prisoner on my own ship!"

"Aye, Captain," I answered pleasantly enough. "I have come to release you. Everything is now in order. You'll find your forward bulkhead badly smashed and the four deserters skulking behind—"

"What?" roared the Captain, taken full aback by that. "Ye found—"

"Aye, sir, I found them in spite of your ingenuity. A clever Captain, you have, Mr. Aborn, but I advise him to save his tricks to try on the British. They cost too much when played on other Yankees. I've been obliged to leave you somewhat short-handed, in accordance with the orders of his Excellency, Ezek Hopkins, who will explain further to you if you wish. He disapproves of privateers enveigling away his seamen and hath devised a method to discourage it, of whose efficacy you will soon discover proof. And now, sirs, I bid you both good-morning!" I finished, waving my seamen out and following them myself so swiftly that neither of the two before me, looking decidedly puzzled over my cryptic remark, had opportunity to say more.

Down the gangway with me shot Henry Gardner and the last half-dozen of his men on deck, so that in another moment, our three boats, heavily laden now, were all shoved off and we were underway before those left on the *Eagle* well realized we were gone. And to avoid any difficulties with our new shipmates, I deemed it prudent when we were well clear of that privateer to put them all at the oars for the journey back to the *Alfred*, considering that with their hands well occupied, they would work no mischief at being so suddenly taken into their country's Navy.

36

On October 27, 1776, a raw day chill with the sharp bite of approaching winter, we weighed anchor to drop down Providence River on the outgoing tide.

With spyglass tucked under his arm and looking wan and worn, for he had hardly slept the last five days, Paul Jones paced the *Alfred's* quarterdeck impatiently while Jack Robinson, bosun, together with all hands and the cook heaved short our cable and struggled to break out our anchor. That was a task, for the *Alfred* had swung so long to her mooring there, our anchor was apparently buried deep in the mud, stock and flukes, and beyond the power of our short-handed crew, heaving all on the capstan bars, to break free of the bottom. Mr. Stacy braced our fore yards hard one way and those on the main hard the other to help out with the sails, so that, broadside to the wind, we heeled to bring the strain of a fresh breeze also on our hawser, and not till then did we break clear the anchor.

Then indeed it walked merrily enough up to the chant of heaving seamen and the rattle of the capstan pawls, while on deck our sailing master hastily squared away all his spars on the starboard tack and clewed up his courses that we should not gather too much headway till we had more sea-room for maneuver.

The *Hampden* had similar difficulty in weighing and when we were well down the bay there was still no sign of motion on that brig, so that it began to be a question whether she would weigh at all on that tide.

Impatient as a race horse to be off, our Captain in exasperation scanned the *Hampden* all this while, fearing that ship might delay him enough to miss the tide in getting out the harbor and lose a day in his start for Newfoundland. He had scant patience now, for the nerve-racking toil of five days of loading stores, of rerigging, of spurring into action the balky Captain of the *Hampden*, of watching closely every nearing shoreboat night and day, lest he find himself suddenly short some of his hard-won seamen, had all worn him down and he was chafing to be well clear of any sight of land and far out at sea where nothing worse than enemy cruisers might rise up to annoy him on his mission north.

At last with a sigh of relief Paul Jones telescoped his spyglass. The topsails of the *Hampden* had filled and she was underway after us, five miles astern.

Off Bristol we loosed courses, and with our skipper himself cutting in bearings on every headland to keep us well clear of all the shoals, we stood with wind abeam and increasing speed past Prudence Island into the deeper water of the bay.

Some three hours later we were off Newport and steering close hauled for the open sea, holding well up to windward in order not to make too close acquaintance with Brenton Reef. That danger cleared, we eased sheets and braces and bore away for Vineyard Sound. It was our Captain's thought that in those sheltered waters we were less likely to encounter any blockading frigates till we had cleared Monomoy Point on Cape Cod at nightfall and were in the open Atlantic.

Running free with doubled lookouts at every masthead, we stood east before the wind. Still tense, our Captain's keen grey eyes alternated between gazing aloft at our lookouts that they mind sharply their business, and off our larboard quarter toward the *Hampden*, yet close hauled beating to windward to clear the reefs. For Paul Jones was praying earnestly not to meet the *Cerberus* nor any other enemy frigate till he had had at least one day at sea maneuvering in formation with the *Hampden*, so that his two ships might have some experience in operating together as a squadron before they engaged.

[345]

For that purpose I had practised in the harbor on the code of signal hoists which Paul Jones, a keen student of naval tactics, had made out for the cruise. Cooperating to that end was little Charley Hill, whom Jones had transferred to the *Hampden* as her signal officer. And now our skipper with drawn face and eyes burning from lack of sleep was impatiently waiting for his consort to close up so we might try our skill in signalling at sea, and he might determine how well or how ill the ship-rigged *Alfred* and the brig-rigged *Hampden* sailed together in line of battle.

With the quartermaster ready by my side, the signal flags in orderly rows stowed snugly in their racks, and halliards to all our topgallant yards clear and streaming forward in the breeze, I stood with the signal code ready in my pocket to make up and break smartly out the first hoist. And meanwhile, with my spyglass trained on the *Hampden*, I watched her carefully for any signal fluttering to her yardarm for us.

Suddenly as I watched that brig I was petrified to see her taut topsails shiver violently and her masts lay far over to windward. Crazily the *Hampden* careened and swung up into the wind, taking instantly aback all her sails!

"The *Hampden's* on the reef, sir!" I sang out.

Aghast, Paul Jones spun sharply about, lifted his spyglass. It was so beyond question. There was the brig with her every spar swaying drunkenly and her sails slatting against the masts, bumping erratically along out of all control, obviously scraping a reef!

In agony we watched. If she stranded on that falling tide, long before we might haul her off, a British squadron would be there to take her, ship and crew! And then to our intense relief, she drove over the rocks, gradually fell off from the wind, and her sails again steadying her, ceased her wild rolling. She was clear.

Not till then did Paul Jones drop his glass, but his worn face was the very picture of despair. After all his superhuman efforts to get his little squadron underway for his first cruise, that clumsy dolt on the *Hampden* had driven his ship on the best charted rocks in those waters. The *Hampden* would be lucky not to founder before she could get back to harbor!

"Mr. Stacy!" called out our Captain, with great effort suppressing his fierce anger. "Haul by the wind and beat back to convoy the *Hampden* into Newport!"

We ran close aboard the brig, sent a party to her to help her man her pumps, and escorted our badly leaking consort back to port. There it was swiftly determined she was unseaworthy with part of her keel knocked off.

Muttering curses at what incompetence had done to wreck the expedition by this delay, Jones transferred Hacker and his crew to the empty *Providence*, had her sailed down to Newport, and there again night and day worked all hands to move the stores and the powder from the damaged *Hampden* to the *Providence* sloop.

He got only one relief. Throwing discretion to the winds, our overwrought Captain wrote a bitter letter to Ezek Hopkins, excoriating him in no uncertain terms as the cause of this disaster.

I looked for that letter to result immediately in trouble for Paul Jones for it was too much to expect that Hopkins would willingly assume the blame for Captain Hacker's stupidity. But nothing happened—then. Our Commodore meekly swallowed Paul Jones' denunciations over having had the incompetent Hacker forced on him, and in reply merely confirmed the substitution of the *Providence* and directed the following out of the former instructions. I could only judge that it was of such importance to Ezek Hopkins that some semblance of a squadron sail to save him from the wrath of Congress, that at the moment he would overlook any insult to accomplish it.

On November 2, we sailed again, our force as a fighting squadron much weakened at the replacement of the *Hampden's* fourteen six-pounders by the twelve fours on the *Providence*. And we were pitifully short-handed—only eighty men aboard the *Alfred* and sixty on the sloop, a hundred and forty only all told to assault what forces we

[347]

might meet in Isle Royale and in Newfoundland.

So badly had we missed the season for going north, that we ran into atrocious weather from the start, cold rain, dull skies, head seas, and then that dread of every mariner—fog.

Our first night out in the Atlantic, battling temptestuous seas, we had hardly cleared Cape Cod and met the cold waters of the Labrador Current than we were enveloped in a blanket of dense mist. And instead of keeping close up in our lee to maintain touch, that villain, Hoysted Hacker, seized the opportunity offered him to give us the slip and desert, vanishing astern in the fog and the dark with the *Providence,* to return incontinently, as we learned afterwards, to the safety of Newport!

But all we knew then when day broke again over the cold Atlantic and the fog thinned somewhat, was that we were alone in the *Alfred* on a waste of wintry seas, standing northeast toward the enemy coasts with a scant eighty men for our assault. When we sighted nothing of our consort after another day of battling gales and fog, I looked for Paul Jones to give over the venture and return also in the storm tossed *Alfred.*

But doggedly he stood on alone. There were some hundred American prisoners held virtually as slaves in the coal mines at Isle Royale. And their release was a project he assured his officers gathered in his cabin to hear his revised plans, that "aroused all my feelings of humanity."

So we fought our way alone northward against the sea till one week out we made the coast off Cape Breton. There we fell in with the Liverpool brigantine *Active.* This merchantman we overhauled and took with little trouble. Out of gratitude to his friend and patron, Joseph Hewes, Paul Jones dispatched this vessel with a small prize crew to Robert Smith at Edenton, where that partner of Hewes was prize agent.

Then in swift raids we fell on the Acadian coast, working with our ice-coated boats to take and burn a transport which the enemy had beached to escape us, and to ravage and burn every warehouse on that shore.

Standing off again, we steered for Isle Royale, but before we made that haven, the fog shut us in again. But this time the marrow-chilling mist proved our friend, for in the eerie vagueness of the fog we made out the hazy outlines of the *Flora* frigate, 32, before she recognized us for an enemy. Thus warned, we worked gradually to leeward of her to join her convoy without in the least exciting the suspicions of that powerful man-of-war.

There with impudence beyond belief, while the *Flora* to windward still sailed unsuspectingly on in the fog, Paul Jones in quick succession laid aboard and took one by one the entire convoy—four transports laden with coal, cod, and furs! And soon with prize crews on each, the *Alfred* was convoying that same fleet of transports off toward Isle Royale from whence they had just come, while the *Flora* stood on in the thickening mists with nothing in her charge!

Now we were quite an imposing squadron in appearance at least, as we made all sail for Isle Royale and our next raid ashore. But in all truth we were weaker than ever, for having manned five prizes, there were but a scant fifty souls left on the *Alfred* to fight her.

However, we never made the raid. The captured Captains of the transports were all brought aboard the *Alfred* with their other officers as prisoners for the greater security of the trifling prize crews we could place on their vessels. We learned from them that the harbor at Isle Royale was already frozen solidly over and no ship could enter any longer.

Our own ship with ice-coated rigging and bulwarks solid now in late November with frozen spray, made this easily believable, but Paul Jones was not one ever to be deterred in his purposes by ice or man or devil. However, something else crossed his path to change his plans completely.

While still well off shore, near Louisburg we made out a large vessel bound for the mouth of the St. Lawrence. Signalling our convoy to stay well together, we speedily ran her down to find under our guns a ship with decks scarlet with the red coats of a company of British soldiers standing with bayonets fixed to repel us should we board!

[349]

Up went our Continental colors to the gaff. Seizing his trumpet, Paul Jones hailed,

"Do you strike?"

Across the water came the answer,

"Aye, I'll strike!" and immediately the deck of that transport burst into flame, with a volley of musketry and six great guns pouring shot into us!

We gave her one broadside only, purposely aimed high to go whistling through her rigging. It left her sails with many a gaping rent to mark the passage of our round shot.

Again our Captain sang out, in a cold fury that left no doubt over his intentions,

"The next broadside sweeps your deck with grape! Strike or die!"

That thundering voice and the sight of our twelve nine-pounders running out again leveled point-blank on their gunwales, cooled the theatric ardor of our enemy. They had no chance. Down came the British ensign.

With the *Alfred* lying prudently off at half pistol shot from our hove-to capture and with our guns loaded with grape and matches ready should there be any sign of treachery, Paul Jones went in our longboat to take possession and to examine his prize. He returned aboard shortly in raptures, with the crestfallen Captain of the *Mellish* transport, a British army Captain and two marine officers as prisoners, and the manifest of the *Mellish*. We had taken the richest prize which had yet fallen in the war to American arms! The *Mellish*, an armed transport whose bulk far exceeded that of the *Alfred*, was laden with military stores of the last importance. And aside from the full company of soldiers she was carrying, stowed in her holds were bale on bale of blankets and ten thousand complete suits of winter uniforms destined for the army of Burgoyne gathering in Canada for their descent into New York! How Washington's shivering Continentals, freezing in their tattered rags, would rejoice at that!

For the next several hours as both the *Mellish* and the *Alfred* wallowed hove to in a cross sea, we were busy transporting boatload after boatload of captured redcoats to the *Alfred* to fill our fore hold with them as prisoners, so that our prize crew on the *Mellish* would not face the danger of having that valuable ship retaken from them by an uprising.

When all this was finally completed, and our prize crew placed aboard the *Mellish*, the *Alfred* was no longer in condition for any further raids ashore. Our holds were jammed with prisoners from the six ships taken. We were stripped of half our insignificant crew by the men and officers sent from the *Alfred* to man the prizes, and in our lee we had a squadron of five vessels to get home. By no conceit could we make up a landing party again to raid Isle Royale, even though we somehow forced our way into the ice there. Regardless of his humane desire to free the American captives in the Isle Royale mines, cold-blooded military necessity dictated to Paul Jones he must not hazard what he had already captured by a mad venture, so with keen regret he made signal to his fleet for all to stand to the southwest, headed for home.

Shepherded by the *Alfred* running to windward all ships in a close knit squadron obediently made sail.

Exultantly our Captain looked across the heaving seas at the fruits of his adventure. The *Mellish* alone, looming loftily in hull and spars above every other ship, was such a prize as would delay for months Burgoyne's expedition by her loss, and he could well imagine with what joy Washington and his men would fall on those uniforms.

But ahead of us lay many a British frigate guarding the coast, and we still had the task of getting our prizes through that enemy screen and into port. That was a nightmare, for any frigate we might meet was sure to outclass the *Alfred* even if we had had a full crew for our guns. And as we were, with scarce men enough to handle sail with any expedition, our fighting power was pitifully reduced. Then there were some hundreds of prisoners in our holds, a constant menace to us should they get free, especially in action.

The situation preyed heavily on Paul Jones' mind, who

made the round of our gun deck hourly with anxious eyes assuring himself that every hatch below was battened down and guarded by seamen with pistols loose and bared cutlasses, lest our prisoners break out and overwhelm us by sheer force of numbers.

Still I could see by his constant watch on the *Mellish*, hovering always close by her in the *Alfred*, that the fate of that rich argosy weighed most upon him. Could seamanlike skill and strategy get her in, I had no doubt as to the outcome, but if we met such force that we had to fight for her, where would we be then? We could not man a quarter of our guns to defend ourselves, let alone the prize.

At last Paul Jones beckoned me to him from across the quarterdeck. I came running to look into my Captain's wan and weary face.

"Tom," he said, "who can tell what we may encounter before we make Boston? But the British must not profit by laying hands again on what I have reft them of. Washington may never enjoy the cargo of yon transport, but in that case, neither shall Burgoyne. Signal the prize master on the *Mellish*, 'If in danger of recapture, sink your ship!'"

"Aye, aye, sir." Soberly I called the quartermaster to me, and soon that ominous signal was fluttering in hoist after hoist, spelled out from our yardarms.

Several days more still under that strain we stood on. Now it was December, with winter weather in those latitudes striking us in full fury, and our under-manned ships, the *Alfred* as well as all our prizes, hard put to it to handle sail with all our lines frozen stiff and canvas heavy with snow and ice.

We took one more prize, a Liverpool privateer of sixteen guns which, scenting loot, came foaming up out of the mists to fall on us from windward.

Immediately we bore up athwart his hawse, with every gun port on our weather side flung suddenly open together to disclose to him our full broadside, twelve nine-pounders trained on him, ready to rake. This menacing display of our teeth so startled the corsair's Captain that he struck to us immediately as before superior force.

But to us worn mariners his chagrin was comical to the last degree when he came aboard us a prisoner to find we had not men enough to have reloaded our guns had he stood our one discharge. He might then have taken us and all our prizes if he had fought his vessel manfully.

Now we were hard put to it to find room to jam the captured crew of that privateer into our already overcrowded holds, and even in worse case to squeeze out from our scant remaining ship's company a prize crew for her. When Lieutenant Saunders and his little group of men shoved off from the *Alfred* to man her for the trip home, it left on the *Alfred* only myself and our sailing master as officers and just thirty seamen as our crew.

With six prizes sailing in our convoy, again we made sail for Boston. And for once Paul Jones earnestly prayed that we sight no more tempting prizes on our way.

We saw nothing more and had only the common enemy of all seamen, the sea itself, to battle till late next afternoon off George's Bank. There, well to windward, we made out an enemy man-of-war standing for us.

Immediately the half deserted gun deck of the *Alfred* echoed hollowly to the roll of the drum beating to quarters. In great dismay we scanned the topsails of that vessel, for her hull was much obscured by the heaving seas, to make out her force. But if she closed on us, her force was of slight moment, for we were in no condition to fight off even a sloop-of-war, let alone a frigate such as the towering masts of that distant ship indicated her to be. To add to our torments, from our holds came such a continuous roar of shrieks and curses from our prisoners scenting freedom that scarce could an order on our decks be heard.

We had only one resource—flight. Immediately the *Alfred* made signal to the prizes to bear away southward dead before the wind, with ourselves and our captured letter of marque (which had been directed to follow all our movements) taking station astern them. This put us between our squadron and the enemy for what little protection ten men

[353]

on the Liverpool privateer and thirty on the *Alfred* could offer in pitched battle to the enemy.

It was soon evident that the enemy vessel was a faster sailer than our huddled squadron driving before a winter gale, but one thing favored us—that short December day was near its ending. By strenuous exertion of the trifling crews aboard each vessel we all managed to spread sail enough so that when darkness fell at last, the enemy while closer was still well out of cannon shot.

Seeing that our pursuer could not close on us before night, in the fast fading twilight Paul Jones made his last signal to his prizes,

"Disregard all further signals of every nature. Extinguish all your lights. Stand on together on this course through the night. At dawn, separate and make the best of your way to port."

Soon after, the black December night closed in, and in the darkness and the cold we plunged ahead through heavy seas, the letter of marque abeam us on our starboard hand, the other vessels invisible altogether. As if to guide our squadron, we hoisted to our masthead a single lantern, and with that the only gleam of light on the black ocean (for our pursuer showed no lights either) we stood on till midnight.

The cold wind whistled through our rigging, the unseen waves foamed up astern to break against our poop. Below at the great guns, the three crews I could still muster slept beside their gun carriages.

With straining eyes, I sought some sign on deck of the whereabouts of friend or foe but so dark was the night and so foam-crested every breaking wave that I could make out neither wakes of ships ahead nor bow wave of ship astern. Not even the letter of marque, a cable's length away on our quarter steering by our masthead light, was visible any longer.

At last came midnight. In preparation for that hour, our lamp-lighter had gathered at our Captain's order half a dozen battle lanterns which he held shielded from view astern by the poop bulkhead. With swollen fingers stiff from cold, the quartermaster and I bent these individually on to the halliards to our yardarms in vertical rows, three to the foremast halliards, two to the main, one to the mizzen.

When eight bells came, that significant array of lights was smartly run up to our topsail yards, there for a moment to sway in the wind as if for a signal gleaming brightly through the thick night to our convoy and then as suddenly as they had been hoisted they were hauled down and doused, again leaving only our masthead light aglow.

And immediately with the striking of those lights, Mr. Stacy swung into action with every man jack of our crew to hand the sheets and haul by the wind, so that shortly, as close hauled as we could lay the clumsy *Alfred*, she was clawing up to windward to the east away from the coast with that solitary light at our masthead cleaving the darkness on a course some eight points to larboard of our previous heading.

What came of all this, neither Paul Jones, Mr. Stacy, nor I, all gathered on the poop endeavoring anxiously to pierce the darkness astern, could in any wise tell. We could see nothing before while we were running free in the darkness; nor were we now in any better case heeled down and plunging heavily into head seas with the cold wind and biting spray driving fiercely into our faces. Not anywhere in that inky blackness was anything visible save only our masthead lantern—a will-o'-the-wisp glowing in the night to lead astray, we hoped, our enemy.

So, wholly unprotected, we left our prizes to drive on through the night before the wind while we sailed away from them. And torn between hope and doubt, Paul Jones paced the poop the whole night through beside the helmsman, ready at hand instantly should anything eventuate.

The late dawn came at last, to break in vague illumination on leaden skies and a forbidding ocean wreathed everywhere in driving spray and tumbling seas. And grimly did Paul Jones' grey eyes sparkle to light upon our enemy some miles off on our lee quarter, while, save for the letter

[355]

of marque still close aboard in company, over that vast expanse of winter sea there was not visible another sail anywhere! His stratagem had succeeded. Come now what might, the priceless *Mellish* and our other prizes had escaped into the southern board, and we had led the warship blockading Boston far out to sea to leave an open road for them to enter port!

Now if we could, it was our turn to escape. Immediately we tacked, to beat back toward the Massachusetts coast, leaving our enemy still well to leeward of us, and at a disadvantage in the chase by so much. He followed suit, of course, and gradually as we might, we bore off, till by midmorning once again we three vessels were driving madly before the wind, on which point of sailing the *Alfred*, but a dull vessel, went best.

It was quickly obvious the Liverpool privateer had the speed of us, and might soon have outsailed either us or our pursuer. Noting this, and desiring to learn what was the force of the vessel chasing us, which in that state of the sea we had still not made out, Paul Jones signalled to Lieutenant Saunders to drop cautiously back and reconnoiter her. For it was certain that long before the day was over, she would have hauled up within gunshot of the *Alfred* and willy-nilly we would be in action, so that our anxious Captain felt it imperative to discover with what he would then have to deal.

Accordingly Saunders shortened sail and slowly dropped astern, till, as he thought, well out of gunshot on her starboard side, he was practically abeam her. From that excellent point of observation, he signalled us,

"The frigate *Milford*, 32."

So the vessel astern was our old friend the *Milford!* Well did we know her. With the fleet *Providence* beneath our feet we had led her a merry chase, and not a man transferred to the *Alfred* from that vessel but remembered well enough the force of those broadsides we had enticed her over-eager Captain to fire at our elusive sloop.

But now that signal fell on our spirits like an icy bath.

No longer were the *Milford's* heavy broadsides anything to laugh away. In deadly earnest we would face them now, for we had under us not the fast-sailing *Providence* but the dull *Alfred,* and not again would an encounter with that frigate be a jest to be ended with a mocking musket shot!

Our worst fears were swiftly realized. Lieutenant Saunders, an inexperienced officer sailing his first independent command as prize master, had sadly under-estimated the *Milford's* range. Scarce had he made signal of her name when her side opened on him in a flaming broadside, and to his stunned amazement the volley landed squarely on his ship to leave his top hamper a mass of severed rigging and wildly flapping canvas!

With not men enough aboard to repair damages, let alone to man the privateer's guns, the letter of marque helplessly broached to, wallowing crazily in the trough of the sea. Instantly the *Milford* luffed under her stern to rake her with a second broadside. But ere it was fired, Lieutenant Saunders struck his colors, and we had lost that prize!

The *Milford* then perforce hove to, and sent a boat with a prize crew to take possession of our late consort, while we, with this as an earnest of our own impending fate, kept on our way, thankful only that the delay thus forced on the *Milford* gave us some opportunity to open on her.

The frigate did not tarry long however, for no sooner was her boat alongside that retaken privateer and her boarding party, covered still by the frigate's guns, clambering over the gunwales, than she was underway again in hot pursuit of us, leaving the recaptured letter of marque a dismal wreck in her wake.

We gained three miles on the frigate perhaps, in that sad interlude, enough to give us some faint chance and that was all. Before the wind in a gale that did not warrant such a spread, we still crowded on all sail, our few seamen scrambling in succession from one ice-coated yard to the next to run out our stu'n'sail booms and get aloft that light canvas, together with every staysail that we had in our hold. So that soon with all the canvas flying that we might with

[357]

safety have spread in a gentle zephyr, we staggered on before the wind, our bending topmasts and taut backstays groaning ominously under their load, and our vast array of running rigging singing like harp strings in the wind as never have I heard the like.

But the *Milford*, a larger frigate by far than the *Alfred*, still made better weather of that wintry sea and slowly gained on our converted merchantman, whose tubby hull had been designed to carry cargo, not for speed.

I made the round of our gun deck with Paul Jones. There, where he had fought the guns with full a hundred men against the *Glasgow* frigate, now I had but eighteen to man the twenty nine-pounders of that battery. But unperturbed, Paul Jones ordered me to load every gun with chain shot, which Henry Gardner, going from one gun to another down one side of the deck and up the other, soon accomplished. Then under our Captain's eye we ran all the guns out and trained them fair abeam so that the fire of each broadside converged at what should be maximum range with all guns at full elevation. And thus we left the battery after much toil—gun ports open, guns trained, elevated, and run out so that we could fire one broadside on each side at least, though with so few men down below I could never hope to reload and fire again in close action before we were battered to pieces.

In that condition our Captain left me to go on deck again, where I followed him shortly, leaving Henry at the battery.

It was noon. The *Milford* had already closed half the distance between us since morning and before night would close the other half in spite of all we might do. And then she would shortly discover from our ragged fire we had but an insignificant crew to fight the ship, so that most probably all would end by her ranging alongside to carry us by boarding. Ruefully I smiled at what would happen when the boarding officer broached our hatches to find the *Alfred* laden with captured redcoats and a vast assortment of British tars taken from our prizes, for immediately I would change places in that gloomy hold with the prisoners making a bedlam of it now with their wild yells.

We stood on with the weather getting worse, and the light canvas of our stu'n'sails threatening with every gust that struck us to bid farewell to the boltropes and go flying down to leeward. But not a stitch of canvas would our Captain strike.

By three o'clock the *Milford* had drawn up within long cannon shot, and her chase guns began to play on us. There were yet two hours till darkness would close in, and it was certain this time that the enemy, if the chase continued unchanged, would have us at his mercy well before night came to save us.

Broodingly Paul Jones leaned over the high railing of our poop to mark the fall of each round shot whistling toward us. Firing dead to leeward, the British gunners made fair practise and the balls splashing about our counters might any moment crash down on our deck. There was no question now—unless we struck, we must fight, either on the enemy's terms from whichever position the *Milford's* Captain might choose, or, while we yet had the chance, on ours.

It was never in Paul Jones' character to surrender the initiative, nor did he now. Leaving the after rail for the quarterdeck, he summoned to him the sailing master and me, the only two officers he had left aboard.

"Soon we shall have to fight, gentlemen, and if I judge aright the weather, the sooner for us the better. See you yonder clouds on our quarter?"

I looked over as directed toward the horizon on our larboard quarter, and there the sky was almost black.

"We must slow up our friend astern till that storm strikes. After that, there will be no further fighting today. Stand by below, Tom!"

I laid below and scattered my few men along the larboard battery, two men at some of the guns, one only at the rest. Over the priming trains already laid, the gun captains started to blow their slow matches.

On deck the helm was put suddenly hard astarboard, the

weather sheets let fly to all our sails. Swiftly the *Alfred* swung into the wind to present her larboard side to the enemy astern, and as soon as the gun through the midship port bore fair upon the *Milford's* bow, I roared out,

"Fire!"

Ten whirling pairs of double-headed shot went flying to windward at that broadside to throw up fountains of spray all about the *Milford's* jibboom, but so far as I could see, not one shot reached her.

Still we did not fail wholly, for thinking from that smartly fired volley we meant to engage now broadside to broadside, the *Milford* trimmed sails and hauled by the wind on a course parallel to ours. But the instant the enemy frigate hauled up, up went our helm again and our flapping sails were sheeted home to lay us once more dead before the wind, having gained perhaps two ship lengths before the *Milford*, after firing two wholly futile broadsides at our swiftly turning vessel, eased her sheets again to follow in our wake.

The *Milford* did not make up that lost distance to bring her chase guns again in range for half an hour, but then at last came a round shot crashing down fairly on our poop to smash the cabin skylight and go tearing downwards through the empty cabin.

By now I had reloaded all the larboard guns and from the lowering darkness it was evident that it would not be much longer till the storm struck. Less than two miles off on our larboard quarter clouds and sea were mingling in one black mass.

Paul Jones looked ruefully from the smashed skylight to the nearing storm. If the next shot carried away our wheel, we would be helpless in the face of both our enemies. He decided not to wait. The sooner he drove into that tempest now, the better.

"All hands aloft, Mr. Stacy, to shorten sail! We're going close hauled for that storm! Tom! Send all your men on deck, except you and your quarter gunner, to reef down canvas!"

Hard astarboard once again went our helm, and we bore up this time with every man we had frantically handing sheets and dousing stu'n'sails to lay us close hauled. This maneuver brought us swiftly off the *Milford's* bow and driving diagonally athwart her course. Below on the deserted gun deck Henry and I stood by, blowing a pair of matches, and once again as our guns bore on the *Milford* we ran rapidly down the line of breeches to give her a very ragged broadside.

What trick of ours the *Milford* thought this was I know not. But she was apparently determined to be fooled no longer by our maneuvers. This time she disdained to haul by the wind after us and held her fire till we were fairly abeam, by which moment such a roaring gale of snow suddenly enveloped us as to hide her completely from our sight and make us lose all interest in everything save reefing down before our whipping masts went by the board.

Our next half hour was a nightmare alow and aloft, with part of our small crew on the yards battling the roaring wind and the thick snow, striving to shorten sail, while below on the gun deck the other half struggled like demons to run in our guns and seal the gun ports before the entering seas caused us to capsize. Which was worse, the howling of the gale tearing our light canvas to tatters or the shrieks of our prisoners battened down in the holds, imploring us to release them before we foundered, who could tell?

But whether on swaying yards or heaving gun carriages, our few stout seamen facing instant death stuck manfully by their tasks till at last all was snug, and under stormsails only we were driving before the storm into the winter night, no longer concerned in the slightest over the *Milford*.

Twenty-four hours later, with food low and water practically all gone, our anchor splashed down near Fort William in Boston harbor and the cruise of the *Alfred* was over.

Hardly two cables off lay the huge *Mellish*, already unloading for General Washington's army the clothing and the military stores which were shortly to assist in his Christmas Eve descent on Trenton and his capture of the Hessian army there. And nearby also swung at anchor most of our other prizes.

Paul Jones, with his haggard face and worn eyes aglow in triumph at the sight of such a blow to King George as had not before been struck on the seas, called me into his cabin. I made copies while he wrote out his reports to Commodore Hopkins and to Robert Morris of the Marine Committee of the Congress. As he listed one by one the captures of the *Alfred* and the havoc he had wreaked on the Acadian coast with that lone ship, I could see his active mind running far ahead of that report to what he would accomplish on his next cruise with all the vessels of our fleet sailing under his command.

But scarcely were these reports finished and the originals signed, sealed, and dispatched than two strangers came on board the *Alfred* who completely wrecked his peace of mind and all his hopes.

The first was Captain Elisha Hinman of the Continental Navy, an officer of no particular prominence, lately Paul Jones' junior on the list of Captains by eight numbers, with orders in his hand from Ezek Hopkins to take immediate command of the *Alfred* as his senior, superseding Jones who was ordered back to the little *Providence*.

And the second was the sheriff, to serve him with papers in a suit for damages brought against him personally for £10,000, in favor of Samuel Aborn, Esquire, and others of Providence, for the taking of certain members of the crew of the privateer schooner *Eagle*, which seizure, it was stated, Commodore Ezek Hopkins wholly disavowed.

37

NOT since I saw young Captain Paul staring horror-stricken at the bleeding figure of the mutineer Jack Fry dead at his feet on deck the *Betsey*, had I seen Paul Jones so broken. To be superseded by an officer of no distinction whatever, claiming now to be his senior, and to be ordered back to the insignificant *Providence* as his reward for his desperate venture in the *Alfred*, stabbed him to the heart. And to be left in the lurch by our Commodore for carrying out his orders, passed all belief.

But if that were not bad enough, soon came worse. Aboard came other dispatches, long delayed in delivery, to show that early in October, just as we were sailing on our last cruise, the Congress had drawn up a new Navy list, on which Paul Jones, who originally had stood fifth in naval seniority, now was numbered eighteen, with thirteen Captains most of whom had not even been in the Navy at the time of his original commission as senior First Lieutenant, all outranking him! Even the incompetent Hoysted Hacker who, as his subordinate a few months before, had first wrecked the *Hampden* and then deserted him in the *Providence*, was now his senior on that list, and should they serve together, would command him!

By this was Paul Jones utterly broken. To him, rank opened the door to action and to glory, and with thirteen men put thus ahead of him, how should he ever again get an important command in our little Navy? That Commodore Hopkins should deny his word and refuse to defend him in the suit over the seizure of the privateersmen, because forsooth that order was not given him in writing, he could now understand. For with much cause he looked on

Ezek Hopkins as capable of any baseness, as one beneath the condition of the poorest reptile that crawls the earth. And he was not wholly alone in that opinion, for others beside himself were beginning to entertain the same idea, though the Congress, disorganized and a prey to sectional jealousies, took no action to remove as Commander-in-Chief that contemptible scoundrel who was strangling the Navy with his petty jealousies, his double-dealing, and his gross incompetence.

But to be superseded in rank by thirteen men, not one of whom had shown in action the slightest claim to such promotion over him, was unbearable. Ever a fertile letter writer, now the impetuous Jones kept me busy copying correspondence the while he bombarded Robert Morris, the Marine Committee of Congress, and Joseph Hewes with such violent and insubordinate letters denouncing that injustice and flaying those involved in it, that daily I expected my fiery Captain to be hanged, drawn, and quartered for his outspoken words.

My young fingers, long trained in due respect for all in authority, burned as I set down the hot words flung at those directing America's destinies by Paul Jones, wounded where it stung him worst, in his pride and his opportunity to fight.

He emphatically demanded of Robert Morris and of the Marine Committee of the Congress that he be fairly broke and expelled the Service rather than be disgraced before the world by being superseded by officers previously junior to him, whose naval abilities could at the most be only presumptive, and with some of whom as a private gentleman he would disdain to sit at table, so low were their characters. He refused flatly to serve under them, and in closing pointedly stated his case,

"I should prove my degeneracy were I not in the highest degree tenacious of my rank and seniority. As a gentleman, I can yield this point up only to a gentleman of superior abilities and of superior merit, and under such a man it is my highest ambition to learn.

"Could I, which I never can, bear to be superseded I

[364]

should indeed deserve your contempt and total neglect. I am therefore to entreat you to employ me in the most enterprising and active service, accountable to your honorable Board only for my conduct, and connected as much as possible with gentlemen and men of sense."

And with that barbed comment on his new seniors on its way to the Marine Board, Paul Jones turned for the moment to his seamen on the *Alfred*. It made his heart bleed to observe them, half clad and freezing in the New England winter.

Not a shilling in prize money had any man of us received, due to the accursed regulations regarding prizes which our Commodore was enforcing. And neither Ezek Hopkins nor the Congress, so prompt in relieving our Captain of his command and his seniority, had in the slightest bothered to send any money to pay off his men for their late cruise.

This was more than the warm-hearted Paul Jones, in close contact with the suffering seamen who had fought for him, could stand. Out of his own funds he paid off not only every seaman on the *Alfred*, but also every one of those aboard the *Providence*, though he knew well the chance of any reimbursement to himself was very slight.

Back again on the *Providence* sloop, Paul Jones eagerly awaited the rectification by the Congress of the injury done him. But the mails were slow, and when finally answers came, they carried nothing but explanations. The Congress, it seems, had drawn up the new list in October before the news of his first cruise in the *Providence* had reached Philadelphia to set him aside from the incompetents they had originally named. And on that list the order of ranking Captains, new and old, was beyond any understanding save one—that those states or cities which had contributed the money to build new ships could name their favorite sons. So Paul Jones with his only friend in the Congress, Joseph Hewes, temporarily broken in health by overwork and home in North Carolina when the new list was being adopted, was pushed far down in seniority to make way for the newcomers. But there would be no change now in the list adopted.

[365]

Paul Jones refused to believe that such a glaring injustice could be permitted to continue. Immediately he got leave to go to Philadelphia, there personally to lay before John Hancock, President of the Congress, his Captain's commission signed by that very gentleman, prior in date by far to every one of the thirteen Captains placed over him.

That august statesman, confronted with his own flourishing signature as palpable evidence of error in the ranking, requested Jones to leave the document till he could find time to fill out a new commission, the which of course Jones did. Upon returning some days later for it, to his intense surprise, Hancock handed him a new commission as Captain still marked number 18.

Jones was furious. Even Hancock could not do that to him. Bursting out that this was not what he had expected, he demanded back his old commission as evidence of his proper rank. Hancock, much embarrassed, began turning over various papers on his desk, to claim at last that he was sorry to have lost or mislaid it.

But the courteous John Hancock suavely extricated himself from his dilemma with this insistent Captain. In glowing terms he began to compliment Jones on the service he had rendered America in vessels of slight force, and to assure him that no officer stood higher in the estimation of the Congress than he. In earnest of which, till the Congress could rectify a list drawn up without well knowing the merits of the various officers concerned, he assured Paul Jones that he should shortly receive a very agreeable appointment and until he was satisfied respecting his rank, in accordance with his own previous request he should have a separate command, responsible to no one but the Congress.

And with that Jones, ever soothed by praise, was content. A separate command! Rank meant nothing to him but that. He wanted nothing more to show the President of the Congress his faith in Paul Jones was not misplaced.

38

IF the situation of America had not been so desperate in the spring of 1777, with urgent need at sea for any Captain who could do more than lose his ship (as within the twelve-month occurred to every vessel of our original fleet) the furnishing of Paul Jones with his separate command would indeed have been comical.

In Philadelphia, Robert Morris, convinced by Paul Jones' startling achievements that in him the Congress really had a naval genius, proceeded to carry out John Hancock's promise in full measure. In late February he drew up elaborate orders for two cruises, of which Paul Jones might take his choice—one a vast raid on the West Indies, the other a descent in force on the African coast. To accomplish these, he sent Paul Jones orders to take command of practically the entire fleet, *Alfred, Columbus, Cabot, Hampden* and *Providence*, informing also Ezek Hopkins of the same.

But Ezek Hopkins, still Commander-in-Chief, though no longer in the good graces of the Congress, was determined apparently that never should Paul Jones, now the object of his venomous hatred, get to sea again if he could prevent it. Pretending not to have received any orders himself (though he had them then in hand), he promptly ordered to sea on independent cruises the *Alfred*, the *Cabot*, and the *Hampden*, thus leaving Jones helpless to do anything except accuse his vindictive Commodore to his face of prevarication, the which in bald terms he immediately did. But the ships were gone and only embittered correspondence over the next month resulted.

Next the Congress sent him orders that he should take command of one of three ships to be purchased and armed in

Boston. In early April Paul Jones hurried there posthaste to supervise the fitting out of whichever of those three he should choose, that he might get to sea with all expedition as he was ordered. And I, as usual, tagged at his heels to help him in the business, wondering whether this time it should be with handbills or with cutlasses I should be sent out to recruit the crew for his new ship.

But nothing came of all the hurry. Unfortunately it took money to buy ships, and the Congress at the moment had neither money nor credit, so, while many letters passed on the subject, the ships remained unpurchased and another month was lost. In desperation, Paul Jones suggested that his prize, the *Mellish*, lying idle in Boston, be fitted out as a warship, using guns available in New London.

While this suggestion was pending, the Marine Committee developed a better idea. In mid-May there arrived at Portsmouth, New Hampshire, the French ship *Amphitrite* of twenty guns, laden with ammunition and stores clandestinely shipped by Baron Beaumarchais, a friendly Frenchman, to aid the rebellious colonies against France's ancient enemy.

The Congress promptly directed Paul Jones to take command of the *Amphitrite* and proceed with her to France, making what prizes he could on the way. Once he was in France, he was to report immediately to my cousin Ben Franklin, American Commissioner in Paris, who would provide for him the *Indien*, a huge frigate being built secretly (with borrowed French funds) in Holland to America's order.

At these orders, Paul Jones' heart was fairly bursting with gratitude to the Congress. The *Indien!* What could he not do to the Royal Navy with such a ship armed with thirty-two-pounders, superior in gun power to any frigate afloat!

Instantly Paul Jones and I packed our belongings and departed for Portsmouth and the *Amphitrite*. But in Portsmouth was confusion worse confounded, and my expectant Captain subjected only to indignity. For the French Captain of that vessel, having no such orders either from Beaumarchais or from his own government, refused point-blank to give up his command to any American, though generously enough he offered to take Jones aboard as a passenger.

Some slight discussion, conducted in bad English and worse French, disclosed that the Congress had gone somewhat far in ordering Paul Jones to take command of a vessel over which it had not a shadow of control. There was nothing for him, mortified beyond expression at such bungling, to do save thank the Frenchman for his courteous offer and report to the Congress that somehow the essential preliminaries to his carrying out their orders had been overlooked.

Perishing with inaction after six months ashore, Paul Jones was thus again left to cool his heels in Portsmouth while the Continental cause faced ruin. Everywhere the British armies were successful. General Clinton had New York, General Howe was threatening Philadelphia, General Burgoyne was actually on the march from Canada. And feeding all these armies were the endless streams of convoys flowing from England with supplies, tempting game for any daring commander willing to battle English frigates for them. And yet Paul Jones could get no ship at all, while our fleet, the plaything of politicians, lay hamstrung in port under a Commodore who dared not take his ships to sea.

Then unexpectedly came a ray of hope. We had taken rooms when first we came to Portsmouth with Mrs. Purcell, a genteel lady whose husband, a merchant sea captain, had unfortunately died the year before, by which circumstance she was reduced to taking boarders into her home.

It so happened that next door to her lived Woodbury Langdon, one of Portsmouth's most influential citizens, and soon Paul Jones, more now than ever a welcome guest in every patriot household, was a daily visitor to his gracious mansion. Shortly, as at The Grove, he was in the center of Portsmouth society, with the Langdons, the Wentworths, the Wendells, and the Whipples his constant hosts.

But here there was much difference from what I had seen at The Grove. The wealth of Portsmouth was built on trade.

[369]

Ships and shipping were the interests of the Portsmouth gentry rather than fox-hunting, and while Paul Jones cut a very fair figure astride a hunter with the hounds before him in full cry, still in a seagoing community he was even more at home.

He immediately commanded the attention of Woodbury Langdon's younger brother, Colonel John Langdon. This gentleman, New Hampshire's leading light, was prominent indeed in the patriot cause. Like Patrick Henry he had led a force early in the rebellion to seize the King's stores of powder. A delegate to the Congress at the opening of the war, he had been member of the original Marine Committee and was a person therefore of no mean influence in naval affairs.

With intense satisfaction Colonel Langdon's eyes lighted up on meeting Paul Jones, the Captain without a ship. For John Langdon had a ship in which his heart was completely wrapped up, which lay without a Captain. Across the Piscataqua, hard by the Maine shore, on Badger's Island he was building the Continental ship-of-war *Ranger*, into which vessel was going all the pride of craftsmanship of that ship-minded community and the fond hopes of its builder that it might win fame for Portsmouth and for him upon the seas.

As usual in such cases, local influence had procured the appointment of a local favorite, Captain Roach, to the command, but Roach had just been suspended under charges pending trial, and the *Ranger*, soon to be completed, was left without a skipper.

Intently, over his brother's dinner table where first they met, did John Langdon scrutinize the young Scotchman whose uncanny skill upon the seas had already won him much acclaim. With what mingled feelings Langdon looked upon him, I could well guess, for it had been down John Langdon's throat as well as those of his fellow members of the Marine Committee, John Adams and Stephen Hopkins, fighting all for a strictly New England Navy, that Joseph Hewes had rammed this then unknown emigrant from the south. And now Paul Jones sat across the table from him, gay, handsome, admired, the center of attention of those

[370]

solid Portsmouth citizens and their wives to whom ships were life, all caring little whence he came as they eagerly plied him with question after question over his adventures in the *Providence* and the *Alfred*.

John Langdon was not the man to miss an opportunity. The success of the *Ranger* meant more to him than whether her Captain came backed by Carolina or New Hampshire, and plain enough it was to all the world that with this man, regardless of what he commanded, went success. The cloth was hardly drawn and the ladies retired, when he dragged Paul Jones aside.

"Your appointment to the *Amphitrite* appears a sad mistake I understand now, Captain Jones?" he asked.

Jones blushed.

"Aye, sir. Unfortunately the Congress seems to have forgot that one must own a ship ere he may appoint her Captain. I know not who was more confused when I presented my orders to him—that Frenchman on the *Amphitrite*, who now is assured Americans are beyond all understanding, or your very mortified servant, that he should be the agent of such a breach of courtesy as to demand his ship of him."

Langdon laughed.

"Concern yourself not too much over it, Captain. Had you seen as much of the workings of the Congress as I have, you would better appreciate the happening. The Congress seems to think it can run a war without money, a government without taxes, and a Navy without a head. That it should think also it might appoint a Captain to any foreign vessel that touches at our shores is but a trifle."

"'Twas no trifle to me, sir," answered Jones ruefully, "'twas a tragedy! For the fourth time in succession, I am left without a ship."

Langdon drew a little closer.

"That is exactly my present concern, Captain Jones. As perhaps you have heard, I am near completing the *Ranger* here, a fine man-of-war, though somewhat small. And due to Captain Roach's difficulties, she is left without a skipper.

Would the command of that ship interest you, could I procure it for you?"

"Interest me, sir?" In his enthusiasm, Paul Jones almost embraced the dignified Colonel. "Apologize not for the *Ranger's* size. An' you see your way clear to get me that command, I am in your debt for life!"

"I have little doubt it can be managed. Robert Morris is evidently well disposed toward you, and if Portsmouth requests your appointment to its ship, rest assured it is as good as made. Leave the matter in my hands."

Colonel Langdon was as good as his word. By the next post he wrote his former associates on the Marine Committee strongly urging the appointment. And on June 14, 1777, the Congress adopted among others, the two following resolutions which, by a freak which gave Paul Jones much satisfaction, stood in juxtaposition upon the records:

"Resolved: That the flag of the thirteen United States be thirteen stripes, alternate red and white, that the Union be thirteen stars, white on a blue field, representing a new constellation.

Resolved: That Captain Paul Jones be appointed to command the ship *Ranger*."

39

At last Paul Jones' months of soul-racking uncertainty were at an end. There at Badger's Island in the tides swirling up and down the Piscataqua lay the *Ranger* nearly completed—a ship actually in the water, not a chimera to mock him when he sought to take command.

In heartfelt gratitude he thanked Colonel Langdon for the opportunity, assuring him he considered the little *Ranger* the best cruiser in America and that since the establishment of the Navy, no person in it had so good, so fair a prospect of success. And then he settled down to the task of outfitting his ship and recruiting his officers and men.

To supervise the outfitting he remained in Portsmouth himself. But in high hopes of getting back again under his flag his old crews of the *Alfred* and of the *Providence*, seamen in whose loyalty and doggedness he had much faith, he sent me off in mid-July with letters to the Continental agents in Providence and New Bedford to aid me in that mission.

With much eagerness, I set out, to go to Rhode Island first. In Providence, scouting the shipping agents and the seamen's boarding houses, I managed to find some twenty of our former seamen. Since their original terms of service of one year had expired, they had left the Service, disgusted with their many disappointments over the payment of their hard-won prize money. But on representing to them that should they reenlist, they might serve under their old Captain on the new *Ranger* abroad, in no way subject to Commodore Hopkins and his fantastic rules of prize money, one and all they consented enthusiastically to go with me before the Continental shipping agent to sign on again.

[373]

Leaving these men in the charge of the agent in Providence till my recruiting should be finished, I set out for New Bedford. To this port many of my old shipmates had gone for service in privateers, and I thought I might under fairer circumstances persuade those who were not yet at sea in those corsairs, to return to their country's service on the *Ranger*.

I had no great luck in New Bedford, however. Diligent search of every seaman's haunt failed to disclose any former seamen of the *Providence*, or in truth, any seamen at all, who were not already engaged. That this was not surprising became clear when I had come in closer contact with those supplying crews for privateersmen. Such were the wild tales of riches to be got and so many the private ships at sea or fitting out that real seamen were not to be had. But to supply the deficiency, agriculture had been in great measure abandoned for that lure and every wharf was crowded with loutish laborers just off the farms, all parading as seamen, and eager for loot.

Feeling that if only farmers were to be had, they might as well be farmers close at hand about the Piscataqua where the *Ranger* lay, I was on the point of abandoning further effort thereabout in Buzzards Bay to return to Providence and start north with the men I had obtained in Providence when I received sad news to upset that plan.

With great regret (so he stated by post) the Continental agent in Providence had to inform me that every man I had enticed back into the Navy by promise of service under Paul Jones, had been pressed by his Excellency Commodore Ezek Hopkins and put aboard the new frigate *Warren*, to be commanded by his son!

So after several weeks of toil, I lost wholly the fruits of all my labors—worse even, for I had been the means of seducing honest sailors to serve under men and conditions they had no stomach for. But there was no help for it. My men were gone.

With imprecations on the head of Ezek Hopkins for this injury, I hastily recast my intentions. Not till I had ex-

[374]

hausted every resource did I care to return to Portsmouth empty-handed. A fair number of seamen for our early cruises had come originally from amongst the whalers at Nantucket, and should any have returned there, I might get them.

I had no orders to go to Nantucket, but in New Bedford I was close. So feeling that my Captain would appreciate the extension of my search was in some measure at least dictated by military considerations, I set about discovering some means of obtaining passage from the Continent.

There was no longer any regular packet; there was indeed no regular communication at all, which confirmed my worst fears as to the situation at home. Not for two days, till a fishing boat going out agreed to land me on Brant Point at night, could I get any passage. So surreptitiously, like a thief in the night, I returned to Nantucket to be landed by a small boat in the early dawn on that sandy point so rich to me in memories.

Perhaps the manner of my coming was symbolic. In my worst imaginings, I had not conceived Nantucket might be so stricken. I trudged up in the breaking day to find no masts towering alongside the wharves, no ships in the harbor. By their desolate appearance it was clear that all the warehouses had long been empty and many were not even locked.

Ere anyone was yet awake, I went out Orange Street to Rose Lane, where in better days dwelt Henry Gardner's family, in some hope that Henry, who had left the Navy when the *Alfred* was paid off in Boston, might be there. To my great joy and his intense surprise, it was Henry himself, as unseagoing a sight as can be imagined in his nightgown, who with sleepy eyes opened the door in answer to my knock.

"Hullo, Tom!" he burst out. "Have you too quit the sea?"

"Hardly, Henry." I stepped inside. "But never mind that just now. I'm fair famished after a long night in an open fishing boat making the island from New Bedford. What's for breakfast?"

Henry's face fell.

"Not much. Some codfish cakes, same's for dinner and supper, less'n ye brought it with ye, Tom. We've backslid here considerable when it comes to table, and ye're lucky this morning to have the codfish. Some days we're short even o' that. Why don't ye go round to your Aunt Keziah's house? Delight can show ye there a breakfast that'll make ye glad ye came home, but in nary another house in this town'll ye get aught but codfish and maybe not so much o' that! But ye're welcome to what we've got here, Tom, which is more'n I can promise ye'll be at Aunt Keziah's." He showed me into the kitchen. "Wait a minute till I put on some clothes, and then we'll see what we can do with the codfish, though there ain't no flour to make any biscuits to go with it. Sit ye down."

Henry vanished. I looked about that kitchen, where hundreds of times as boys Henry and I had eagerly haunted the oven and robbed the shelves of the pies, the cookies, and the jams which motherly Mrs. Gardner had always at hand. Nantucket kitchens were famous for their cookery, Nantucket wives most liberal in their hospitality, especially at sheep shearing time when even total strangers were made welcome. But now as my hungry eyes swept over that kitchen, I found the shelves as bare as Mother Hubbard's and every one of the appetizing odors which always as a hungry lad seemed to me linked up with that kitchen, completely gone.

Shortly Henry came down again and we turned to making codfish cakes. But there was neither tea nor coffee nor bread nor butter to go with them, and we washed down the fish-cakes with cold water only.

"I should think a sailor like you could do better than this, Henry," I complained. "Can't you run in things from the Continent, in spite of the blockade? You've had experience enough not to mind a British cruiser."

"An' how'd I pay for 'em, Tom?" countered Henry bitterly. "With the prize money I never got? Ye can't imagine how bad times are here. We ain't got a barrel o' oil left to trade with. If it weren't for the fish I catch working off-

[376]

shore in a dory, we'd all starve, same's everybody else save those doing business with your Aunt Keziah."

"My aunt?" I asked. "I should think she'd be out like everybody else, Henry, with the war on now over two years and no ships coming in any more."

"That damned witch?" Henry looked at me in surprise. "Not she! Ain't ye heard what she's doing?"

"Not a word, Henry," I confessed. "Delight never mentioned her mother in the only letter that ever caught up with me since I left here. What's happened?"

"Ye don't know, eh? Well, I'll tell ye then and it'll sure make ye proud o' your Tory aunt. She wrote a letter to Admiral Digby, commanding the station here since the British took New York, saying we was all Tories here and loyal subjects o' the King, only we was starving because the rebels on the Continent wouldn't sell us anything and we couldn't get food nohow. And blow me, Tom, if she didn't bamboozle the old boy into feeling so sorry over the treatment she was getting from the rebels for her loyalty that he sent her papers to show any King's cruiser, giving her ships permission to trade through his blockade line with New York! So now she's got a monopoly of all the trade there is, and she's bringing in supplies from the merchants in New York. Ye can buy anything ye want at Aunt Keziah's, tea, coffee, bacon, flour, sugar, anything at all—at her price! Only in this house, so long as I can catch codfish, we're damned if we'll mortgage our home to her to pay that price, though she's got mortgages already on nearly everything else in this town against the food she's bringing in on her permit to feed us starving Tories! Have another codfish cake, Tom, and some more o' that fine water! It's all ye'll get on Nantucket that somebody ain't mortgaged their home or their warehouse to your dear old Aunt Keziah for! Steer clear o' the old bitch if ye want anyone else here to treat ye like a friend!"

I blushed. There was no doubting from Henry's vindictive tone how Keziah Coffin was looked on now by all the islanders. But if I knew her at all, I doubted that with mortgages on all their property in her bony fists, she cared the slightest what her neighbors thought of her.

I pushed away the proffered fishcake. Food was evidently too scant now in Henry's household for me to make so free with it.

"Thanks, Henry, for the information. Don't worry, I'll keep well to windward of the old girl, since she'd throw me out of her house anyway if she found out why I'm here. But how's Delight?" I finished anxiously.

"Dunno," said Henry curtly. "I never go near the place, and Delight never goes out so far's I've seen since I came home. But why're ye here, Tom? Ye ain't said yet. To see Delight, I suppose? A fine family ye chose to go sparking in!"

"Not exactly." I blushed again at the malice in Henry's voice. "Now I'm here, I'll see her, of course, if I can get by her mother somehow. But I'm here recruiting, Henry, for Paul Jones. He's got a new ship in Portsmouth, the *Ranger*, bound soon for France, and he wants his old men back if he can get 'em. Anybody here on Nantucket beside you, Henry, who'd like to ship with him again?"

"Who said I'd like to?" Henry looked at me belligerently. "Cap'n Jones is all right, but I've had my fill o' fighting to bring in prizes for them thieves in Providence River to do me out of. And ye'll not get anyone else here to go on them terms, neither. Not while we got fishhooks and the cod holds out! We'd rather be robbed by home folks like Aunt Keziah, where we can take it or leave it, than by that off-island old woman in Providence who goes round dressed up like a Commodore and don't give us no choice at all!"

"Now listen, Henry," I pleaded. "It won't be that way at all this time," and carefully I explained why not as best I could. "Paul Jones'll be on his own in France," I concluded. "The *Ranger* doesn't belong to the fleet; it'll be a completely independent cruise. What we capture'll be ours."

Though somewhat dubious, Henry agreed finally to ship if I could guarantee that. And he promised further to find and persuade Red Jerry, who alone of all those he knew was back on the island, to go with him. If I wanted more men, I

[378]

should have to seek them out myself.

"There's thirty good men, some of 'em harpooners too, drifting around this island ye might speak, Tom. They ain't been in the Navy, and I'll have no hand in enveigling 'em to join, but ye might try yourself. Ye can start on Reuben Chase; he's as good as two ordinary men himself. And if only ye can talk him into it, maybe the others'll go along. But if ye want to see Reuben, ye'd better hurry. He goes out fishing mighty early."

"Thanks, Henry. I'll get to it right away," and pushing away my plate, I seized my hat and hurried around to find Reuben Chase.

From my recollection of him, I quite agreed with Henry that if I could persuade Reuben Chase to ship with me, his example was likely to be followed by many others. I hardly knew Reuben myself, he being some four years older than I, and away whaling when I was but twelve, since which time our paths had never crossed.

It was well I had wasted nothing in dallying further over Henry's scant breakfast, for scarce was I in the street when I saw Reuben heading down the empty street toward Old North Wharf with a pair of oars over his shoulder.

I gasped when I saw Reuben Chase full grown now. Here was a seaman! Towering six feet six inches as he strode easily along, his great height was accentuated by his angular figure, lean and muscular to the last degree. And the hand encircling the oars, both gripped negligently in one palm, was the largest I have ever seen on any man, a hand on which the sinews on the back stood out like mountain ridges and the huge fingers, bronzed and bony, bespoke a giant's grip. Well could I vision a harpoon, encompassed in those vast hands as if it were but a straw, sinking solidly to the hitches into a luckless whale whenever he darted his iron. If I could only get Reuben Chase aboard the *Ranger*, he would be a whole gun crew in himself, slewing a six-pounder about with his bared hands with greater ease than four men might ordinarily with the training tackles.

"Morning, Reuben," I said, falling in beside him, where

[379]

though I was tall myself, I looked but insignificant. "I'm Tom Folger; maybe you remember me as a lad."

Reuben looked down on me with his rugged features and deep-set eyes wrinkling up into crow's feet as he scanned my face.

"Aye, Tom, though I'd not recognize ye now. Ye've grown some from the lad I recollect running around the docks with Henry Gardner. You're a sailorman now yourself, so I've heard from Henry. Right?"

"Aye, Reuben, and that's why I'm here." And with no more ado, I plunged directly into convincing him of the attractions of sailing with Paul Jones, the Captain of Captains. Solemnly Reuben listened, leaning on his oars there in the street, while I dwelt on what Jones had done, on what more he would do in the *Ranger*, soon to sail to carry the war directly into Britain.

Fired with enthusiasm myself for my Captain, I soon had Reuben interested, but he had qualms.

"It may all be as ye say, Tom. But how're my old father and mother going to eat if I go? They don't never get paid in this Navy o' yours, so I heard."

"I wouldn't fool you, Reuben," I answered honestly. "That's so. I haven't drawn a penny in pay from the government for well over a year. Congress just hasn't got the money for it. But in a way I've been paid part, and you'll be paid. Paul Jones paid out of his own pocket the crew on his last ship, and he'll guarantee your pay on the *Ranger* six months anyway. He's good for it."

Still Reuben was dubious, but at any rate, he turned about.

"Let's go home and see Debbie. If my sister's willing, I'll sign with ye."

So back to the Chase household we went, where Deborah Chase, just busying herself over breakfast, peered out of the kitchen at us, skillet in hand.

"Debbie, this is Tom Folger," said Reuben, adding bluntly, "He's trying to get me to ship in the Navy with

[380]

him under Paul Jones to fight King George. What d'ye think on it?"

Debbie looked at me. I looked at Debbie with bulging eyes. They certainly ran to gigantic proportions in the Chase family. Here was a strapping damsel that, if I could ship her, might lead a boarding party with a cutlass instead of a skillet in that massive arm to sweep all before her! More than six feet herself and, unlike her brother, well filled out so that she weighed at the very least over three hundred pounds, she was an Amazon indeed!

"So you're Delight Coffin's young man," remarked Deborah, scanning me with some interest while ignoring her brother's question. "You'll do her no favor rantum-scooting all over the ocean again with that Paul Jones. King George indeed! There's more tyranny in Keziah Coffin than in George and all his Ministers! The men on this island make me sick the way they just gam and don't do anything about that woman! If you're a fighting man, Tom Folger, why don't you stay home, marry Delight, and fight your mother-in-law? That'll do Nantucket some real good!"

Abashed, I shrank back behind Reuben's mighty frame.

"Now, Debbie," cautioned Reuben, "that's no way to talk. Ye know very well Tom here can't do that. He's in the Navy a'ready and that'd make a deserter out of him. Besides, how d'ye know Delight'd fall in with all that? But ye've settled my ideas, sis, all the same. If we lick King George, that'll settle Keziah too and we'll have no more tyranny on our island. I'm with you, Tom, pay or no pay. Debbie here can make out somehow for the old folks."

With that promise I hurriedly withdrew ere Deborah Chase could open on me again. What a woman! I had little doubt Reuben need have no worries over his parents in her charge. She would provide, could strength and resolution manage it.

All morning I chased about the town, seeking out every idle whaler I could get track of with my story. Now I had better luck, with Reuben Chase as well as Henry Gardner to hold out before them as their shipmates on the *Ranger*,

[381]

and I enlisted altogether nineteen, from young Thomas Turner whose mother tearfully consented to his departure, to grizzled Jerry Evans, a hard-bitten whaler, whose wife, unaccustomed to such an extended sojourn at home of her mate, practically pushed him into enlisting.

Meanwhile, in all my dashing to and fro along the dusty streets from one whaleman's modest house to another, I had kept a weather eye on Keziah Coffin's mansion, hoping to discover some indication that she had gone out.

Fortune favored me at last. I was still inside Mrs. Turner's doorway, for the third time promising that weeping mother that I would personally keep an eye out on her boy, when I spotted my Aunt Keziah's sparse figure swinging firmly along toward the waterfront.

Delaying only till her angular frame had turned the corner, I abruptly broke away from Mrs. Turner and dashed for Centre Street, to bang the knocker there furiously against the door lest I waste even a second of my opportunity.

Delight opened the door. In an instant, I had slammed it behind me to sweep that startled Quaker maid to me in a mad embrace.

"Oh, Tom!" she sobbed. "It's so long I heard from thee I thought for certain thou wert dead in some sea battle!" and as if never again would she risk that chance, she twined her arms so tightly round my neck I scarce could breathe. "Thou'rt home now to stay?" she asked anxiously, releasing me somewhat at last that she might look up to my eyes.

I shook my head.

"Nay, dear; but for a few hours. That I'm here at all comes only that I'm recruiting seamen for another cruise."

"I had thought when I saw thee thou hadst come—" And then Delight broke off abruptly, releasing me altogether. Looking into her brown eyes, as suddenly the joyous light faded from them, it wrung my heart to see what change the year had wrought in her. All the suffering of Nantucket seemed reflected in her face. "Nay, it matters not what I had thought, since thou art safe, my darling. I should thank the

[382]

good Lord he favors me thus, when all here live in such misery!" Gently she stroked my hair, looking appealingly up at me.

"Must thou take up the sword again, dear Tom? Surely two years is enough! And how I can live longer here without thee, I know not. Oh, Tom, surely I have cross enough to bear through my mother's doings here without further anguish over thee! Stay with me, darling!"

"I know, dearest. Henry Gardner told me what goes on from your mother's trading. I'm sorry."

"What can Henry know of it?" burst out Delight bitterly. "Does he know how every mouthful I eat in this house of abundance is dust and ashes on my tongue when my mother robs others of their substance that they may eat at all? Daily I pray the Lord I may obey his commandment to honor my father and my mother. But how can I honor my mother when everyone upon this island who was once my friend curses her daily for her covetousness? I dare not show my face upon the street for shame!"

"I would to God I might take you hence immediately!" I burst out. "But I can't, Delight. Almost as soon as I return to Portsmouth, we sail to raid the English coast. What happens to me then, who knows? I can't take you away from here to leave you stranded in a strange seaport without a farthing!"

"I am glad to see thou hast that much sense," broke in a harsh voice. "It is more than I gave thee credit for."

I spun about. There in the doorway stood my Aunt Keziah, her angular face grimly fixed on me.

"I heard on the waterfront thou wert back in town, Tom Folger, and it occurred to me that did I hurry home, I might find thee here in my absence. I see I was right. Hast come to bring me another message from that villain Paul Jones?" she finished sarcastically. "If I recall rightly, thou slipped out of my house last time the instant my back was turned without delivering his message then."

"Nay, Aunt Keziah. He has no part in this visit. I came but to see Delight, a-a-and you," I added lamely.

[383]

"I have no doubt of it. Well, thou hast seen Delight, and I do not care to see more of thee, so thou canst leave now. And I warn thee, Thomas. Consort not with that arch rebel Paul Jones if ever thou wish to enter my home again. That villain has done me more harm than Sam Adams! I'll have naught to do with any that aid in his scandalous attacks upon our good King's ships. Begone now!" and Keziah Coffin flung wide open the door, vindictively motioning me out.

I stood a moment uncertain over what I had best do, but Delight settled it for me.

"Goodbye, Tom," she said sadly. "Fail not to write me of thy whereabouts." And as if desirous of not stirring up her mother's wrath further, she turned and started for the stairs. Without a word, for indeed what could I say either to Delight or to my Aunt Keziah that would not make matters worse, I stepped through the open door. Immediately it slammed shut behind me.

40

I RETURNED to Portsmouth the second week in August
with my party of seamen, hot, dusty, fatigued and much anguished over what I had seen on Nantucket. Thankfully I
turned my recruits over to Paul Jones who received them
even more thankfully, welcoming Red Jerry and Henry
Gardner especially almost as long-lost brothers and fairly
gloating over the seaman I had brought him in Reuben
Chase.

The *Ranger* was now in commission and to the casual view
practically ready to sail as soon as the crew should be
aboard. We were, however, still decidedly short of our complement, and again immediately I was busied trying to get
more men who had some claim to call themselves sailors.

As always in that dismal business, I ran instantly up
against the twin obstacles of pay and prize money. Congress
had promised an advance of twenty dollars to every seaman
enlisting for a year or longer, which inducement I set out on
my hand bills in large type, but little good it did me. Neither
in Boston nor in Portsmouth could I find seamen willing to
enlist for more than just the one cruise and under those conditions no advance of public money was payable.

Then there was the matter of pay. Patriotism and resistance to tyranny went perfectly well on my circulars, but
after two years of battling King George, the flush of enthusiasm was forever gone and common seamen could not get
mercenary considerations wholly out of their heads. Since
they were little likely to get aught else save hardship,
wounds, and death out of the struggle I could not but secretly sympathize with them. On a privateer, where they
could resist tyranny with more profit also, they knew whom

[385]

to look to for their wages and their share of the loot.

But in the Navy, it was notorious that paydays were rare and arguments with unknown and distant officials over prize money quite fruitless. My recruiting went slowly. That it went at all was due solely to Paul Jones. Out of his own pocket he paid to every man the twenty-dollar advance. And further, he deposited himself in Boston a sum of money to pay to every sailor on the *Ranger* half his monthly wages while we were gone, this to be drawn upon by the families of his crew during their absence.

With these concrete rewards assured, I made some progress, but only at the cost of a bitter fight with privateering agents for nearly every seaman I cajoled into shipping on the *Ranger*.

Providing the officers on the ship went in sharp contrast to furnishing the crew. Jones could get his crew by paying them out of his own pocket. Local pride went not so far as to step into the breach there, even with those who shipped from Portsmouth. But as regards the officers, by direction of the Congress, these were to be commissioned by a joint Board on which Colonel Langdon and another gentleman of Portsmouth, Colonel Whipple, had most say, so that it was natural enough Portsmouth men were chosen, and these perforce Jones had to take for better or for worse. Those named were Thomas Simpson, First Lieutenant; Elijah Hall, Second Lieutenant; and Samuel Wallingford, Third Lieutenant—all of Portsmouth, and none of whom had ever sailed before in a man-of-war.

Only in the naming of our marine officer was Jones allowed his own choice, and for that post he named Captain Parke of Providence, of whose ability he had some knowledge.

By September first, the ship was completed, we had our officers, we had our crew, and we were ready to sail—only we had no sails! That such a thing could happen in fitting out a public vessel of the United States seems unbelievable, but so it was. So completely had the vast number of private ships-of-war stripped New England of its sailcloth, that not anywhere could the canvas for the *Ranger's* suit of sails be got by the builders.

So for two months more we lay in port, while our Captain had added to all his other concerns the problem of finding canvas if he ever wished to get to sea.

Now indeed did the days drag hard, while Paul Jones by post and messenger, using every contact his years at sea had got him, scoured the Atlantic seaboard for sailcloth. By dribs and drabs it came in, some good, some so coarse and thin as to be almost worthless. But however it was, so only it passed for canvas, it was hurriedly bundled off to the Portsmouth sail lofts to be sewed into our slowly growing suit of sails.

While Jones struggled over this vexation, his gnawing sense of grievance over his supersedure in rank flamed violently out into fresh letters of protest over what he saw in Portsmouth harbor.

For there alongside a wharf, loading stores for a cruise, lay the new frigate *Raleigh,* commanded by one of the thirteen Captains placed over him. That the *Raleigh,* a fine vessel of twice the *Ranger's* force, had been given to one of his former juniors, was gall enough to set his teeth on edge. But what was insufferable to contemplate was that Captain Thompson, her commander, had orders also for a cruise to France. For Captain Thompson's ability as a naval officer Paul Jones had only the deepest contempt, but Thompson was his senior now, and should their paths cross in France, he must sail under Thompson's orders, obey his commands, and even go into battle under Thompson's flag—sure road to disaster!

Between that torment, the struggles to get canvas for our sails, and the gloomy forebodings with which he looked on his unpromising officers and crew (who regarded the *Ranger* not as a man-of-war to harass our enemy but rather as a privateer bound out for personal gain), I marvelled he did not throw up his commission and quit the service in disgust. Under less provocation, already many another officer (even some of his new seniors) had taken leave of such a Navy to

[387]

enrich themselves in privateers.

But Paul Jones only set his teeth and grimly faced his trials. If it killed him, till the Congress should do him right, with the last penny of his fortune and his last drop of blood he intended to battle for the flag which first he had hoisted that January day of '76 over the flagship of the new Navy.

Still he was only human. Had not my worn Captain in some degree beguiled himself with visions of the "calm contemplation and poetic ease" for which his heart yearned to follow all this hectic activity, I know not how he should have survived his trials.

By every post (though I never saw the contents of those missives) letters went off to Dorothea Dandridge. With much misgiving I looked on his hopes there, for even in my young eyes, that one might leave such a sought-for beauty amongst all the suitors of Virginia with never a visit for two years and nothing more than letters to compete with the ardent presence of flesh and blood lovers, was pressing fate too far.

That Dorothea had waited two years already was a miracle, I thought. That she should wait yet unnumbered years more till we should be victorious over the British and Paul Jones footloose to return, was wholly inconceivable. Yet Paul Jones looked confidently forward to it. Nothing I know of showed better his colossal faith in himself than this.

We had with us now on the *Ranger*, Major John Gizzard Frazer of Virginia, a convivial Army officer who seemed to know everybody. Months before he had come to Paul Jones with a letter of introduction from Robert Morris, since which time he had on several matters acted as intermediary between that dignitary and Jones. Genial Major Frazer had found life in the Army not altogether to his liking, so he had persuaded our Captain to intercede with Morris that he might go with us on the *Ranger* as a volunteer on foreign service, to act perhaps as an additional officer of our marines. Nothing loath to oblige such a friendly character, Jones had made the request and Morris had granted it.

It was the gallant Major, on whose gay soul wars bore

[388]

lightly, who more than anyone else kept Paul Jones' spirits up by his lively stories of recent happenings in Virginia society, for with him (unlike Jones) never had his addiction to warfare kept him more than a few months at a time from the attractions of his native state.

In particular as October passed along and our one suit of sails approached completion, he caught Paul Jones' fancy with his beguiling description of an estate on the Mattapony in Virginia, a place truly Elysian in all its qualities and to be had at a marvelous bargain considering its unusual character. Instantly my poetic Captain, visioning himself ensconced there with Dorothea, forwarded through Robert Morris the necessary funds for the purchase, though with a little more prudence, he wrote also to his friend Joseph Hewes to verify the Major's description of its merits ere the money should pass.

On October 20, our suit of sails was finished at last, and bent to our yards. Now Paul Jones was two different people at once, the one the impatient sailor burning to be off, all over the ship supervising the bending of our canvas; the other the dreamy lover visioning the "calm contemplation and poetic ease" to be enjoyed on that Elysian estate on the banks of the Mattapony, inditing lyric letters directing its purchase.

Thus divided in his interests, Jones dropped down the Piscataqua towards its mouth ready to sail on the next tide, only to be caught there in a fierce northeast gale. Promptly this welded his divergent interests, making him wholly the sailor, for in the teeth of that gale nothing mattered save the safety of his ship. A week we lay there with yards and topmasts struck, whole cables paid out ahead and two anchors down, with difficulty riding the storm.

But finally, the wind shifted to the northwest, the weather cleared somewhat and on November 2, 1777, Paul Jones boldly thrust the prow of the *Ranger* out into the broad Atlantic to carry the war to Europe, headed at last on the great adventure of his life. And to add to his joy, he was made the bearer of despatches just come to hand, notifying Ben Franklin and his fellow American Commissioners in France of the most glorious achievement yet of American arms in the war—the surrender of Burgoyne and all his army at Saratoga on October 17!

41

FOR practically a year Paul Jones had not been afloat. So it was with wild exhilaration that he felt again beneath his foot the heave of the *Ranger's* quarterdeck and listened to the symphony of taut rigging singing in the cold wind as we ploughed eastward with a fresh gale driving us.

He had some reason for his exaltation—behind him at last were all the vexations of the land. Now he was at sea—lord of creation, absolute master of the *Ranger,* her destinies, and all in her.

With much pride his eyes swept over the *Ranger,* driving hard before a quartering sea. By him who knew ships well, she was thus described in one of those poetic moments which interlarded his dreams,

"In outward appearance, she is a perfect beauty, her sheer being as delicate as the lines of a pretty woman's arm. And as she is rather low in the water for her length, and her masts rake two or three degrees more than any other ship of the day, she is on the whole the sauciest craft afloat."

That she was. With masts as tall as might have graced a three-decker, the low-hulled *Ranger* with her well raked sticks gave an impression of speed and grace to make any Captain's heart throb. To a Captain who in anguish had seen one ship after another slip from beneath his feet, she was quite enough to justify poetic outbursts.

The weather was stormy to start with and so continued. Through one cold gale after another we drove eastward, all sail continuously set, our Captain burning to get to France with his great news, and then to lose no time in falling upon the enemy coasts.

But if our Captain was burning with that desire, I swiftly

found that most of his officers were not. The cross currents flowing in the *Ranger's* wardroom and steerage disturbed me much. The *Ranger*, in spite of her ship rig, was but a small vessel with all her guns mounted in the open on her upper deck. As there was no great amount of room available for berthing either the 140 men in the crew nor the large number of officers we carried, we Midshipmen of the steerage found ourselves in closer contact even than was usual with the wardroom and its officers just abaft the cramped quarters in which we swung our hammocks on the lower deck.

In the cabin aft our Captain lived and messed in solitary grandeur. But in sharp contrast to his state was the crowded condition of the wardroom, where Lieutenants Simpson, Hall, and Wallingford, Captain Parke of the marines, Major Frazer, volunteer, and Dr. Ezra Green, surgeon, were jammed together, a diverse group of personalities bound to cause trouble.

I soon had cause to look with much foreboding especially on Lieutenant Simpson. There being nothing but latticed gratings to separate the wardroom from the damp and gloomy steerage in which we Midshipmen contrived to keep alive when not on deck, whatever was said in the wardroom came plainly to our eager ears.

Lieutenant Simpson, who always went about with a sour look on his rough face, seemed to regard himself as Captain already of the *Ranger*, deluded with the idea that Paul Jones was aboard as hardly more than a passenger to France. That he had some little warrant for his hopes of future command was true enough, for like the rest of us, he well knew that once in France Jones had been promised command of the huge frigate, *Indien*, building for us in Amsterdam, so that then he might as First Lieutenant succeed to the *Ranger*. But so little experience did our First Lieutenant have in anything, that he seemed not to distinguish between future prospects and present facts, with the result that he seemed hardly to realize that he was not yet Captain and might never be.

At any rate, regarding Paul Jones as little more than an

intruder on the *Ranger*, to be got rid of the moment we sighted France, he hesitated not at all to air his plans on what then he intended to do with the *Ranger*. Baldly put, it was to make what amounted to a privateering cruise, avoiding all warships and attacking only merchantmen.

In voicing these plans, he came promptly into collision with our marine officer, Captain Parke. Having had considerable previous service in men-of-war, he had no liking for such an idea for a warship like the *Ranger*, and in no uncertain terms disagreed with our First Lieutenant. Much hard feeling came from this immediately and continual bickering which upset the wardroom, a condition not helped at all by our volunteer, convivial Major Frazer, who having nothing else to do, egged on both disputants. To make matters here somewhat worse, the good Major had brought with him a considerable stock of whisky, in which he indulged himself without stint. More or less intoxicated all the time, he kept the wardroom in a turmoil and Simpson and Parke at each other's throats to the serious hurt of the discipline of the ship, though truth to tell, to the continual joy of us Midshipmen listening through the gratings to the wrangling of our seniors on how a war should be conducted.

Save for the fact that our passage was one endless series of drills at our guns, it was uneventful. Day after day for nearly a month we hammered eastward over stormy seas, close hauled mostly, heeled down on our beam ends always under the press of sail our skipper kept spread. Every man in the crew was driven hard at the never-ending drills, but none could very well complain for our Captain drove himself harder almost every hour of the night and day than he did his seamen.

Three weeks out, we raised the Azores. Up to then, we had seen nothing in the way of strange sails, but from then on we saw plenty, unfortunately mostly neutral. We then sighted a fleet of ten British sail heading north from the Mediterranean through the Bay of Biscay, but convoyed to our distress by the largest man-of-war that I had yet seen, the *Invincible*, 74, a huge three-decker with tier on tier of eighteen-pounders, making the little *Ranger*, 18, with but one row of six-pounders on our upper deck, look small indeed.

But undismayed by this disparity in force, for two days we harried the flanks of that convoy, continually chased off by the *Invincible* each time we made a close approach from leeward, always coming back in the hope that some opportune shift in the wind or some lapse on the part of the convoying man-of-war might put us to windward and give opportunity to dart in and cut out one of those fat merchantmen ere that overpowering ship-of-the-line could beat up to prevent the capture.

But the wind stayed steady, none of that closely huddled convoy fell behind, and the prudent Captain of the *Invincible*, who knew his business well, kept always to windward of his charges, refusing to be decoyed down to leeward of them by any artifice. Nothing resulted therefore from our aggravating two day game of tag with the *Invincible* and her convoy save that we lost two days and were finally compelled to abandon further effort, setting our course again for Nantes as empty-handed as when we first sighted the convoy.

Next day, however, our luck improved somewhat. In rapid succession we raised and overhauled two brigantines from Malaga, both of which we took. Despatching one to Brest, we convoyed the other into the Loire, coming to anchor finally toward evening of December 2, 1777, just off the port of Nantes.

Immediately on arrival, Jones started his despatches regarding Burgoyne on their way to Paris, though to his chagrin he learned that a packet from Boston had arrived two days before with the same news, which was therefore already on its way to Franklin's ears in Paris, our delay over the *Invincible* having cost us our chance to be first with that good news.

We were welcomed in Nantes by the American agent there, Jonathan Williams, a grand-nephew of my cousin, Ben Franklin, and a most amiable young gentleman who received Paul Jones like a brother, assisting him particularly in the disposal of his prizes and in handling his correspondence.

Jones had some need of such friendship, for soon again disappointments started to descend on him, of which the worst was the loss of the promised *Indien*, the frigate building in Amsterdam. This disaster came about through the carelessness of Arthur Lee, one of the American commissioners, who while in Berlin left his papers where they were stolen, as a consequence of which they swiftly fell into the hands of Elliot, the British ambassador to Prussia, disclosing the *Indien's* character, and forcing an immediate sale of her to the French king, lest under British compulsion the Dutch confiscate the ship.

This blow, the loss of command of the finest frigate ever built, Paul Jones took philosophically, realizing there was no alternative. But, if he took it philosophically, it was hardly received that way by Lieutenant Simpson, who had been looking forward confidently to taking over the *Ranger* immediately on our arrival. Now he looked surlily on Jones' continuance in command, and amongst both officers and crew undertook immediately a cabal to undermine his Captain's authority and his right to continue in command.

But at the moment, our Captain was too concerned over more important matters to bother with Simpson and his childish delusions. Immediately on arrival, he reported to Ben Franklin his presence at Nantes and requested orders, meanwhile busying himself in some modifications of the *Ranger's* masts and ballast which our first voyage showed to be imperative. For the *Ranger*, like many another beauty, had some shortcomings for the vicissitudes of practical life, hers being that she was "crank" in a seaway, over-sparred, and under-ballasted.

So Paul Jones' first concern was to cut down the unduly long masts of his ship, rerig her, remove two of her guns which he found her unable to carry safely, and rearrange and increase her ballast that she might stand up better under sail and enable him to fight his remaining guns in bad weather.

Not for three weeks therefore after his arrival at Nantes was our Captain able to leave his ship to journey to Paris in obedience to the summons of the Commissioners, Ben Franklin, Silas Deane, and Arthur Lee. But a few days after Christmas, taking me with him as his secretary, he set out by coach from Nantes to Paris to report personally, make known his plan of action, and receive his orders.

In Passy, a neat village on high ground on the outskirts of Paris, two nights later we made our way through the garden of the Hôtel Valentinois to the house lent by the courtesy of de Chaumont to Franklin to serve him as unofficial embassy.

I say we made our way through that garden, but rather should I say by force we fought our way along it through almost a mob struggling for admission about that door. I had thought I had seen every conceivable type of uniform in the world when first I went to Philadelphia to attend the session of the Continental Congress two years before, but in all stages of decrepitude, decking out the figures of that crowd swirling about the doorsteps to Ben Franklin's house was a gaudy array of such varied military dresses as I had not imagined could exist.

In every color of the rainbow swarmed about us, pushing to get to the door, a motley crowd of obviously impecunious adventurers—French, Prussians, Italians, Poles, Swedes, aye, even English! And almost lost in that brilliant glow of color, in our plain blue cloaks, Paul Jones and I thrust our way rudely forward, shoving and pushing with the rest till my tall figure and Jones' broad shoulders and long arms had elbowed for us a path to the steps.

Here Paul Jones, breathing hard from his exertions, paused a moment to glower on the angry faces of the fiercely mustached and bearded gentry we had displaced.

"Tom," he said, "there are Generals and Admirals enough here, judging by their regimentals and epaulettes, to furnish out all the armies and navies of Europe! God help Benjamin Franklin if this is his nightly grist of callers!" and he seized the knocker to bang it loudly against the door.

That we got in at all without being followed by a flood of others, resulted only from my dexterity in slamming the door instantly I had crossed after Jones, whose name proved a password to the harassed French doorman. But once inside, we were met graciously enough by young Temple Franklin, a youth of about my own age serving as his grandfather's secretary, who conducted us immediately into the study where, in severely plain garb, stood waiting us the aged Ben Franklin.

With what veneration I looked for the first time on my benignant kinsman as we entered his house at Passy I need not state. But I doubt if it matched that evident on Paul Jones' countenance as he bowed humbly to present to America's representative in France his credentials, the letter of introduction from Robert Morris and the Marine Committee in Philadelphia.

"Pray, gentlemen, be seated," said my cousin simply, adjusting his glasses the while, still standing, he opened and scanned the letter, and I looked inquisitively from my famous relative wrinkling his broad brows over the script, to self-possessed Temple Franklin, in all the assurance of his position as confidential secretary, coolly eyeing his country cousin from Nantucket.

"I see," said Franklin finally, looking curiously up at Jones, "that the Congress recommends you to me as an active and brave commander in our Navy, who has already performed signal services in vessels of little force, and directs you to follow my orders. You are very welcome, Captain Jones." He paused, and over the rims of his large glasses, examined Jones carefully. "You are but young, I see, to have warranted what Robert Morris says of you here. But still, I suppose, that the perilous business of revolutions is better carried through by those in whom the blood of youth runs hot, than by elderly gentlemen like me who too much desire the comforts of their firesides."

Worn and tired, Ben Franklin's appearance well bore out his words as his aged frame sagged into a chair alongside us, with Temple hovering solicitously behind him.

"I note the Congress desires of me I should procure you a fine fast sailing frigate or larger ship, Captain," continued Franklin. "I had some hopes of it till shortly, as Silas Deane had one such secretly on the stocks at Amsterdam. But such is the dissension hereabouts, and so much are we surrounded by spies and thieves, that that plan was discovered," he sighed, "and we have lost the ship. You must content yourself with the vessel you have come in, sir. It is not within my power to procure you such a ship as you expected."

"My unfeigned thanks are equally due for the intention as for the act, sir," answered Paul Jones whole-heartedly. "The *Ranger*, though small, will serve. It is my wish to be employed in active and enterprising service where there is prospect of rendering acceptable aid to America. The enemy has many important places in such defenseless situations that they might effectually be surprised and attacked with no very considerable force."

Franklin's weary face lighted up, and he gazed with fresh interest on the impetuous features of Paul Jones with those deep-set grey eyes burning for action.

"Aye, young man. How long have I waited here for someone willing to act with what he has! All I hear hour after hour, months on end, are demands for money, ships, arms, and armies, with which this volunteer or that will accomplish wonders when I get them for him. But where can I get these things when we have little credit, and every penny I can borrow in France on our poor prospects has been sent to aid Washington? So the loss of the *Indien* frigate discourages you not, and you will make the little *Ranger* serve, eh? Fine! It encourages me to find you in agreement with my reflections on the many instances in history which prove that in war, attempts thought to be impossible do often, for that very reason, become possible and practicable because nobody expects them and no precautions are taken to guard against them."

Wholly forgetful of his years, Franklin, disdaining young Temple's aid, rose from his chair and laid an enthusiastic hand on Paul Jones' shoulder.

[398]

"You shall have your chance, sir. I doubt I can get Arthur Lee, who suspects everyone, including me, and doubts everything, to agree to it, but I can sway Silas Deane, and that will be enough. Go back to your ship, and you shall shortly have orders there from the Commissioners to put your plans to the touch!" Then apparently wearied by even this slight exertion, he walked unsteadily again to his chair, sank into it.

"And you, sir," he looked benevolently at me, "I understand from Temple here, are that cousin I promised some years ago to take as apprentice? What changed your mind, that instead you sail with Captain Jones?"

I blushed with pride that amongst all the cares of his office he should remember that trifling circumstance.

"A whaling accident, sir, forced it on me, and instead I had to go awhaling like my fathers."

" 'Tis no loss," mused Franklin. "There be others of my kin I have tried to make into printers with no great success, but I never saw a Folger who made not a good seaman. And you are in good hands for that profession now, I'll warrant." He smiled encouragingly, glancing over his glasses at Paul Jones, and then, evidently worn, tired, and anxious to conclude his day, asked,

"Were there many waiting me yet when you came in, Captain?"

"Some score at least, I judge, sir," answered Jones, "and a more pressing lot I never saw."

Franklin shook his venerable head sadly.

"You see then what I must contend with. Half of them are probably English spies seeking employment that they may betray me. And the other half are no doubt as usual the riff-raff of all the courts of Europe, each one with a grandiose plan to free America if only I fit him out with a General's commission to supersede Washington in command (or mayhap a Commodore's), an army, or a fleet, and send him to America." With a deep sigh, he turned toward his grandson, "Temple, I am too worn to see anyone else tonight. Give each of those outside a letter of recommendation from me to

[399]

whom he wishes in America, and send him on his way. And you, gentlemen," he turned his wan eyes again on us, "I bid you now good night. You will hear from me on the *Ranger*."

We both rose, bowed deeply, and followed Temple out into the hall.

"If you are staying in Paris, Cousin Tom," said Temple in all friendliness, "perhaps I can be of service to you."

I looked uncertainly at Paul Jones, not knowing what his plans might be. Jones shook his head decisively.

"No, thank you. We return immediately to Nantes and the *Ranger*, which is left in none too good hands." He reached toward the cloak which a servant was holding out for him, then a thought struck him. "This mob of military ragamuffins outside—can it be that I heard His Excellency aright in directing you to give them recommendations from him when he knows nothing of them?" he asked incredulously.

"Aye," replied Temple. "Each of them. Would you like one also?" and without waiting an answer, reached to a pile of neatly stacked letters on the table nearby, thrust one into the hands of both of us. "Read it," he urged. I read,

"The bearer of this, who is going to America, presses me to give him a letter of recommendation, though I know nothing of him, not even his name. This may seem extraordinary, but I assure you it is not uncommon here. Sometimes, indeed, one unknown person brings another, equally unknown, to recommend him; and sometimes they recommend one another. As to this gentleman, I must refer you to himself for his character and merits, with which he is certainly better acquainted than I can possibly be. I recommend him, however, to those civilities which every stranger of whom one knows no harm has a right to; and I request you will do him all the good offices, and show him all the favour, that on further acquaintance you shall find him to deserve.—Benjamin Franklin."

Paul Jones finished reading, laughed aloud as he thrust the letter into his pocket.

"I think I see here the hand of Poor Richard, come to Paris to save your grandfather much annoyance from need-

[400]

less interviews. Good night, sir," and he stepped out the door.

Immediately he was almost mobbed by the waiting crowd, in a bedlam of languages shouting requests for the recommendations which Temple Franklin began to hand out.

42

BACK in Nantes, the refitting of the *Ranger* went slowly. In some measure this was due to lack of funds, for while Jonathan Williams shortly transmitted to Paul Jones a draft for five hundred louis d'or, this our Captain hesitated to draw upon, reserving it for dire emergency. But the major obstacle to any progress lay in the sullenness of our officers and crew.

That Paul Jones, now the *Indien* had slipped from his hands, was to remain as Captain of the *Ranger* was disappointment enough to our First Lieutenant who already had considered himself its commanding officer, but when it was noised about the decks what manner of cruise our Captain proposed, so unheroic was the reaction of our mercenary senior Lieutenant and many of the crew, that every artifice was resorted to that might hinder the sailing of the ship.

On January 16, young Jonathan Williams came aboard, overflowing with enthusiasm, to place our orders in our Captain's hands.

"Here, sir," he said proudly, delivering the instructions, "are such orders from the Commissioners in Paris as I hardly hoped might be sent you! You are ordered in your discretion without restriction, after equipping the *Ranger* in the best manner, to proceed with her as you shall judge best for distressing the enemies of the United States by sea, or otherwise! What you choose to do is wholly in your own hands."

Eagerly Jones seized the document, scanned it.

"Aye," he commented after a hurried perusal. "I see Ben Franklin shows more faith in me than almost I dare have in myself. It is just as you say. But," he added with a dubious frown, "these orders are signed only by Franklin and by Silas Deane. The third Commissioner's signature is absent. What think you Arthur Lee means by that?"

Williams laughed sourly.

"It means that since Arthur Lee was not permitted to write the orders, he refuses to concur in them as usual. No one, save himself, is in his opinion fit to manage our affairs. A narrower minded bigot than Arthur Lee I have not met. So pure is his patriotism that he suspects everyone else. Ben Franklin, he is assured, is a doddering dolt sold out to the Court of France and is but putty in the hands of the spies with which the British Ambassador surrounds him in Passy. Lee has already denounced his associate, Silas Deane, to the Congress as a peculator and a swindler. He suspects me, whom he had no hand in appointing, as a dishonest agent of the government. And you, dear sir, you may rest assured, have already earned his bitter enmity, if there be no other reasons, by having been born a Scot, which race he detests. Arthur Lee sign your orders? Not if his co-commissioners, Ben Franklin and Silas Deane, thought fit to issue them to you! But do not distress yourself—here at least are such orders as no other American commander has ever received. When do you expect to sail?"

"As soon as I can put the *Ranger* in such trim that I may safely sail her out without being overhauled and taken by the first British ship-of-force I fall in with. But how soon that may be, I cannot say yet. My crew has little stomach to go out and face the enemy and the work goes slowly."

At Jones' direction, I locked away the orders, the while he and Jonathan Williams each partook of a glass of Madeira in celebration of the coming cruise.

How those orders got out, I know not, for certainly neither I nor Paul Jones discussed them with anyone and it is little likely that Jonathan Williams, a person of much prudence, did either. Williams, indeed, believed that Arthur Lee's own secretary was a British agent, and responsible for the leak. But however it came about, in three days it was public property in Nantes and, of course, all over the

Ranger, that our Captain had discretionary orders to sail, with the disastrous results I have mentioned.

What manner of cruise Paul Jones intended if left to choose his own course, our hulking First Lieutenant could easily guess. Hardly had the disgruntled Simpson heard the news than he rushed below to the wardroom with it, there to stir up trouble, in the which effort he had little difficulty with his juniors, and less with our seamen, all appalled like himself at the dangers to be encountered.

Perhaps there was something to extenuate their state of mind. For of our predecessors in British waters, Captain Wickes of the *Reprisal* had been peremptorily ordered out of French waters the moment he brought in his first prize without being allowed even to refit his own ship, to be lost at sea as a result on his way home. The *Lexington,* next to make such a cruise, had swiftly been captured, and her officers, Captain Johnson and Richard Dale, were now ignominiously imprisoned in England. And lastly, Gustavus Conyngham, our immediate precursor in such an attempt, who had alarmed the British by boldly seizing the Harwich packet, was also soon taken, to be confined in a vile dungeon loaded with fetters as a felon and a traitor, and daily threatened with hanging.

With these examples that cruising in English waters resulted in prisons instead of profit, Simpson had little difficulty in working up his associates to the same point of view as himself and, as he hobnobbed much with that part of the crew which came from Portsmouth, in infecting them also with the same beliefs.

The result of all this was that shortly the crew of the *Ranger* was in such a state of insubordination that our refitting went distressingly slowly, and disaster impended if we sailed against anything but merchantmen.

One interlude lightened a little this situation. By the middle of February, we had our rerigged masts stepped again and our top hamper sufficiently refitted so that our Captain deemed he might make trial of our sailing qualities. Inviting Jonathan Williams aboard as a spectator of what he hoped to accomplish, we sailed out of Nantes for Quiberon Bay to the north.

In Quiberon lay the French fleet under Admiral La Motte Picquet. Paul Jones was determined to maneuver him into an open acknowledgment of American independence which should better our position in using French ports as bases, though not yet had France or any foreign power so recognized America.

Accordingly, lying off Quiberon Bay, Captain Jones sent in a boat to board the French flagship, with a note saying that as the Senior American Officer in Europe, he was about to salute La Motte Picquet's flag from the ship-of-war *Ranger*, and demanded a return salute, gun for gun.

Shortly our boat returned with the answer. Should we salute, the salute would be returned in the manner authorized by the Court of France to an Admiral of Holland or any other republic, that is, four guns less than the salute given.

Over this our Captain hesitated, having demanded gun for gun, but after a particular inquiry disclosed that the offer was in fact the truth, and that by such a return La Motte Picquet acknowledged him on a par with an Admiral commanding, and America as an independent republic, late in the afternoon we beat our way in the *Ranger* against a hard wind into the bay.

There, tugging at their cables, in long lines lay the naval might of France—vast three- and four-deckers armed with tier on tier of forty-two-pounders, amongst which the little *Ranger* with our single deck of six-pounders, looked small indeed.

With the new Stars and Stripes floating proudly at our gaff, we luffed close up alongside the French flagship and over the white-capped waters of Quiberon Bay roared out the first gun of our salute, followed alternately larboard and starboard by billowing clouds of smoke and flame from our other guns till we had fired thirteen all told.

Anxiously as the echo of our last six-pounder died away we waited on the *Ranger*, all eyes fixed now on the huge

[405]

ship-of-the-line towering above us. At rigid attention on his quarterdeck, with Jonathan Williams at his side, Paul Jones stood in his most brilliant coat, tense and eager.

From the upper tier of that mountainous wooden wall across the waves, level almost with our own main yard, thundered out the first gun of the answering salute, a volcano of flame and smoke dwarfing the feeble bark of our six-pounders. Then leisurely roared forth the remaining discharges, till nine guns in all had been fired, while beneath the new banner of the United States whipping in the stiff breeze overhead, Paul Jones glowed in ecstasy. Till this moment, in the eyes of the world had we of America been but rebels in arms against our lawful King. Now the thunder of those guns and the clouds of smoke drifting past the *Ranger* and her proud Captain were notice one of the oldest Courts in Europe recognized us as a nation—and Paul Jones equal in authority in European waters to any Admiral!

Followed then on both sides visits of ceremony, with Paul Jones, bursting with pride, received through long lines of side boys aboard the French flagship, and in our turn, a continuous stream of courtly French officers to be welcomed on our quarterdeck, curious to see what manner of warship America could build.

Jones found the courteous French a very well-bred set of men. They on their part expressed great satisfaction with the *Ranger*, in extravagant French, declaring her "un bijou parfait," which, so I learned, meant a perfect jewel. And with all hands thus pleased with one another, we sailed away from Quiberon Bay for Brest for our final fitting out. But not till eight of our men, assured now by all this naval display that their mad Captain meant to go through with his assault on the British Navy, had deserted the ship rather than risk such a crack-brained enterprise.

We lay some time in Brest, amidst many discouragements for want of money and want of faith, finishing our changes and lading stores. Our gallant volunteer, Major Frazer, took French leave, explaining in a casual note that he was going to Bordeaux where the inhabitants seemed to live in

[406]

more style, and requesting our Captain to take care of certain debts of his which no doubt would be brought to his attention. Save for this last presumption, I think Paul Jones heard of his decampment without regret, for the Major's constant intoxication was to him, who never himself drank ardent spirits, a constant trial and the drunken Major a sore disappointment as a fighting man.

But if he witnessed Major Frazer's vanishing with complacence, not so could he look on the growing animosity of Lieutenant Simpson and Captain Parke, our marine officer.

On this feud he gazed with dismay. Parke he had himself selected for his post; Simpson, relative to the influential Mr. Wendell of Portsmouth, had been chosen for him. Between the two, no harmony at all was possible. The loyal Parke backed his Captain in carrying the war home to the British, be the risk to ourselves what it might. The venal Simpson, like a rank privateersman, saw in the war only an opportunity for loot, to be seized with as little risk as possible. These ideas, vehemently expressed on both sides in the most personal terms, kept the wardroom in such an embittered state that duelling and death were close in the offing, threatening disaster to what slight discipline we had left.

There was only one solution for Paul Jones. Either he must part with Parke or with all his Lieutenants, since the two juniors sympathized with Simpson. A marine officer, especially one he had appointed, he might make shift to do without. Not so however with his Lieutenants, commissioned by the Congress, whom he could not displace without court-martial, nor in France find replacements for them should he do so. So for the sake of harmony, with great regret he detached Captain Parke, ordering him home to America, in the earnest hope that this might heal the breach.

But the effect unfortunately was only to strengthen Lieutenant Simpson's position on the *Ranger*. With Parke, the loyal captain of marines gone, the way shortly looked clear toward eliminating Paul Jones himself.

On all this, Paul Jones resolutely turned his back. He

[407]

could do little to cure the situation. A court-martial, if attempted, would tie the *Ranger* hopelessly up in port and stifle his enterprise. That his officers were disaffected and had undermined the loyalty of his crew was plain, but nothing could be done save only to proceed with a mutinous crew or abandon all.

We took aboard as a marine officer another volunteer, Lieutenant Jean Meyer, a slight, keen-eyed Swedish army officer, on leave from Sweden and bearing orders from Silas Deane authorizing him to serve in our Navy. And with Lieutenant Meyer, reserved but observant, to complete our complement, on April 10, 1778, we sailed at last from Brest, a ship seething with discontent and on the verge of open mutiny.

That any Captain ever sailed under more nerve-racking conditions, I much doubt. What he might expect at the hands of Lieutenant Simpson and his own men, he knew only too well. And that the British were waiting only to get their hands on him to hang him as a renegade and a pirate was common knowledge in Brest long ere we sailed. With ignominious death staring him in the face from friend and foe alike, any prudent Captain would have fled his ship for what safety Ben Franklin could offer him in Paris. But Paul Jones, to whom in the ordinary sense prudence was a stranger, went boldly forth to beard both his crew and the British, sending a last message to Ben Franklin before we weighed anchor.

"It is true I must run great risk, but no gallant action was ever accomplished without danger. Therefore, although I cannot ensure success, I will endeavor to deserve it."

And hardly were we in the stream and clear of the distractions of the port, than officers and crew alike were turned to on ceaseless gun drills.

43

WHATEVER may have been Paul Jones' intentions as we heaved in our cable and made sail from Brest, he kept them wholly to himself. Brest, like every other French port, was so full of British spies as to ensure immediate transmission of every rumor direct to Whitehall. But mainly I think he desired to get his faint-hearted crew somewhat in hand ere he attempted anything, lest he be incontinently tossed overboard and the *Ranger* headed immediately for America.

For several days therefore we cruised to the northwest looking only for merchantmen bound for the Channel. We took off the Scilly Islands and sank one brigantine laden with flaxseed, the which seemed not worth a prize crew, and then stood for St. George's Channel. There, five days out of port, we fell in with a large ship, the *Lord Chatham*, almost in sight of her Irish destination and brought her to, an easy prize. This vessel, laden with porter and a wide variety of merchandise, and by great good fortune, carrying the baggage and plate of General Irwin to the value of some £5000, a rich haul indeed, Paul Jones manned and ordered for Brest, thereby assuaging the worst fears of our crew that the cruise would be wholly profitless and reducing them for the moment to some semblance of subordination.

We stood north into the Irish Sea, coming on April 18 off the Isle of Man, from which point we steered direct for Whitehaven on the English coast. That it was our Captain's intent to raid that port was fairly evident from the orders to clear away our boats. What might have resulted in the dubious temper of our crew is uncertain. But as we stood in late at night, the wind suddenly shifted in direction to blow landward and increased so much in force that landing in small boats was obviously out of question. Only by consummate seamanship was our Captain able to claw off that lee shore, the which in the darkness he accomplished without discovery.

Offshore again, with the grumblings of our crew, which temporarily had been quieted by the taking of the *Lord Chatham*, once more ominously in evidence, Paul Jones gave over any further immediate attempt at a raid and we stood northward through the Irish Sea looking for merchantmen.

At daybreak, we sighted to the southward a lugger heading in for Scotland, hotly pursued by a revenue cutter. Immediately we bore away before the wind for the cutter, but such good sailers did both pursuers and pursued prove, that we closed but slowly in the dull-sailing *Ranger*.

Thoroughly disappointed in the speed of his ship and despairing of overhauling the cutter should she take alarm, Paul Jones silently sent the crew to quarters, but kept the *Ranger* disguised in that all our ports remained closed and our guns hidden, with the gun crews crouching low out of sight behind the bulwarks, hoping to entice our prey under our masked guns.

While closing, we had showed no colors at all, but now at the Captain's orders, we ran up a British ensign and made signal to the cutter, asking for a pilot.

At that, the cutter obligingly veered somewhat toward us till she was within long hail on our lee quarter, though still with all sail set in pursuit of the lugger ahead of her, and sang out,

"What ship is that?"

"The ship *Molly*, of Glasgow!" roared back Paul Jones. "What ship is that, and can ye let us ha' a pilot? We be strangers on this coast!"

"His Majesty's armed revenue cutter *Hussar* of Whitehaven, Captain Gurley commanding!" came back the reply. "I'm in chase of yonder smuggler! I can't stop to help you!" and to our disappointment, with no more ado, the *Hussar* sheered off to follow again dead in the wake of the fleeing lugger.

Further concealment was useless.

"*Hussar* there! Heave to or I'll sink you!" shouted Captain Jones, and instantly at that, our gun ports flew up, out rolled our gun carriages, down from the gaff came the British ensign, and up from behind our bulwarks leaped Lieutenant Jean Meyer and his marines, to convert the innocent-looking *Molly* of Glasgow into a threatening man-of-war.

But Captain Gurley, faced now by overwhelming force, proved no coward. Startled he must have been by our sudden unmasking, but he neither struck nor heaved to. Instantly he hauled the agile *Hussar* up into the wind, to tack away off our quarter, where at the moment only our aftermost guns bore on him. Seeing he meant to try escape, with both musketry and such great guns as could be brought to bear, we opened fire. But to our intense chagrin, though we managed to cut up his sails and rigging considerably, the fleet *Hussar*, tacking frequently, outsailed us to windward, finally drawing out of gunshot completely and escaping in the direction of Belfast Lough.

In much disappointment, Captain Jones ordered Lieutenant Simpson to secure our battery, and the drummer to beat retreat from quarters. Hardly was this done than our burly First Lieutenant came striding aft to the quarterdeck.

"Do we sail now for America or for France?" he demanded bluntly of the Captain.

"Neither, Mr. Simpson," answered Paul Jones. "We stay yet awhile in the Irish Sea till we have accomplished something here. Why should we leave?"

"Why?" echoed Simpson, his ox-like features staring wide-eyed at his Captain. "Are you blind?" He swept his arm about the horizon, where in plain sight over our rail to larboard lay the Irish coast, to starboard rose the Scottish mountains, and over our stern might faintly be seen the English coast off Cumberland. "D'ye want to get us all killed? We lie in plain sight from all three kingdoms at once, and now that revenue cutter's escaped us to give the

[411]

alarm, shortly there'll be the whole English fleet out to cut off our escape both north and south. We'll all be dead or prisoners by tomorrow if we stay here another minute!"

"You give the English too much credit, sir," disagreed Paul Jones, a faint smile playing in his grey eyes. "You know not the English Navy as well as I, or you would know that from Jemmy Twitcher, First Lord of the Admiralty, down, there's no one in that Service today capable of such expedition as you imagine. Calm yourself. I came here to make the British fear me, not to flee from shadows, Mr. Simpson," and turning abruptly on his heel, he vanished down the after hatch.

We stood now for the Scotch coast, where next morning off the Mull of Galloway we sank a coasting schooner and shortly a sloop bound for Dublin. Standing over for Ireland in search of larger game, off Carrick Fergus we were boarded by an open fishing boat, the which, unsuspicious of our character, our Captain permitted to come alongside that he might gain some information regarding a vessel he could see anchored well up in Belfast Lough.

Hardly had the three fishermen at the invitation of our quartermaster clambered up our innocent-looking side, leaving their bobbing boat tied at the foot of our sea steps, than they found themselves to their utter bewilderment on deck a man-of-war with gun carriages, red-coated marines, and pigtailed seamen on every hand. Those dumbfounded Irishmen, certain now of being pressed into the King's Service (for such they thought our ship in) would fain have leaped overboard to escape had they not immediately been seized and hustled aft to confront our Captain.

Quickly calming the quaking fishermen's fears of being impressed, Paul Jones learned from them that the ship he saw anchored in the distance was His Majesty's man-of-war *Drake* of twenty guns, a vessel somewhat larger than the *Ranger*, which carried now but eighteen.

Longingly Paul Jones scanned the distant *Drake* through his glass. Here was what he had been seeking—a British ship-of-force! But now that he had her in sight and had but to stand in another league to ensure an engagement, well he realized that should he attempt it, he would but precipitate instantly the brewing mutiny. Still, what he could not get his men to face directly, he might persuade them to attempt by strategy. He called all his officers aft.

"Gentlemen," he said, fixing his gaze most particularly upon Simpson's rebellious countenance, "yonder two leagues off lies the man-o'-war *Drake* of twenty guns, guardship for northern Ireland. Scan her well, all of you, through your glasses for in a moment we are tacking out to sea that we excite not her suspicions. But tonight we stand in again to lay aboard her in the darkness and sweep her decks ere they have time on the *Drake* even to beat to quarters. You, Lieutenant Meyer," and he turned to our volunteer Swedish marine officer, "prepare your men with muskets and grenades to sweep her decks from our tops. And you, Lieutenant Simpson, muster the boarders on our fo'c'sle and lead the attack. Success is certain, and you will gain such glory tonight that posterity will not forget you. On your stations, gentlemen. We stand out till darkness falls!"

Even to the dubious Simpson, it was evident that plan involved slight risk, and while he showed no enthusiasm, neither had he any objections. So as if the *Ranger* were the best-disciplined ship in the Continental Navy, we stood out of Belfast Lough in a bustle of preparation for boarding, taking with us still as prisoners the three Irish fishermen so that our presence remain a secret.

Once night fell, with tops crowded with marines, fo'c'sle jammed with boarders, guns loaded and run out should we have need of them, we beat our way back up Belfast Lough through the darkness against a rising wind, already blowing that estuary into a mass of vaguely seen white caps.

Alongside the helmsman aft stood our Captain, in the waist the sailing master, David Cullen (a sorry substitute for Sam Stacy of the *Providence* and the *Alfred*), in the bow, peering anxiously out through the night, Lieutenant Simpson.

With a cutlass slung to my waist and a brace of pistols

stuck in my belt, I stood myself with a wildly beating heart, fortified on one side by Reuben Chase's towering figure and on the other by Red Jerry's barrel-chested brawn. Never yet had I any occasion for the hand-to-hand melee of boarding an enemy, and truth to tell, my shivering limbs might well have failed me had not the gleaming pikes in the hands of the two harpooners flanking me in the gloom somewhat stiffened up my resolution.

Silently we waited. Our plan, as we all knew, was to stand down on the starboard tack across the hawse of the *Drake*, let go our anchor as soon as we overlay her cable, and then swing down at short stay with the wind so we fell across her bow, when without further orders as we fouled her sides, we were to sweep over our gunwales onto the deck of the unsuspecting enemy.

Soon in the night we made out the *Drake*, a vague blotch in the darkness, riding to her surging cable headed dead into the wind. Close hauled on the starboard tack, with our lee bower anchor acockbill at the cathead, we clawed to windward to weather her bow, till we had drawn athwart her hawse. From my position in the eyes of the heaving *Ranger*, it seemed that on the *Drake*, unalarmed and showing no sign of life upon her deck, the masts were beginning to come into line. And then from aft, relayed by the sailing master, came the hoarse order,

"Let go the larboard anchor!"

Instinctively my fingers closed upon my cutlass, waiting the splash of the anchor dropping clear of the cathead and the surging of our hawser which should follow it. But nothing happened. Instead I heard only the curses of our clumsy bosun, who somehow in the dark had fouled up the releasing pendant on the cathead, so that ere the anchor dropped free at last, we were well across the bows of the *Drake*. And alas, when we swung into the wind to ride at short scope to our hook, so far had we overridden our objective that we brought up on the enemy's quarter instead of afoul her, in bafflement looking across half a cable's length of foaming water between our side and hers!

[414]

Instantly racing forward came our Captain. What inner rage he may have felt at having his plan thus foiled by lubberly incompetence in letting go the anchor, he kept concealed, striving only to retrieve the blunder. We had made no warlike appearance in our approach. We had given no alarm. And still the *Drake*, which seemed not even to have an alert anchor watch, appeared to apprehend nothing untoward from our maneuvers in the dark.

"Cut that cable!" sang out Paul Jones sharply. "They'll think it's parted on us! We'll make another approach and try again!"

Down on the stout hempen hawser swung the carpenter's axe. In a moment, as if indeed our cable had parted under the strain of snubbing us up short, we were drifting free down to leeward before the wind. The *Drake*, wholly unaware of what she had by that mischance escaped, was swiftly swallowed up in the darkness.

Unfortunately however, so speedily was the wind rising that soon to the accompaniment of heavy snow which blotted from sight all landmarks, it was blowing a fresh gale against which there was not the slightest chance of our beating back dead to windward and finding the *Drake* again. So we had no option save to drive before it out of Belfast Lough, the which perforce we did, by great good luck in the blinding snow barely escaping the lighthouse rocks ere we got clear.

For two days, hove to in the open Irish Sea, we rode out the storm, with Paul Jones so chagrined at the failure of his surprise attack on the *Drake* that in a taciturn mood he scarce spoke to anyone. But there was conversation enough below decks on the heaving *Ranger*, where from fo'c'sle to wardroom, seamen, midshipmen, and wardroom officers alike argued endlessly over whether that scheme had not indeed been doomed to failure regardless, being beyond seamanlike ability to accomplish.

Morning dawned on April 22 with the weather fair and clear again, though the three kingdoms, once more spread out before us, were covered with snow as far as the eye could reach, and only the tumbling sea stood out grey and wrinkled like an elephant's hide against a world of white.

We made sail and stood southeastward toward Solway Firth. That our Captain once again was contemplating action was clear from the increased vigor with which, alone as usual, he trod the *Ranger's* quarterdeck. So that it was no great surprise when we had raised the coast off Cumberland and vaguely could make out the distant spires in Whitehaven, he sent for the First Lieutenant and ordered our two longboats cleared away.

"What for?" asked Simpson, making no move toward obeying.

"To raid Whitehaven, Mr. Simpson." With cold fury Paul Jones looked into his insubordinate Lieutenant's eyes. "I intend to make such a bonfire of the shipping in that port as will pay out the burning of Falmouth and many another American town. After tonight, King George and his Ministers will have much cause to think on the dangers of reprisal ere ever they set torch to our homes again!"

"You'll not get me in those boats," said Lieutenant Simpson flatly. " 'Tis a rash business, and there's nothing to be got by burning people's property!"

"So, Mr. Simpson?" In disgust, Captain Jones looked up at his recalcitrant Lieutenant. "Do America's interests in this war affect you not, save only as you may *get* something out of it? Enough, sir! Have those boats cleared for lowering at once!"

"Aye, I'll clear them," grumbled Simpson, overawed by the steel in Paul Jones' voice. "But be not too sure you get the crews to man them for you!" and he slouched forward to set the bosun about the business of clearing away our two largest boats.

That there was much truth in Simpson's parting shot was soon proved. We stood in with the boats at the davit heads ready for lowering. But while I had no great difficulty in mustering ten men (mostly from those I had recruited on Nantucket) for the boat Paul Jones himself was to lead for the dangerous business of silencing the forts at Whitehaven the while the other boat's crew fired the shipping, the remaining twenty men and officers for his boat and the second boat's crew were hardly to be had.

Our Second Lieutenant, Elijah Hall, backed up our First in refusing to go, in which example most of the seamen followed them, terrified at the prospect of what the guns on the forts overlooking Whitehaven could do to fragile pulling boats once they got them in range of grape and solid shot.

It was only with the greatest difficulty that Paul Jones persuaded our half-hearted Third Lieutenant, young Sam Wallingford, that the expedition did not mean certain death, and as a matter of fact, so sure was he of English blindness to the possibility of attack, that it involved no danger at all. Using these arguments, our skipper managed then in some degree enough to overcome the fears of sixteen seamen more, to furnish out the crews. That he had even that much success, however, I gathered was due more to the hope of looting ashore in the minds of these men, rather than to any willingness to take part in a reprisal expedition.

As night fell we worked our way inshore on the *Ranger*, impeded considerably in our design by the lightness of the wind which barely filled our sails. Not till midnight, against an ebbing tide did we manage to fetch within two miles of the harbor, which was as close as the *Ranger* could safely lie off. There, leaving the ship in charge of Lieutenant Simpson, we lowered our two boats.

In the first went Paul Jones, Lieutenant Jean Meyer of the marines, myself, and fifteen seamen, all armed with pistols and cutlasses. In the second went Lieutenant Wallingford, Midshipman Hill, and eleven seamen, similarly armed, while in both boats went several candles carefully shielded in lanterns, to light off the fires we purposed starting.

Silently in the black night we dropped away from the low sides of the *Ranger*, to find ourselves immediately in the grip of such a strong ebb tide running out the Solway Firth that the oarsmen in each boat could make little way against it, and not till we had double-banked the oars with every man in each boat pulling, did we make much progress battling the outgoing tide.

[417]

At near three in the morning, with the sky in that high latitude already beginning to show the first faint streaks of dawn, we arrived off the docks. Eagerly Paul Jones strained his eyes to scan once again the harbor from which, a boy of twelve, he had first sailed for America, and which many a time since as mate and master, he had threaded in merchantmen. About that harbor lay all the memories of his tormented youth and round about it lived those who had persecuted him for the death of Mungo Maxwell. Now had their day of reckoning come.

With fierce satisfaction, he eyed the two basins, separated by a long stone quay, where, left stranded on the mud flats by the tide which was nearly at dead low, lay some hundreds of vessels of all sizes, tempting fuel certainly for our conflagration. But to the north and to the south of these docks stood two stone forts guarding the harbor entrance, the broken outlines of their stone walls ominously significant of the great guns hidden in those embrasures waiting to loose a hail of iron on us, should the sentries there challenge our approach. Still, so quietly had we come in, there was as yet no sign of any alarm.

Just off the end of the quay separating the two shipping basins, Jones in a low voice ordered,

"Oars!" and then motioned Wallingford to bring his boat alongside.

"Lieutenant, with your boat proceed immediately into that north basin and fire the shipping there," he ordered softly. "I'll take my boat and spike the guns in both forts to cover our retreat, and then I'll fire the ships in the south basin. Shove off and get your ships blazing!"

"Aye, aye, sir!" responded Wallingford, though now that the moment for action was at hand, very dubiously I thought. Nevertheless, his boat headed away in the half light of the early dawn toward the north side of the quay, where it was swiftly lost in the shadow, while with helm hard over, Paul Jones sheered our boat toward the northern fort.

Now indeed we rowed with the utmost silence toward that

fort, to beach our boat gently on the sand fringing the foot of the lowering stone walls. Leaving Lieutenant Meyer with half a dozen men in the boat to cover his retreat, Jones took the rest of us for the assault.

Quietly, that we alarm not the sentinels, we stole across the beach, each instant expecting to hear from the stone walls above us a sharp challenge and the roar of musketry in our faces. But with no sign of an alarm, we made the wall of the fort, wholly undiscovered. So far, so good.

Twelve feet sheer above us rose the stone walls of the fort, slippery with moss. We had no scaling ladders. But that was swiftly overcome.

"Chase!" breathed Paul Jones.

Reuben Chase moved to his side.

"Put your back to the wall, Reuben, under this embrasure!" whispered the skipper. "Give me a hand up!"

"Aye, aye, sir!" Reuben Chase placed his lanky back against the wall where it reached two-thirds of the way to the embrasure, clasped his prodigious hands together to form a step. With both his pistols jammed in his belt to leave his hands free, Paul Jones placed his hands on Reuben's shoulders, lifted one foot into the stirrup formed by Chase's huge paws, and the next instant was catapulted violently upward over Reuben's head against the wall so that with no difficulty at all he fell into the embrasure and scrambled through!

Instantly, by the same means I followed him, as did some eight more, to find ourselves, pistols and cutlasses loosed for action, on the parapet of the fort ringed about by fifteen heavy guns all run in, ready for loading.

Still to our amazement, there was no alarm, no challenge. Separating and treading softly along the parapet to the sentry boxes at the corners, we saw why. So remote from England's shores was any thought of the war she was waging on distant America, every one of the sentries was sound asleep! One by one, without a sound we seized and gagged them, so that they awoke in stupefied surprise to find themselves with pistols at their heads, already prisoners!

[419]

Descending then to the guardhouse, it was no problem at all to secure and bind the remainder of the trifling garrison similarly in their beds. In a few minutes, without harming anyone, or even firing a shot, we were masters of the main fort guarding Whitehaven, and town and shipping were wholly at our mercy, for we learned from the prisoners that the southern fort had no garrison at all!

We lost no time. Leaving our prisoners firmly lashed, the which Reuben Chase in grim silence personally and expertly attended to, with sledge and spikes we went to work on the battery guarding Whitehaven. In fifteen minutes, with its touchhole solidly plugged off, every gun on the ramparts was out of commission, the fort as useless as a warehouse, and we were tumbling pell-mell back into our boat, with all Whitehaven still peacefully asleep.

Swiftly then in the growing light we rowed across the harbor toward the southern fort, where once again we beached our boat. Here, with the keys to that fort in his possession, Paul Jones landed with only one man carrying the sledge and the spikes to assist him, leaving all the rest of us to start out with our combustibles to spread amongst the vessels in the southern basin, waiting only his return to the boat as the signal to fire them.

Hardly had the sounds of a spike being sledged down the touchhole of the first gun inside that fort come to our ears to show that all was going as expected, than Reuben Chase and some half dozen of the seamen who had taken the northern fort, left the boat laden with canvas and oakum matches soaked in brimstone to spread them on the decks of the nearby ships, high and dry on the mud flats.

I was myself about to swing over the gunwale with the candle (now unfortunately almost guttering out, so much time had we lost in battling the tide coming in) to light off the fires, when Lieutenant Meyer seized my arm and held me in the boat.

"Wait, Mr. Folger," he whispered softly. "It is dangerous to leave!"

Puzzled, I set the lantern with my flickering candle gently

down again in the sternsheets.

"What's the matter?" I asked. "The danger's all over; the forts are both ours now."

"It is not the English. It is your own men! You don't see yet any fire where Lieutenant Wallingford should be, do you?"

I looked. Not a sign of fire, not a sign of smoke, came from the silent northern basin where Wallingford and his men, unmolested, had already had over half an hour to get to work amongst that helpless forest of masts and spars and hulls. What could have gone wrong?

Jean Meyer drew me closer to him.

"Shoondelin, that man rowing bow in this boat, he's a Swede. When I was going to follow Captain Jones ashore at the northern fort, he held me back, telling me in Swedish so none of the others of his shipmates knew what he said, not to go! For, he warned me, the men left in this boat had already concerted with Wallingford and the men in the other boat (who as you see have not landed yet in spite of their orders) that should there be any resistance at all so Captain Jones did not immediately return, they would all abandon him ashore and flee back to the ship. Stay here with me, or it may happen yet! You see already Wallingford has disobeyed his orders; if he becomes panic-stricken, he will certainly fly. And this boat then will follow, unless we stay to prevent it so that our valiant Captain may have some escape if Wallingford abandons him!"

So that was the reason no flames were showing in the shipping. Wallingford and all his men must be skulking in the shadow of the quay, afraid to leave their boat, ready to fly ignobly seaward the instant there was any alarm!

From the fort above us came the clang of sledge on spikes as gun after gun was rendered impotent. What Paul Jones had expected of Whitehaven and its negligent defenses was proving exactly right, but all was being rendered futile by his timorous assistants. Now the sun was peeping over the horizon, day had come, and not a ship had yet been fired!

[421]

At that instant, while yet I was hesitating over what to do, out from the lee of the quay pushed the stem of our other boat, heading seaward. In a few minutes some dozen boat-lengths off, the cutter paused a moment to hail us, and save for Wallingford himself, a drunker set of seamen I never saw! They had landed all right, but instead of firing the shipping as ordered, they had taken possession of a public house near the head of the quay, whose sign I could now easily make out in the daylight. There they had brazenly made prisoners of the proprietor, Nick Allison, and his wife, whom they routed out of bed, and then having hurriedly guzzled all the liquor they could find on the premises, were on their way back!

And now, there were they all in the boat (save one seaman, David Freeman, whose absence they could not account for and made no moment of) drunk as lords, waving us to return to the *Ranger* with them, and not a finger lifted yet toward carrying through the mission for which we had come! In anguish, I looked at Lieutenant Meyer. His worst suspicions of our crew were justified.

"Shove off there, mates!" sang out Wallingford. "It's daylight! We can't stay any longer or we'll have the whole town on our necks! One of my men gave me the slip while we were ashore, and I fear he'll spread the alarm all through Whitehaven. Shake a leg! We've got to get clear!"

My fingers tightened on my cutlass, ready to cut down any man in our boat who showed sign of obeying that order. But at that instant on the ramparts of the fort over my head, clearly outlined against the morning sky appeared Paul Jones, sledge in hand. The final gun was spiked. Triumphantly he flung the sledge away, and then turned to stare off northward toward the shipping.

It was pitiful to see the look of triumph fade from his features. Not even a wisp of smoke met his gaze. Dumbfounded, he bent his head to look into my boat, and his eye for the first time lighted on Wallingford and the other boat's crew lying a little off.

[422]

"Row back there, you scoundrels!" he roared. "Fire those ships!"

"It's too late, Captain. The town's been roused! And besides, our light's gone. My candle's all burned out!" sang out Wallingford.

Paul Jones made no answer. Instead he slipped out an embrasure, hung down a second, dropped to the ground, to come running headlong for my boat followed by the solitary seaman he had taken with him to the fort. He came tumbling over the gunwale, his face a thundercloud.

"Shove off, Tom!" he ordered sharply. "Make that quay! Lay back, lads! Bend those oars!"

In a moment our boat was clear, under straining sweeps heading across the mouth of the south basin for the stone quay, the while, almost too enraged for speech, our Captain motioned Wallingford to follow him back. But for my part, my own heart sank as I peered down in the sternsheets at my lanterns. The candles there, lighted almost four hours before on the *Ranger*, had burned out completely! In neither boat now did we have any fire, nor any means of starting one! In dismay, I silently pointed out to my Captain the guttered lanterns.

"If that lout Wallingford had carried out my orders, the whole harbor would be this instant flaming in such a blaze it could be seen in London!" muttered Jones. "And now he's botched my plans so we haven't even a lighted candle! Never mind, Tom. We'll get a light ashore. Only make haste. But who's that?" he finished sharply, pointing shoreward.

Along the street fronting the water some squares off I saw a seaman in the rig of our Continental Navy flying from door to door, banging on the knockers, bawling at the top of his voice,

"Turn out! The Americans have landed to burn the town!" while from various windows above him up and down the street, night-capped heads started to pop out.

"That must be David Freeman, sir. The villain deserted Wallingford's boat the while his men were making free with

[423]

the spirits in that pub on the dock. Now he's waking the town!"

"So?" With narrowing eyes, Paul Jones peered across the water at one of his own seamen frantically striving to frustrate our expedition. "A traitor, eh, to top off the mutineers and the skulking cowards I have already to contend with on the *Ranger!* We've got to take that quay before the citizenry get there!" He turned to face the laboring seamen before him, sang out fiercely,

"Give way, my hearties! Lay back! Heave and snap those oars!"

We made the slimy steps at the seaward end of the quay with a bang, went scrambling up them led by Paul Jones almost before the way was off our boat.

"Tom!" ordered Jones curtly. "Get a light somewhere, anywhere! But get it!"

He turned immediately to Lieutenant Meyer, just as I dashed off for Nicholas Allison's looted pub, which stood at the head of the quay, ordered him, "Lieutenant! Take half a dozen seamen to the head of this quay! Let no one down the dock!"

With drawn cutlasses, behind me Meyer and his men came running heavily, to pass me when I paused before the pub. The door of that inn having already been smashed in, I had no difficulty in entering, to find the floor littered with empty bottles, the bar overturned, and the place a wreck. From a back room I caught the muffled groans of the gagged proprietor and his wife, but I had no time for them. Before me in the fireplace were the dulling coals of a fire now nearly out. I seized a pair of bellows from the hearth, started fiercely blowing on those embers to fan them back to life ere it was too late.

While I pumped furiously, outside I heard the hoarse cries of the citizens of Whitehaven running toward the quay and the clanging of church bells pealing wildly out far and near. The alarm had been given now in all truth; from the noise, the whole of Whitehaven was rushing toward the

[424]

waterfront. As frantically I plied the bellows, I cursed vehemently Wallingford's disobedience and folly which had brought matters to this pass. Now indeed, if Lieutenant Meyer and his slight force should be overwhelmed by the shouting mob gathering outside, we faced disaster!

Spurred by the uproar on the waterfront, I soon had the dying coals glowing brightly again and flung away the bellows to seize the tongs and pile the hot coals into an iron pot hanging from the crane. Gripping that pot, I rushed headlong from the pub, to see in one fleeting glimpse Lieutenant Meyer with raised pistols and his six seamen with cutlasses bared, stretched across the head of the quay, menacingly facing a crowd of hundreds of half-dressed citizens pressing in a solid semi-circle round about them, but fortunately held back by the sight of their threatening weapons.

I fairly flew down the dock with that pot of coals, without delay to flounder waist-deep in mud and water some few fathoms to the gangway of the stranded *Thomson*, the largest vessel thereabouts, where Paul Jones awaited me.

He seized avidly on the pot.

"Tom," he ordered, "while I work here with these coals firing this ship, you take the boat to the south basin, and gather up all the men you left there. Bring them back with you instantly; there's not time now to light fires anywhere but here!"

"Aye, aye, sir!" While Paul Jones vanished down the hatch of the *Thomson* to her steerage, into which two of our men were already busily engaged lowering a tar barrel they had found on deck, I sped over the gangway, to clamber, all coated with mud and slime, into the boat.

Nearby, at the seaward end of the quay Wallingford's boat and its drunken crew still lay, loaded and ready to leave, doing nothing apparently to help out. But disregarding them, I rowed speedily toward the south basin and beached my boat in the ooze amongst the ships stranded there. With some shouting, I called back to me Reuben Chase and his shipmates who, alarmed at all the clamor in the town, were already on deck the vessels where they had spread combustibles, waiting only my arrival with the candles to light off. After much floundering about through the mud, all managed to regain the boat, surprised and disappointed at finding I had no fire with which they might complete their work.

"That's all belayed," I explained briefly. "Tumble aboard!" Hurriedly I counted noses to ensure I had them all, then shoved clear.

This time as we came about for the quay again, I could see some results of our enterprise. In huge billows, smoke was pouring out the hatches of the *Thomson* already, with tiny tongues of flame licking round her cabin ports.

Lying now a little off the quay was Wallingford and his crew. Slowly retreating down the dock, still facing the mob, came Lieutenant Meyer and his squad of seamen, while on the end of the pier waiting them stood our Captain and the few seamen who had helped him fire the *Thomson*. Immediately I drove my boat into the stone steps to pick them up. Soon, one by one, flying down the steps and into the longboat came all that party, Meyer last.

Only our Captain was now left on the quay, he having stayed apparently to cover the embarkation of Meyer's landing force. Already Wallingford and his boat's crew were underway headed out, pulling vigorously in spite of their inebriation. With all oars manned in my boat and Reuben Chase with boat hook poised in the bow ready to shove clear, I waited, expecting the skipper immediately to follow Lieutenant Meyer down.

But he made no move. Instead, alone upon that pierhead, pistols in hand he faced the crowd surging forward toward the burning *Thomson*, bringing them to a sudden halt.

"Back!" he ordered. "Let her burn!"

"Why, that be Captain Paul o' Kirkcudbright across the Firth!" shouted a voice in the crowd. "He murdered Mungo Maxwell and now the bloody pirate's come back to murder all the rest o' his old neighbors!" And instantly, as if indeed they feared that fate, in the wildest panic the mob fell precipitantly back before those coolly levelled pistols, leaving Paul Jones a solitary form sharply outlined on the end of the quay against the roaring flames leaping from the *Thomson*.

Some minutes more he stood there, the center of attention of all Whitehaven with thousands on thousands of the amazed citizens who had turned out on the wild alarm, gazing awestruck and silent from every eminence in the town upon this fearsome figure and the blazing ship behind him. But to them, save to keep his pistols levelled, Paul Jones paid little attention. Only the *Thomson*, with the flames momentarily leaping higher through the hatches and curling out the cabin ports, interested him. Not till they had reached the rigging and were licking fiercely skyward up the tarred hempen shrouds so that the conflagration had fair opportunity to spread to the surrounding maze of masts and spars, was he content. Turning his back then contemptuously on Whitehaven and its awed citizenry, he descended to the boat, leaped lightly into the sternsheets, and ordered calmly,

"Shove off now, Tom. I think this fire is going well enough to teach King George the distress he has occasioned in America can be brought home to his own door!"

Reuben Chase with one mighty heave shoved us clear. In a moment, with oars swinging smoothly and unhurried, we were out in the stream, standing seaward. The sight of our boat drawing rapidly out of pistol shot broke the spell which held the awed crowd back, and immediately it broke into action. Some sped down the quay toward the burning ship. Others ran back to town to get their fire engines. But the largest numbers, by the thousands it seemed to me, remembering suddenly we were yet within easy reach of their cannon, rushed en masse to the forts flanking both sides of the harbor to turn the thirty heavy guns there upon our helpless boats. What was their chagrin upon finding these instruments of their vengeance rendered useless may easily be imagined. Beside those spiked guns the outraged inhabitants of Whitehaven impotently shook their fists at Paul Jones who was coolly looking back on the ever-mounting flames in the harbor—at Paul Jones, escaping with impunity from the first foreign raid on English soil since the days of William the Conqueror.

44

AN hour later we were back aboard and the *Ranger* underway again with all hands, save for our solitary deserter, safe and uninjured. And to my surprise, without a word of censure to anyone on his conduct once the boats were hoisted in, the skipper dismissed the landing party to tumble into their hammocks for some hours' rest.

But instead of setting our course straight out to sea, Paul Jones laid the *Ranger's* bow northwest across Solway Firth, and not until we were well steadied on that course with all sail set and Elijah Hall, who had the watch, warned to hold it till land was in sight ahead, did our Captain lay below.

A quick glance at the chart showed we were pointed fair for Kirkcudbright in Scotland, which, alone of all those aboard, I well knew was our Captain's birthplace. I began to wonder whether he intended a raid there to burn that place of miserable boyhood memories also. If that were so, considering what Lieutenant Meyer had told me of the cabal to abandon him in Whitehaven, I judged it but the part of prudence now to warn him of what he faced should he land again, lest this time, should all not go well, he find himself marooned ashore indeed.

So going below to Meyer's tiny stateroom, I routed that gentleman, who had but a moment before climbed into it, out of his berth and giving him scarce time to dress again, dragged him aft to the Captain's cabin. Through the empty wardroom and down the passage abaft it, Meyer followed me till in the cabin country we came upon a red-coated marine sentry, rigidly at attention before the cabin door, guarding with fixed bayonet the entrance to that sacred spot. Stiffly the sentry saluted us.

"Tell the Captain," said our marine officer, "that Lieutenant Meyer and Mr. Midshipman Folger beg permission to see him."

Silently the sentry saluted again, rapped on the door, waited a moment, till from inside came the word, "Come!" then entered, closing the door gently behind him. In another moment, he was out again, to hold the door respectfully open for us the while we entered.

Hats in hand (for on Paul Jones' ship one uncovered to his Captain as to his God) we passed through, to find our commanding officer beside a table covered with charts looking inquiringly at us.

"Lieutenant Meyer, sir," I began, "told me something while we were ashore of which I think you should know immediately. So I asked him to pass it along to you."

"About my crew?" Paul Jones looked quizzically from me to Meyer. "If you can tell me anything of them I have not already good reason to suspect, you will surprise me."

"Aye, sir, about both officers and crew," said Meyer in utmost gravity. "That this ship's company is full of plots and cabals against its Captain is evident. This morning on the beach I warned Mr. Folger here of one when there was much danger you would be deserted. He will tell you of it. But since our return, sir, I have more questioned the seaman Shoondelin, who first warned me. He is, like myself, a Swede, and I know him for a seaman who has learned discipline in Sweden and is not, like so many of your crew, poisoned by false notions of equality they have brought from America. To put it plainly, Captain, your officers and crew wish only ardently to return to America, and since they wish it, such are their beliefs they think it should be done regardless of their duty or the orders of their Captain. Never in my military service have I seen such a thing!"

"You should serve a while in Washington's army and you would not be shocked so easily, Lieutenant," replied Jones, smiling on him with some amusement. "Every General almost is plotting to displace him as Commander-in-Chief; his troops, led by such scheming officers, are as likely to mutiny

[430]

or desert as to obey his orders. Being cursed on the *Ranger* with officers of that same stripe, I can expect no better here. Subordination and discipline are hardly natural to rebels in arms against ancient authority. So I must now make out as best I can. But what else? Surely you have not come here to tell me what is plain to every powder monkey aboard?"

"No, sir, there is worse," continued Meyer sadly. "Shoondelin tells me there is a definite plot afoot among the men (of which Lieutenant Simpson at least is well aware) to mutiny should they be called on to go into battle, throw you overboard, make Lieutenant Simpson their Captain, and sail immediately back to America. Of this plot, the sailing master is the leader. He waits only the propitious moment to attack you when the men will back him up, and you will find then your officers all strangely scattered so that you can expect no help from them!"

"So that fool Cullen is to be ringleader, eh?" Reflectively Paul Jones thought over our dull-witted sailing master. "Thanks, Lieutenant, for your warning. I'll keep a weather eye out for Cullen. Concern yourself no further. If I can't handle him and the pack of home-sick idiots he's leading astray, he deserves success. Good morning, gentlemen," and abruptly our Captain terminated the discussion to return to poring over his charts. Immediately we withdrew.

"The Captain is too sure," muttered Meyer as soon as we were in the passage. "He should put the sailing master instantly in irons and keep my marine guard under arms constantly to overawe the crew."

I shrugged my shoulders.

"Aye, Lieutenant. That would save the Captain, but also it might immediately bring on mutiny and end the cruise even though the Captain and your marines triumphed. Paul Jones would die first ere he took that chance of ending his enterprise."

"He stands a fine chance of dying now," said Meyer pessimistically, "and you too. The sailors, Shoondelin says, know you for a loyal friend of the Captain. Beware!" and Lieutenant Jean Meyer ducked into his stateroom, leaving me

[431]

alone in no very happy frame of mind to pass on to the steerage a little forward, where weary from a long night's work, I tossed aside my mud-caked clothes to crawl naked into my hammock.

Hardly it seemed to me had I closed my eyes when along the berth deck echoed the roll of the drum beating to quarters. Hurriedly I tumbled out, snatched my clothes. From the hammock alongside me, as sleepy as I, fell out Charley Hill, who had accompanied Wallingford ashore in Whitehaven. Round about us in the crowded steerage, my fellow Midshipmen, Bill Green and Pierce Powers, flighty lads both, were already buckling on cutlasses. Powers, a fair-haired youngster of sixteen, led the way out to scramble nimbly up the berth deck hatch, with the rest of us, still buttoning up our clothing, at his heels.

All about us, the men were running to their guns, casting loose, but a swift glance around showed no sign at all of any enemy man-of-war, nor indeed of any ship at all. The rugged coast of Scotland, not half a mile ahead, was the only thing in sight.

In silence, I attended the after battery while Henry Gardner, quarter gunner, saw to the loading of the guns. In a minute perhaps, all were ready and run out, and still wondering what the reason for all this might be, I looked curiously aft, to see flying from our gaff the ensign of St. George. And there paraded on the quarterdeck where they would be plainly visible over the rail, was the marine guard, dressed not in the Continental green of our Navy as the Regulations called for, but in flaming red coats so that they much resembled British marines. Whatever the reason, it was plain Paul Jones was anxious the *Ranger* be recognized on shore not only as a man-of-war but as a British one.

With the final thud of the rammer and the rumble of the last carriage rolling out dying away, complete silence fell on the *Ranger*. We were ready for action, though clear it was to all hands that none impended.

Shrill over the decks then came the trilling of the bosun's pipe and the hoarse call,

"Lay aft on the quarterdeck, all the officers!"

Obediently I followed Lieutenant Simpson, who commanded the after guns, down past the breeches of our guns to where, abreast the mizzenmast, the Captain awaited us.

In three lines, our backs to the mast, we drew up facing the Captain, our three Lieutenants, the marine officer, and the surgeon in the foremost line, the sailing master and the four Midshipmen next, and behind us the warrant officers.

"Gentlemen," said Paul Jones quietly, "close aboard now is the coast of Scotland. We are about to make our second raid there. The point of land we approach ahead is called St. Mary's Isle, the seat of the castle of the Earl of Selkirk."

The Earl of Selkirk? Involuntarily I started. From Captain Paul's own lips, long before on that weary journey overland from Edenton to Fredericksburg, I had it that he thought himself the illegitimate son of that Scotch peer, lord of Castle Douglas on St. Mary's Isle!

"Thousands of Yankee seamen," went on the Captain coolly, "are slowly dying now in English prisons, vilely mistreated as felons and traitors, daily threatened with ignominious death. Since no one else has yet been able to do anything effective toward their exchange, I purpose attaining it by seizing the person of the Earl of Selkirk and holding him as the instrument of alleviation of the horrors of their hopeless captivity till King George and his Ministers see matters in a different light. In this aim of relieving our suffering countrymen, I look, gentlemen, to your wholehearted cooperation."

Though he well knew that in nothing whatever save in the order to make sail for home, could he expect that from his Lieutenants who were uneasily eyeing the nearing coast to avoid the piercing gaze their Captain fixed steadily on them, he continued as if wholly unaware of it.

"We are plainly sighted already from ashore in the guise of a British man-of-war. I want that impression to continue. All officers going in the boats which shortly I shall land, will go out of uniform, and we are to create the impression that our men are press gangs landed from one of George's warships to seize and impress every able-bodied man we sight for His Majesty's Navy. So wholeheartedly do the British support their King in his war on us, that instantly such a rumor will ensure the flight of every man on the place," and here Paul Jones' lips curled in contempt, "lest he suddenly find himself serving good King George. As a consequence of this odd trait, on which confidently we may rely, we shall meet no resistance at all in approaching the Earl and seizing him."

And with all that in the way of explanation, he remarked casually, "I shall go in command of the first boat, gentlemen." And then his voice suddenly hardened.

"Lieutenant Simpson!" he finished abruptly. "You will go with me to seize the Earl. Lay below, sir, and change that uniform coat for any nondescript cloak you may have."

So Paul Jones was determined to take no chances this time in leaving Simpson in possession of the *Ranger* during his absence. But would Simpson go? Directly behind him, I watched his broad shoulders twitching nervously under his Captain's stern eyes. Simpson was obviously in a quandary. He had no stomach for any kind of landing party on enemy soil. But to refuse outright to take part in what on its face was but a bold attempt to help our captured Yankee shipmates would do him little good with the seamen of the *Ranger* he hoped soon to captain. That Paul Jones might have personal (and not so laudable) reasons for wanting to seize the Earl of Selkirk, he was, of course, wholly unaware.

Outmaneuvered, Simpson gave way.

"Aye, aye, sir," he said haltingly, and fell out to go below as ordered.

"Mr. Wallingford," continued the skipper, turning his cold eyes next on that officer, "you will go in command of the second boat. And mind this time you keep your men in good order, and obedient to my commands, or it will go hard with you, sir. I overlook disobedience but once. Lay below now and change your coat."

"I can't, sir," said Wallingford hesitantly, his eyes falling under the sting of the Captain's reprimand. "I have no

[434]

clothes with me but my uniforms."

"Very well then. Go as you are, but keep back among your men and let Lieutenant Simpson go ahead. And now, sir, muster immediately at the boats the same crews we had this morning, and no others. You shall have one more chance to show you are able to control them. That's all, gentlemen," he concluded. "Back on your stations."

So with our Second Lieutenant, Elijah Hall, left this time in command, the *Ranger* was shortly hove to half a mile off the coast. Down the Jacob's ladders into the boats tossing alongside went the men who had raided Whitehaven, but with what change in their demeanor it took no practised eye to see. Wholly gone was that ill-concealed fear that before they had shown at setting foot on enemy soil. The ease with which we had taken and spiked the guns at Whitehaven had effectually cured all hands of that. So it was with a will the men laid back on their oars, and coarse jests flew back and forth over the thwarts on how the peers of Britain would take this seizure of a noble lord in his own castle by the despised Yankees.

But for my part, I looked with ill-foreboding on the venture. That the seizure of the Earl of Selkirk might indeed open the door to better treatment of our mates in English gaols and perhaps even to their exchange, was plausible enough. For with one of Scotland's peers thus rudely swept up by Continental raiders from his own home, no peer of the realm might longer feel safe from a like fate. But what mad strain in Paul Jones' mind prompted him thus to fall on the man whom in his own heart he regarded as his father? What did he really expect to result from such a Quixotic enterprise? That the Earl acknowledge his captor as his son? I shook my head wearily. What Paul Jones, wrapped in an old cloak, had in mind as he sat exultantly looking shoreward in the sternsheets of that boat bearing down on the scenes of his childhood, was beyond me.

Jones silently pointed out the place of our disembarkation, a small stone pier at the foot of the gardens stretching far back toward the castle. The two boats ran smoothly alongside, our landing made easy by the fact that it was just ten in the morning and the hour of high tide. Our Captain leaped out nimbly, followed immediately by all save those detailed as boat-keepers.

Grimly Paul Jones looked at the men tumbling over the gunwales. With pistols plentifully stuck in their belts, cutlasses drawn, and a sprinkling of muskets carrying bayonets fixed, they were ready enough to beat down any resistance. And led now by Lieutenant Simpson, whose visage, naturally of a blackguardly cast, excellently suited the business he was about, there was no doubt it would be easy to carry through the illusion they were a soulless press gang, bent on seizing every luckless able-bodied male they ran across.

We met with luck immediately. Hard by were three Scotch peasants who had been spading up a garden bed, till alarmed by our near approach to shore, they had quit work to scan us dubiously. Scarce had the first boat bumped the little pier and its crew leaped ashore, than one of these three flung down his spade, shouted wildly,

"Run, mon! The press gang!" and instantly he was off, followed by the others.

"Catch me one of those gillies!" shouted Paul Jones.

"Aye, aye, sir!" In a flash, Reuben Chase was off across the turned sod after them, his long legs giving him such an advantage that in a few dozen strides he had overhauled the hindmost of the trio to bring him to a sudden stop. Gripping his victim firmly with one vast hand that completely encircled that cringing peasant's arm, he held his prisoner helpless the while the rest of us trudged swiftly up.

"Want another one, Cap'n?" asked Reuben, releasing his captive to look hurriedly round where the other two, separated now, were disappearing amongst the trees. "I can lay either of 'em alongside in three jumps."

"No, Reuben; one's enough. The others are doing exactly what I want of them—spreading the alarm. In two minutes the Earl won't have a man whose legs are sound enough to take him off, left about the place to defend him. The cat-o'-nine-tails till they die of scurvy is all they can expect in the

[436]

King's Navy, and well they know it!"

At that, the shaking peasant whom Reuben had caught flung himself on the ground before Paul Jones, seized both his knees in supplication.

"Spare a puir mon wi' four bairns and nain to feed 'em if he's pressed! Ha' peety, your worship! Wull ye ken, it'll freighten my puir woman out o' her wuts d'ye tak her mon in sic a wa!"

So thick was his brogue and so odd his dialect, I could not make out half of what he said, but there was no mistaking the abject fear in his quavering voice. Had he been in danger of instant death and not, as he thought, only of being pressed into his King's Navy, he could not have been in greater terror.

But if I understood him not, Paul Jones did well enough.

"Get up!" he ordered, gripping the quaking gillie by the shoulder, and dragging him to his feet. "I'll think on it, provided the Earl is willing to say a good word for you. Take us to him instantly!"

But instead of being in any way relieved at this prospect of being let off, the poor Scot burst out wailing afresh.

"Ah, wae's me! Wha kens what'll come to my wee bairns noo? I hae lang been a faithfu' servant to my laird, and wull wud he say it o' me. But wi' my laird awa from hame, wha'll say the guid word o' me? Peety, your hon—!"

"What?" His face black as a thundercloud, Paul Jones roughly jerked the man about, looked him fair in the eyes. "You say your lord is not at home?"

"Nay, but his guid lady is, your honor. My laird is in London these twa days gone. Wud na my lady's word o' me do ye? Wull she kens me for a faithfu' husband and a guid gardener, but I'm na a sailor at a', as she wud tell ye," he pleaded.

There could be no doubt of the man's honesty. The Earl of Selkirk was beyond our reach!

With his eyes, haggard already from strain and loss of sleep, now suddenly lusterless at this unexpected termination

[437]

to his hopes, Paul Jones turned his back upon the gardener, dully ordered,

"Let that man go."

Incredulously almost the gillie gaped open-mouthed at him, then finding no hand stretched out to stop him, fled like a frightened hare for the nearest thicket.

"Back to the boats, men," muttered Jones in a voice from which all life had departed. "There's naught for us here. The Earl is gone," and he started for the pier.

"Why bother our heads about the Earl, Cap'n?" spoke up Lieutenant Simpson who all this time had been staring eagerly at the castle in plain view across the lawn stretching back from the water. "There's his house completely at our mercy, and I'll warrant you, jammed full o' plate too! A torch'll go fine there after we've looted it, to pay out the English for what they've done in Falmouth in the province o' Maine, where many a poor man's house went up in smoke and even his milch cows were stolen and butchered for beef by a landing party o' British tars. Who's this Scotch Earl that we should treat him any better than they served us back home in Maine, lads?" he asked loudly, ignoring his commanding officer to address directly the seamen who like himself had been casting covetous eyes on that lordly mansion.

"Aye, burn it down!" came almost in a chorus from the sailors, many of whom, hailing from Portsmouth, had with their own eyes seen the charred ruins of Falmouth lying but a few leagues to the north of them.

"There, Cap'n, ye see what the men think?" exclaimed Simpson belligerently, as if that settled it. "Let's give these lords a bellyful o' what they've been dishing out to us Yankees and see how that sits with 'em!"

Abruptly Paul Jones faced about, scanned the seamen. Now that Simpson had planted the idea, there was no mistaking the temper of the men—they were wild to loot and burn! Simpson, whom he had forced ashore as a precaution, had turned the tables on him. How could he, who with his own hands had fired the shipping in Whitehaven a few hours

[438]

before under the noses of these very men, order them now to withdraw, leaving scathless that tempting Scotch castle?

Curiously I watched Jones' twitching face. I knew well that while Jones might justify to himself the seizure of the Earl of Selkirk as a hostage, to burn *that* Earl's house would seem to all thereabouts who knew the rumors of his birth, such an unnatural act of personal vengeance that never would his queer conscience give him rest. But how could he explain that delicate point in ethics to these seamen, inflamed already by the twin lures of reprisal by way of arson and profit by way of loot dangled before them by his insubordinate Lieutenant?

In truth, all my forebodings over this mad venture were now justified. Paul Jones, I knew, could never permit the burning of *that* house. Yet if he persisted in his order for embarkation, then and there he might precipitate open mutiny, for what better chance would Simpson ever have than this Jones himself had providentially afforded him? Ashore already, it would be easy for our scheming First Lieutenant, were he resolute, to maroon his Captain amongst his enemies and flee with the *Ranger*.

Cautiously, with pistols loosed beneath my greatcoat, I began to edge round toward my Captain, to back him up when the break came. And catching Reuben Chase's eye, I winked significantly at him to do likewise.

"Aye, men," said Paul Jones in an astonishingly conciliatory tone, "I agree with you. You volunteered to accompany me to Whitehaven to face the guns there, and something is your due for that complaisance. Within reason, you shall have your way now."

Intensely relieved though much amazed at this concession, I dropped my hands from my pistol butts. So Paul Jones would provoke no mutiny there. Evidently the man knew when to give way as well as when to fight, a trait in him wholly new to me, but for which I was now decidedly thankful. Had it come to blows, though I meant immediately to see that Simpson fell with us, still in a moment after should the Captain and any who stood with him have been cut down under a dozen slashing cutlasses. And I cared not so much for ethics and the Earl of Selkirk's castle as willingly to die for them.

"Lieutenant Simpson," continued Jones, fixing that officer with his compelling eyes, "you told me last night, I think, that there was nothing to be got by burning people's property. I cannot countenance your being of one mind when my orders are concerned, and of another when your own wishes are in question. There will be no burning here! But as for the getting, you may proceed with that. The plate in that castle is yours. Take the men with you, demand of Lady Selkirk all the plate in my name, and then leave her in peace."

With a melancholy glance over the lawn to distant Castle Douglas where as a little child, the petted darling of the young bachelor Earl of Selkirk, he had often played, he faced again the fierce looking group of whiskered seamen roundabout him, fingering their weapons, itching to get their hands on the treasures of that defenseless mansion.

"None but the officers shall enter that house," he ordered sternly. "They will take only the plate that's offered them and retire without a search. No man on my ship hath tasted of the lash yet, but this time the cat-o'-nine-tails will mercilessly claw the flesh from off the back of any man who lifts a finger against the women in that house! And," he concluded ominously, "the man, be he who he may, who sets torch to Castle Douglas will see his last sunset swinging from the *Ranger's* yardarm tonight!" In deadly earnest, his eyes icy, his deep voice hard as iron, he swept his gaze slowly over that rough crowd of fighting men, finishing at last with eyes riveted on our First Lieutenant, towering half a head above him.

"Take charge, Mr. Simpson, and mind my orders are strictly obeyed. I shall not go with you," and turning abruptly on his heel, Paul Jones flung his cloak about his shoulders and started for the boats.

"Aye, aye, sir," mumbled Simpson, obviously abashed that in front of all hands the burden of maintaining discipline had shrewdly been put upon his shoulders. Now with these men whom he aspired to lead, he must carry out the Captain's orders or stand discredited before them, an officer incapable of commanding obedience. "Forward, men!"

At Lieutenant Simpson's heels, silently we tramped upward over the sloping lawn toward Castle Douglas, spreading somewhat as we came closer the more easily to surround it.

I must own that castle much disappointed me in its appearance. For wide-spread and lordly in aspect as the Earl of Selkirk's castle was, it lacked wholly the turrets and parapets with which in my imagination since youth, castles were inseparably connected, being simply an ivy covered stone mansion of considerable extent, with innumerable chimneys and chimneypots only to take the place of the more warlike battlements.

With no noise at all, Lieutenant Simpson rapidly deployed the advancing sailors to surround the house that our object be not foiled by servants fleeing with the plate when our true character was discovered. Posting two men with fixed bayonets before the door, he beckoned Wallingford and me to accompany him, and flinging back his blue greatcoat, rapped loudly for admittance.

A grizzled major-domo, bent and gnarled with age, who very obviously had been expecting us, immediately flung wide open the door.

"There's na a yonker aboot to press," he broke out before ever a word was said to him. "Dinna ye think it shame to come wi' a' yer claymores bared to the hoose to freight her ladyship? The Laird o' Selkirk, when he hears o' it, will ha' ye all flogged by yer ain Captain for this!"

"Never mind your lord nor my Captain," said Simpson roughly, pushing by him through the hall into the parlor, a vast room just beyond. "Tell your mistress immediately I must speak to her!"

Still grumbling protests, the butler started up the stairs, but hardly had he mounted the first step when down the stairway in quiet dignity came to meet us Lady Selkirk, a

[441]

woman who I judged must be much younger than her husband, since she seemed scarce past thirty.

She looked us three intruders over calmly, and then selecting Simpson as apparently our leader (though plainly enough his disagreeable visage gave her pause), she spoke out bravely,

"Who is your Captain, sirrah? It surprises me that any of His Majesty's commanders allows his press gangs to trespass upon the Earl of Selkirk's estates. His Grace, the Earl of Sandwich, your First Lord of the Admiralty, will, I think, be equally displeased when he hears of it."

"You are quite right, my lady," replied Simpson, civilly enough. "I have no doubt that Jemmy Twitcher" (ribaldly he called the Earl of Sandwich by his ironic nickname), "will be more than displeased when he hears of this—he'll be furious! Madam, we meant so to deceive you, but it is needless any longer. We are no press gang, and we're not British! We belong to the *Ranger* frigate, Captain Paul Jones, Esquire, commander, in the service of the States of America. Our business was with the Lord of Selkirk, to take him on board our prisoner. But as he is absent, madam, our next orders by our Captain's direction are to demand all your plate. Produce it immediately! We are masters of this house and everything in it. It is needless to resist."

At this startling statement, Lady Selkirk paled, but I must do her justice in saying she lost no whit in self-possession. Through the windows on her lawn came the glint of bayonets and the flash of cutlasses, thus suddenly disclosed to her as being in the hands of rebels she had never dreamed of as closer than a month's journey off across seas closed to them by Britain's mighty Navy! But fantastic as that idea was, there we were!

"I am very sensible of that," she murmured, looking out upon the gleaming cutlasses and the tightly drawn cordon of fierce seamen who bore them. "There will be no resistance in my house to your Captain's orders." She raised her voice, called,

"Daniel!"

Immediately the butler entered; so quickly indeed he must have been listening behind the door and heard all, for now there was a gleam of hatred in his eyes I had not seen there before.

"Daniel," ordered his mistress quietly, "these gentlemen have orders from their Captain to take away our plate. Go into the pantry and gather it all up directly for them."

Dumbfounded, Daniel made no move, for the which state I hardly blamed him. It was all incredible.

"Instantly, Daniel!" Lady Selkirk looked imperiously at him. "You are delaying these gentlemen in their duty!"

"Aye, my lady." Dismally Daniel stamped out of the parlor into the hall and down it toward the pantry.

I could have sunk through the floor for shame. Gentlemen, indeed! Here we were, thieves practically, and this gentle lady, with no irony in her voice, was calling us gentlemen and having regard to our duty the while we robbed her! With pleasure almost, I could have shot Simpson for having suggested this outrage!

"You must excuse me a moment, sirs," she begged. "Daniel, I fear, still fails to comprehend I am not jesting. I must go see that he obeys," and she stepped out to follow him.

Simpson looked uncertainly after her a moment.

"You, Mr. Folger, go with her and see there's no tricks played on us about that silver," he muttered finally. "And you, Wallingford, take a look about outside to see the men obey the Captain's orders to destroy nothing and molest nobody. I'll stay here."

With a choked, "Aye, aye, sir," I stepped into the hall. This was getting worse and worse—I, Tom Folger, Midshipman in the Continental Navy, being sent to spy on a lady to see that she do nothing to mitigate her losses by robbery! To hell with Simpson and his orders, I swore inwardly. For all of me, Lady Selkirk could do what she pleased in directing the concealment of her plate!

But if Daniel had been dumbfounded at his mistress' order to gather up the plate for us, I was even more startled at what I saw in the hall. For through the open pantry door, there in plain sight was Daniel, who had seized the opportunity to fill the apron of a maid before him with what he could first lift into it that she might flee and hide it somewhere, unwillingly lifting it all out again! And over him stood Lady Selkirk, resolved evidently not to dispute or deny us anything, forcing him to take that silver out of the sagging apron and restore it to the shelves! Hastily I turned my back upon that scene lest I embarrass her, to study ostentatiously the portraits of the Earls of Selkirk lining the walls of the hall.

I was thus engrossed, seeking perchance to see if I could find any resemblance between Captain Paul as I first knew him and the last Earl whom he thought his father (though truth to tell, I could discern none) when I heard a light step at my elbow.

"The plate, sir, is all ready, and I have sent Daniel for some sacks to take it away in. Here is the inventory, if you care to have it," and Lady Selkirk held out for me a yellowing sheet of paper listing the Selkirk plate. "You seem but young to be in so ill a business. Robbing a house is certainly below the dignity of the States of America or its officers."

I blushed at that, but said nothing. How could I explain to her that only by acquiescing in the looting of that plate had Paul Jones kept his men under control and saved the house from being burned over her head? And God knows what worse to her and the helpless maids I saw peeping from every door (for save Daniel, every man had fled the place), once Jones' authority was gone and in the flames of Castle Douglas the mutinous seamen seized the opportunity for rape as well as arson and loot?

So I went back to the parlor silently, to present the inventory to Lieutenant Simpson and tell him the plate was ready to be loaded into sacks, if he cared to check it first.

"Aye, Mr. Folger; of course!" He looked at me for a fool that I should consider that omission for a moment, and stepped out into the hall. "Which way?" he demanded.

I pointed to the pantry, and there he strode, the inventory in hand, checking off with his thumbnail each item as the

[444]

mumbling Daniel, scarce able to restrain his rage at being any party to such a proceeding, took it from the shelves and dropped it into the sacks. Platters, tankards, bowls, huge covered dishes, cups, knives, forks, and spoons—into the sacks went the silver till the shelves and drawers were wholly bare.

"'Tis a'," muttered Daniel, straightening up as he dropped in the last cup, "and may the Deil tak ye for the taen o' it!"

"Then where's the teapot and the coffeepot?" demanded Simpson gruffly, looking from the thumbnailed list to the mistress of Castle Douglas. "And what else are you trying to hide on me?"

"Hide, sir?" Plainly insulted, Lady Selkirk blazed up. "Do you think I should voluntarily have given you that inventory if I were trying to save my silver?" She turned to the butler. "Daniel, where are the teapot and the coffeepot? Have you hidden them?"

"Na', my lady," answered Daniel humbly. "They're yet on the breakfast table wi' the tea and the coffee, still fu' o' it."

"Bring them instantly!" ordered his mistress, which Daniel left to do, returning in a moment with the two silver pots evidently still hot, to fling them angrily as they were into the last sack, from which a steaming mixture of coffee and tea began immediately to ooze.

At that instant, Lieutenant Wallingford returned. "Lend a hand, Sam," ordered Simpson. "And you too, Folger," with which he seized a pair of sacks and carted them to the door, where he passed them to the men outside, in the which action perforce we two followed him dragging the rest of the sacks.

"And that is all, madam," said Simpson as we passed through. "Our Captain has strictly enjoined us to behave civilly, to make no search, but to accept what was offered us and leave you in peace. Our Captain knows your lord, has a great opinion of him, and for that reason gave orders that no more should be done. I trust you will observe that we have

[445]

but carried out his orders."

"That you certainly have," answered Lady Selkirk, smiling enigmatically at him in recollection no doubt of how the teapot, tea leaves and all, had been offered him. "I must do your Captain justice to say he has his men under good discipline. Not a man has entered the house, nor asked nor taken anything, though we poor women here are at their mercy. My thanks to your Captain for that." She peered out the door at the seamen gathering there under Wallingford's orders, ready to leave. " 'Tis a cold morning and your men look chilled. For their behavior, they should be rewarded. Permit me, sir," and she turned indoors to call out,

"Daniel! Bring immediately half a dozen bottles of your master's best whisky!"

Reluctantly Daniel produced the whisky, passing the bottles out to the struggling knots of sailors clutching wildly at them. For a moment, I feared Lady Selkirk's kindness was like to bring on the outbreak I had dreaded. But soon (principally I think lest the fiery liquid be lost in a general melee) the bottles were passing more peaceably from hand, with the whisky being guzzled in swift gulps by each in the few seconds he was permitted to tip a bottle aloft ere it was torn from his lips by the next. In hardly a minute the bottles were all emptied.

"Thanks, madam," said Lieutenant Simpson, and with that we set off down the slope toward the waterfront where pacing nervously to and fro under the trees, our Captain waited us.

"Into the boats, men!" he ordered curtly, after a swift glance over the party showed clearly no signs of loot on anyone save only the sacks of plate. "Shake a leg! I see a mob coming out from Kirkcudbright to defend the castle, and I want no blood shed on St. Mary's Isle!"

45

WE stood out Solway Firth in the *Ranger* with the ebbing
tide, headed southwestward for the Irish Sea. In evident
gloom, every trace of exultation over his raid on Whitehaven
washed out by the outcome of the foray on Castle Douglas,
Paul Jones retired immediately to his cabin once we were
underway.

Quixotic as his idea in seizing Lord Selkirk might have
seemed, at least it was designed for the altruistic purpose of
forcing Britain into an exchange of prisoners. And now instead of that, his madcap venture had ended with Paul Jones
standing before the world as plundering a private house for
personal gain—a pirate indeed! What his old neighbors and
all Britain would make of that was clear. Only too well the
anguish in his face, as at the rail he watched the sacks of
Selkirk plate being swayed up over the *Ranger's* bulwarks,
showed the agony in his heart. In almost feudal Virginia, in
chivalrous Fredericksburg, before stern old Captain Dandridge, how should he ever explain that? And what would
Dorothea think of a lover coming back to her from across
the seas enriched by robbing a lady in her own home? That
stolen plate had smirched the honor he prized above all
things beyond possible repair. Now in his own eyes he was
below even the privateers he despised in plundering for
profit, and clearly the hopeless drooping of his shoulders
disappearing down the hatchway to his cabin painted his despair. Not for anything like this had he brought the *Ranger*
across the seas to attack the coasts of Britain.

But if Paul Jones was sunk in gloom, not so was the rest
of the crew. Hardly had we scrambled up the sea steps to the
deck, when each man in the party was the center of an en-

vious knot of his shipmates, for the smell of Scotch whisky was only too evident and the heft of those bags of plate going below to the Captain's storeroom roused the fires of cupidity in every seaman that handled them. I turned away in disgust to lay below to the steerage. The desperadoes composing the crew of the *Santissima Trinidad*, outright pirates, could hardly have shown more interest in their loot.

Divested of my weapons, I came again on deck to see the gunner, Nathan Sargent, and the quarter gunners, Henry Gardner and Ezekiel Falls, busily engaged in supervising the unloading of our run-in guns, at the which task all the guns' crews were turned to. That done and the powder cartridges sent below again to the magazines, we resumed our appearance as an innocuous merchantman, cruising toward the North Channel to see what further game afloat we might entice beneath our hidden guns.

Idly then I watched Henry Gardner, assisted by Red Jerry and Reuben Chase, going from gun to gun, meticulously cleaning out the touchholes with wisps of oakum spun round a long wire, refitting the tompions lest spray get down the muzzles, and then scanning carefully each of those iron monsters for scars on the muzzles. Here and there, gently they smoothly filed away the scratches and then delicately brushed on some black paint to cover such spots, leaving each gun at last all over an unbroken mass of glistening paint, oiled and as solicitously tucked up in its breechings and tackles as any infant tenderly put to bed in its crib by its doting mother.

"Why the bother, Reuben?" I asked. "You couldn't hurt one of those chunks of iron with a sledge. They'll do as well in action even with a few scratches, and they'll be just as scarred again the next time they're cast loose."

"I see ye ain't never been a harpooner, Tom," replied Chase, uncoiling his vast length from about a six-pounder on which he was bent double oiling an already well-oiled pair of trunnions. "A harpooner always keeps his irons slicked up even if a few dull spots on the barbs'ld make no difference to the whale he heaves it into. And a gunner likes to see his guns glistening like the sun. It ain't what it does fer the guns, Tom; maybe they would do as well with some rust from the salt spray coming over the rail. But it's fer what it does to the gunner's heart, he's always shining away on his pets. Show me a battery that ain't slicked up, and I'll show you a gunner that ain't worth the powder to blow him to hell, where he belongs! The chances are a gunner like that'll short weight the powder cartridges so's he can sneak what he's skimped ashore and sell it to line his own pockets, and the devil take his poor shipmates who've got to go into action with charges o' powder so light the balls won't carry through a mainsail, let alone a ship's side! No, Tom; harpooner or gunner, a good man always keeps his weapons shining!" and down over his beloved guns went his long body and those huge paws to caress their ugly muzzles with paint brush and oily rags.

Remembering the care Red Jerry had shown for the implements of his profession on the *Beaver*, I nodded understandingly. Polished weapons did something inwardly to the owner thereof; I said nothing further as Jerry, Reuben and Henry, harpooners all, moved on to the next gun, leaving the one I stood by gleaming like a jewel.

All the rest of that day we cruised in the open Irish Sea, seeing nothing at all worth attention. As darkness fell, for the first time since morning the Captain came on deck again, morose and taciturn, but I noted, with a pistol stuck in his belt as never before had been his wont on board. Evidently he was taking seriously the warning our Swedish Lieutenant had transmitted to him.

After a brief glimpse about at the distant coasts fading in the night, and another at the sky, he curtly ordered David Cullen, sailing master, to furl topgallants and clew up courses. So shortly, under topsails only and spritsails set as steering sails, and with bare steerageway, we were standing to the northward in the darkness toward the North Channel between Scotland and Ireland.

Morning found us still on the same course just off Belfast Lough again. I came on deck for the first watch to find our crew gathered in little knots all about the fo'c'sle and the waist, gazing uneasily from our scant canvas overhead to the quarterdeck to see what the Captain might order when he came up. For in the distance off to larboard, coming into view as we opened the southern point of Belfast Lough, still anchored off Carrick Fergus was plainly to be seen the man-of-war *Drake*, which some nights before by stealth and strategy we had so futilely sought to take.

I needed no gift of mind-reading to divine the cause of the unconcealed grumbling on deck. The *Drake*, not half a day's sail in any fleet cutter from Whitehaven, by now had certainly been fully warned of our presence and the hysterical terror we had engendered by our descent on that town. Indeed it would surely be to the *Drake*, the closest ship-of-force, that the first wild appeal for protection to all the ravished coasts thereabouts would instantly be sent via the swiftest craft available to them by the frightened inhabitants of Whitehaven and of Kirkcudbright. And from both of those raided spots the *Ranger* had been in the plain sight of thousands who could well describe her to the King's ships. So there could no longer be any hope in anyone's mind aboard our little frigate that, night or day, we might again surprise the *Drake* and catch her at a disadvantage.

Instead of that, the *Drake* would be out seeking us shortly, though plainly enough she was not yet underway, and what alarmed our crew was that while yet we had good opportunity to flee, there we were under much reduced sail like men reft of our wits, casting away our chance to escape!

Our Captain was, of course, immediately notified of the sighting of the *Drake* by Elijah Hall, our Second Lieutenant, who happened to have the deck. But not till eight bells had struck and the watch was being changed, did Paul Jones come leisurely up from his cabin to cast an eye westward into the Lough where the enemy lay.

By that time, it was evident our crew was in a ferment, with the seamen, topmen, fo'c'sle gang, and waisters without orders taking stations ready to loose all sail and get hastily away ere the *Drake* weighed in pursuit of us. For just shoving off from our enemy's quarter and heading for us was a boat loaded with armed men so that very soon, in spite of our sealed ports, our character as a man-of-war must be discovered. And by then, were we no further off than now, in the dull-sailing *Ranger* escape would be wholly impossible.

Our agitated sailing master was so perturbed at that danger that had not the situation been serious, his nervousness would have seemed comical. He rushed up to the Captain almost the instant his foot hit the quarterdeck, to point out to him the boat approaching us.

"Shall I make sail, Cap'n?" he queried.

Paul Jones lifted his spyglass, gazed off a moment at the distant boat, then shook his head.

"Nay, Mr. Cullen. 'Tis but an armed boat coming to speak us. Let 'em come alongside; they can do us no harm. From a distance, the *Drake* takes us yet for a merchantman, and wants doubtless to press a few of our most likely looking hands for the King's service. I trust the boat gets close aboard before it discovers the error."

"But the *Drake*, sir! She's a reg'lar man-o'-war, and she'll be underway for us the instant her boat makes us out!" groaned Cullen.

"Aye, Mr. Cullen; without doubt," placidly agreed Paul Jones. "Think you any British Captain with a ship like the *Drake* under him would miss such a glorious chance to take the pirate Paul Jones who has been distressing this coast?"

Taken completely aback by that, Cullen stared at his Captain speechless a moment, then without a word turned and went forward, leaving Paul Jones alone on the quarterdeck. But I judged from his strained features, our sailing master was through talking. That Paul Jones should be so mad as deliberately to invite attack from a British man-of-war larger than his own was too much for Cullen. So awed was he by what Britain's invincible wooden walls had done even to the well trained navies of Spain, of Holland, and of France, he had no stomach for facing any of them in a Yankee frigate. Not for that had he shipped in the *Ranger*. And rendered desperate by the imminence of an encounter, that he meant swiftly to do something to avoid it was (in the light of what Jean Meyer had said) now plain as day.

Though still distant, the oncoming boat steadily stood for us, headed to cross our bows.

"Down with the helm!" sang out the Captain, and then, "Mr. Cullen, trim topsails to bring that boat astern of us and hold her there!"

With alacrity the disgruntled sailing master lifted his trumpet to execute that order, thinking the Captain had at last come to his senses and was preparing to flee. But when with sheets hauled taut and the yards braced hard over we had swung up into the wind sufficiently to put the oncoming boat into our wake, and still the Captain gave no orders to shake out our furled sails, it became clear to all hands the maneuver was merely better to conceal our character as a warship, not to make off. Even at close range, our stern with its large cabin windows, differed in no way from that of any merchantman; never could the *Drake's* boat learn from that it was running into a ship-of-force. And once its boat had been taken, the *Drake* was sure to weigh immediately, and then willy-nilly, we were in for a battle. Without a long start it was impossible for the *Ranger* to outfoot her.

Cullen, his features grimly set now that he finally saw the skipper's intentions, began to ease unostentatiously over to the rack outboard the mainmast where the boarding cutlasses were stowed. Uneasily I looked about. In sullen knots, eyes on the sailing master, some others of the crew began edging casually in the same direction, while Lieutenant Simpson, who had just relieved Hall of the deck, found occasion to hurry forward immediately. Every other officer was below.

Just as it was dawning on me that the scene exactly suited what Lieutenant Meyer had prophesied as portending trouble, Paul Jones sang out,

"Back the main topsail, Mr. Cullen! Let that boat come up astern."

With a snarl, Cullen sent his trumpet flying across the deck to bring up in the lee waterway.

[452]

"Come on, lads!" he shrieked, seizing a cutlass and whirling about with blade swinging to hurl himself upon the Captain, and cut him down in one wild slash. But hardly had he raised that cutlass aloft than he halted dead in his tracks, his face suddenly chalk. For there, coolly waiting him with pistol levelled at his breast and trigger cocked, stood Paul Jones. The cutlass clattered to the deck.

"Stow that cutlass, Mr. Cullen, and go about your duty." Contemptuously the skipper eyed him, thrusting his pistol back into his belt. "You dolt! You cut so sorry a figure as a mutineer, no seaman in his senses would risk his neck following your lead! You're not worth wasting time on punishing. Get that main topsail backed now!"

"Aye, aye, sir!" Thoroughly cowed, Cullen picked up the cutlass, restored it to the rack, scrambled hastily across the deck to retrieve his trumpet. Then in a broken voice he began singing out orders to the astounded men about him, not one of whom had yet laid hand upon a cutlass so swiftly had everything happened. He bade them haul aft the weather sheets and braces on the main topsail yards, while disregarding him entirely, Paul Jones strolled calmly aft to scan the boat bouncing along over a cross sea in our wake.

So startlingly had Paul Jones made a fool of our sailing master and so cruelly had his caustic comment, echoing loud over the decks, stripped him of every shred of self-respect under the very eyes of the men he had long plotted to lead in mutiny, that verily I believe the sailors leaping to back the main yards looked on the cringing Cullen, scarce able now to bark out his orders, with even more contempt than had our Captain a moment before. And certainly, as Jones had stated, no man there who had seen Cullen so suddenly turned into a limp rag at the sight of the Captain's pistol, would risk swinging at the yardarm in any plot he fathered again. Not till some better ringleader was developed would there be more talk of mutiny on the *Ranger*. With a heart intensely relieved by that knowledge, I looked aft. Now we had but one enemy, not two, to face on the *Ranger*.

Once that topsail was backed, the boat astern gained rapidly on us.

"What ship is that?" hailed the Midshipman in its stern-sheets, an insignificant figure there alongside the brawny coxswain steering.

"The *John* o' Kirkcudbright!" replied Paul Jones in a rich Scotch brogue to give verisimilitude to his statement. "I'm michty short o' seamen and ye'll nae find ony aboard here tae press!"

"Heave to for search!" shouted the Midshipman in a shrill treble, completely unimpressed by the statement, for no doubt such an answer was routine from every ship he spoke. "I'm coming aboard to see! Put over your starboard Jacob's ladder!"

"Aye, aye, but I warn ye, mon, ye waste yer time!"

Hastily coming forward to the gangway, the Captain softly bade all hands keep low behind the gunwale save some few to toss over the ladder and take lines from the boat, while he sent me flying below to muster Lieutenant Meyer and a platoon of marines armed with muskets. Shortly they came tumbling up from the hatchway, also to crouch low out of sight, and we were ready.

The cutter, rowed by ten stout oarsmen and carrying half a dozen seamen more armed with pistols and hangers, ran smartly up under our counter. There the bowman, boating his oar as the others tossed theirs, dexterously caught the heaving line flung him by our bosun who with difficulty kept his face straight while he leaned over the rail to watch it made fast below.

The Midshipman, a ruddy-faced lad who could have scarce been thirteen, immediately came scrambling up the swaying Jacob's ladder like a monkey, his armed squad at his heels. But hardly had he topped the rail, poised a moment to leap down on our deck, when his glance fell on the long rows of six-pounders just below him and he stood transfixed there, his boyish eyes suddenly wide in astonishment. This was no merchantman, Scotch or otherwise!

"Welcome, sir, to the *Ranger* frigate, eighteen guns, of

which no doubt you have heard," said our Captain, bowing slightly. "I am Paul Jones, commanding officer. Let me give you a hand down, sir. You block the way for the men behind you!"

In a daze the youthful Midshipman, his knees shaking at the muskets levelled on him, complied, for indeed there was little else he could do. Round about him, everywhere now our deck seemed to be spouting marines, who with muskets sweeping the rail and covering the helpless boarders clinging to the ladder as well as those still in the boat alongside, made all resistance or hope of flight utterly futile.

In a few minutes, all disarmed, they stood in a dismal group, sixteen stunned seamen and Mr. Midshipman Wilson of H.M.S. *Drake*, gazing fearsomely on the dreaded Paul Jones!

"Cast the boat adrift," ordered the Captain, addressing himself to our bosun. "We can't stow it, and it only impedes our sailing while alongside. And you, Lieutenant," he ordered Simpson, who since just before Cullen's abortive attack had kept discreetly out of sight till now, "have the master-at-arms confine these seamen out of harm's way in the hold. I have little doubt they'll find that safer shortly than their late stations on deck the *Drake*," he concluded grimly.

While the bosun was casting off the empty boat, and the master-at-arms, aided by a squad of marines with bayonets fixed, was unceremoniously herding our prisoners down the hatch toward the forehold, there to batten them down, our Captain beckoned to little Mr. Wilson, pale, shaking, and altogether pitiful standing alone abreast the mizzenmast, his youthful eyes tearful almost at having blundered himself and his men into the enemy's hands.

"Cheer up, Mr. Wilson," said Jones kindly. "Older officers than you have been taken by artifice before. And besides," he added, though it was dubious that the thought should convey much comfort, "as a prisoner of war you have preceded your Captain by only a few hours. Come, sir! Will the *Drake* there weigh to engage, or must I go in after her?"

"You're not making off for America with us? You'll stay

to fight?" burst out Wilson in a high-pitched voice, brightening up perceptibly at the thought. "Then, sir, I'm sorry for you. Captain Burden was preparing to weigh to go out in search of the *Ranger* when I left, and he'll thank you for saving him the trouble. The *Drake's* men-o'-warsmen'll knock this fir-built Yankee privateer and yon hungry-looking Yankee freebooters into kindling in one broadside!" he bragged boyishly, looking disdainfully about him at the *Ranger* and her lean seamen. "We had an express from Whitehaven last night about you. And if you're not swinging from the *Drake's* yardarm for a pirate by night," he added defiantly, "it'll only be because Captain Burden wants to deliver you to Whitehaven where they'll take more pleasure in the sight of you dancing on a gibbet!"

"Aye, lad; doubtless they would," agreed Paul Jones, warming up visibly at the news that the *Drake* would force an engagement. "You but echo your Captain's opinions, the which I'm glad to hear of, since he'll not hang back in his bounden duty in the taking of a pirate." He lifted his glass to scan again the *Drake*. "I see her anchor's aweigh now and she's making sail." Very deliberately he telescoped the glass. "Lay below to my cabin, Mr. Wilson; I'll speak further with you there about my hanging. This way, sir," and he pointed out the hatch. Then turning forward, he shouted savagely,

"Beat to quarters!"

No longer was our Captain desirous of concealing the *Ranger's* identity. On the contrary his only interest lay now in flaunting it in the face of the enemy, so that she would force the engagement, and willing or no, his crew would have to fight. And so it proved.

With the decks of the *Ranger* echoing deafeningly to the long roll of the drum, both the watch below and those on deck came tumbling up with alacrity to fling up the gun ports and roll out the carriages. For now in the plain sight of all hands, there was the *Drake* underway for us, her sides bristling with guns run out and ready. There was no longer the slightest chance of avoiding action. And clear was it to every man, though but a short hour before he had been ready to mutiny and assist in flinging his butchered Captain's body overside, that now his best chance for life and the longed-for return to America rather than swift acquaintance with vile English gaols, lay wholly in prompt and cheerful obedience to that Captain's commands.

So with no skulking and no hanging back on the part of anyone, for the next few minutes the *Ranger* was a madhouse of ordered activity. The topmen leaped aloft to sling the yards in chains. On the berth deck, down in a flat heap came wardroom and stateroom bulkheads to reduce the chance of flying splinters from them. Through every hatch went hurtling below to the holds every chest about the decks. Up from our bulwarks rose the boarding nets. In a steady stream from the shot locker down on our keel, came pouring up in slings the round shot to be stowed in pyramids abaft the guns.

The gun tubs were hastily filled with water, and with hoses swelling under the pressure of the groaning pumps, our decks, bulwarks, canvas, and rigging were speedily wet down to lessen any hazard of fire from red-hot shot. And most ominous of all, far and wide over our gun deck and more particularly about the guns, sand was scattered everywhere, that come what might, the toiling gunners could keep sure footing while they heaved on the tackles and train bars on decks slippery with blood.

The little powder monkeys were scurrying frantically up the ladders from the berth deck, where through a small armhole in a wet woolen blanket which screened the handling room they received the powder charges. They raced up the ladders with cartridges wrapped tightly in their jackets, to pass them to the waiting loaders and hurry below for the next charge. And over all, drowning out every other sound, came endlessly the mad roll of the drum, reverberating wildly from our echoing sides, beating to quarters in a barbaric rumbling rhythm fit to stir the dead to fight!

In five minutes we were cleared for action, our guns run out and matches lighted. In little clusters about each gun

[457]

stood its silent crew looking nervously aft along our open deck at the oncoming *Drake*, an awesome sight under full canvas standing out against the tide to bear down on us.

That the citizens of Belfast and of Carrick Fergus deemed the taking of the insolent Yankee privateer (as in spite of our character as a regularly commissioned warship the English persisted in miscalling her) a mere lark to be ended by the *Drake's* peremptory call on us to strike, seemed attested by the fact that the *Drake* was attended by five small vessels jammed with spectators led by curiosity to come out to witness our surrender. But on closer approach, no doubt affrighted by the sight of our own long guns which promised no such quick ending, they wisely dropped back, leaving the *Drake* clear.

Apparently the news of our presence had been widely spread ashore by expresses sent in all directions from White-haven, for now alarm smokes appeared in great abundance on both sides of the channel, so that as we stood slowly away from the coast with the *Drake* closing in our wake, it seemed all Ireland and Scotland was flaming out with signals warning shipping far and wide of danger.

We stood away from Belfast Lough heading eastward for the Scotch coast to get well out in open water with searoom for maneuver. Since the tide was adverse and the wind not strong this took some hours, and not till mid-afternoon, being then fairly in mid-channel, did Paul Jones permit the eager *Drake*, straining after us, to come even within long cannon shot.

By then, both from observation of her and from close questioning of our captured Midshipman, our Captain was fully acquainted with our antagonist. That she was crowded with men was plain to the naked eye. Everywhere her decks and tops were dotted with redcoats, who we learned from Mr. Wilson belonged to two companies of soldiers she had taken aboard that morning as marines. So it was clear that we should fare ill if the *Drake* should ever manage to lay us alongside, her complement approaching all told one hundred and ninety men as against scarce half that number which the *Ranger*, depleted by desertions and prize crews, now bore. If it came to boarding, we were lost. And aside from being a somewhat larger and more heavily built ship, the *Drake* carried twenty guns against our eighteen, so there again we were outclassed. Cocky little Mr. Midshipman Wilson, sent finally below to join his shipmates in the hold, had not the slightest doubt what the issue should be, once action were commenced.

It seemed passing strange that Paul Jones, bursting with eagerness to engage after a year of inaction since his last cruise in the *Alfred*, should wear away most of the day leading his enemy off the coast. But so it was. Not till late afternoon when we had finally beaten out into North Channel, well clear of land on both hands, did he make the last preparation. Into the tops, fore, main, and mizzen, he sent the marines, good riflemen all from the forests of Maine and New Hampshire, to crowd those swaying platforms far above our decks with the best marksmen aboard.

Satisfied, Paul Jones dressed in his best, silk-stockinged like a dandy going to a ball, gazed about him. The wind was light, blowing from Scotland across a moderate sea, fairly on our starboard beam as we stood north. Dead astern us was the *Drake*, just beyond long cannon shot, straining to close. All was now ready on the *Ranger* for close action.

"Trice up courses! Back the main topsail, Mr. Cullen!" sang out the Captain. "Let 'em close!"

Up to the yards went our courses, aft came the weather sheets and braces on the main topsail, and immediately our headway was deadened, so that the *Drake*, sheering off a little to leeward, started to draw up swiftly on our lee quarter. Simultaneously up to the *Drake's* gaff went her colors, a huge St. George's Cross. At that, on a nod from Paul Jones, our quartermaster ran up the Stars and Stripes, the identical ensign indeed which Admiral La Motte Picquet had saluted in recognition of the United States in Quiberon Bay under the eyes of the French fleet.

With our character as an American man-of-war thus boldly disclosed, I had thought all preface was now at an

[459]

end, and looked anxiously from my gun captains, blowing their glowing matches, across the quartedeck to see what maneuver our Captain proposed. For the *Drake*, while within easy gunshot, was still astern, and neither her broadsides nor ours yet bore.

But loud and clear over the sea from the *Drake* came a hail,

"What ship is that?"

Impatiently Paul Jones beckoned our sailing master to his side.

"You may have the honor of replying, Mr. Cullen," he said ironically, "and since he desires answer, of bearding yon British Captain into the engagement which but this morning you sought to murder your own Captain to avoid. Tell him this, loudly now, that every seaman on this ship as well as those on the *Drake* may hear you—

" 'The American Continental ship *Ranger!* We wait for you and desire you to come on! The sun is now little more than an hour from setting and it is therefore time to begin! Come on, you waste our time!'

"But hurry not your phrases, Mr. Cullen. While they are listening to your reply, I have an idea they will pay little attention to our movements, and I may take them somewhat at a disadvantage. Proceed now!"

"Aye, aye, sir." Obediently poor Cullen, every whit of mutinous insubordination gone out of him, lifted his trumpet, and at the top of his lungs began slowly to bawl out that lengthy challenge.

But hardly had the first hoarse word started to drift down our wake, than Paul Jones sang out forward,

"Stand by, larboard battery! Blow your matches, boys! Aim for her crosstrees!" and then jumped inboard to take station alongside the helmsman. Hurriedly he looked aft. As he had hoped, her officers were gathered in a little knot of vivid crimson on the *Drake's* weather bow, straining forward over the bulwarks to catch the answering hail—in no good

[460]

position for the swift maneuvering of their vessel to meet any movement on our part.

"Hard up the helm!" shouted our skipper. "Square the yards!" and immediately the *Ranger* fell away from the wind to swing smartly athwart the bow of the oncoming *Drake*. There she lay under our guns at easy musket shot, her towering masts all in line, her yards, her rigging and her spreading canvas offering such a target for a raking broadside, no gun could miss!

Only an instant after that Paul Jones waited while the helmsman spun his wheel about to meet her and steady us before the wind and the straining gunners, heaving madly at training bars and tackles, slewed the guns to concentrate their fire on the line of masts abeam us, and drew back the quoins to elevate the muzzles till all lay fair on the foremast crosstrees.

"Fire!"

Down came the glowing matches. Our side burst into flame, a volcano of sulphurous smoke poured from our gun ports, our larboard guns came hurtling back into their breechings to heel the reeling *Ranger* hard to starboard.

In a thundering volley our round shot went screaming through the air to rip through the *Drake's* rigging from bowsprit to mizzen, tearing gaping holes in her bellying sails, and bringing her fore topsail yard crashing down on the cap, there to sway drunkenly in a tangle of flapping canvas and severed lines!

Our first broadside had sadly crippled the *Drake's* headsails, leaving her able only to run before the wind. Certainly she could no longer outsail or outmaneuver us to close for boarding with those companies of soldiers clustered on her decks. From that moment on, the initiative in how that action should thereafter be fought, lay wholly with Paul Jones.

Vastly heartened at the sight of the havoc that devastating broadside had wrought on the *Drake*, with wild yells our gunners leaped at the smoking throats of the guns hurled inboard by the recoil, with sponge and rammer to swab out, shove home fresh powder, shot, and wad, and then

[461]

heaving all together on the tackles, to run out the carriages again.

The *Drake* meanwhile, fearful lest we rake again, had immediately fallen off also from the wind to parallel our course, thus presenting her starboard battery to us, and now broadside to broadside, the action opened in earnest. Simultaneously this time, both ships let go with full volleys, but we were steady on our course and the *Drake*, firing in haste, was still swinging off our larboard quarter. The result was that our shot, aimed high as before, further galled her rigging and did great execution in her tops on the marines stationed there, while her shot, fired from a ship still rolling from the effects of hard over weather helm, splashed all short, to ricochet harmlessly against our hull.

From then on, it was hammer and tongs in a gunnery duel, with both ships going free before the wind just out of musket shot, the which range was our Captain's choice to keep the *Drake's* vast superiority in marines out of action— a decision in which Captain Burden of the *Drake*, confident of what British gunnery would do to the despised Yankees once his ship had steadied on her course, obligingly acquiesced.

But there he made a grave mistake. Not for naught had Paul Jones day after day, month after month, in port and at sea, ceaselessly drilled our men at gunnery exercises. Never have I seen guns handled the way the *Ranger's* six-pounders ran in and out that day. Now that the *Drake* was belching shot at them across the water, all was forgot amongst our crew save what their martinet Captain had made second nature to them. After each recoil, our men savagely flung themselves upon the smoking guns to sponge out, load and send the carriages flying back to battery, ready at the next command to fire again in unison. It was swiftly evident that we were firing at least three broadsides to every two from the *Drake*, rapidly and visibly cutting her rigging to shreds to the great distress of her sailing qualities, which her topmen in face of our deadly fire could not get aloft to repair.

[462]

On their part, the *Drake's* gunners, following the ancient British tradition in action, were firing low into our hull, in the confident expectation shortly of sinking us. But of that Paul Jones had little fear. Striding fore and aft behind his flaming larboard battery, encouraging both officers and men, not only could he see we were outshooting our enemy, but that by his unconventional plan of battle, he would have the *Drake* reduced to a hulk helpless under his guns long before Captain Burden for all the *Drake's* more numerous battery could possibly hole our hull sufficiently to distress us.

And so with each Captain content to follow his own plan we blazed out at each other across three scant ship lengths of water in crashing broadsides, nine guns from the *Ranger*, ten from the *Drake*.

Now nothing was heard but the thunder of the guns and the rumbling of the gun carriages. Stripped to the waist, barefooted on the wet sanded decks, 'kerchiefed in vivid bandanas to keep the pouring sweat from out of their eyes, nostrils inflamed with acrid powder smoke, our gunners toiled furiously at tackles and rammers, serving their hot pieces.

Behind the three after guns, Lieutenant Simpson whom I assisted, grim and silent now that battle was joined, watched with a careful eye the laying of his guns, wholly wrapped up in bringing down the enemy's mizzen yards on which he was ordered to concentrate his fire. And with Reuben Chase, disdaining the elevating bar to lay his gun with his huge hands, sighting along the barrel of the aftermost piece; Red Jerry, whooping like the wild Indian he was at every shot, laying the one just forward of it; and Henry Gardner, quarter gunner, coolly laying the third, we were in a fair way to achieve our object soon. Already we had the *Drake's* topgallant yard hanging up and down in its slings, the lifts cut and the sails useless. Now we were working on the gaff, hurling solid shot at the mizzen crosstrees.

Just forward of me abreast our mainmast was Lieutenant Wallingford, pale and nervous at his first smell of

[463]

powder smoke, shrinking involuntarily each time a broadside smashed into our hull. I could scarce blame him for this
reaction, however, remembering well my own fears when
first the *Glasgow's* shot came crashing through the *Alfred's*
gun deck. But Wallingford stood manfully to his guns
nevertheless, directing them against the enemy's mainmast,
though his gunlayers, being not so good as ours aft, were
seemingly doing less execution.

After the first half dozen broadsides, Paul Jones, wholly
convinced his men needed no coercion to hold them to their
guns, came aft to the quarterdeck to scrutinize critically
what damage he had done.

He was satisfied that the *Drake* could no longer work to
windward, being able with the loss of her fore topsail and
mizzen topgallant to sail only before the wind and none too
well even there. So he ordered the sailing master to spread
our fore course, that we might haul forward and take up a
position on the enemy's bow, there to rake her again.

Slowly that sail caught the wind and we started to forge
ahead. In desperation, Captain Burden, a stout figure
plainly visible in epaulettes and red dress coat on the
Drake's quarterdeck, seeing us drawing away, ordered his
helm hard down and sheered his ship toward us, intent on
laying us alongside where we could no longer work on his
spars. At close quarters, between his more numerous guns
and his overwhelming force of boarders, he would there
shortly cut us to pieces. And lest we get away, the *Drake's*
gunners, who had all this time been hammering at our waterline, suddenly lifted their muzzles and let go a whole broadside aimed fair for the base of our mainmast.

Instantly a hail of cannon balls smashed into our bulwarks amidships, sending the splintering timbers flying inboard over our decks to knock down gunners right and left.
And to my horror, where an instant before had stood Lieutenant Wallingford, sword in hand behind his guns, now
before my eyes there swayed only his headless body spurting
blood, his head taken clean off by a whistling round shot!
A second more and the corpse crumpled up in a sodden heap,

fingers still twitching, to lie in a widening pool of red gushing out on the sanded deck. And just beyond him, gazing stupidly at his right side was little Midshipman Powers, a sorry sight bathed in blood, clutching convulsively at a gory stump where once had been his arm!

From all up and down our larboard side came the shrieks and groans of wounded men, gashed by splinters and torn by shot. Almost at my feet, still clutching his rammer, in a welter of mashed flesh and broken ribs lay the torso of John Dougall, first loader on Red Jerry's gun. Literally cut in half by a double-headed chain shot which had come smashing through the bulwarks, with eyeballs protruding startlingly from their sockets, with mouth wide open gasping horribly for breath, Dougall died before my gaze.

Suddenly sick, I turned away as Red Jerry dived forward, tore the rammer from his nerveless fingers, rammed home the charge. And then, seizing Dougall's severed body lest he jam the wheels of the gun about to be run out, he flung first the trunk, then the legs out the gunport to splash overside. A second later, his naked chest dripping now with blood as well as sweat, Red Jerry was back on his station, his copper face immobile, heaving madly on the gun tackle, intent only on rolling his piece back to battery, ready to sight it.

"Take over the waist battery, Mr. Folger!" sang out Paul Jones, noting both officers there gone, with Wallingford dead and Powers staggering drunkenly below to the cockpit where Surgeon Ezra Green waited with his tourniquets and saws. "Keep those guns firing!"

"Aye, aye, sir!" Choking with fear, I leaped forward to take Wallingford's place, eyeing gruesomely the hole in the mainmast oozing blood and spattered with his brains where the ball which had carried away our Third Lieutenant's head had buried itself. If the *Drake*, closing on us as she sheered over to starboard, was concentrating her fire on our mainmast, trying to bring it down, now indeed was I in the slaughterhouse!

But Paul Jones had no intention of letting the *Drake*

[465]

close to get in another such broadside. His voice rang out sharply above the groans of the wounded,

"Hard alee!" and obediently the *Ranger* swung away to starboard. With far more canvas drawing than the crippled *Drake* had spread, we shot speedily ahead off her starboard bow, ending any chance she had of laying us alongside. And by the time our wounded had all been dragged clear and the loaded guns run out and reported ready, once again we were well ahead on her weather bow.

Now Paul Jones had the *Drake* where he wanted her. Holding our fire, he bade us aim thereafter at her decks, while he raked her from ahead. From then on, sailing two feet to the *Drake's* one, we did nothing but that. Luffing first to get the *Ranger* well up to windward off the enemy's bow, he then wore ship to come down running free so that we passed diagonally across the *Drake's* forefoot, pouring in on her at close range a murderous broadside which went screaming down her deck crowded with men to fill the air with flying splinters and the agonizing shrieks of wounded men.

After that discharge we promptly wore ship again under her bows to come back on the opposite tack, presenting for the first time our starboard battery to deliver its initial broadside with like results.

From then on, we had the unwieldy *Drake* at our mercy, outsailing her, outshooting her, wearing back and forth across her shattered bows to pour in broadside after broadside, raking her decks from stem to stern. It was no longer worth while aiming at her rigging—her sails were too much cut to pieces to warrant further attempt at damage there. With the taste of victory already in our mouths, stained with powder smoke, deafened by the concussion of heavy ordnance, fiercely we served our guns, madly heaving at the tackles to send the rumbling gun carriages back to battery after every discharge. Each time now our guns were laid point-blank on the *Drake's* bulwarks, to send our round shot crashing through her oaken sides onto her gunners, with our every discharge almost, visibly reducing her volume of fire as she tried by yawing wildly from side to side to present her broadsides to us.

Now coolly, like a surgeon dissecting a cadaver, Paul Jones directed his fire upon his victim. We cut away the *Drake's* bowsprit, leaving her wholly devoid of headsails. Part of our next broadside, flying a little high, cut away the gaff from her mizzen, dropping her ensign into the water, the which, however, was promptly rehoisted on her main truck. Next we finished smashing in her bulwarks forward, dismounting the guns there, and leaving a clear passage down her deck along which our solid shot from then on went ricocheting aft to bowl over the gunners at their pieces and sadly to slow up their fire.

By now it was near sunset, and shortly it would be dark. Abandoning any further efforts at maneuvering, Paul Jones ordered sail shortened and we dropped quickly back abeam the *Drake* to make an end. At half pistol shot almost, we poured in another broadside to send the planking of her starboard bulwarks flying inward. And almost like an echo to the thunder of the great guns came a rattling volley from our tops as our marines, good marksmen all, opened fire to deluge the *Drake's* quarterdeck with musket balls.

Which did the most damage, there was no telling. Immediately with that last shattering broadside, we could see the British gunners skulking below, driven finally from their guns. And on the heels of that withering volley of musketry, on the quarterdeck of the *Drake* we saw her Captain stagger and drop, pierced through the head by a musket ball.

The next instant, every sign of resistance thoroughly beaten out of her, across the water came to us the anguished cry,

"Quarter! Cease firing, for God's sake! Quarter!"

Against the sun setting behind her, down from the enemy's main truck fluttered the Cross of St. George and the battle was over. In his despised "fir-built Yankee privateer," invading the very heart of the closed British seas with a mutinous crew wanting only to run, Paul Jones had taken in fair combat a heavier British man-of-war!

Exultantly Red Jerry leaped atop his half-loaded gun, with fierce Indian war-whoops echoing wildly over the darkening seas, started a mad dance of victory on its smoking muzzle.

46

IT was a ghastly sight that met our eyes on the *Drake* when in a boat I accompanied our Captain to take possession of our prize.

Smashed gun carriages, dismounted guns, and severed rigging so encumbered her deck that it was with difficulty we made our way over the battered bulwarks. On the quarterdeck, breathing his last lay Captain Burden. Abreast the mainmast, in the scarlet uniform of a Lieutenant of Infantry lay dead the army officer who had come out to command the land forces serving as marines. Nearby with a leg missing and bleeding horribly from its shattered stump was the First Lieutenant, Mr. Dobbs.

Only the *Drake's* Second Lieutenant was on his feet to meet us as we set foot aboard, and tender his sword in token of surrender. Jones waved it aside.

"No formalities, sir. Bother not over us. Muster all the men still able and attend your wounded!"

And indeed there was much need of it. Now that the thunder of the cannonading had died away, the moans and shrieks of the wounded, begging for aid, rose on every hand. On deck the *Drake*, a shambles battered by solid shot and musket balls, lay dead or wounded forty-two men and officers, near a quarter of the whole ship's company, so terrible had been the slaughter wrought by our broadsides ere that ship hauled down her flag.

We counted later in her hull some hundred holes where our shot had struck, many piercing her through from side to side. Amidships, just abaft the mainmast, smashed by a round shot lay a hogshead of rum brought aboard to serve in celebration of their victory over the Yankee buccaneers.

Aloft, save for the main yard, there was scarce a spar still crossed, and the rigging was but a tangle of frayed lines and severed shrouds.

Exultant in his triumph but grimly conscious of the agony involved, Paul Jones looked sadly about.

"A dreadful spectacle, Mr. Folger," he groaned. "Humanity starts back from such scenes of horror, and cannot but execrate the vile promoters of this detested war! Take the boat and go back to the *Ranger*. If our surgeon, Ezra Green, has by now attended the cases of our six wounded (with which few we have by God's grace escaped in this awful carnage) send him immediately aboard the *Drake* to help the British surgeon here. Heaven knows how many of these mangled tars will die if they are not swiftly amputated!"

As bade, I hastily returned to the *Ranger* and clambered down the steep ladders to the orlop deck where our cockpit lay below the waterline, damp, unventilated, hardly illuminated by a few oil lanterns, to have my ears assailed by the most agonizing shrieks that ever I have heard. For there on a rough table, held down by four stout seamen scarce able to cling to his struggling frame, lay my shipmate, young Midshipman Powers, screaming from pain and writhing in anguish, with Ezra Green grimly sawing away the shattered stump of his arm.

Silent, sick all over and near fainting, I stood by till the stump was severed, the ligatures tied, and the raw flesh drawn down to cover the end of the bone and the whole bandaged up. Then hardly able to speak, such was my nausea, I delivered my message.

"Aye, immediately," grunted out the surgeon, starting to bundle up his bloody instruments. "That's the last of ours, thank God!" Waiting not an instant more, I shot up out of that butcher's pen.

All night long, hove to under shortened sail, we drifted with the *Drake* secured to us by a hawser, repairing our own damages first. The bosun and his mates hurriedly rove off new lines aloft to replace those cut, while on deck our carpenter, Sam Hichborn, and his gang toiled to patch up our shattered larboard bulwarks and what was more important, to plug the shot holes made by the *Drake's* broadsides in our lower hull ere the sea kicked up and we made water through them.

By dawn we were shipshape again on the *Ranger* and ready to fight should another enemy appear, but the day brought no rest for our weary seamen. Boatload after boatload, seamen and carpenter's gang alike, they were ferried over to the *Drake* to turn to on that wreck and make her seaworthy again. Alow and aloft, fishing topmasts, reeving off cordage, putting stoppers on parted stays and shrouds, clearing away broken timbers, plugging innumerable holes in the hull, with what little aid we could get from the sullen prisoners we had taken we kept on without sleep till midafternoon.

That was a task racking our nerves as well as our worn bodies, for by the hundreds spectators from small craft about had witnessed the taking of the *Drake*, to vanish in all directions thereafter in the night with news of that incredible event. What moment now we might expect another frigate or even a squadron of them to loom up on the horizon seeking us, no one knew. But in spite of many alarms each time a sail was sighted, nothing larger than a fishing smack showed up save one. That vessel was the brig *Elizabeth* of Glasgow, which incautiously ventured within hail. We brought her to by a round shot cross her bows and promptly made a prize of her, to send off to Brest with a prize crew under Midshipman Charley Hill.

By late afternoon, we were underway again, beating northward. We hove to briefly close inshore in the north side of Belfast Lough. There, with all our boats and those of the *Drake* which would still float assisting, Paul Jones sent ashore a landing party to bury the dead, save Wallingford, all British.

In a spacious grave atop a promontory overlooking the scene of their last battle, with the honors due their rank and the respect due their memory, Paul Jones, head bared, buried them.

When that last office for our late enemies had been dispatched, we stood out to round northern Ireland and return to Brest through the western ocean. It was now time to release the honest fishermen whom we had lured aboard four days before. Since the poor fellows had lost their boat, our Captain gave them another, and the necessary sum to purchase everything new which their craft had contained in the way of fishing gear. Giving them also one of the *Drake's* sails which would explain sufficiently to any ashore who doubted what had happened to that man-of-war, we cast them adrift, whereupon the grateful fishermen expressed their regard by three hearty cheers for our Captain as they passed the *Ranger's* quarter.

We stood as the day waned, through North Channel in plain sight of both Ireland and Scotland with the *Drake* in tow astern, though able now to sail if need arose. From various small craft we spoke, we learned that all the coast towns were in such a state of hysteria lest we land again and burn them, that the inhabitants were fleeing inland, banks were closing and carting away their specie, and insurance rates to Ireland had leaped so high, scarce a vessel could get cargo even if she dared to sail.

In particular Paul Jones was amused to hear that in Glasgow it was sarcastically rumored that such was the panic verging on insanity he had created in Whitehaven, all the physicians in Scotland were being hastily gathered up to be sent en masse to that raided port to restore the inhabitants there to their senses. But should not those gentlemen succeed in it, a subscription must be started to build them a madhouse.

We did not need these tales to convince us of the panic our raids and the taking of the *Drake* had created, for before our eyes as night fell, far and wide along the coasts signal fires blazed out on every headland. Truly we had converted the shores of the three kingdoms into a *tierra del fuego*, a land of fire surpassing that which greeted Magellan's eyes as he threaded his new found straits. If Paul Jones had hoped by his raids to alarm the English, here was evidence surely that he had succeeded in full measure.

But what was not so heartening to us tired seamen we heard also. The *Thetis* frigate from Glasgow, the *Boston* frigate from Dublin, the *Heart of Oak*, letter of marque from Liverpool, and such lesser craft as the *Hussar* cutter and the *Cumbras* wherry were all out near about, scouring the seas for the buccaneer Paul Jones, so that it seemed certain we should soon fall in with such superior force we should be taken, together with our hard won prize.

But at that and our fears of it, Paul Jones only scoffed.

"Aye," he remarked to the sailing master who came to him for the night orders, obviously sadly shaken by what was about to happen. "I know these unready English. Those ships will be out when the wind serves, when they have finished lading stores, when they have pressed some dozens more reluctant seamen for their crews! By that time, we shall be far in the open Atlantic. Hold her full and by as she goes now, Mr. Cullen, and call me instantly should the wind change. Good night, sir," and he went below.

Our Captain was right. North about Ireland and then far offshore down its western coast, for ten days we struggled slowly along towing the *Drake* and not an enemy man-of-war did we ever sight. By then, laboring steadily on her, our carpenter's gang and our quarter gunners had restored our prize to some semblance of a man-of-war so that over half her guns could again be served. Under those conditions, considering that we might yet be in action again ere we reached Brest, Paul Jones placed Lieutenant Simpson aboard with men enough to man eight guns and transferred all the prisoners to our own hold so that they constituted no danger to Simpson's scant crew. Then he strictly enjoined our First Lieutenant that should it be necessary to cast him loose, he should stay closely in company, assist should we fall in with British ships-of-force, and should he unavoidably be separated from us by stress of weather, to steer directly for Brest.

Thus bolstered up in our fighting power, we cleared the coast of Ireland and stood southeast across the mouth of the English Channel. Our Captain was confident that in those waters, thick with shipping, he should top off his cruise by picking us some prizes ere we made port.

We did not sight anything worthy to pursue till we were well across the Channel mouth and only some fifteen leagues off Ushant, but then on the morning of May 5, in the eastern board we picked up some miles off to leeward a vessel of considerable size standing before the wind up the Channel.

Casting off the hawser to the *Drake*, we immediately started in pursuit with the *Ranger* under a full press of canvas. Since the stranger made no effort to escape, we soon overhauled her, to find to our disgust our chase was a Swede and immune to capture.

Muttering maledictions at this ill-luck, our grumbling seamen handed sheets and tacks, so that we were soon close hauled beating back to pick up again our consort, now some miles to windward of us.

But if we had been disgruntled over our fruitless pursuit of the Swede, now we were astonished on coming about to see that the *Drake*, instead of waiting our return, had made sail, hauled close by the wind herself, and was already hull down on the horizon, fleeing westward from us with every rag set she could get to draw!

Paul Jones eyed the rapidly vanishing *Drake* incredulously. Then by gunfire and flags at our main truck, he made signal to her to heave to, but all to no avail. There was naught left to do but go in chase of our prize, the which perforce we did.

To add to our exasperation, several fat merchantmen now appeared standing by us up the Channel, all of which we must needs wholly ignore to pursue our flying consort, still steering away from us.

By noon we had drawn up abreast the *Drake* but considerably to leeward of her, though in such plain sight of her there could be no mistaking us for an enemy. Again we made signal to heave to.

Still our First Lieutenant on the *Drake* showed not the slightest sign of compliance. In a cold fury, Paul Jones beat to quarters, and we boarded our tacks, laying the *Ranger* as close to the wind as was possible that we might claw up to windward within gunshot and pound our runaway First Lieutenant into submission.

Unfortunately however, the wind shifted suddenly and hauled aft, so that running now free, the *Drake* was enabled to make off again before the wind, easily outfooting the *Ranger*.

There was no telling what Lieutenant Simpson was up to, but clearly it was his intent to make off with the prize. So, vainly flying signals to heave to, all afternoon we stood on in chase till night fell, when once again the *Drake* had us hull down.

There was nothing we could do now save stand on through the night, our Captain believing the dull-witted Simpson was most likely to keep away dead before the wind, heading westward for America. So westward also we went through the dark hours, sighting nothing at all, till at dawn we made out ahead a sail at a great distance, somewhat on our larboard bow.

There was no telling what this might be, but nothing else being in sight, we went in chase, with every scrap of canvas we had on board spread—stu'n'sails, spritsails, staysails, and a ringtail on our spanker that gave the final touch to hide the *Ranger* in a vast cloud of canvas.

With all this, it was shortly evident we were gaining on the chase, but not till noon had we hauled up close enough to recognize her for the fleeing *Drake*. When that was clear, once again we went to quarters, so that it was with all guns run out and ready to give her a broadside we drew finally close enough under her quarter to hail.

"Heave to, you scoundrel, or I fire!" roared out Paul Jones across the waves.

If Lieutenant Simpson had any hope that his shipmates on the *Ranger* could not be persuaded or bullied into firing on their comrades, the sight of the *Ranger's* guns slewed all forward to bear on his quarterdeck with matches glowing ominously over the touchholes, disabused him of it.

The *Drake* promptly hove to.

We triced up courses swiftly, though keeping all our muzzles trained on our consort lest yet she give us the slip again, furled topgallants, hove in stays and steering sails, backed our main topsail, and lay to abeam her, scarce a ship length off.

"Mr. Folger!" sang out our Captain.

"Aye, aye, sir!" I spun about from my station in command of our after battery, hurried to the wheel where the skipper stood grimly eyeing the *Drake* as she wallowed close aboard in the trough of the sea.

"Mr. Folger, muster an armed boat's crew on whom you can rely, and take a squad of marines with you. Board the *Drake* yonder and bring back Lieutenant Simpson a prisoner! If he resists, use what force you need, but bring him off!"

"Aye, aye, sir!"

I soberly thrust a pistol in my belt, motioned to Red Jerry, Reuben Chase, Henry Gardner and some half dozen other Nantucketers at the great guns to seize cutlasses and pikes, and with a squad of red-coated marines whom Jean Meyer hurriedly gathered up for me, we shoved off, prepared for a hand to hand fight.

As the cutter pulled away from the low side of the *Ranger*, our long guns thrust out threateningly over our heads, covering our consort. We drove hurriedly over the sea pulling strongly to make the *Drake's* larboard sea steps. Up I scrambled, cocked pistol in hand, followed closely by my men with the pikes, ready for action. What the insubordinate Simpson, ever an enigma to me, might attempt was beyond me, but his running off with the *Drake* made anything seem possible.

But there was no resistance. Save for the helmsman, there was scarce a man on deck. The prize crew had all skulked below leaving their guns, lest a broadside of grapeshot catch them. And Simpson, abandoned thus by all hands, waited me himself at the gangway, glumly eyeing the pistol in my hand and the grim-visaged boarders at my back with cutlasses bared.

"The Captain's orders, sir, are to take you aboard the *Ranger* under arrest! Get in the boat!" I ordered, levelling my cocked pistol at him.

"Aye, aye." Without another word, the cowed Lieutenant obeyed.

We were back aboard the *Ranger* shortly, where on the quarterdeck, stern but quiet in spite of his inner rage over this final trouble, Paul Jones waited us.

"Your sword, sir," he demanded, as Simpson, flanked each side by a marine with bayonet fixed, faced him. Silently the First Lieutenant delivered it up.

"Lieutenant Meyer," ordered the skipper, turning to the marine officer, "Mr. Simpson remains confined to his room under arrest! Post a sentry over him!"

Meyer saluted smartly, faced about to see the order executed, but the Captain motioned him to wait.

Looking up into our hulking First Lieutenant's sullen countenance, he asked sharply,

"What, sirrah, did you expect to do with my prize, the *Drake?*"

Eagerly I leaned forward for the answer, for on that matter, like all aboard, I was much puzzled.

But Simpson, making no reply at all, only stood there scowling so that his naturally brutal countenance seemed even more villainous. A moment longer the Captain waited, wondering himself, no doubt, why the man before him, who after all had fought bravely enough in the *Drake* action, should have attempted so stupid a trick, but no explanation was vouchsafed him.

Paul Jones gazed contemptuously up at his shaggy features.

"The trouble with you, Mr. Simpson, is that while you have the heart of a lion, you have the head of a sheep!"

Turning on his heel, he motioned the marines to take the

prisoner below, then looked off to starboard where the *Drake* lay, unofficered. He brusquely beckoned to him Elijah Hall, our Second Lieutenant, and now with Wallingford dead and Simpson a prisoner, our sole remaining Lieutenant.

"Mr. Hall," he ordered, "go aboard the *Drake* and take command there in Mr. Simpson's room. I shall pass you immediately another hawser. You know what my orders are for the *Drake*. Mind that this time they are obeyed!"

"Aye, aye, sir," answered Hall obediently.

And so shortly we were standing once more for Brest, again towing that man-of-war as a prize, with our Captain furiously pacing the quarterdeck over having lost two days and no one knows what other rich prizes, by Simpson's scandalous conduct.

But Paul Jones, volatile always in his passions, was soon over his fury. Hour after hour as we plunged headlong into the long Atlantic seas, he stood on the poop, feasting his eyes on the *Drake* ploughing obediently along in our wake, that hawser to her nose symbolic of her submission.

Now truly was he in Elysium. The capture of the *Drake* intoxicated his glory-loving soul, and here at last, I knew, was a deed for which the posterity that so often he spoke of, might well remember him. But more than that, as I copied in his cabin the letters and reports concerning the cruise which now began to pour from his pen to Franklin, to the Marine Committee in America, to his friend Joseph Hewes, to others, I saw something else. I could only judge from those he directed to Robert Morris and good Dr. Read, inquiring on how his purchase stood of that estate on the Mattapony in Virginia, that now the door to glory had opened to him, again his thoughts were turning to "calm contemplation and poetic ease."

One letter only of all those he wrote did not come into my hands to be copied—a letter to Dorothea, which from the time and care put on it and the many glances aft through the great cabin windows to the *Drake* astern the while he composed it, I concluded must carry at last the word that their long wait was over. Now his fame would be

[478]

such that he could dare ask her hand of pompous Nathaniel Dandridge, and she might marry him without shock to the family pride. For of all America's Captains on the sea, he alone could lay at her feet a British man-of-war seized on Britain's doorstep!

And so, absorbed in the fame awaiting him in France and the rosy glow of love awaiting him in Virginia, Paul Jones drove eastward across the seas toward Brest with the future looking glorious indeed.

On the evening of May 8, 1778, with the sun just setting behind us we arrived off Brest, where a huge French fleet lay under le Comte d'Orvilliers, Admiral of France.

With great care, we prepared to enter. At our gaff flew the Stars and Stripes, the same we had fought under. And from the fished gaff on the *Drake* flew the largest American ensign we could find aboard, with the Cross of St. George, the *Drake's* own battle flag, upside down beneath it!

And thus under the eyes of the whole French fleet we entered, the little *Ranger* towing astern the bulky *Drake*. The French, incredulous at first that a British man-of-war should actually strike to an inferior enemy, soon hailed us with frenzied cheers, the which we Yankees on the *Ranger* answered heartily.

Paul Jones, a gallant figure in his brilliant uniform, young, graceful, handsome, in solitary grandeur on his quarterdeck as we swept by the towering sides of those cheering ships-of-the-line, glowed with pride.

But brute fate came swiftly to shatter his dreams. Hardly had our anchor splashed overboard and our debonair Captain gone below than the mail from America, waiting us, came aboard. I took the packet for the Captain to his cabin, helped him sort them. Despatches, orders, bills, hastily we ran them over. Ah! A letter from Fredericksburg.

"From our old friend, Dr. Read, Tom!"

Gaily Paul Jones seized it from me, tore it open, read,

"You tell me you are under some expectation of purchasing a Virginia estate. But some more agreeable idea will, I fear, call you off now and deprive us of you. Miss Dandridge is no more, that is, she a few months ago gave herself into the arms of Patrick Henry."

Dorothea married? Utterly crushed, Paul Jones stared unbelievingly at that letter. Married! And to Patrick Henry, old enough to be her father, an uncouth widower with six children!

47

GLUMLY Paul Jones received now the adulation his victory swiftly brought him. From Admiral le Comte d'Orvilliers, from the Duc de Chartres, his second in command, from the Captains of the French squadrons, extravagant praises showered down on him.

Not in the memory of any Frenchman had they seen their ancient enemy thus humbled. Only too well they recalled through the last half century how their own fleets and frigates had crumpled up beneath the guns of Britain's mighty Navy till the legend of British invincibility on the seas was almost an article of faith with them. To get away uncaptured after an engagement with British seamen was the most any French Captain in his innermost soul dared hope for. That a British man-of-war might be battered into submission save by vastly superior force had seemed unthinkable.

Yet there before their eyes in Brest, outmaneuvered, outgunned, outfought, lay the *Drake*, her colors floating humbly in submission beneath those of her smaller antagonist. The French were keenly aware that they were again on the brink of war with Britain. Their enthusiasm for Paul Jones who had wrought that miracle, was overwhelming in its spontaneity.

From morning colors till sunset the day following our arrival, our quarterdeck echoed continuously to the roll of the drum, the blaring of ruffles, the shrill wailing of the bosun's pipes, while one after another between stiff rows of side boys, Paul Jones welcomed aboard the *Ranger's* quarterdeck the Admirals and Captains of France's men-of-war, come to embrace him and inspect at close range his victorious ship and its prize.

But Admiral d'Orvilliers brought prudent counsel as well as praise.

Jammed in the *Ranger's* hold we now held two hundred British seamen, men and officers, taken on the *Drake* and our other prizes. These were to Paul Jones our most valuable booty and he proudly explained to the Admiral he meant to hold them close prisoners till he had forced the British Ministry into an exchange for an equal number of our countrymen, and further extorted a promise of treatment as ordinary prisoners of war instead of as traitors for such as remained unexchanged. The protests of Dr. Franklin had been many over the villainous way our shipmates taken at sea had been mistreated in British gaols, but all to no avail. Now, however, with a sizeable batch of their own officers and men in our hands, the obstinate British Ministry must give over their cruelties to captured Americans or see their own men treated likewise in reprisal.

Gravely d'Orvilliers nodded approval of the plan but pointed out pitfalls.

"*Monsieur le Capitaine,*" he advised, "take not any chances. What outcry Stormont, the British Ambassador in Paris, will make over this, you may guess as well as I, even to a threat of war if these men are not instantly released by us. The Court of France has not yet made up its mind to war, and may comply. I must report immediately your captures to the King, but to avoid disaster to your plans, delay not, *monsieur!* Put your captives all aboard your prize, the *Drake,* man her, and send her off to America, ship and prisoners together, ere any orders can come to me by post from Paris to take them from you and return them to King George with whom France is still at peace! I implore you, *mon Capitaine,* act thus immediately to save your prize, your prisoners, and much embarrassment to you!"

Courteously Paul Jones thanked him, but delayed any action in compliance. Close to England's shores, something might be done in forcing an exchange; once the captured

[482]

English were three thousand miles and a month's journey off across the sea, it was unlikely. He rested on my cousin, Ben Franklin, in whose diplomacy he had utter faith, to foil Stormont in any attempts at the release of his prisoners.

There was another matter that weighed on him—the Selkirk plate. Long and earnestly he had pondered how in any degree he might clear that stain on his honor. Now back in port, he acted.

Strange as such a thing might seem, he wrote personally to Lady Selkirk, explaining what really had occasioned that raid, how it came her plate was seized, apologizing profusely to her for the seizure which he had permitted to keep his crew in hand and stating that now he had gratified his crew, he would gratify himself by purchasing the plate when it was sold by the prize agent in Brest, and restore it to her by such conveyance as she should direct.

Stranger yet, in this letter, of the which I made several copies for him, he seized the opportunity in writing to a woman, though to one he had never seen, of pouring out his heart in the hurt he had received in Dorothea's marriage, though I think that Lady Selkirk might little understand the anguish which lay behind the phrase,

"Before this war began, I had at an early time of life, withdrawn from the sea service, in favor of 'calm contemplation and poetic ease.' I have sacrificed not only my favorite scheme of life, but the softer affections of the heart and my prospects of domestic happiness. And I am ready to sacrifice life also with cheerfulness, if that forfeiture could restore peace and goodwill among mankind."

What Lady Selkirk might make of that, and of the man who wrote it, I greatly wondered. But the offer of restitution much relieved Paul Jones' mind, and with that letter posted, he turned now to another matter which cried haste.

His prizes were yet unsold, his crew unpaid. The wounded, both British and American, were in urgent need of hospital care ashore. Naturally provisions had to be secured to feed his own crew and his prisoners. With no money to effect all this, he turned to M. Bersolle, a merchant of Brest who gladly undertook to advance him daily supplies as needed to the ultimate total of 24,000 livres, against drafts in his favor drawn immediately for that amount on the American Commissioners in Paris.

But now came more blows. Our crew, enraged that they did not receive their prize money immediately, sent off post-haste to Paris a letter expressing sympathy with the arrested Lieutenant Simpson and requesting his release as well as their own prompt departure for America. Then crowning shock of all, a few days later came aboard Monsieur Bersolle, inarticulate with rage and gesticulating wildly, flaunting in our Captain's face for want of words, the drafts he had drawn on our Commissioners, dishonored every one! When the frantic Frenchman finally found voice, it was to bellow out that till those bills were paid, not another sou of credit should Jones receive, and with that he stamped wildly down the gangway and ashore to sue out immediately attachments on all the *Ranger's* prizes against the stores already issued.

Haggard to be thus left in the lurch, knowing not where to find tomorrow's dinner for his crew, let alone the materials to refit his damaged ship, certain only that in some way Arthur Lee must have gained ascendancy amongst the Commissioners in Paris thus to humiliate him, he wrote the Commissioners in rage,

"That America should suffer this damned disgrace in the presence of the French fleet and to the knowledge of every officer and person here, covers me with shame. None of my prizes can be sold, and my officers and men want the withal to cover their nakedness!"

And with that off his mind, he turned to seek what remedies he could. His men at least must eat, and somehow he must find the funds to feed his prisoners also, for never did he mean to let them go till an equal number of Americans were released from British gaols.

He had one resource. Somehow in their meeting, as had

[484]

before twice happened at critical periods in his life with Joseph Hewes and Dr. Read, he had again struck a responsive chord of friendship in the Duc de Chartres. Instantly on their first contact that hereditary Prince of France and Admiral in her fleet had been warmly attracted to this handsome young Captain who had come across the seas so superbly to humble the ancient enemy, and he had since in many instances gone out of his way to manifest his friendship.

To the wealthy Duc de Chartres, Paul Jones now brought his troubles, to be furnished with a loan on his personal credit sufficient to feed for some time yet the hungry men dependent on him.

That done and with a letter commending him to the attention of the Duchesse de Chartres from her husband, Paul Jones hurriedly bundled up his papers, left the *Ranger* temporarily in charge of Lieutenant Elijah Hall, and taking me as secretary, posted off to Paris to see what was wrong.

There we learned swiftly from Jonathan Williams, late Continental Agent at Nantes. Williams, who met us on the arrival of our coach in Paris, sadly informed us that Arthur Lee's neurotic actions were bearing fruit. Silas Deane, co-commissioner with himself and Franklin, had been recalled to America to face there the slanderous charges adduced by Lee that his every act in France had been to line his own pockets. And in his place as Commissioner had been sent over John Adams, sympathetic with Lee and his suspicions, openly envious of Franklin!

Paul Jones groaned at that. Of Lee's distrust and hatred of himself as a Scot he was already well acquainted. And now to have as Lee's supporter John Adams, explained all! John Adams, who mistrusted Jones as "an emigrant foreigner from the South" and moreover had been bitterly and personally affronted when Joseph Hewes had thrust aside one of his New England appointees to make a place for Paul Jones as a Lieutenant in our infant Navy! With those two as Commissioners, a majority now since all were equal in authority, he could expect little but enmity and frustration.

But still there was Ben Franklin, whom he reverenced as a father. Anxiously Paul Jones turned on Williams with that. Surely Franklin knew better than to let America's interests suffer from his colleagues' personal animosities?

"Aye," agreed Jonathan Williams to that. "But Ben Franklin has lived long enough to know when he must bend in order not to break. Arthur Lee he despises, feeling that in sowing suspicions and jealousies, in creating misunderstandings and quarrels, in malice and in subtilty, he has no equal. But of John Adams, though at present he be swayed by Lee, he has a higher opinion, knowing that in time Adams will see the truth and abide thereby. Still, pending that, lest worse happen he must give way to them. Complain not, my friend, over what Lee and Adams have done in humiliating you. I have been dismissed wholly from my post! What can that mean save that Arthur Lee holds me up to all the world as a thief? And yet Ben Franklin who is my uncle, must acquiesce even in that!"

Understandingly Paul Jones nodded. So the wind lay in that quarter. Still there was hope, if what Franklin had acquiesced in had been only under compulsion, not from lack of faith in him.

We went next day, all three of us together, to pay our respects to Ben Franklin. There admitted once again by young Temple Franklin, we were received with the utmost cordiality by the aged Doctor himself.

"Ah, my son!" he exclaimed on taking Paul Jones' hand, "how can I congratulate you sufficiently for your late success! And now by your victory you have given me something to work with in my efforts to succor our suffering compatriots. Already I have written to England about the exchange of your prisoners. Sit you down, sir, and tell me how went your cruise, and what difficulties you now labor under."

Instantly under the warm glow of Ben Franklin's open

approbation, Paul Jones lost every sign of the cankerous fury which had been gnawing at his heart. Like a son indeed, he cast all his troubles at Franklin's feet—his hurt over the dishonored drafts, his worries over his insubordinate Lieutenant, the raw wound to his honor over the Selkirk plate.

"I have received also some roses from those who should be my friends," he concluded finally after a description of the taking of the *Drake*, "but they, alas, have had a superabundance of thorns!"

Franklin laughed.

"You are young yet. With more years, you may acquire philosophy enough to bear up under their pricks. Look at my situation! With Arthur Lee telling me to my face I connive at peculation! And John Adams, cold in his Puritanic conscience, thwarting my plans, unable to comprehend why the deluded French should prefer to deal with me on the public business when he is certain his abilities overmatch mine! But I answer them nothing, for I am old, cannot have long to live, have much to do, and have no time for altercation. I bear all their rebukes for the good of the service, though it goes a little hard with me. I commend the same attitude to you, my impetuous friend."

Paul Jones humbly nodded acquiescence. If Franklin could thus silently stand calumny, he also should try.

"You tell me the Duc de Chartes has personally loaned you money?" continued Franklin, his aged face wrinkling inquiringly as he directed a benevolent glance on the young Captain. "Yes? Then you are fortunate, for I have found the best manner in which to secure a person's support is to put him in the way of doing you a favor. You have secured a powerful friend there, my son, and one who can do America much good through you—more so perhaps than you know, for Madame la Duchesse to whom he commends you is even more influential with the King than he, and she can help you at the Court." He meditated a moment, eyeing Paul Jones keenly, then asked,

[487]

"The *Indien* frigate in Holland; you remember her? Would that command still interest you?"

"The *Indien?*" Transported with joy at the thought, Paul Jones leaped buoyantly to his feet. "The *Indien,* sir? For the command of that powerful frigate, I should give my right arm!"

"Be not so rash," sagely Franklin admonished him. "It does not demand so great a sacrifice. To prevent seizure, we have transferred title to the *Indien* to France, but with your fame now and what interest the Duchesse de Chartres can exert on Louis, that huge frigate may yet be obtained for you. The occasion seems propitious, as Sartine, the Minister of Marine, has requested I detain you in France for further service. Therefore present your letter to Madame la Duchesse, and since women have more influence at Court even than Ministers, I shall give you another to the Comtesse d'Houdetot."

And rising from his chair, he made his way slowly but with the dignity of age to his desk, where seizing a quill, he began to write.

"Here," he said finally, handing Paul Jones the missive, open and unsealed. "I have minced no words about you. You may read it, but I charge you, hesitate not to deliver it, for attention to the ladies here in France, I find, is the surest way of getting the King's ear."

Paul Jones read. That he immediately blushed was not surprising, for in black and white on that freshly sanded paper the canny Franklin, surely a keen judge of men, had written of him,

"You will take pleasure, I am sure, Madame, in receiving the brave Captain Paul Jones, not for his bravery, but for himself. For when face to face with him, neither man, nor, so far as I can judge, woman can resist the strange magnetism of his presence, the indescribable charm of his manner."

Gracefully Paul Jones bowed in acknowledgment, but with a wry grimace, covering a raw inner hurt, countered,

"You mistake, sir. One there is in America, so I have just learned from your nephew, Dr. Read, who has most successfully resisted my manner, to give herself to Patrick Henry, whose charm, if he has any, certainly lies elsewhere than in manner."

"Aye," replied Franklin. "My nephew has written me also of how Patrick Henry has taken the fairest maid in all Virginia to himself as his second wife. But note well, sir, still I am right. I say there, 'When face to face with him.' My years have taught me much concerning women. You have so far blundered with Miss Dandridge, in your close attention to the public business, as to keep your face too far apart from her. As with electricity, in which subject I have also done some delving, I find that the power of charm and the magnetism of presence decrease rapidly in potency with distance. Never, my son, make that mistake again with any woman, especially not here in Paris!"

"*Touché!*" admitted Paul Jones ruefully. "Not for three years have I been in Virginia, thinking the post would serve me the while I plied the oceans seeking the enemy. But no longer, sir!"

And with that we left, Paul Jones mightily changed by his new hopes for the *Indien* and even more from having basked in Franklin's friendly smiles.

We stayed some months in Paris. At first a frequent visitor to Passy, Jones who enchanted my philosophic cousin as much as any other man, was soon invited to become a member of the household, an invitation in which I as a somewhat distant relative was included.

In the delightful villa overlooking Paris occupied by Franklin, the "petit hôtel" donated by Monsieur le Ray de Chaumont, Commissary to the French Marine, Paul Jones blossomed. Surrounded by the throngs of French soldiers and of statesmen constantly in attendance upon the venerated Franklin, he swiftly became acquainted with the major figures of the Court, friends all to the rising young Republic of America. And Paul Jones, on whom were centered their hopes on the sea of humbling hated Britain, was particularly the object of their close attention, the which attention Franklin, possessed at last of a Captain who he believed could do it, cannily fostered.

Under Franklin's wing, Paul Jones, relieved of all fear that he was in disfavor, managed at last to secure the permission of the French Ministry for the sale of his prizes, and happy in that permission, immediately wrote his disaffected crew in Brest to that effect, promising further his utmost endeavors to secure the prompt return of the *Ranger* to America.

To this end, having received from Lieutenant Simpson earnest expressions of regret for his conduct, he ordered that officer released from his arrest. He even went so far in his generosity as to recommend to the Commissioners that since he was to stay in France, the *Ranger* would be wanting a new Captain, and that Lieutenant Simpson be allowed the post.

This the Commissioners acceded to, so with Simpson at last Captain of the vessel to which he had so long aspired, and given permission to sail for home as soon as he could get the *Ranger* ready, Paul Jones washed his hands of that vessel and turned to other prospects.

With war impending between France and England, alluring prospects were dangled before Paul Jones' eyes.

His letter to the Duchesse de Chartres had promptly procured him an invitation to attend on that great lady, wife to France's Sailor Prince, herself a Princess of the royal house. At her levee at the Palais Royal, Paul Jones, youthful, graceful, courtly, handsome in gorgeous uniform, hero of the *Drake* victory, immediately took the eye of the motherly Duchesse; and from that moment, his position in Parisian society was assured.

To me, humbly lost in the edges of the crowd fringing that salon in the Palais Royal, the way this man, gardener's son, ex-slaver, ex-merchant seaman, ex-buccaneer, sea captain now, rose to the occasion to enchant the eyes of gracious ladies and of their bewigged and silk-clad consorts, fair startled me. No courtier to the manner born could have accepted more naturally the attention centered on him, nor half so gallantly dispensed the subtle compliments with which he held enchanted about him the perfumed and beauty-patched ladies attending on the Duchesse de Chartres.

From then on, in one way at least, Paul Jones changed radically. Never save in Dorothea, had he taken much interest in women, ships wholly absorbing him. But now, the welcome guest at one salon after another, he flitted gracefully amongst the ladies in the most indiscreet society in all Europe.

Still, heeding Franklin's advice, he did not lose the chance to use what influence these ladies, and particularly Madame la Duchesse, had at Court, and shortly as a result of their intrigues, he was personally received by Sartine, Minister of Marine, and Vergennes, Minister of State, next to Louis, the most powerful men in the kingdom.

To these Ministers he set out his plans for a raid on England by combined land and sea forces, to strike such a swift blow on unprotected cities as should leave England reeling.

Many a time in the past the French had dreamed of such a thing, always to have their unseagoing Admirals outmaneuvered and outfought, and their shattered fleets thrown back ere ever a French soldier set foot on English soil. Now such an attack had for long been held impossible. But Vergennes, infected by Paul Jones' enthusiasm and affected certainly by the success attending his raids in the *Ranger*, promised again to give the matter consideration.

Soon the plan flowered—from Sartine came word the King approved. The dilatory Louis had at last decided for war. Among other projects, a joint land and sea expedition under the American flag was to be undertaken, with the ships commanded by Paul Jones, and the troops led—of all persons—by the Marquis de Lafayette, the idol of France, who was to be brought home from America for that purpose!

[491]

Deliriously Paul Jones rushed off to thank the Duchesse de Chartres for what she had done for him—now indeed the path to glory and to eternal fame was opened to his thirsting soul! That elegant lady, indulgent to Paul Jones as any doting mother might have been to an impetuous son, received him in her boudoir, where she still lay abed though it was near noon. Wildly Paul Jones flung himself on the silken coverlets to kiss her hands and in extravagant phrases pour out his heart in gratitude.

Then that no time be lost, Jones flung together his belongings in frantic haste, bade farewell to Franklin and to Passy, and we posted off to L'Orient.

There Paul Jones feasted his eyes on the *Epervier*, a large French frigate promised him as flagship of his squadron, to which were to be joined two other frigates and two cutters lying at St. Malo and the *Indien* when she should arrive from Holland.

L'Orient was bustling with activity. At last the French had openly declared war in assistance to America. Just a week before off Ushant, the fleets of France under d'Orvilliers and the Duc de Chartres had met the British under Keppel and Palliser. That battle, however, with some sixty huge ships-of-the-line engaged, had like many another, lacking a vigorous Admiral on either side, ended in futility. No ships were taken by either the British or the French, none destroyed, and after fruitless cannonading, both fleets had retired, the French to Brest, the British to Portsmouth.

Paul Jones scanned the *Epervier*, lying without a Captain in L'Orient, and his heart swelled. There was a frigate! With a few more fast-sailing ships like her to form his fleet, he would show Britain that not all her lordly squadrons of towering men-of-war could save her coasts and her cities. When he sailed, there should be no bloodless ocean parades like the battle off Ushant with perfunctory broadsides at long range satisfying the honor of both combatants, and getting nowhere. His ideas on warfare on the sea were quite otherwise.

Fully satisfied with his inspection of the *Epervier*, we posted off to Brest for a double purpose—to get from the *Ranger* ere she sailed for home such seamen as might choose to remain behind to sail again under Paul Jones' flag, and to arrange with the French Admiral for the promised squadron.

The first part of our mission in Brest was quickly accomplished. Still the *Ranger* lay in port with Lieutenant Simpson, Captain now, finding to his dismay the difficulty of fitting out a ship with only a bankrupt government at his back and funds hardly obtainable. Lack of food, lack of money, lack of naval stores, all of which lacks he had previously used to inflame the crew against Paul Jones as due to his personal shortcomings, he had now to struggle with himself in outfitting for the voyage home, and though many weeks had gone by since his sailing orders had come, there in Brest lay the unready ship.

Under such circumstances, Paul Jones had not much difficulty, even though he was received aboard but sourly by Captain Simpson who owed only to his former commander's generosity the fact he was on the quarterdeck and not in prison awaiting court-martial. On his reading to the mustered crew Dr. Franklin's orders authorizing the proposal, some twenty-seven men (practically all being the Nantucketers I had recruited) volunteered to join Paul Jones for his future squadron in France, and gathering up their dunnage swiftly, went ashore with him.

Next day, Paul Jones waited on the Admiral d'Orvilliers to see about his ships. D'Orvilliers, certainly his friend, received the request with frank bewilderment, and to his stunned surprise, Paul Jones learned that the promises of princes were as worthless as those of the Continental Congress!

In evident distress, d'Orvilliers had to inform him that on the day after Jones had left Paris, orders had come to him to send the frigates at St. Malo on a cruise to the Baltic. And as for the *Epervier*, knowing nothing of the promises

[493]

made to the American Captain, he had himself just given her to an officer in his fleet. Not a vessel of the promised squadron was available to Paul Jones!

Dazed, sick almost, Paul Jones came away from that sad conference a broken man. Once again he was a Captain without a ship!

48

NOW began a dreary time like unto nothing so much as those tragic months following the day Ezek Hopkins had snatched from him the command of the *Alfred*. Then he had worn his heart out pursuing one ship after another dangled before him by the Marine Committee, only on coming up with them to find them as unsubstantial as an idle dream.

It was the same now, save that in place of the Marine Committee stood de Sartine, Vergennes, and behind them Louis, forever dangling before his eyes the promise of fine ships, of powerful squadrons, never making good on them.

Heartbroken, Jones watched the *Ranger* sail from Brest for home. He had voluntarily given up that command; now the feel of the quarterdeck of even that little frigate lifting to the seas beneath his feet would have been heavenly balm to his oppressed soul.

To add to his miseries, there soon came to his ears the story that ere his departure from Brest, the villainous Simpson, his pardoned Lieutenant, had maliciously spread the story that Jones had peremptorily been removed from command of the *Ranger* by the American Commissioners with whom he was in deep disgrace!

That such a thing was plausible was obvious enough. There was the *Ranger* gone away, in command of her late First Lieutenant. There in Brest was her late commander, beached with no ship at all in sight for him, American or French. What use to argue in such a situation?

Ashamed to show himself in Paris again, ashamed almost to show himself amongst the French officers in Brest, Paul Jones kept himself indoors wholly wretched, glum and taciturn, so that it was a trial for me to live with him.

But one resource remained to him, his pen. I copied his letters endlessly, the originals of which went off to Franklin, to de Sartine, to de Chaumont demanding that the promises of the Minister of Marine be fulfilled. That Franklin and de Chaumont both did their best was evidenced in the fact that soon apologies came from de Sartine for the lost squadron, with promises of other ships.

One by one these glittering rainbows of ships were danced before his eyes—the ever-recurrent *Indien*, the mention of which now almost nauseated him, the *Renommee*, the *Fox*, the *Lively*, the *Alert*, each time however the promised ship shrinking from great to less, from less to little.

But like their counterparts in America, Jones found them, great or little, vanishing into thin air when he reached out to clutch them. America was at war with Britain. France was at war with Britain. All over the Western Ocean the ships of Britain's enemies under workaday Captains or worse were mainly bungling their opportunities when they were not actually hauling down their flags to "superior force." But for Paul Jones, who never yet had met a force of any kind on any ocean, superior or otherwise, from which encounter he had not come off both with his ship and with honor, there was no ship.

The months went by, the war went on. Like a mist vanishing before the sun, under the Captains who had been placed ahead of Jones in rank and thereby got commands, one by one the ships of our Navy were lost. The *Alfred*, the *Cabot*, the *Andrea Doria*, the *Providence*—all the original fleet. Then the fine new frigates built thereafter—the *Raleigh*, the *Warren*, the *Hancock*, the *Randolph*—bravely fought, some of them ere they struck, were sunk, or run ashore to avoid capture. But bravely fought or not, lost they all were with slight damage to the enemy, and wars are not won that way.

Paul Jones, beached in Brest, heard in anguish of the destruction one after another of the ships he knew, and might perhaps, save for that unjust supersedure in his rank, have had command of to do something vital for America other than to lose her ships. But there stood that fatal list of Captains in America, with his name so low on the list it was improbable, should he take passage home, there would be now any ship for him.

The summer drifted away, then autumn, and still Paul Jones lingered in Brest, so distraught that he would not have wished even his worst enemy in like position.

Monsieur de Chaumont, despairing that Jones ever should get a warship, wrote him in all kindness offering to fit out for him a privateer.

Jones was purple almost. Go privateering? He would die first!

Too wrought up to write himself, he turned to me.

"Tell Monsieur de Chaumont, Tom, in what terms you will, that as an officer in the American Navy, I can serve neither myself nor even my best friend in any private line whatsoever, unless either the honor or interest of America is the premier object! And who can say such of that damnable business of privateering?"

That insult, though de Chaumont meant it not as such, determined Jones. He had worn away his heart appealing to the Ministers, to Franklin, to de Chaumont, to the Duc de Rochefoucauld, to the Prince de Nassau, to the Chevalier Baudouine—to every Frenchman of high or low degree he knew who might help get him a command. Now he was through with men. Women, Franklin had told him, ruled France. If that were so, he would try what influence he had with women to provide himself a ship.

So casting aside all reserve, he wrote the Duchesse de Chartres, setting forth his miseries, explaining his hopes, imploring that gracious lady to intercede for him directly with the King!

That letter, wonder of wonders, brought immediate results. Hardly had it arrived in Paris than a message came back to Brest which lifted instantly my Captain from the depths of his despondency. Franklin wrote back to inform him that Monsieur de Sartine had just been to call, formally

to promise Jones a ship. With the war on, none of the
King's ships would be available, but a large ship which
might well be converted to a warship could be purchased,
together with some smaller consorts. Would Paul Jones be
so good as to go to L'Orient where the vessel in question lay,
to inspect her and report? If the ship were suitable, Monsieur de Chaumont, Commissary of Marine, should be instructed to purchase her for Jones and provide the remainder of his fleet.

Half killed with grief over his long inaction and heartily
sick of Brest where he considered himself now but an eye-
sore, Jones packed immediately and we set off south for
L'Orient where we arrived on the evening of December 6,
1778, tired and frozen.

Jones was worn and cold from the wintry journey, and
immediately turned in, leaving me to locate for him the vessel we were interested in. I soon learned by inquiries along
the darkened waterfront, that this ship, an old East Indiaman by the name of the *Duras,* was lying out of commission
in the basin along with a number of the King's ships considered altogether unfit for service and condemned for sale
as hulks. With many misgivings therefore as to what daylight might reveal regarding our particular ship, I wended
my way back to our inn. Jones was already asleep, so I
deemed it unwise to waken him merely to communicate my
fears.

Next morning without breakfast, so eager was Paul
Jones to lay eyes on his new ship, we journeyed to the basin.
What Jones may inwardly have expected, I know not, but
that he did not expire of mortification then and there at
first sight of the *Duras* I still regard as a miracle.

It was fitting that the *Duras* lay surrounded by vessels
condemned for hulks. There she was, an East Indiaman of
ancient pattern, with a high poop sure to make her a bad
sailer to windward, a rotten hull, decaying masts and spars,
worthy herself only to be sold as a hulk to lie in the mud up
some river far from the waves, a warehouse only!

How old was the *Duras?* None of the French, mariners.

or landsmen, round the basin could recall exactly. Some thought sixty years; some thought less. Amid their shrugs and gesticulations, all we could discover for certain was that for twelve years she had plied to the Indies, armed with six-pounders to defend herself from pirates, till the French East India Company had decided she was worn out and had laid her up for sale. Now there she was.

Had not Paul Jones literally been through purgatory for five months at Brest, I doubt not but one glimpse at the *Duras* would have sufficed him. But his soul thirsted for a ship, and now it seemed it must be the *Duras* or nothing.

He looked her over critically. At least she was large, and might mount a fair number of guns, if her decayed timbers could sustain their weight. And on her roomy decks might be carried considerable numbers of soldiers. As for spars and rigging, a good bosun and a good carpenter might do something to make her shipshape aloft. She had large tops to all her masts, and on these platforms his eyes dwelt at length.

At last he turned to me.

"She'll do, Tom. On that hull I can mount guns enough to capture an English sixty-four, provided only I have fair play for it. We go to sea on the *Duras*."

Returning to the inn, he wrote immediately to M. de Chaumont, assuring him the *Duras* would answer. Two weeks went by unaccountably with no reply to this letter from the Commissary of Marine.

At the end of that time, the agent for the East India Company informed my Captain that even old ships being now in some demand with a war raging, he could give Jones but ten days' refusal on the ship, after which she would be sold for a merchantman to one of the other expectant purchasers.

In anguish lest even this old tub escape him and never should he get to sea again, he wrote imploringly to de Chaumont,

"So much indeed have I suffered through the severity of my situation, I find my health much impaired. I can no

[499]

longer sleep. The *Duras* will certainly be sold if you do not promptly make decision. If you really love me, you will remove my doubts, or tell me that my fears are true, else I shall believe I have been betrayed and sacrificed with premeditation."

In an agony of suspense, Jones waited his fate.

Three days before the refusal period was up, there came to M. Gourlade, commercial agent of the Ministry at L'Orient, definite word to purchase the ship. Paul Jones breathed again.

But hardly had my Captain's pulse returned to normal and the next post come in, when there arrived from M. de Chaumont another letter so dubious in its tone regarding the purchase as to leave all again uncertain. In a torment, Paul Jones paced endlessly back and forth in his room. He had given up his American command to stay in France at de Sartine's request. Now he had exhausted every resource amongst his friends in Paris and still he had not received the promised ship. Even Franklin had apparently been unable to hold the slippery Minister of Marine to his promise. In despair, Paul Jones sank down on his bed, his youthful face haggard and suddenly aged. Everything had failed him. Caught between the politicians of France and the politicians of America, he was doomed now to the one thing that most certainly would kill him and that soon—inaction.

In sympathetic silence I gazed on him there, convulsively gripping the sheets. Nothing I might say would ease his torment, and well I knew already that in his moments of anguish, he always became taciturn and did not welcome any attempts at conversation.

At last he sat up, reached on the table for a paper-backed volume he had lately acquired, Ben Franklin's "Maxims of Poor Richard," then widely popular in France.

"Your venerable cousin, Tom," he remarked to me, wanly attempting a smile, "has managed to survive through much adversity. Perhaps Poor Richard's philosophy will help reconcile me also to bearing up under a miserable fate," and idly he began to thumb the pages.

[500]

Some thirty minutes he continued thus, to no great degree lifted up in spirits. For what interest could Poor Richard's sage remarks on thrift have to one who was recklessly dissipating his own wealth in support of a bankrupt Treasury without hope of reimbursement? Surely Poor Richard could not commend that as the road to fortune for any man. In my chair, slumped down myself as dispirited as my Captain, I dozed off.

A wild war-whoop which would have done credit to Red Jerry himself brought me suddenly wide awake again. On his feet, his sunken eyes glowing almost as if an enemy ship had just struck to him, was Paul Jones, reaching for his cloak.

"Come, Tom!" he ordered impetuously. "Underway, my lad; we've just time to catch the coach for Paris. Poor Richard has opened my eyes to my folly in expecting anything other than what has happened to me in this matter of the *Duras*. Never said Franklin a truer thing than what in those Maxims he has put into Poor Richard's mouth,

'If you would have business done, go yourself. If not, send.'

"Come! We fly to Paris to get that business done ere it is too late!"

Within a quarter of an hour, wrapped in our heaviest cloaks, we were inside the lumbering post coach, with Paul Jones impatiently counting almost every beat of the flying hoofs on the rough road bringing us nearer to Paris.

In Paris, all succeeded to his wish. Confronted face to face with the Captain he had personally requested be kept in France, the dilatory de Sartine received Jones with utmost courtesy, apologized for all delays as being incident only to the vast labor of carrying on the war, and sent off instantly peremptory orders for the purchase of the *Duras*.

That settled, he was at once content to await, though with impatience, the slow process with which full well he realized now the French Ministry, like every bureaucracy, would unwind itself from the red tape involved in the actual transfer of the ship. A month, two months? Who knew? He could but wait, certain however that it was in process.

Meanwhile, as guests we were once again installed at Passy, with Franklin smiling benevolently on his ardent Captain, burning at the prospect for action. Out of a heart overflowing with gratitude at what had brought escape from his agonies, Paul Jones had hardly greeted his host when he burst out,

"Sir, under your name shall the *Duras* go into battle. Poor Richard's advice has brought me this ship, and she shall henceforth be called for that great man who guides the destinies of America, *Bon Homme Richard!*"

Six weeks more went by till all the formalities were completed, and in the name of Louis XVI, the *Duras* was formally bestowed on Paul Jones and renamed in accordance with his wish, a suggestion which the French enthusiastically fell in with. For amongst high and low, the fame of the good Doctor Franklin shined in France above that of any living man.

Those were a busy six weeks, with Paul Jones constantly in attendance on Count Garnier, designated by de Sartine to handle the affair, over the details attending the transfer of the *Duras*. But at last they drew near an end, and in early February, Paul Jones was ready to depart for L'Orient to supervise the fitting out.

His last duty ere he left was to call on the Duchesse de Chartres.

In high spirits at the thought of being afloat soon again, he gaily called to me as the last of our effects were being carried from "le petit hôtel" in Passy,

"Come, Tom! Your best cloak! My *devoir* now is at the Palais Royal to thank the more than royal—the divine— woman to whose grace I feel I owe all."

And well might he say so. For surely no doting mother exhibited more solicitude for the welfare of her son than that bestowed by the unaffected Duchesse de Chartres on young Paul Jones.

In the grand salon of the Palais Royal, he was soon pouring out as he bent to kiss her hand impassioned sentiments of gratitude for the *Duras.*

"*Bon voyage,*" smiled the Duchesse, indulgent to his youthful enthusiasm. "Do not forget me." Anxiously she looked into Paul Jones' eager eyes. "Do you have everything you need now?"

"Aye, madame," exclaimed my Captain exuberantly. "The King has given me the ship, good Doctor Franklin has bestowed on it his name, and on the sea the enemy is waiting. Nothing is wanting to complete my happiness."

"Nothing?" Mischievously that great lady gazed at him. "It may be that in love you can get along without money, *mon enfant,* but having lived more years than you, I know that in war it is impossible. You will find the King's Ministers niggardly. Go when you get to L'Orient to Monsieur Gourlade. In his hands I have placed 10,000 louis d'or that you may draw on to assist in properly fitting out your ship that you may come home again in triumph."

Enraptured Paul Jones kissed her hands again.

"Madame, I shall lay an English frigate at your feet!"

49

BACK in L'Orient, with infinite vigor Paul Jones set about converting the *Duras* into a man-of-war.

His first concern, of course, was cannon, the insignificant battery of six-pounders she carried already being worthless to him. So, after starting the artisans in the dockyard at L'Orient upon replacing the rotten spars and decayed rigging of the *Duras*, and cutting through her hull the gun ports for her new battery, he looked about for artillery.

Since there was none whatever available on hand, Jones left to see what he could do in the way of locating a foundry to cast a set for him. And I, under no illusions now as to what was involved, set ruefully about the task of recruiting a crew.

I immediately brought down as a nucleus from Brest my twenty-seven shipmates left there when the *Ranger* sailed, mostly my old neighbors from Nantucket—Henry Gardner, Reuben Chase, Red Jerry—all overjoyed to be aboard ship again.

But after that small group had come aboard, getting more men was next to impossible. Since the *Bon Homme Richard* was an American ship now, we were forbidden to enlist French seamen, all those being desperately wanted for the King's own ships. How then to obtain a crew of some three hundred and eighty Americans in a French port, or indeed in all France where there were but few, was a task that might well have given pause to Solomon, let alone to poor Tom Folger who laid no claim to his unbounded wisdom.

In despair, I racked my wits for solutions, for the thousandth time looking longingly back at the day there had tumbled aboard the *Alfred* in Philadelphia in answer to my handbills, seamen enough to have manned a squadron. Never again would I see anything like that. What could I do now? There in L'Orient, every device I had previously used was worthless. Handbills calling on patriotic Americans to ship were of no avail where there were no Americans, patriotic or otherwise. Nor for the same reason would the lure of prize money have any effect. And least of all could I go raiding American privateers in French ports, as I had the *Eagle* in Tarpawling Cove, to seize deserters and all the rest of their men, to fill out my empty billets on the *Bon Homme Richard*.

Here and there, traveling up and down the coast in St. Malo, Brest, L'Orient and Nantes, I picked up a few more men, chiefly American prisoners who by devious means had escaped from English gaols to work their way to France through Holland.

Consequently, when after a month's journeying Paul Jones had discovered in Angoulême a foundry capable of casting his guns, and having ordered them, had returned to L'Orient, I had hardly fifty seamen recruited for the ship, and was at my wit's end as to how to get more.

Now indeed did Paul Jones have everything on his own head to solve, and a less resourceful organizer would have thrown up his hands in despair. Crew, officers, guns, even the ship itself, had all somehow to be improvised from nothing or in the case of the decayed *Duras*, from something almost worse than nothing.

Paul Jones energetically turned to, to produce a warship ready for action from this sad state of affairs. The guns at least he had ordered. Whether he should ever get delivery on them remained yet to be seen. He prodded the dockyard artisans into activity which promised in some months to deliver the *Bon Homme Richard* in such a state of repair that provided we did not meet any weather too bad for her aged timbers, we might hope to remain afloat. But officers and crew, especially the last, were a puzzle.

He was little worried over officers, for we had now a First

Lieutenant who had come from America to join us, and Jones felt that in a pinch he could commission the remainder from amongst his seamen and still be better off than he had been on the *Ranger*, where the officers foisted on him with commissions from the Congress were but a hindrance when they were not worse.

But the crew! He must have seamen to man his guns and handle the sails, or the ship was worthless. I had failed to get them. What could Paul Jones do? I started to explain the impossibility of getting American seamen, and we were barred from recruiting French sailors.

"Belay the explanations," interrupted Paul Jones. "Why waste my time? I expect no miracles of you, Tom. American seamen? Unobtainable, you say. Aye, I will not argue the point. We are barred from recruiting Frenchmen? That also Monsieur de Sartine made plain to me. But what of that? Had you done as much seagoing as I ere you joined the Navy, you would know that there are dozens of other nationalities to serve our purpose—Swedes, Portuguese, Dutch, Maltese, Danes—good seamen, too. Don't worry over their nationality. Go out and get them!"

I did, and gradually our crew increased.

Meanwhile, Lafayette arrived home in Nantes, coming in the finest frigate yet built in America, and graciously named in honor of our new allies, the *Alliance*.

Immediately the plans for the joint military and naval descent on England were taken in hand, and Jones was called to Paris, where with Vergennes and Franklin the details were settled.

My Captain came back glowing. He was enchanted with the Marquis de Lafayette, who promised cordial cooperation. And de Chaumont was adding to his command the small French frigate *Pallas*, the brig *Vengeance*, and the cutter *Cerf*, all (though manned by Frenchmen) to be placed under the American flag with their Captains commissioned for the cruise by Franklin.

Finally to make his joy complete, at his request Franklin was holding in France and adding also to the squadron the only other American warship in France, the newly-arrived *Alliance*, a 36 gun frigate, and next to the *Bon Homme Richard*, the largest vessel in it. Oddly enough this American frigate, making her first voyage since completion, had out of compliment to France been given to Captain Pierre Landais, a Frenchman once in Louis's Navy who had come to America conveying supplies from Beaumarchais. On Pierre Landais, cashiered by de Sartine for an ungovernable temper, the Congress in a fit of sentimentality and without looking into his qualifications, had bestowed an American commission as Captain and the finest vessel in its possession. And going even further in its desire to show its appreciation of French aid, the Congress had sent the *Alliance*, commanded by Landais, to convey Lafayette, covered with laurels as aide to Washington, in triumph back to France.

There was, however, some slight miscarriage in all these trans-Atlantic compliments. Vergennes and de Sartine, good diplomats both, lifted their eyebrows at the lack of tact of America in sending Landais whom they had dismissed in disgrace, to enter a French harbor in command of a finer ship than ever he had had in France. And Lafayette, having had some experience with Landais on his crossing, wrote Paul Jones that none of his troops were to be embarked on the *Alliance*. The Marquis declared he did not desire to subject any of his officers to contact with the quarrelsome Pierre Landais.

A little perturbed, Paul Jones looked questioningly across the water from the *Bon Homme Richard*, ringing to the clatter of shipwrights' mauls, to the *Alliance* swinging clear in the stream. No soldiers to be carried on her? Then his troop capacity would be reduced at least a third. What kind of Captain was this Pierre Landais, that Lafayette, his own countryman, should prefer such a reduction in his fighting force rather than compel French army officers to travel on his ship?

But Jones had little time to worry over the idiosyncrasies of Pierre Landais. In spite of a windfall of some hundred Portuguese, Maltese, and Malay seamen who came to

[507]

L'Orient in the *Epervier* and whom I promptly enlisted, we were still far short of our complement. And with the time rapidly approaching for the embarkation of Lafayette and his troops, not a single cannon had the foundry at Angoulême delivered, regardless of all its promises!

Hurriedly Jones dashed off to Angoulême, to come back near distracted. Not for months could he expect completion of his guns. As a last resource, lest he go to sea unarmed, he was compelled to accept from the French arsenal at L'Orient a set of worn out cannon too old for use in the French Navy —6 six-pounders for his upper decks, 14 nine-pounders and 14 twelve-pounders for his middle gun deck, and 6 eighteen-pounders for the lower gun deck, 40 guns all told. Even with this ancient battery, we were left short, for on our lower gun deck, Jones had cut through six ports on each side, expecting to carry 12 eighteen-pounders for our main resource.

As it was, now he could mount but three heavy guns on each side, but this shortage in weight of metal on either side he hoped to overcome by rolling all six guns out the lower ports on whichever side he found himself engaged, leaving the unengaged side barren altogether of heavy artillery.

With that solution, we took aboard and mounted our guns, such as they were, and now the only problem left was the crew.

With all my efforts resulting in bringing aboard such a vast number of differing nationalities that our decks were a veritable babel of strange tongues, I had still no more than two hundred seamen, and by no conceivable means were more to be got.

Glumly I reported my failure to Paul Jones.

"I have one more shot in the locker, Tom," was his comment, "though I had hoped not to be forced to use it. While de Sartine has forbidden the recruiting of French seamen, I have his permission to top off my crew with Englishmen."

"Englishmen?" I looked at him with astonishment. "Our enemies? Where will you get Englishmen to fight for America against their own countrymen?"

"Out of French prisons, Tom. There are hundreds of

English seamen rotting there, who for release from those dungeons would fight for the devil himself! Go you to the Commandant of Fort Louis at the harbor mouth, present my compliments, and request of him that he pass the word amongst his prisoners that by the King's grace, such of his captured English sailors as wish to ship aboard the *Bon Homme Richard* will immediately be released. But warn him, a hundred such volunteers are all I can take, no more."

Dubiously I proceeded to Fort Louis on that errand. Was it possible that Englishmen, even to obtain release from prison, would take up arms against their own country?

It turned out to be possible. Such was the misery in which the captives lived even as prisoners of war that I might easily have chosen far more than a hundred men from among the ill-fed and filthy volunteers clamoring for release on any terms at all.

With my recruits under guard of a company of French marines, I brought them aboard the *Bon Homme Richard*, to complete the worst crew, I think, that ever a man-of-war went to sea with. How we should avoid mutiny at the earliest opportunity, or the seizure and surrender of our vessel the first time a British ship-of-force hove in sight, I could not imagine.

But Paul Jones could.

"Avast worrying, Tom," he counseled me. "Lafayette's soldiers will keep 'em in order and at their guns."

In late May, we were at last all ready to shove off, with orders issued for the embarkation of the troops. Nothing was wanting save the arrival of Lafayette, and we should set sail on our great adventure, a descent in force on Liverpool.

Then instead of the coming of the General, came instead a message that the plan had been suddenly changed, Lafayette's orders cancelled, the troops withdrawn. Someone (the talkative de Chaumont himself, Jones feared) had gabbled, news of the sailing had reached England, the project was abandoned!

Paul Jones, philosophic now under repeated disappointments, took the blow with fortitude. Instead of sailing to raid England, he was ordered out with his squadron to convoy a fleet of French merchantmen from L'Orient to Bordeaux and then to chase all British cruisers from the Bay of Biscay, this voyage, limited to ten days, being in the nature of a shakedown cruise.

With some foreboding as to what might result from his heterogeneous crew with no troops aboard to maintain order, Paul Jones, Commodore now, sailed on June 19, 1779, on that duty.

Such a crazy cruise resulted as I think had not heretofore occurred. Hardly had we cleared port and settled down on a southerly course, when trouble started.

In fairly heavy weather, we were standing southward in the night with our convoy in our lee, our new First Lieutenant, Richard Robinson, having the deck, and our squadron in some disarray as regards alignment.

As a consequence the Commodore (who was below) sent word to the officer of the deck to signal all ships to form line astern the *Bon Homme Richard*.

The *Alliance*, disregarding our signal however, stood on to cross our bows, so that a collision seemed imminent, at which critical moment when action was demanded on both quarterdecks, the situation degenerated into farce.

On the *Alliance's* poop, Captain Pierre Landais stood an instant screaming in profane French across the water for the *Bon Homme Richard* to give way to him, but seeing no sign of that, gave no orders himself to his own ship which might have obviated the danger and instead rushed below to load his pistols.

On the *Bon Homme Richard*, our First Lieutenant, confused perhaps by the unintelligible torrent of abuse coming through the darkness and being no very good seaman himself, lost his head and did nothing either, so that the ships were left in the hands of the two quartermasters at the wheels. These sailors, finding themselves without directions, stolidly held on their courses, with the result that ere the Commodore, seeing through his cabin windows the dark mass of the *Alliance* looming up on our larboard quarter, could

[510]

get on deck, the *Alliance* had driven athwart our hawse.

With the crash of splintering timbers rising above the whistling of the wind, the ships collided, our bowsprit smashing over the *Alliance's* poop, so we lost our cutwater and our jibboom and the *Alliance* her mizzenmast.

With imprecations on all hands who had stupidly stood by while that happened, Jones, roaring orders, extricated the two ships, reformed the squadron, and making what repairs were possible at sea, stood on for Bordeaux.

But the accident gave the Commodore much cause for thought. Under what hallucination was Pierre Landais, that in a moment of danger he should abandon his quarterdeck, scream for the right of way, and rush for his pistols? Whom had he meant to shoot? And as for Lieutenant Richard Robinson, what sort of seaman might he be to stand by speechless while his ship was driving headlong into a collision?

That was the start. We kept on with our convoy, but next day the *Cerf* was compelled to put back to L'Orient to refit.

Having safely delivered our convoy to Bordeaux, we turned northward to clear enemy cruisers out of the Bay of Biscay the while we steered for our home port. But it proved a hopeless task.

Two days out in the Bay of Biscay, three enemy ships of war were sighted to windward coming down on us. Promptly the Commodore made signal to form line of battle and we stood for them. Seeing our readiness to engage, they immediately hauled by the wind and made off, to escape shortly by outsailing us.

Then what I most feared happened. Through one of the Maltese sailors came to the Commodore's ears news of a plot on the part of the English seamen to seize the ship when the close presence of an enemy promised success. Fortunately it had not yet been put to execution, the first enemies sighted having fled with too much precipitation to warrant the rising.

A swift inquiry having showed the impending mutiny was a reality, it was for the moment squelched by seizing and

[511]

putting into irons two British quartermasters who turned out to be the ringleaders. But there was no way of wholly removing the danger by ironing all the English participants, for that would have left us short a full third of our crew and sadly crippled in manning our battery.

Several days later in a thick fog, the *Alliance* and the *Pallas* parted company and we saw no more of them. Being thus deserted by our most powerful consorts and left only with the *Vengeance* brig, we steered for L'Orient, off which port we arrived on June 30. But the wind was foul, and it was hopeless to enter in the *Bon Homme Richard*. The *Vengeance*, however, with the Commodore's permission, left us to beat her way in.

We stood alone offshore, when as night fell, we sighted not far off two British frigates bearing down on us, both at least thirty-twos, and thus in combination more powerful than we.

Paul Jones was immediately all eagerness for battle, sure, could he but get the *Bon Homme Richard* between them, of capturing both.

With the roll of the drum beating to quarters echoing everywhere in the *Richard*, Paul Jones wore ship and stood away while we rigged for action, after which we hove about and stood by with courses hauled up and topgallant sails handed to engage them both.

But immediately on perceiving that, the two poltroons tacked ship and stood to windward, to our Captain's intense mortification easily outsailing the *Bon Homme Richard* close hauled, since we with our high poop, reminiscent of Columbus' towering caravels, could not lie close to the wind.

And with that final fiasco, we returned to L'Orient. Not a gun had we fired, not a ship had we taken. What Paul Jones thought of that brief cruise he never said, but certainly it illuminated to him that never could the clumsy *Bon Homme Richard* catch a ship-of-force that sought to elude her. And between a mutinous crew, the incompetence of his own officers, and the lack of attention to orders displayed by Captain Landais, the future of the *Bon Homme Richard* when she actually sailed to raid England looked gloomy indeed.

Once in L'Orient, Paul Jones set out grimly to rectify matters. With the assistance of Lafayette, the Minister of Marine was persuaded to detail to the ship four French marine officers, a dozen French marines, and a hundred and twenty-one French soldiers from the garrison at L'Orient who volunteered to go as marines, so that any future tendency of our seamen to mutiny might be dealt with properly.

Then came a real blessing. A number of American seamen, released at last from prison in exchange for the seamen we had taken in the *Drake*, arrived in a cartel from England at the port of Nantes. Hurriedly I was rushed down there to recruit those I could for the *Bon Homme Richard*. Out of this sorry lot of half-starved sailors, I managed to enlist some thirty-odd for the *Richard* and a like number for the *Alliance*, which also badly wanted men.

Since the number of released captives exceeded a hundred, I had expected to do better, but most of the poor devils after several years of torture and abuse, had had quite enough of war in any form and wanted nothing but a chance to sail for home, in which desire I could not but sympathize with them. So with those I had, I returned to L'Orient, leaving the others to find their way back across the ocean to America, if they could.

Amongst my new recruits for the *Bon Homme Richard*, thus providentially delivered from English prisons to help fill up our complement, I was overjoyed to find two old shipmates—Sam Stacy and Jack Robinson, late of the *Alfred*, and taken by the British with that ship. And my joy was even exceeded by that of Paul Jones. When he saw them, he promptly reinstated them on the *Richard* in their old positions of sailing master and bosun respectively, giving him in those stations men on whose competence and loyalty he could rely.

Meanwhile throughout the ship, Paul Jones was busy winnowing out the chaff our late cruise had so mercilessly exposed. Our First Lieutenant, Richard Robinson, was tried by court-martial and broke for his incompetence in the late

[513]

collision. The two ringleaders in the abortive mutiny were similarly tried and by the court sentenced to death. But on the Commodore's intercession, this was commuted to flogging, a doubtful mercy, for the cat-o'-nine-tails, for the first time wielded on a man-of-war commanded by Paul Jones, cut their backs to ribbons.

Since there were now aboard from amongst those lately arrived from English prisons, some who had been officers, Jones seized the chance to improve his situation. The berth of First Lieutenant being vacant, Jones filled it by commissioning as such a daring and capable young officer, Richard Dale, who had escaped from Mill Prison by his own efforts, made his way to France, and had joined us.

As Second and Third Lieutenants he appointed two brothers, Henry and Cutting Lunt, late prisoners also, and filled our mess in the steerage by appointing as Midshipmen, Nathaniel Fanning, Thomas Potter and John Mayrant, all recent captives, and to my delight, by promoting gigantic Reuben Chase. These men, with Richard Coram, Benjamin Stubbs, Gilbert Watt, Beaumont Groube, and John Linthwaite, all lately from America, gave a liveliness to our steerage mess I had not before seen there on any ship.

Dr. Lawrence Brooke now joined to complete our personnel. He came all the way from Virginia to volunteer as Surgeon. A merchant from Philadelphia, Mr. Matthew Mease, insisted on accompanying us as Purser, and two Irish Lieutenants fighting in the French Army joined up—Edward Stack and Eugene McCarty. These last, with Colonel Paul de Chamillard, Lieutenant Colonel Antoine Weibert, Lieutenant de la Bernerie, and Ensign François Kuelain, all of the French Marines, gave our officer personnel nearly as cosmopolitan a character as had our crew.

Paul Jones feverishly repaired and refitted his ships, drew up minute instructions in their duties for his new officers, and half-killed himself (as well as them) by keeping all hands endlessly at gun-drills. Such was his fervor in this that from reveille to taps, the *Bon Homme Richard* was shaking continuously to the rumble of gun carriages on all her three decks. From waterline to poop and forecastle the whole ship was daily a madhouse of cursing in strange tongues the while they all—Malays, English, Maltese, Spaniards, Portuguese, Danes, Italians, Dutch, Swedes, Americans, and Heaven alone knows what others—toiled on tackles and rammers drilling at the great guns.

Only one thing could now draw Paul Jones, beating his odd crew into shape as men-of-warsmen, off his ship—the appearance on the quay of any man who, to his practised eye, showed the slightest signs of the rolling gait of an American seaman.

Invariably when that happened, the drill was promptly turned over to the hands of Lieutenant Dale while Jones himself shot over the gangway to make acquaintance with a potential recruit. The one relaxation we had aboard ship while we labored at the guns in L'Orient was to watch our Commodore through a port, for hours together did the occasion require, strolling on the quay beside some reluctant seaman (usually an exchanged prisoner desirous only of getting home to America), plying him with flattery, dangling before him the glory and the wealth to be gained aboard the *Richard*, working on his sense of patriotism. And such were the charm of his manner and the deep conviction burning in his own soul (in both of which qualities no man approached him) that almost every time the seaman ended following our Commodore aboard to sign the ship's articles, all reluctance forgot, eager to serve under such a commander.

One thing, coming more and more to the fore as the day of our departure approached, greatly disturbed our Commodore—the strange actions of Monsieur le Ray de Chaumont, Commissary of Marine, the representative of de Sartine and the actual French agent in the management of the squadron. De Chaumont, most indiscreet in conversation, discoursed at full table before all and sundry who might be present, concerning the objectives of the expedition. But worse than that, de Chaumont gave every Captain in the

[515]

squadron to understand that it was but an association of equals, in which no commander was required to obey an order contrary to his own judgment. This strange doctrine, subversive to all military discipline, struck directly at the authority of the Commodore over all the vessels of the fleet save only the *Bon Homme Richard*, which he commanded, and the *Alliance*, which as an undisputed American man-of-war, was subject by the laws of our Navy to his orders without qualification.

But in spite of all, the ill-assorted squadron was at last got ready to sail, composed as follows:

Bon Homme Richard, 40, Commodore Paul Jones.
Alliance frigate, 36, Captain Pierre Landais.
Pallas frigate, 32, Captain Denis Cottineau.
Cerf cutter, 18, Captain Joseph Varage.
Vengeance brig, 12, Captain Philippe Ricot.

To these ships, composing Commodore Jones' squadron, were added two French privateers, the *Monsieur*, 40, and the *Granville*, 14, both volunteers which desired to join the expedition and agreed to abide by its rules.

So with his force finally all equipped, Jones made ready to sail in mid-August. Then at this last moment again Monsieur le Ray de Chaumont appeared aboard with a document entitled a "Concordat" to which he requested Jones' signature.

Jones, impatient to weigh anchor and be off, hurriedly scanned it. The Concordat, signed already by each of the other Captains, confirmed in writing what previously had rested only on de Chaumont's ill-advised gabblings—that the expedition was in essence a partnership of colleagues, with each Captain bound only by his judgment rather than compelled to obey the orders of the Commodore.

Courteously de Chaumont made known his ultimatum— Jones must sign with the others, accepting those terms, or he should not sail at all!

Shaking with inward fury, Jones signed. There was no

other option save to abandon the enterprise in which his whole soul was bound up. But now was everything of a piece —his ship was decayed, his guns worn out, his polyglot crew of poor quality, and as a final blow, by the Concordat his authority over his Captains was rendered quite as uncertain as all else.

50

WE weighed at 4 A.M. on August 14, 1779.

Worn though he was and still quivering with rage at the final hurt done him, we had hardly cleared the roadstead off the Isle de Groix and the *Bon Homme Richard* began lifting to the ocean swells than all Paul Jones' troubles dropped magically away from him. He was at last at sea!

Beneath his feet heaved and rolled the *Bon Homme Richard*, driving before a fair wind for the British Isles. Under her forefoot the waves broke to come washing in a mass of foam down her sides. Overhead the wind sang through the rigging in strange harmony. From all our decks came the everlasting thud of rammers and the rumble of wood wheels on wooden planks—as usual the crews were exercising at all our forty guns.

With the beatific look of one transported at last to his longed-for Paradise, Paul Jones drank in the music of a ship at sea. He was free at last of the shore, of its politicians, its intrigues, its spies. Shaken though he was by that Concordat, still it was the last wound. The land could do no worse to him now. About him lay the sea with the waves driving before the wind, the salt spray flying from the breaking crests to come aboard dashing refreshingly into his face.

Astern our towering poop in our wake came his squadron, six ships beautiful to see in their widespread canvas bellied full out before the wind. Six ships, though smaller than the lumbering *Bon Homme Richard*, more modern in design and faster than we, ready all at his command to loose their broadsides, the most powerful squadron he had yet commanded.

And ahead of him beyond those waves lay the enemy of

America and its liberties, with its ships and its cities, fair targets all for the havoc he could wreak with those broadsides at his back.

That ahead of him in Britain also lay the most powerful fleets in all the world, against which his squadron and its broadsides were but nothing, and that spreading wide above those British ships-of-war were numberless yardarms from the nearest of which the English meant ignominiously to hang him the instant they got their itching fingers on him, was to Paul Jones of no moment. Their major fleets he was supremely confident he could evade; anything less, he was burning to encounter.

Watch and watch, course northwest, the squadron plowed along, the people on deck the *Richard* employed in sundry jobs setting up the backstays, making all shipshape aloft. And Richard Dale and Sam Stacy, stretching their legs almost unbelievingly again on deck an American ship instead of in an English gaol, eyed professionally the sails on the *Richard* from spritsail to spanker, experimenting constantly with their trim to see how each sail might draw best.

So we stood on through the day with pleasant weather. Nothing remarkable occurred except that we sighted a large convoy bound north, which the *Cerf*, ordered to speak, found to be French, bound from Nantes to Brest.

Two days more went by with still nothing sighted, the while we stood for the west coast of Ireland. But on our fourth day, being now well at sea and distant from the French coast, enemy sails began to be more plentiful.

At two bells in the afternoon watch came a cry from the masthead,

"Sail ho!"

This sail, on the western board, the *Monsieur* was ordered to chase. It was, however, all to no purpose, the chase when overhauled proving to be a Dutchman, so that by eight bells the *Monsieur* was back in formation.

But this was not for long, as scarce an hour later, another sail was sighted, and once again the *Monsieur* was signalled

[519]

to go in pursuit of the stranger.

The chase proving but a dull sailer, the *Monsieur* swiftly brought her to with a shot across her bows, to find on investigation she was good prize, though another Dutchman.

For this vessel, the *Verwagting*, bound originally from Barcelona to Dunkirk heavily laden with brandy and wine for that French port, had some days before on that voyage been taken by an English privateersman in the Bay of Biscay. Now, in the hands of an English prize crew bound for Liverpool, she was of course an enemy vessel and as such, good prize when retaken.

Now came trouble. With that fat Dutchman in our hands, a rich prize to gladden the heart of any captor, the Concordat began to bear fruit. Captain de Roberdeau of the *Monsieur*, who had brought the prize to, exercised also his discretion. This, influenced no doubt by the sight of tier on tier of casks of wine jamming the holds of the *Verwagting*, led him to the conclusion he should claim the prize as his alone.

Consequently he was in the very act of placing his own prize crew aboard with orders to take the *Verwagting* into Ostend under his name only, when the rest of the squadron came up and hove to.

On discovering this breach of faith, Jones promptly stopped it by placing on board the Dutchman his own prize crew and sending her to L'Orient, consigned to de Chaumont for the account of the squadron.

The *Verwagting* was hardly on her way in the night under the charge of James O'Kelly, master's mate, and the signal hung out by lanterns from our poop for the squadron to make sail again, than there came the splash of oars in the darkness under our counter.

"What boat is that?" sang out Sam Stacy through his trumpet.

"*Monsieur!*" came back a hail in French, and hurriedly our sailing master sent an orderly flying to the cabin to inform the Commodore that Captain de Roberdeau of the *Monsieur* was boarding us.

[520]

It being after sunset, no side honors were accorded Captain de Roberdeau as he clambered up our side, but he wanted none. He had scarce climbed through the gangway opening where Paul Jones courteously awaited him, than in a mixture of fluent French and broken English, poured forth together in such a torrent that I made out but a few words, he began to protest violently against the taking of the *Verwagting* from his hands.

Paul Jones diplomatically endeavored to draw him aft off the quarterdeck into the great cabin, that such a scene of open insubordination become not the subject of discussion amongst our people round about the scuttled butts to undermine our shaky discipline still further.

But de Roberdeau obstinately refused to budge. Gesticulating wildly with both hands at the lights of the *Verwagting* fading now into the night, he delivered his ultimatum.

"Signal her *à l'instant* she heave to and deliver her to me! *Sacrebleu,* otherwise I take her again, put on her a prize crew from *le Monsieur* and despatch her once more for Ostend! She is mine!"

"That prize, like all prizes taken by any ship here, goes to de Chaumont for the whole squadron, *mon Capitaine,*" answered Paul Jones coldly. "Return to your ship, sir, and follow the movements of the flagship."

De Roberdeau shoved off still infuriated, but that he meant to obey was highly dubious.

On the *Richard* we fired a swivel gun to signal the squadron to get underway and shook out our sails, heading northwest again for Ireland. But it was noticeable that the Commodore, instead of retiring to his cabin while the First Lieutenant got the ship away before the wind, climbed to the poop with his spyglass to scan what went on aft.

Shortly all vessels were underway before the wind following us, and save for the wash of the waves alongside and the creaking of our spars swaying in the breeze, all was again quiet on the *Richard*.

We stood on thus for an hour, with the lights of our consorts bobbing erratically in our wake, dull yellow blotches in the dark. Then from the poop, sharp in the quiet night, came a command,

"Haul by the wind, Mr. Stacy, and make all sail after the *Monsieur!*"

Our deck immediately came to life, with Mr. Stacy bawling orders, the bosun's mates shrilling on their pipes for the watch below to tumble up, and the stamp and go of the watch on deck, already heaving on sheets and braces to bring us close hauled on the larboard tack.

We fell out of line, of course, and as we luffed up to windward, one by one, dark masses against the foaming water of our wake, our consorts sailed by ghostlike under our stern, still steering northwest before the wind. All save one, that is, the cause of our sudden maneuver, for there with all lights suddenly doused to obscure her movements, was the *Monsieur*, close hauled also on the larboard tack, stealing away in the darkness!

Another order from the poop, cutting through the turmoil of belaying lines,

"Beat to quarters!" To the mad roll of the drum, all hands rushed to battle stations to engage the fleeing *Monsieur*.

All night long we stood to our guns, ports open, matches glowing, wondering nervously what was to ensue, for the *Monsieur*, like us, carried forty guns, and being newer, might perhaps overpower us. But we never did draw up close enough to bring that deserter to with our chase guns, let alone to get her under our broadsides. And when dawn came, the *Monsieur* had reached so far ahead and to windward of us, it was hopeless we should ever catch her.

Furious at de Roberdeau's disobedience and desertion and even more wroth at the clumsy sailing of the *Bon Homme Richard* which put it out of his power to prevent it, Jones ordered Midshipman Fanning to the masthead with a glass to see whether the *Verwagting*, the cause of all this insubordination, was in sight. Fanning's report from aloft was in the negative, so Jones concluded that his prize at least was safe from de Roberdeau's further molestation. Muttering

[522]

curses on the Concordat as being at the bottom of all, our baffled Commodore ordered Sam Stacy to lay the ship before the wind and rejoin our squadron, giving up the futile chase.

In another hour the distant *Monsieur* had dropped completely from sight below the horizon, and we saw no more of her on our cruise.

Crowding on all sail, by afternoon we had rejoined our squadron, which obedient to signal ere we left them, had stood on northwest under reduced canvas. With the *Richard* again taking station in the van, our consorts loosed topgallants and once more, a squadron reduced now to six ships, we made sail for the enemy coasts. But it was no longer any secret on our lower decks that something was amiss among their commanders, and the seamen excitedly gathered between the gun carriages in strange tongues to argue over what was wrong.

Early next morning, expecting momentarily to make a landfall off Cape Clear, we picked up instead when the day broke, a sail in the northeast quarter and to windward.

Being well assured that the *Bon Homme Richard* could overhaul nothing to windward of her, Paul Jones made signal for the *Alliance* to go in chase of the stranger, and accordingly she luffed to go in pursuit, with the whole squadron hauling by the wind to stand on as well as might be in support of her.

The *Alliance*, which was of the latest design and a very fast sailer, made no difficulty of drawing quickly away from us to windward and closing on the stranger.

Within an hour, it appeared from our decks that the *Alliance* was within cannon shot of the chase and should shortly bring her to. But to our astonishment, instead of firing a gun across the bows of the stranger to heave her to, the *Alliance* hurriedly wore ship and bore away dead before the wind to rejoin us.

Our squadron continued on close hauled as before and it was no long while before the *Alliance* was passing close aboard us headed opposite, at which Captain Landais leaned over the rail, so close indeed that his face, small and sharp

[523]

and now apparently much bewildered, was plainly evident to us as he shouted,

"Come about, *monsieur!* That vessel, she is an English line-of-battleship, for I did go near enough to see her upper battery! *Mon dieu,* we must flee!"

Paul Jones, high on his poop, looked off to windward over the sea where hull down but obviously under a full press of canvas and still on her original course striving to escape, was the stranger. His lips curled. No English ship-of-the-line would be doing that in the face of a frigate like the *Alliance* or half a dozen like her; she would already have come about in hot pursuit. The timorous Landais, affrighted at the sight of some guns, had magnified a large armed merchantman into a line-of-battleship.

"You damned coward!" sang out Paul Jones contemptuously, and disdaining to waste further time on Landais, he shouted,

"Quartermaster! Make signal for a general chase!"

Accordingly, no longer in formation, our squadron settled down for a stern chase, but by noon it was evident that our hoped for prize, having now taken fright (which till the *Alliance's* close approach she had not before) had the heels of us.

The case was hopeless with the stranger topsails down below the horizon and gaining steadily, so Paul Jones gave over the chase. But such was his passion that had he had the coward aboard, he would have smashed his speaking trumpet over Landais' head. And this temper was scarce improved when shortly after there came alongside us a small fishing smack to inform us in answer to an inquiry that the chase (which had passed close aboard them in flight) was an English East Indiaman.

Standing again to the northward, we soon sighted a brigantine to which we gave chase ourselves in the *Richard*. As she obligingly kept off before the wind (on which point of sailing we went best) we were soon enabled to bring her to with a round shot.

Our prize this time proved to be the *Mayflower* from Limerick to London laden with butter and provisions, and these delicacies were shortly on their way to L'Orient in charge of a prize crew.

Somewhat calmed by this stroke of luck, Jones bore away for Cape Clear, with a fine breeze serving. By the next midnight being, as he supposed, past that Cape, the Commodore hoisted five lanterns as a signal for the fleet to tack ship and then fired a gun that all observe the order.

Immediately on that, down went our helm and slowly we swung up into the wind to fill away on the larboard tack, heading northward. But scarce had we come about, with our yards not yet braced up on the new course, when, not obeying the signal, the *Alliance* loomed up on our quarter with her starboard tacks aboard, still on her original course, and bidding fair to cause another collision by her obstinacy, as once already she had in the Bay of Biscay.

But this time we had seamen on the *Richard*.

"Hard alee!" sang out instantly Lieutenant Dale, while simultaneously Sam Stacy let fly the fore sheets and braces so that immediately we shot up into the wind to lie there with sails and yards banging the masts the while the *Alliance* drove by us in the darkness.

With such cursing as may well be imagined at the clumsiness of our consort, our sailing master hove our lines taut again to lay us once more close hauled and we stood north. But every officer from our Captain down had now good cause to wonder what manner of skipper it was the Congress had placed in command of America's best frigate, for surely we seemed to be in more danger of being sunk by the erratic Landais than by the enemy.

51

A⊤ 8 A.M. on August 23, 1779, we made the land of Ireland called the Mizzen Head, and shortly our squadron, already seething with unrest, had what little concord yet remained completely dissipated.

As we drew abeam the land, the wind died away to a near calm, leaving us to drift with sails hanging idly from the yards off the mouth of a deep and dangerous bay situated between some rocks on the south called the Skallocks and on the north called the Blaskets.

In this situation, we made out in the western board, drifting slowly toward us on the incoming tide, a brigantine similarly becalmed and helpless.

Deeming her an enemy merchantman and easily to be taken, the Commodore called to him Lieutenant Henry Lunt and ordered him to muster a boarding party of twenty men to man two boats and take the stranger. Accordingly Mr. Lunt, being left to his own devices as to whom he should choose for the cutting out party and having a wide variety of seamen to make selection from, mustered on deck some twenty Algerines, Turks, Genoese and Maltese who from long service amongst the Mediterranean corsairs had much knowledge of that business.

This party, all brawny fellows, came each to the gangway stark naked save for a pair of light linen drawers, with their swarthy skins glistening with oil, their heads bound up in gay 'kerchiefs, and armed only with long knives for work at close quarters, in anticipation of which their bared teeth and black eyes gleamed as evilly as their wicked knives.

A more ferocious-appearing gang it would have been impossible to gather, and one well calculated to strike panic to

[526]

the heart of any honest tar. With these men at his back, Lieutenant Lunt shoved off, to sweep across a smooth sea for the brigantine. Since she was helpless to make off, they swiftly closed upon her.

In such a bedlam of fierce cries as might have froze the blood even of tried men-o'-warsmen, these naked devils drove aboard their hapless victim to scramble wildly up the chains and over her gunwales, knives in their teeth. At this sight the terrified crew, making no resistance at all, fled incontinently below to save their lives, and the master, bawling for quarter, surrendered his ship.

Being thus easily in possession of the brigantine *Fortune*, bound from Newfoundland for Bristol with a cargo of oil, blubber, and barrel staves, Lieutenant Lunt sent back one boat for a prize master and a crew of seamen better fitted than his fanatic boarders to take the ship to L'Orient. Meanwhile, pending their arrival and the removal of the prisoners, he remained aboard with some half of his men lest a breeze spring up and the vessel take to her heels.

Since this transfer had to be made across several miles of calm ocean, it occupied us the rest of the afternoon and the evening, with our longboats plying back and forth between the *Bon Homme Richard* and the *Fortune*. Long before it was completed, the tide had begun to run a strong flood and we found ourselves athwart the current being set into the nearby bay with grave danger of being stranded.

In this emergency, our consorts made shift in the light airs to head offshore. But we found it impossible on the unhandy *Richard* with her high poop, no more manageable than an ancient galleon, so that we drifted broadside to the tide inexorably shoreward in the deepening darkness.

Our sails doing us no good, Paul Jones ordered the pinnace and his own barge overside (our longboats being engaged with the *Fortune*), and sent them ahead of us on a light hawser. In this endeavor, the boats were secured in tandem with the pinnace nearest the *Richard* and the barge leading, to tow our head around so that we might then spread our sails and work to seaward against the tide.

[527]

I went in command of the pinnace with seven Nantucketers stroked by Red Jerry. Little Midshipman Gilbert Watt, scarce seventeen years, took the Captain's barge, and thinking no doubt to excite some competition between Yankees and English tars, boyishly selected seven of the stoutest Englishmen we had aboard to man his boat.

The matter worked out to his wish, for indeed when once we had the cable stretched away from our stern to the *Richard's* hawse and from our bow to Watt's boat, one might well have thought from Red Jerry's wild yells and the way the men behind him lay back, we were in chase of a spermaceti, with the English, heaving madly on their oars ahead of us, striving to get an iron in him first.

With the two boats' crews thus fiercely bending to their sweeps in the darkness, we managed to start the *Richard's* head offshore. We were in a fair way shortly to finish the task, when in the barge ahead of me, the stroke oarsman, a stalwart British tar, suddenly threw aside his oar and leaped full on unsuspecting little Watt to tear the tiller from his hands and fling him headlong into the sternsheets. Then with a wild slash of his sheath-knife, he cut the hawser to my boat, and bearing hard down on the helm, made for the shore with his mates pulling harder now than ever!

We were helpless to pursue the scoundrels for I dared not cast off myself lest the *Richard* be stranded. I could but shout a warning to our forecastle, while I desperately urged on my oarsmen to redouble their own efforts to save what ground we had already gained in swinging our ship's head against the tide.

Instantly all was turmoil. Astern me on the *Richard's* forecastle I heard a gun port fly open, a gun carriage being run out, then the deep voice of Paul Jones roaring,

"Come back, you villains, or I fire!"

But ahead of me, with Midshipman Watt hurled unceremoniously beneath a thwart, were seven frenzied Englishmen, lately prisoners in French dungeons, now unwilling recruits on an enemy ship, pulling madly for British soil and freedom not a mile away, with not the slightest intention of turning back, come what might.

Another instant and a nine-pounder thundered out directly over our heads in a blinding flash, well-nigh bursting my eardrums with the blast, of which we in the pinnace under the bows got the full benefit.

A round shot, a little short, splashed astern the barge to go skipping over the sea past it. A miss, unfortunately.

"Load with grape, lads!" sang out our Captain. But since no action had been in prospect, ere a second charge of powder could be brought up from the magazine and the starboard chase gun (the only one which bore on the fugitives) reloaded, something else chanced which prevented.

While the gunners on the forecastle were sponging out under our Captain's eye, there came to me the splash of oars close at hand. In another moment our Third Lieutenant, Cutting Lunt, who without orders had hurriedly manned the jollyboat at the gangway aft, drove by me in hot pursuit, with six seamen heaving at the oars and six marines armed with muskets crowded in the sternsheets beside him.

The result was that by the time our chase gun was run out again, Mr. Lunt and the jollyboat were directly in the line of fire and close enough behind the runaway barge so that there was grave danger the spreading charge of grape might spray his men as well as the eloping Englishmen. In that predicament, there was naught Paul Jones could do save order the gun run in again, the charge of grape drawn, and the gun reloaded again with a solid shot which might be better directed.

But by that time the barge had drawn so far away it was out of sight altogether in the darkness and the second shot was never fired. So with what philosophy he could muster, Paul Jones, having not a boat left on the ship save the one beneath the jibboom in which I was still struggling to swing our head offshore, could but encourage us to hold her up while he stared landward and hoped that Cutting Lunt, rushing off with no orders toward an enemy coast, might use due prudence in not being himself taken with all his men in his pursuit of the fugitives.

[529]

In my boat we tugged endlessly on the monstrous cutwater looming up in its gilt carving over our heads. With all the war whoops gone from him, Red Jerry heaved silently on the stroke oar, panting in what seemed a fruitless effort to swing the vast bulk towering astern us. Not till our longboat, laden with some dozen naked corsairs come back from the taking of the *Fortune*, picked up the slashed hawser ahead, did we manage to get the ship's bow swung fair into the current so that with our sails then drawing we could make shift to claw off the threatening rocks. With that at last assured, we cast off the towing lines on the Captain's orders and came wearily aboard.

Now unfortunately a fog rolled up in the night, to make the lights we had hanging out for Cutting Lunt's guidance in his return wholly useless. What was worse, however, was that to avoid being cast away by treacherous currents on rocks masked now in fog as well as darkness, we had to stand offshore, leaving our men ever farther behind. But to direct them should they be trying to find us in the fog, every fifteen minutes through the night we fired a signal gun.

Dawn came. With the sun, the fog soon lifted, to show the squadron and our prize all in sight and some miles off the coast. First ordering the prize to make sail for L'Orient, we slowly stood in to reconnoiter the shore for any sign of our missing boats, when the *Alliance* made signal she wished to speak us.

Accordingly we hove to, and shortly the Captain's gig of that ship made our side, bearing in it Pierre Landais.

Respectfully received by saluting side boys, to the whistling of the bosun's pipe he came over the side, there to be greeted by the Commodore. Landais lost not an instant in getting to the point. With his sharp features so contorted that his small face took on a most remarkable resemblance to an enraged rat, he burst out,

"*Cochon!* You call me coward when I not attack a ship-of-the-line. But you lower two boats for to seize prize when it shows no sagacity. Now you lose them in fogs, and keep me here where the English come soon to take us. Before God! I leave you!"

What the incoherent Landais in his garbled English meant save to flaunt his insubordination before the whole crew of the flagship, I know not. Surely in any Service such an outburst should have landed him in irons immediately, but there behind him was the Concordat, and well Jones knew it.

So since any direct show of military authority was inadvisable, Jones tried indulgence.

"Come, sir," he said, indicating the entrance to the poop. "In my cabin you may set out what complaints you wish. But you seem to labor under some misapprehensions which may easily be cleared up."

He looked about him, motioned to Colonel Chamillard, Lieutenant Colonel Weibert, and to me, standing all near by on the quarterdeck with our fellow officers, to precede him into the cabin.

Once inside, with his French orderly, Pierre Gerard, posted at the closed door with fixed bayonet that no eavesdroppers might overhear, he motioned Landais to be seated but to no avail.

"Very well, sir, you may stand if it suit you better." He turned to me. "Mr. Folger, Captain Landais upbraids me for losing my boats through lowering them in a fog to take a prize. Since you were in the best position to observe, inform him, please, of how actually we lost those boats."

"Aye, sir." I faced Landais, who was pacing rapidly across the stern windows in great agitation. "The first boat lost, sir, was the Commodore's barge, engaged in pulling on a hawser ahead of my boat, in an endeavor to swing this ship's head seaward to save her from grounding. The Englishmen in it suddenly cut the line and decamped with their officer and the barge. The prize was in no way involved."

"And the second boat, Mr. Folger?" asked Jones.

"That was the jollyboat manned by Lieutenant Cutting Lunt, who went off immediately in chase of the deserters, to my knowledge without orders. It had nothing to do with the

[531]

prize either, sir. None but the longboats ever went to the prize and they're both safely aboard now with all their crews and Lieutenant Henry Lunt commanding them."

"Aye, Mr. Folger." Paul Jones looked calmly now at the skipper of the *Alliance*. "I trust that allays your distress, sir. You see the occasion involved not the prize, but only an endeavor to keep the *Bon Homme Richard* off the rocks, the obligation of any prudent Captain."

"Bah! You think me fool who believe this boy?" Contemptuously Landais eyed me. "Who is he?"

Involuntarily my gorge rose and had I been ashore, I would gladly have seized that sharp-faced scoundrel with his weasel eyes and with my bare hands made an end of him. But this was aboard a ship-of-war off an enemy coast, and he was Captain of our strongest consort. If those circumstances forced my commander to swallow insult, so might I.

"Mr. Folger is an officer of the *Bon Homme Richard* whose word is good, sir. But if you think he answers as I wish him, here are Colonel Chamillard and his second, Lieutenant Colonel Weibert. They are your countrymen, whom you must know for gentlemen of honor. Ask them."

There ensued then in rapid French a conversation in which our two marine officers assured their skeptical compatriot that what had happened was as I had related it, but all to no purpose—Landais was convinced we were all deceiving him to cover up our Commodore's incompetence.

"You not fool me!" he screamed shrilly. "I, Pierre Landais, am command the *Alliance*, the only American ship here by commission direct from Congress and I am the only American *de l'escadre!* Now I go. If I stay here three days yet with this Scotch *insensé*, all are taken!" and he stamped out of the cabin, flinging over his shoulder some further French epithets at the Commodore the which I understood not, but which caused our two French colonels, scandalized apparently at his obscenities, to reach instinctively for the hilts of their swords and start after him.

"Nay, gentlemen!" Paul Jones halted them. "His insults are personal and my affair only. I understand your outrage,

[532]

that your Commodore should be thus treated, but this is a strangely constituted squadron, and till our enterprise is over, he must go unpunished, lest the common cause suffer. Tom," he turned abruptly to me. "Tell the officer of the deck to see Captain Landais receives the full honors due his rank on his departure."

"Aye, aye, sir," and I hastened after Landais to pass along the message. And then, most humiliating of all, I must needs stand myself respectfully at salute while with much solemnity we piped over the side into his boat a Captain in the Navy of the United States, whom, had I instead pitched bodily overboard then and there to drown beneath the weight of his epaulettes, I would have done my country the greatest service of my naval career.

We never recovered our lost boats. We stood in closer but got no sight of them. All day we stood off and on, hoping Cutting Lunt and his boat's crew at least might return. In the late afternoon, fearing again the effects of a flood tide on our large vessel, we sheered out, but in our place sent in the *Cerf*, smaller and more manageable.

From far offshore as evening fell, we could see the *Cerf*, a fine cutter commanded by Captain Varage, cruising close along the coast. Then out at last from among the rocks where it had been hiding during the daylight hours, came the jollyboat with Lieutenant Cutting Lunt and his men making gladly for the *Cerf*. Apparently the deserters in the other boat had landed and made good their escape, for there was no sign of them.

And then, for God knows what reason, the *Cerf* suddenly hoisted English colors and opened fire on the boat!

Thus assailed, Cutting Lunt, lest he be sunk, could do nothing but row pell-mell for the shore, there promptly to be seized by a company of redcoats, which under the guidance of our deserters had been searching all day for him, and was now attracted to the spot by the firing.

And so, aside from the desertion of seven stalwart English seamen and the Midshipman they had kidnapped in their flight, we lost our Third Lieutenant and twelve loyal members of our crew.

Finally to put the last touch to this crazy drama enacted off the Mizzen Head, the *Cerf* herself made off in the darkness, accompanied possibly by the privateer *Granville* which had taken and manned another prize that afternoon, so that we never saw anything of either of them again, though we cruised off the coast all next day hoping they might rejoin.

52

As night fell on August 26, 1779, our further stay off that coast became somewhat hazardous. The countryside was well aroused by the intelligence imparted by the deserters, and signal fires began to blaze in warning all up and down the shores. So reluctantly the Commodore made signal to stand northward.

Accordingly, with the wind increasing, we bore away from the coast, our fleet reduced to only four ships, the *Bon Homme Richard*, the *Alliance*, the *Pallas* and the *Vengeance*, hardly more than half the force with which we had sailed twelve days before from L'Orient.

As it drew on towards midnight, the wind rose steadily till it was blowing a whole gale from the northeast. Before this we drove with royal and topgallant yards sent down, topsails handed, and courses close reefed, going to the west with the sea rising and the motion of the *Bon Homme Richard* increasing almost with every wave which struck us.

Soon in the driving rain we lost sight of the lights of our consorts, and then, alone in a mad world of tumbling waves, shrieking wind, and utter darkness the aged *Bon Homme Richard* fought the storm.

By two bells in the midwatch it was blowing so violently we could not bear a yard of canvas lest our masts leave us. In the wildest night that ever I have seen at sea, I laid out on the end of the main yard with the topmen. There with the yard swaying drunkenly under me, one moment half burying me in the waves, the next swinging me sickeningly skyward, we handed the main course.

That done on fore and main, with not a rag of sail anywhere, we drove before the gale under bare poles only.

Now was our ancient vessel literally alive. We rolled horribly under the weight of our high poop and our forty guns and pitched with a motion even more horrible as the long seas went sliding by.

One instant our bowsprit would be pointed heavenward riding a mountainous crest; the next, submerged in foam, it would be sliding down into a trough at such a dizzy angle it seemed our ship was headed fair for hell and meant not to stop until her jibboom plumbed its depths.

On the poop four seamen clung to the wheel, struggling to keep our clumsy vessel from broaching to before the rushing seas. Beside them stood Paul Jones, clad in oilskins, his dripping face barely visible in the glow of the binnacle lantern, gazing thoughtfully aloft at the invisible masts and rigging, singing now in a devil's symphony of discords with everything from heavy shrouds to thin signal halliards vibrating in a different screech in the roaring wind. The rigging was new and so were the spars, but the masts? How long would those old sticks, swaying like huge pendulums above us, stand up ere our crazy motion rolled them out and left us a dismasted hulk?

But if our masts were dubious, the same could not be said of our rotten hull. Of that there was not the slightest doubt —it was in imminent and visible danger of going to pieces under our feet if the storm did not abate.

Our decayed timbers were working every one—deck beams, ribs, side planking—all were groaning dismally as sea after sea smote our poop to toss us wildly about. Through every seam of the planks sheathing our sides the sea began to seep in, so that from having to man only one pump, we were soon forced to man all four in an attempt to hold the water down.

Not a man aboard was turned in. Crouching on deck in the lee of the gunwales to avoid being washed overboard were all the able seamen we had, ready with stoppers to fish any shroud or stay should it part, ready with axes to cut away a mast should it go by the board ere it might hammer in our side and cause us to founder out of hand.

But our middle gun deck was a veritable scene of terror. There, turned to on the pump handles were our French soldiers, landsmen all, eight on each side of each pump, sixty-four all told on each shift, swaying up and down on our four pumps, fighting to keep down the flood rising in our holds. Such was the wild motion of the deck that scarce could they keep their feet, and poor devils, all violently seasick from our fierce gyrations, they were in mortal fear that each shuddering plunge of our hull into the trough of the sea was her last, to take them with all their sins unshriven into the depths.

The result of this was that with all hope lost, many of these terrified soldiers quit the pump handles to fling themselves on their knees and cry most dolorously out to God for mercy, to the serious detriment of the pumping on which alone our safety depended.

In vain Colonel Chamillard pleaded and threatened his men, striving to keep the pump handles flying but with no effect, till our sombre Captain, coming up with the carpenter from sounding the rising water in the wells, seized a cutlass and rushing upon the kneeling men, threatened instantly to run them through if they did not stand to the pumps.

For the moment that menacing blade and Paul Jones' savage mien produced the desired effect, but only for a brief time. Not till he had stationed Lieutenant Henry Lunt and three Midshipmen, each with bared hanger flashing over their heads promising instant death to whoever let go to pray, did he succeed in keeping the pump handles flying.

Then came the last blow to insure our destruction. So terrible was our rolling and so rapidly did the decks alternate between rising violently to drive our legs hard up into our stomachs, and dropping from under us with such velocity it seemed we were left with no support at all to fall freely through empty space, that even our veteran seamen were unable to get about without clinging desperately to the nearest line or fife rail.

In that condition then, it was no great surprise when on our lower gun deck, one of our great guns, an eighteen-pounder, tore its securing eyebolts bodily from out the rotten timbers, and started to batter the *Bon Homme Richard's* gunroom to splinters.

Rolling athwartship, it crashed its breech heavily into the planking on the larboard side, starting half a dozen seams, then shot crazily back to starboard on the succeeding roll to bring up against a gun there, wrecking its carriage.

From then on, rolling aimlessly on that careening deck, it smashed from side to side with every heave, leaving destruction in its wake, while all about, crouching with lines ready to encircle it should it but pause a moment, clung the white-faced quarter gunners and the gun crews. But no man dared approach that hurtling gun lest he be caught and crushed against the side in its unpredictable lungings.

All efforts failing to loop a line about it and bring that devastating mass of iron to a stop, it seemed but a matter of minutes when it should smash bodily through our decayed side and go overboard, leaving a yawning hole low down on our waterline through which the raging sea would pour to end at once our miseries.

Reuben Chase saved us. Leaving the lines to others, he seized a wooden training bar, directed Red Jerry to get another, and then, nimbly as if in chase of a whale, those two bare-footed harpooners with bars poised followed back and forth across the heaving deck abreast the gun till it at last crashed muzzle first into the side near where they were.

Instantly at that, Red Jerry shot his bar along the deck behind the rearmost wheels to hinder the backward roll and Reuben, swiftly thrusting the end of his between the wheels, with a mighty heave up of his enormous hands and shoulders, upset the carriage to lay it with wheels spinning idly, flat on its side.

Immediately their mates leaped upon that gun to encircle it with lines hauled taut to other deckbolts ere it could slide away, and thus we lashed it down, leaving our lower gun deck looking as if an enemy broadside had just crashed into it.

For twenty hours all told we battled that storm, our pumps our last resource. Had it lasted but four hours more

[538]

with the violence of its latter part, we should have surely foundered, for the water then was gaining constantly on us, and our old ship was wrung almost to pieces, seemingly having as many joints in her limber hull as any rattlesnake, with all of them started to let the sea pour in.

But with the ending of the day, the wind gradually abated, and with that came some slacking of our motion and a diminution of our leaks. By late afternoon, the sea had gone down so far we could make sail northward again. We were then ahead of the incoming water, and by evening, the French soldiers, an utterly exhausted group of men, were at last allowed to leave the pumps.

Of our squadron, no ship save the *Vengeance* brig and her French crew was left in sight. To her we signalled to follow us, and set our course for the north coast of Scotland, where off Cape Wrath was the appointed rendezvous for all ships in case of separation.

There on September 1 we arrived with the *Vengeance*, to see none of our ships but instead an armed ship to windward bound west.

We promptly went in chase of this vessel in the *Bon Homme Richard*, hoisting English colors meanwhile, but she proved wary of us and stood on. However, as she was deeply laden with naval stores and cordage and therefore sailed but poorly, we were in a fair way to overhaul her when in the northwest quarter appeared the *Alliance* accompanied by a prize she had taken.

While normally the sight of our lost consort rejoining would have gladdened the Commodore's heart, on this occasion it caused him to break out in profanity, for on recognizing us, the *Alliance* imprudently hoisted American colors though we were then ourselves flying a British ensign.

Immediately on this, various packets began to go overboard from our chase which up to then had showed no undue alarm. So that when we brought her to at noon (though armed, she fired not one gun in her defense) and found we had taken the letter of marque *Union* from London for Quebec, we discovered also that she had heaved overside her

[539]

despatches, thus depriving General Washington of what might have been valuable information had we taken them.

The *Alliance's* prize gave me a shock, for it proved to be the West Indiaman *Betsey*, from Liverpool to Jamaica— that very ship on whose deck in Tobago long before I had first met Captain Paul!

But if Paul Jones had any pangs at the plight of the ship on which he had slain the mutineer Jack Fry and from her fled to land ultimately in America, he showed no signs of them nor did he manifest any desire even to set foot again on her. So with the English prisoners from both vessels jammed into our holds and prize crews put aboard them from the *Alliance*, we lay to off Cape Wrath waiting for more victims.

Shortly another sail appeared, and she being to windward, the Commodore made signal to the *Alliance* to chase as that frigate had the best chance of beating up and laying the stranger aboard. But in keeping with all that had gone before, the *Alliance*, instead of tacking to obey, wore ship and headed the other way, in consequence of which the ship escaped.

This strange exercise of discretion on the part of Landais the Commodore had to swallow perforce in view of the Concordat. But wanting at least some explanation of what might be the reasons, he made signal when next the *Alliance* hove in sight to speak her, to which signal not the slightest attention was shown.

Despairing for the moment of any cooperation, Paul Jones then turned to with the *Richard* and the *Vengeance* only, to chase all and sundry sail that hove up over the horizon, with such good results that we took eleven ships bound from Ireland to Norway and Denmark, of which one we manned for L'Orient, and the others we sank.

Having by now a considerable number of prisoners in our hold, we stood away for our second rendezvous near the Shetland Islands, where we were joined by the *Pallas*. Cruising here with our consorts, in a few days we took and burned sixteen further sail, after which having destroyed all the commerce north of Britain, the Commodore signalled the squadron to stand southward into the North Sea, down the east coast of Scotland. That evening, being September 5, we hove to and Paul Jones hung out the signal for the Captains of the squadron to report aboard the *Bon Homme Richard* to consult on future operations.

This brought only further trouble. While Cottineau of the *Pallas* and Ricot of the *Vengeance*, Frenchmen both of them, came promptly aboard, Landais, who had so loudly proclaimed himself an American, refused. Hoping to persuade him, the Commodore despatched our purser, Mr. Mease, together with Colonel Chamillard and Captain Cottineau aboard the *Alliance*. After a fruitless hour with the recalcitrant Landais, the emissaries returned to report that in the most uncivil terms Landais had informed them he had but the lowest opinion of the Commodore, would never set foot on his ship, and would meet him, as Mease transmitted it, only on shore "where they must kill one or the other."

In this dilemma, there was nothing to do, so dismissing Ricot and Cottineau with instructions to steer for our third rendezvous, all of which was signalled also to the *Alliance*, we made sail again.

For the following four days, we had heavy weather, and in the midst of it the *Alliance* once more took occasion to make off, while we ourselves were kept busy rerigging our crosstrees lest we lose our masts.

Being left now only with the more amenable *Pallas* and *Vengeance*, we succeeded when the weather cleared in taking and sinking seven large colliers, after which being well down the coast we stood for the Firth of Forth.

Off the mouth of that wide estuary we chased and took in the *Bon Homme Richard* a ship and a brigantine, both from Edinburgh. Their Captains were immediately sent aboard the flagship on the Commodore's orders for close questioning. In this I was called in as Paul Jones particularly desired their answers recorded.

The information he received from these two prisoners as to the state of affairs off Edinburgh must have agreed with his wish, for he discovered that at Leith, the port of Edinburgh, there lay but one ship-of-force of twenty guns and three armed cutters. He then dismissed the prisoners to be taken below, and made signal to our consorts to send not only their Captains, but also their First Lieutenants on board.

So there gathered that evening in the great cabin of the *Bon Homme Richard*, Captain Cottineau of the *Pallas*, Captain Ricot of the *Vengeance*, their Lieutenants, and from our ship, Richard Dale and myself who was secretary.

"Gentlemen," said Paul Jones, opening the meeting, "to this moment we have been on a cruise only against shipping. I am now to inform you that by the orders of Doctor Franklin who has drawn up the following capitulation," and here he spread before them a paper, "we are instructed to lay the city of Leith under a contribution of £200,000. My instructions are, if it be not promptly paid, to lay the town at once in ashes with red-hot shot from our broadsides! We are to start immediately up the Firth as soon as you have your instructions."

Whatever Captains Cottineau and Ricot may have thought of starting immediately for Leith, they lost not a fraction of a second in starting from their seats in protest.

"But, *monsieur!*" almost in concert they exclaimed, "there is Edinburgh Castle directly on the Firth! Never can we pass that fort! We shall be sunk!"

I sank back into my seat, feverishly trying to keep up with my notes, resigned to the knowledge that we should not start immediately, and probably never. Not while that damnable Concordat removed from Paul Jones all authority to command, and left him free only to argue with his "colleagues."

All night through that discussion lasted, the while we wasted a fair wind which would have landed us before Leith by morning. Sage remarks, pointed objections, doubts, fears —endlessly all were aired, to be met by Paul Jones, who had prepared for every contingency, with such cogent explanation that at last all were agreeable to try. The very boldness of Paul Jones' plan was its best earnest of success. Never would the English expect him to take his squadron directly beneath the guns of the strongest fortress in Great Britain to get up the Firth of Forth to Leith, but by artifice, that was exactly what he meant to do.

So with all hands convinced at last, at dawn the conference broke up. Immediately Paul Jones began issuing instructions.

"Gentlemen," he explained to the departing officers, "you will each of you find at the gangway, ready to be put in your boats, an English naval officer's uniform with the proper insignia of your rank, together with some others for the juniors on your ships. Don them immediately on boarding your ships and wear nothing else till further orders." He turned to Captain Cottineau of the *Pallas*,

"*Monsieur*, you are now Captain Bazely, of His Majesty's frigate *Pegasus*. The *Pallas* is to answer all hails addressed to the *Pegasus*, and you are to require all your officers to address you only as Captain Bazely."

Addressing then Captain Ricot of the *Vengeance*,

"And you, *monsieur*, are now Captain Montague of His Majesty's brig *Medea*. And as for me, I shall shortly be Captain Burnet of His Majesty's two-decker *Prudent*, Commodore of a squadron seeking that villainous pirate, Paul Jones."

He laughed at that conceit, then finished,

"These are the actual names of the ships and their Captains in His Majesty's Navy most like unto your own vessels. Use them with confidence till we are off Leith. After that, there will be no need."

The others, accompanied by the parcels with their new uniforms, shoved off, and shortly on our ship every officer from Commodore Jones down to the youngest Midshipman was apparelled in the scarlet of George's Service.

Soon after, as H.M.S. *Prudent* accompanied by H.M.S. *Pegasus* and *Medea* and the two prizes we had lately taken, we stood into the Firth of Forth and with English colors flying at every gaff, started working up toward Leith Roads.

Since the wind was contrary though of no great force and

the tide not serving, we made slow progress beating to windward up the Forth, so that night found us well inside but still far from our objective. We improved our time, however, by getting up a hawser to use as a spring on our cable, so that when necessary we might wind our ship off Leith to present to that city our full broadside.

Meanwhile Paul Jones instructed Lieutenant Dale in what was expected of him.

"Once we are before Leith, Mr. Dale, and have it under our guns, you are to land under a flag of truce and present this document from Dr. Franklin to the magistrates of the city, and return aboard here immediately. You are to await nothing, sir! You understand?"

"Aye, aye, Captain."

"This capitulation in our Ambassador's own hand will sufficiently set out everything. In reprisal for the barbarous burning of Falmouth, Norfolk, Fairfield and many another American town, Leith is to be laid in ashes. But Dr. Franklin grants to the citizens of Leith, what never was offered to our countrymen. They may, if they wish, save their city by delivering aboard within thirty minutes an indemnity of £200,000. All this they may read, Mr. Dale. What you may tell them is that they lie under the guns of Paul Jones who will hesitate not at all to exact reprisal by opening fire with red-hot shot in precisely thirty minutes if the indemnity be not instantly paid!"

We now finished our preparations for burning Leith. Pyramids of round shot were piled up around the galley in our waist, and stacks of wood brought handy for firing up the galley range to heat the shot. All our boats were cleared away for landing if necessary, swivel guns mounted in the boats, the boat crews told off, and arms issued.

In the morning, with the wind favorable though very light, we made a further stretch up Leith Roads against the tide, bringing to at last a mile short of Edinburgh Castle.

From the waist of the *Bon Homme Richard* I nervously looked over the gunwale upon that gloomy fortress commanding the entrance to the river we must pass. Massive, impregnable to our attack, formidable with its two tiers of huge guns, twenty forty-eight-pounders in its lower ports, twenty twenty-four-pounders in the embrasures above, it lay there capable with one broadside of those huge guns of sinking easily our whole squadron. And we must pass that fortress twice—once on our way to Leith, when we might get by with strategy, a second time after the attack on Leith. That second time, whether we fled laden with booty and Leith intact, or empty handed with Leith in flames, strategy would avail us nothing and we must face those guns. For the fortress lay within twenty minutes by messenger from Leith and certainly an alarm would be sent the moment Richard Dale presented his ultimatum. After that, of what avail artifice?

But of all that Paul Jones made no moment. Calling all his officers on the quarterdeck for inspection to ensure that like himself all were arrayed properly in English uniform, he noted all hands had eyes for naught but that forbidding fortress near at hand.

"Calm yourself, gentlemen. That castle is all teeth and no bite. They lie there like the English always, unprepared, in indolence and perfect security which shall prove their ruin. You shall see." And dismissing us, he audaciously hove to directly under the guns of that fort as any English squadron might do, and boldly made signal for a pilot to take the ships up to Leith!

The matter worked out to his wish. A pilot boat came alongside the flagship and perfunctorily the pilot came aboard, to take station with our sailing master, in no wise suspicious as over his head floated the ensign of St. George, and all about him, reporting occasionally to their commander, English naval officers went about their duty.

Our other ships being likewise supplied with pilots, we wanted nothing more to proceed past the fort up to Leith. But the tide was now running a strong ebb, so the pilot advised we must wait some little time till we had at least slack water, when we might go up on the flood, assisted by what little wind we had.

Since we could do nothing else, we lay thus some little time, in what state of inward excitement may well be imagined. Everyone, that is, save Paul Jones who in all calmness plied the pilot with questions, to learn that the countryside thereabout was much alarmed at the stories of Yankee privateers off the coast.

"An' weel they may be," concluded the pilot gloomily, "for 'tis the report Paul Jones himsel' hae come back tae finish the mischief he's dune a'ready in Whitehaven. An' dinna ye soon lay him by the heels, Cap'n, wi' a' yer michty ships-o'-war, he'll burn a' bonnie Scotland! He's the greatest pireet ever lived, an' if he's not soon hanged, wha kens what he may burn?"

"Aye, pilot," Paul Jones gravely assured him. " 'Tis exactly as you say. Who knows what—"

At that instant came a cry from the quartermaster.

"Shore boat with an officer just shoving off from the castle!"

It was so. Just pushing away from the water gate beneath those menacing forty-eight-pounders, was a boat with an English army officer in the sternsheets and four redcoats heaving on the oars, heading for us.

Immediately our Commodore swung up his spyglass, scanned the boat, then sang out,

"A Lieutenant coming aboard! Officer of the deck, two side boys to receive His Majesty's officer!"

A few minutes later, piped over the side with two side boys saluting, an English Lieutenant, ruddy almost as his scarlet coat, boarded us to be courteously received by the Commodore, gay in his epaulettes and sword, attended by some three or four more of his officers.

The young Lieutenant meticulously raised his hand in salute, awestruck to be received by the Commodore himself.

"The Governor's compliments, sir, and he desires to know which Commodore he has the honor to receive and what are the names of his ships. And should you want provision, he stands ready to accommodate you, sir."

"My compliments to your Commandant, sir," responded

Paul Jones, "and my thanks for his gracious offer. Fortunately, we want for nothing in the squadron, being just started on our cruise. Inform His Excellency, the Governor, his humble servant is Commodore Burnet of H.M.S. *Prudent*, flagship of this squadron, accompanied by H.M.S. *Pegasus*, Captain Bazely, and H.M.S. *Medea*, Captain Montague. The squadron I have the honor to command, sir, is sent in pursuit of Paul Jones, who hath lately been reported on this coast. Perhaps the Governor hath some further information which may assist me?"

The Lieutenant breathed a sigh of deep relief.

"His Grace, the Governor, will be happy to learn that, sir. He has been himself much disturbed at the reports you mention, and in great fear that Paul Jones may attack Leith, the which he is powerless to prevent as he has next to no powder in the castle for his guns. In fact, sir," added the young Lieutenant, obviously ashamed at his admission, "I was really sent by His Grace to beg you take no offense at his not saluting your flag for want of powder, and to request you, if you intend not to lie here at Leith but shortly to leave, that you lend him a barrel or two."

How Paul Jones ever kept a straight face at that news, I wondered. Not another one of us from Lieutenant Dale down but had hurriedly to turn away his face from the embarrassed Lieutenant lest he burst out in laughter. So it was exactly as our canny Commodore had predicted—that huge fortress bristling with monstrous guns was as harmless a mass of stone as the forts we had taken without a scratch at New Providence and Whitehaven. Would these blundering English never learn? In a sudden fit of coughing, I buried my face in my sleeve lest I give all away.

"Aye, it is a pleasure to me to relieve His Excellency's distress." In utmost gravity, Paul Jones turned from the embarrassed aide, sang out to our gunner,

"Mr. Conner! Break out a barrel of powder from the magazine and deliver it immediately over the side into this boat!"

Facing his visitor again, he bowed apologetically,

"Express to the Governor my deep regret I can spare him but a single barrel. I must husband what I have against falling in with that villain, Paul Jones. Allow me, sir," and drawing aside the Lieutenant, he engaged him in questions, the while Mr. Conner and his mates brought up the powder.

Soon the boat with our barrel, hardly enough for three rounds for one of those great guns, was on its way back to the fort, officer and all, laden far more deeply with Paul Jones' compliments to the Governor than with powder.

No longer was anything wanting for the destruction of Leith (or its ransoming) than the nearing turn of the tide to take us the few remaining miles up the Firth of Forth. We were impatiently waiting for that, when suddenly the wind which had been light from the northeast, hauled about to blow very fresh from the southwest directly down the Firth, dead contrary! So that when the tide turned, we found ourselves facing a rapidly rising gale against which, despite our frantic efforts, we could make no headway whatever up the river even with the tide, and found ourselves instead being driven steadily seaward out the Firth.

Here was a contingency against which Paul Jones could make no provision. While with all his seamanship he was struggling to hold the squadron against the storm to beat back for the attack when the wind moderated, there came another mischance.

Down the river from Leith before the wind came a cutter of fourteen guns in the King's Service to pass us close aboard and scan likewise our consorts. After that, coming instantly about, it tacked away from us to beat hurriedly back toward Leith. This the fore-and-aft-rigged cutter was able to do when our square-riggers could not.

At that, Paul Jones in utter dejection made signal to all our ships to wear and stand out before the gale. It was useless now ever to hope to attack Leith. To the practised eye of the Captain of that cutter, a regular naval officer, the deception that had hoodwinked the Governor and the pilots was laid bare—he knew too well the ships of the King's Navy to be likewise deceived. Soon in Leith and in the fort, the alarm would be given, and ample powder would be got from somewhere to give us a proper reception should we return when the storm blew over.

So with set face Paul Jones abandoned the enterprise. First had his fond dreams of sweeping the seas about Britain of all shipping been frustrated in great measure by the insubordination of his "colleagues." Now was his grandest scheme foiled by the elements when on the verge of success!

A few days more and the time allotted for his cruise would be up. He must return to France to face de Sartine, de Chaumont, Franklin, and the Duchesse de Chartres who had expended a fortune on him, with nothing more achieved, despite the imposing squadron he had led out of L'Orient, than might have been accomplished with far less heartburnings and expense in the little *Ranger* had he only kept her.

53

We stood southward down the shores of Scotland when the gale blew over, for our fourth and last rendezvous off Flamborough Head on the coast of Yorkshire.

On the *Bon Homme Richard* our masts were in bad shape from the racking of this second storm, and we had to strike down our fore topgallant mast and our fore topmast in order to renew the trestle trees which were on the point of giving way and letting the foremast go by the board.

Scarce was this done when the same was found necessary on the mainmast, so that it was not until September 21, four days out of Leith, that we had all our masts on end again, our yards swayed up, and were in some condition once more to face a storm.

By now we were off Flamborough Head, a promontory jutting far out into the North Sea between Scarborough and Great Grimsby. Off that point passed all the shipping bound up or down the coast, and in particular past that point must come the great fleet of merchantmen from the Baltic which as a last stroke, Paul Jones hoped to intercept.

The capture or destruction of this fleet would atone for all else, but in vain Paul Jones pleaded with his two remaining colleagues, Cottineau and Ricot, to linger off Flamborough Head till it might arrive.

Both flatly refused. The Baltic fleet, they pointed out, was bound to be strongly convoyed, making successful attack impossible. And if we lingered beyond two days more on the alarmed east coast of England, such a strong force would surely arrive as to take us all. Paul Jones might do what he pleased, but after September 23, which unfortunately they knew to be the date set for closing the cruise, they would themselves sail directly for the Texel in Holland, our final destination.

Since there was no moving them, Paul Jones hoping for the best accepted the inevitable. We should all do what we could in destroying shipping off Flamborough Head in those two days.

So with the *Pallas* working to the northward of the Head toward Scarborough, and the *Bon Homme Richard* and the *Vengeance* together working to the southward of it toward the Humber, we sank that day one brigantine collier, forced another to run aground, and took a third brigantine belonging to Sunderland.

Next day we cruised southward to the Humber with no great success, taking only a small schooner which we manned as a tender. The coast by now was apparently warned so that all large merchantmen had run for shelter. There being no game left, with great reluctance the Commodore turned northward as evening fell to rejoin the *Pallas* off Flamborough Head, from which rendezvous we should all sail by nightfall of next day, September 23, for the Texel and the end of the cruise.

About midnight we saw and chased two ships to the northward, which we found when dawn broke to be our own consorts, the *Pallas* and the *Alliance.* Captain Landais had finally brought his vessel to the rendezvous, knowing the cruise was now to end.

What was left of our squadron was thus all reunited. And in company we lay in wait to the southward of Flamborough Head to see what fortune might send our way on our last day ere we went home.

September 23 began inauspiciously. Not a sail showed up from the south, so, since the wind was from the sou'southwest which would be fair for all northbound vessels, we could only conclude that all shipping from that quarter was being held in harbor for fear of us.

Shortly after noon, however, we made out a brigantine lying at anchor off Bridlington Bay, somewhat to windward of us. On examination, this appeared to be the same brigan-

[551]

tine that two days before we had forced ashore, now apparently refloated.

Deeming it unwise to go into shallow water himself after that brigantine, the Commodore called up the little schooner which was now our tender, placed aboard her our Second Lieutenant, Henry Lunt, with twenty well armed seamen, and sent him off to take the vessel, or if she ran herself aground again, to fire her.

Lunt, with the sheets on his tiny schooner hauled flat aft to beat to windward into Bridlington Bay, had hardly got a mile from us on that mission, when clearing the point of Flamborough Head some leagues to the northeast, we spied from our decks a large ship running close hauled, beating to windward to weather the land.

That ship had hardly cleared the Head when following her came another, and shortly off Flamborough Head and dead to leeward of us the whole ocean was covered with the sails of full-rigged ships—forty-one of them—the largest fleet that ever I had seen at sea!

Immediately Paul Jones had swung up his glass for a glimpse of that vast armada, he dropped it again to turn to his officers nearby on the quarterdeck. In such excitement as never before on any occasion I had observed in him, he cried out,

"Gentlemen, that is the Baltic fleet! The very fleet I have been so long cruising for!"

And well might he be excited. Before him lay a chance with the four ships of his squadron to fall on those fat merchantmen like a pack of wolves on a flock of sheep and deal English shipping and English merchants such a blow as they had never suffered in any war—provided he could defeat the convoying ships-of-force!

Of what strength was the convoy? It was impossible yet to make them out amongst so many distant vessels. But strong or weak, Paul Jones wasted not an instant. Immediately to our yardarm rose the signal,

"General chase!"

And then up went another, to recall aboard our tender

with Lieutenant Lunt and his twenty men for now should we have need of every fighting man.

For once, Paul Jones was impatient with our sailing master, with Richard Dale, with his Midshipmen, with each seaman heaving on lines alow or aloft. On every yard and stay, we were madly running out canvas. Like magic almost the *Bon Homme Richard* blossomed out in stu'n'sails, royals, staysails, spritsails, and ringtail, but however fast we ran them up, it was too slow to suit our Commodore, straining to close that fleet.

Shortly all were set. Nothing we had in the way of canvas but was flying somewhere aloft, pushing us dead before the light wind for that fleet rounding Flamborough Head.

But meanwhile our prey had taken alarm. As they had come down the coast from the north past Scarborough, off which the *Pallas* had taken a brig the day before, evidently they had been warned by some boat sent out from that town of our presence. For immediately on sighting us bearing down on them, though we were too far off to be recognized either as friends or enemies, the foremost ships let fly their topgallant sheets and began firing guns in signal of distress, at the same time tacking to run northwest into the lee of the promontory jutting out into the sea between them and us.

We closed but slowly. The wind was light, hardly a six knot breeze, scarce strong enough to fill out the vast expanse of canvas we had spread.

At five o'clock, being then still some leagues to the southward of the nearest ships, we made out plain from our deck the convoying men-of-war. There they were standing bravely to windward out to sea to take position between the fleeing merchantmen and danger—two warships only, one large, one of medium size, close hauled on the starboard tack heading southeast.

Paul Jones glowed as he scanned them. Here at long last was his opportunity! There were but two, one roughly our size, one about the size of the *Pallas*. With four ships under his command—the *Bon Homme Richard* 40, the *Alliance*

36, the *Pallas* 32, and the *Vengeance* 12—he should be able in line of battle to fall on those two enemies in close action and make short work of them by laying them aboard on both sides at once, after which the whole Baltic fleet of thirty-nine merchantmen must surrender at discretion or be destroyed.

Our squadron was somewhat spread out before the wind in consequence of the order for a general chase, so the Commodore now made signal to form the line of battle on the flagship, the *Alliance* ahead, the others behind. During this maneuver, the *Alliance* was hailed and directed to engage the larger of the two ships-of-war in conjunction with the *Richard*, so that after she had fired her broadsides, as opportunity offered she was to lay the enemy aboard on one side the while we did the like on the other.

To this, Landais himself, as the *Alliance* drove ahead across our bow, replied,

"The Commodore shall be obeyed!" which answer greatly cheered Paul Jones, who was, in view of past events, dubious of how heartily the Captain of the *Alliance* might enter battle.

With that satisfactorily settled, we next hailed the *Pallas*, to order Captain Cottineau he was to engage the smaller vessel of the enemy together with the *Vengeance*, and so to inform Captain Ricot of that ship which was so far astern of us as to be out of hail. All this Captain Cottineau acknowledged, and dropped back between us and the *Vengeance* to form the line.

By now it was approaching six o'clock and the afternoon light was rapidly failing, with the certainty that not for an hour yet should we be close enough in that gentle wind to engage, so that the battle must be fought in the dark.

In order that we might prepare, however, while still we could see, the Commodore ordered,

"Beat to quarters!"

Instantly all over the *Bon Homme Richard* broke forth the savage rattle of the drums calling to action. And almost as an echo to the wild beat of the rolling drumsticks, came

[554]

from our holds where Burbank, the master-at-arms, had battened down two hundred English officers and seamen taken from our prizes, a chorus of hoarse shouts and groans from the crazed prisoners that made such an infernal din as nearly to drown out the drums.

We cleared for action immediately—every seaman stripped to the waist, as weird a crew as ever prepared for battle. Before us lay two British ships-of-war, yet full a third our men who must fight them were English sailors lately taken from French prisons, of whom some had already deserted us and the rest wanted nothing but fair opportunity to do the same. More than another third were of every seagoing nation on the globe save that under whose flag they now sailed. Out of all the three hundred seamen still left in our ship's company, but eighty were Americans or claimed to be. How could any Captain look forward to aught save disaster with a crew like that?

But under Paul Jones' flashing eyes, they cleared for action as men-o'-warsmen should.

Down came our light sails, all over the ship the carpenters knocked down bulkheads, up the masts scrambled the topmen to sling the yards in chains. Up went gun ports, on all our three decks rammers thudded home loading the guns, and with the rumble of gun carriages running out echoing in their ears, the powder monkeys raced below to get more cartridges from the magazine.

Boarding nets, splinter nets, tubs of water—all were provided, the decks wet down, sand scattered everywhere. Pikes and cutlasses were distributed. Up into each of our three tops Paul Jones sent such an array of firearms and combustibles it seemed there would be scarce room left on the platforms for any of the seamen and marines who were to man them—one after another went up muskets, blunderbusses, light swivel guns, coehorns, stinkpots, hand grenades, pistols, powder flasks. For Paul Jones was determined on close action, and for that he intended swiftly to clear the enemy's tops and then her decks that he might board her.

Rapidly as all this was done, it was completely dark on

that late September day when at last all was ready, so with battle lanterns lighted, over a smooth sea only faintly illuminated by the stars, the *Bon Homme Richard* glided slowly along, running free before what wind there was to cover the last mile between us and the enemy ships.

And now came the first shock. With still that mile to go, the *Alliance* boarded her tacks and hauled sharply by the wind to leave the line and run away to windward! In vain we hoisted signal lanterns. The cowardly Landais took himself and his ship, the newest, the best, and, save for our six old eighteen-pounders, the most powerfully gunned in the squadron, out of harm's way to windward, there to lie in safety awaiting the outcome of battle to see then whether he should flee or stay!

Thus deserted on the eve of action ere ever a gun was fired, Paul Jones swiftly recast his plan of battle and stood on. We were now to engage the enemy flagship alone. To the *Pallas* and the *Vengeance* as before were left her consort.

Just at seven o'clock, with the enemy still out of cannon shot ahead, the harvest moon rose above the ocean, a huge round disk majestic beyond description, to cast a golden glow like an arrow of fire from the eastern horizon across the sea to us. In that soft light, the two ships ahead of us were beautifully illumined, the enemy flagship especially with her yellow sides standing clearly out.

Being then somewhat on our starboard bow, the enemy ships tacked, to stand almost directly westward across our bows toward the land. On achieving this, the larger ship made some signal to her consort. Immediately the second ship bore away to leeward, in consequence of which the *Pallas* astern us, in obedience to orders to engage that vessel, made sail after her.

We were left alone with the larger ship, for the *Vengeance* was far astern and the *Alliance* fled, so it was clear that as between us and the enemy, it would be ship to ship with no longer any advantage in numbers on our side.

Now came the last orders. Hard astarboard went our helm, we handed topgallant sails and hauled up courses.

Under topsails only we hauled by the wind to head westward also toward Flamborough Head, a little ahead of the enemy and converging slowly on him.

A deep silence fell on the *Bon Homme Richard*. From every one of our gun ports, the gunners looked out anxiously across the water at that nearby yellow hull and the tall masts over it shining in the moonlight. A large ship certainly. What was her force?

With strained eyes, from our quarterdeck where I stood alongside Paul Jones as his aide, I hurriedly counted up the gun ports illuminated as squares of light against her side. A single-decker evidently, of twenty nine-pounders in her main tier with probably a dozen more on her spar deck. My pounding heart calmed somewhat. We could match that, and still have the six eighteen-pounders in Mayrant's charge on our lower gun deck, all likely soon to be run out to starboard through the six ports cut through there, to throw the weight of metal in our favor. I waited confidently. Against anything like our force, I had firm faith that our gunners, trained by Paul Jones, would shortly pound the enemy into submission as they had the *Drake*.

Now with the two ships within easy pistol shot and we a little ahead still gradually closing the gap between, there came across the moonlit waters to break that eerie silence, an imperious hail,

"What ship is that?"

Paul Jones, desirous if possible of getting close enough to lay the enemy immediately aboard ere action opened, played for a little more time.

"The *Princess Royal!*" he sang out. "What ship is that?"

"His Majesty's ship *Serapis*, Captain Richard Pearson!" came back the answer, but evidently our hail had the Captain of the *Serapis* nonplussed. Could we really be the *Princess Royal?* He doubted it, but still it might be so. In the darkness with our black sides he could not make us out. We flew no colors at all, and might indeed be another of His Majesty's ships looking for Paul Jones.

"Where are you bound?" he asked to clear the matter up.

[557]

Sheering in as best he could in that light breeze, our Commodore sought still to delay matters.

"Come a little closer! I can't hear you!"

At that, Captain Pearson of the *Serapis* concluded he was being trifled with.

"Answer directly, or I shall fire!" he shouted, and all along the tier of gun ports facing us in that yellow side ghostly in the moonlight, we saw the gun captains start to blow their matches.

Paul Jones waited no further.

Up to the head of our ensign staff on the poop at his signal ran the Stars and Stripes, and that same instant he shouted down the main hatch to where waited Richard Dale on our gun deck,

"Fire, Dick!"

Which ship actually fired first I never knew. Ship to ship, across a scant cable's length of smooth water, the two broadsides roared out so that it was impossible to separate the thunder of our guns from the impact of the enemy solid shot smashing into our hull.

But simultaneously with the crash of our guns, the quarterdeck heaved up under my feet, a terrific explosion such as I had never heard before in action rent the air. While I reeled unsteadily alongside the Commodore who was almost tumbled down the hatchway by that shock, a chorus of agonized shrieks rose from far below to cut sharply through all else. Some of the ancient eighteen-pounders on our lower gun deck must have burst at the first discharge!

"Tom!" sang out Paul Jones in my ear. "Get down there! Don't let 'em fire the rest of those guns again! Abandon that battery and secure the lower gun deck ports! Send Midshipman Mayrant and all his men on deck, if," he concluded somberly, "they're still alive!"

I scrambled down the ladder to the middle gun deck, where I caught a brief glimpse of Richard Dale and Colonel Weibert with bared cutlasses driving back to their guns the panic-stricken seamen who had turned to flee at that blast beneath their feet. Then I shot down the next ladder

[558]

through a cloud of smoke curling upward in the hatchway from below.

Immediately I was stifling in an acrid mist of powder fumes in such a scene as hell itself could scarcely match. Two out of the three huge eighteen-pounders fired on the first broadside had blown up, flying to pieces like erupting volcanoes, to fill the gunroom with searing flames and send monstrous chunks of jagged iron hurtling all about to tear their gun crews limb from limb. Scorched torsos, severed arms and legs and heads lay all about the deck amidst the shattered pieces of the guns and their smashed carriages. Amongst all this wreckage and the blinding smoke from the explosion staggered drunkenly about the remainder of those gun crews, some horribly mangled, all coughing and choking and badly scorched.

Fortunately only three guns and their crews were on the starboard side at the instant of firing. But of those thirty men some ten were dead and the rest all terribly burned or wounded. Of the other thirty men belonging to that battery, all had been with Mayrant on the larboard side, engaged in casting loose the breechings of the three larboard guns to roll the carriages across the ship and out the empty starboard ports awaiting them.

Groping about in the smoke, by the dim rays of the solitary battle lantern still lighted overhead, I found Mayrant there, himself badly singed, helping his frantic men to beat out the flames in their tarry canvas trousers.

"On deck, John!" I screamed in his ear to make myself heard above the shrieks. "Secure the ports! Don't fire again!"

"Aye, Tom!" gasped out Midshipman Mayrant. "But no need o' that order! You couldn't get the people left to load another o' these wornout eighteen-pounders again if you ran 'em through! If there are men enough left on their feet, we'll close the ports! Look after that for me while I get the wounded down to the cockpit!"

I staggered to starboard through the debris of shattered iron, splintered wood, and bleeding flesh to see what I could

[559]

do toward releasing the lanyards and dropping the port shutters myself. But there was no need. The shutters over the exploded guns were torn from their hinges and gone overboard, while the side planking between was so bulged out no chance existed of sealing tight the openings even had the shutters still been there. Not till the carpenter and his mates could get down to spike fresh planks across and caulk in oakum could we hope to seal up our side.

Still choked from powder smoke, I thrust my head out the after port to fill my gasping lungs ere I started back through that stifling gunroom. Immediately the night air, cool off the sea rippling by not two feet beneath my burning eyes, revived me. Over my head, I heard the hoarse cries of Dale's gunners running out their pieces on the deck above for the second broadside. Hurriedly I straightened up, started to draw back my head lest I catch the blast from the muzzles only a few feet over me, and my eyes fell on the *Serapis* close abeam us.

Immediately my stomach turned to lead, my breathing stopped. For now, flung wide open all along her side down near her waterline, was a second row of gun ports brightly illuminated by battle lanterns. And running out those ports came thrusting forth into the moonlight, almost in my face it seemed, the ugly muzzles of a whole battery of eighteen-pounders!

The *Serapis* was a two-decker then, with twenty eighteen-pounders as well as the range of guns I had first seen, a man-of-war far more powerful than the *Bon Homme Richard* under any conditions. And now in this terrible moment when we had just lost what few ancient eighteen-pounders we had, she was unmasking that overpowering battery on us!

We no longer had the slightest chance in a gunnery duel with her. Craftily the Captain of the *Serapis* had kept his overwhelming superiority in guns concealed till he had us under their muzzles, lest like our consort, the *Alliance*, we also should flee and deprive him of an easy victory. Now was the *Bon Homme Richard* surely lost!

Spasmodically I jerked my head back from the port lest the coming broadside take me bodily with it through our other side. Those guns were aiming at our waterline, our lower gun deck would shortly be but a mass of flying splinters. In a panic, I ran for the ladder to get speedily on the topside ere those huge solid shot came crashing into us.

Lost immediately in the smoke of the gunroom, I stumbled into someone leaning against a stanchion, together we sprawled out full length near the foot of the ladder.

I got on my knees, grabbed the seaman I had knocked down to help him up.

"Shake a leg, man!" I screamed. "Get out of here!"

He made no move, sagged limply to the floor again. I looked. It was Tommy Turner, powder monkey, the little lad I had recruited in Nantucket, dead! There he lay, eyes glazed, covered with blood, the boy whose tearful mother I had promised to look after, pierced through the chest by a ragged iron splinter from one of the burst guns! In a frenzy, I let go that corpse, seized the ladder, scrambled wildly for the topside to save myself.

Ere I made it, the broadsides on both ships crashed out again and this time the *Bon Homme Richard* literally reeled as she caught the full impact of those eighteen-pound shot smashing into her below. Gasping with fear, I popped out the hatch, looked wildly about for the Commodore to report.

There he stood in the moonlight on the starboard side of the quarterdeck, eyes contracted, intently studying the *Serapis* which was now wreathed from waterline to spar deck with smoke billowing from both tiers of guns.

"Two guns burst, sir!" I gasped out. "Ten dead, maybe twenty-five wounded. Mayrant's getting 'em down to the cockpit, then he'll be up with the rest. Can't close the ports, sir. The shutters are gone!"

"Aye, aye." Paul Jones turned back to studying our opponent. "Those ports, open or shut, will make little difference if our friend gets in a few more broadsides like that last one. We must close him!"

He beckoned the sailing master.

"Sheer in, Mr. Stacy, but not so sharp you mask our fire!"

"Aye, aye, sir!"

Stacy put the helm somewhat aweather, eased the sheets a bit, and we started to close. But Captain Pearson, well realizing his advantage, had not the slightest intention of permitting it.

Immediately he backed his topsails, and the *Serapis* being apparently a new vessel of the latest design and far more manageable than the awkward *Richard*, began to drop back, so that in a few minutes she had gained a position under our stern.

From there she raked us with whole broadsides, her heavy eighteen-pound shot crashing through and through our rotten hull, while from her upper range of nine-pounders and her spar deck guns she poured into our poop a veritable hail of round shot and grape to go flying down our gun deck and make dreadful havoc amongst Dale's gun crews. And then a cannon ball went through our ensign staff, cutting it clean off, to drop both staff and colors into the sea astern.

We backed our own topsails to fall back abeam the enemy and end all this lest we be beaten out of hand. But hardly had we lost headway than the *Serapis*, whose Captain had by now discovered he could outsail the *Bon Homme Richard* handily, filled away and running past our starboard side sheered in across our bow to rake us from forward.

So for half an hour the battle continued in full fury, the *Serapis* outsailing us to alternate between raking us ahead and raking us astern. The sides of both ships flamed out continuously with the crashing of full broadsides. On deck and from the tops came from each ship the incessant fire of small arms which did much execution, since the ships were always within pistol shot of each other and the sea smooth. Under these conditions, muskets and pistols could be aimed and fired in the moonlight with some certainty, and as for the great guns, it was impossible for any shot fired to miss, so close were the contending vessels.

All this time we had been heading directly for Flam-

[562]

borough Head, atop which promontory stood thousands of spectators looking off in the night toward the lurid flames wreathing each ship from waterline to tops. Now we were hardly a league from it, and it seemed to me that we must soon ground there unless we sank first. In the absence of Lieutenant Lunt, who was charged with the navigation, I pointed out that danger to the Commodore.

Jones, intent only on somehow grappling with our enemy, took but a hasty glimpse.

"A league yet, you say? 'Tis ample. Inform me when there's but a half mile left!" and he turned to again on his main problem, closing the enemy ere we were shot to bits.

To me it seemed that all was lost. We had an inferior number of mixed guns from twelve-pounders down to sixes to oppose fifty guns on the *Serapis*, and of those fifty, twenty were eighteen-pounders! And the way Captain Pearson of the *Serapis*, an excellent sailor evidently, was handling his ship, coolly keeping away from us while his great guns battered us to pieces, left no room for hope.

All over the *Bon Homme Richard* our men were falling literally by scores. On the high poop, Colonel Chamillard with twenty French marines had his men literally mowed down at his side by the hail of grape raking us from aft. Under their Colonel's eye these Frenchmen bravely replied with musketry fire till with only a handful left, Chamillard withdrew them from the poop to the quarterdeck, where at least they had the shelter of the bulwarks from those deadly clouds of grape.

Matters went swiftly from bad to worse on the *Bon Homme Richard*. John Gunnison, carpenter, rushed up to report we were holed in sundry places below the waterline and water was rising in the holds. Jones ordered him to plug what holes he might; as for the water, let him gather what men he could to man the pumps and hold it down. Dubiously Gunnison went below to try.

Our fire began to slacken appreciably. Our heaviest guns, of course, had been out of action from the beginning. But now with our decayed sides offering no resistance to the

[563]

steady battering of round shot crashing through from abeam, and from bow and stern ricocheting full length along our gun deck, by ones and twos our broadside guns were dismounted to be strewn with carriages smashed all up and down the gunroom. Soon Richard Dale, in command of that 'tween decks battery, found himself with not a single gun left on its wheels to serve, with the side of the ship a mass of splintered wreckage, with the deck planking ploughed up, and all about him, horribly mangled by shot and flying splinters, the dead and the dying lying in heaps.

He was helpless to injure the enemy longer. With the certain prospect that his remaining men would shortly be slaughtered in that shambles if he stayed there, Dale abandoned the gun deck and sent what men were left up on the topside to arm themselves there with muskets as a last desperate resource.

We had now but three guns left in action—one six-pounder on our forecastle, where Red Jerry, gun captain, was raging behind its breech, with fierce shrieks encouraging his decimated crew to keep up a hot fire, and two six-pounders on our quarterdeck, somewhat more quietly served under the eye of our purser, that mild-mannered merchant from Philadelphia, Mr. Mease.

Paul Jones strove desperately to counter the maneuvers of the *Serapis* and close her where we might try boarding, for it was plain to all hands that otherwise in another few minutes under that devastating fire we should have our last few guns dismounted and our ship sunk—unless our Captain struck our colors first.

But so many of our sheets and braces were already shot away that the lumbering *Bon Homme Richard* responded poorly to his efforts, and our nimble antagonist made the most of his superiority.

Again the *Serapis* swept by our starboard side and luffed across our bows to give us another raking broadside, but so close aboard this time that Paul Jones, putting our helm aweather, drove our bowsprit fair over the enemy's poop.

Seeing at last a slight chance to board, he rushed forward, shouting,

"Boarders away!"

All hands on the forecastle, seizing pikes, sprang into the head rigging to scramble out the jibboom and drop down on our enemy. But ere that could be accomplished, the *Serapis*, smartly handled, put her helm up, slid away from us, and then promptly backed her topsails to fall back abeam us for a broadside at such close quarters as should end all resistance.

And now Paul Jones saw the opportunity he had been looking for, and instantly improved it. At long last had Captain Pearson, over eager for the kill, given him an opening by coming so close. As the *Serapis* with sails aback lost headway and dropped abeam us not a ship length off to deliver that murderous broadside, Paul Jones sang out to the sailing master,

"Hard aweather, Mr. Stacy! Fill away the topsails!"

Instantly up flew our helm. The main and mizzen topsails, which before had been aback, were braced hurriedly over and filled away, so that close aboard the *Serapis* we started to draw ahead of her the while our sails completely blanketed hers, and left her helpless to maneuver!

Now under the influence of our helm, we swung sharp to starboard athwart the hawse of the *Serapis*. She, still coming slowly on, drove her jibboom straight through our starboard mizzen shrouds to come across our poop just abaft the mizzenmast!

Like a cat, Paul Jones leaped from the quarterdeck up the ladder to the poop, laid hold the end of a stout hawser coiled down there, and assisted by Mr. Stacy expertly lashed the enemy's jibboom to our mizzenmast, leaving some slack between, so that by no possibility could the ships tear apart again!

Then loud and clear, triumphantly Paul Jones' deep voice rang out to the seamen manning the sails,

"Well done, my brave lads! We have got her now! Throw on board the grappling irons and stand by to board!"

[565]

As we lay stern to the wind, and the *Serapis* with sails aback lay broadside to it, the wind began immediately to pivot the *Serapis* about her bowsprit, so that she was shortly swinging toward us, her stern closing our bow.

As she swung in, with a wild yell Reuben Chase leaped upon our bulwark amidships, hurled across the gap a grappling hook tailed with chain to catch it in the enemy's rail. Instantly Jack Robinson put a stopper on the chain, ran it through a snatch block, and with all hands laying back on the line, started to drag the *Serapis* hard up against our side.

But no sooner was the hook caught than on deck the *Serapis* a seaman scrambled up the rail and began hacking madly at the chain with an axe to cut it loose.

Hardly had that tar lifted his axe for the first swing when up beside Reuben sprang Red Jerry balancing a pike in his hands. Up went that pike over his shoulder, a moment it hung poised there for all the world as if once again Red Jerry was in the bow of a whaleboat balancing his harpoon for a cast at a whale, then he darted it.

The axe came down, but at that same instant, transfixed by the hurtling pike, so did the seaman wielding it, to go toppling inboard on his deck while the axe splashed overboard.

"Well done, my little Indian!" sang out Paul Jones, and then, "More irons, Reuben, so we hold them fast!"

"Aye, aye, sir!" Down the bulwark ran Reuben Chase, with his huge hands pitching heavy grapnels across our rail as if they had been toys, so that shortly we had the *Serapis* hauled close aboard us, her bow against our stern, the two ships lying headed opposite, starboard to starboard.

From the instant we had laid the *Serapis* athwart her hawse, the fire of her great guns had ceased, for at first none of her guns bore on us, and now on her starboard side, which she presented to us for the first time, all her gun ports were closed.

Captain Pearson, however, had no intention of fighting at close quarters, being well assured that as matters were going, he would shortly silence us completely and then sink us at his leisure. So at the instant of collision he took steps to separate us immediately.

Seeing his bowsprit driving aboard the *Bon Homme Richard*, he promptly let go his larboard anchor, thinking that his men would shortly cast adrift our grapnels and that then we should be drifted clear of him by wind and tide the while his anchor held him fast.

But the matter succeeded not to his wish. Dismayed by the sight of the first man who had tried to cut away the grapplings lying sprawled out on their deck, horribly transfixed by that impromptu harpoon, his shipmates on the *Serapis* were loath to mount the gunwales for another trial, so we had half a dozen others caught ere Captain Pearson had gathered a sufficient party to attempt it in force.

By that time, our own boarders, reenforced by all Dale's men from below, were pouring such a hot fire from muskets and pistols on all and sundry who showed themselves with axes above the enemy's gunwale that it was too late. The grapnels held, even more were thrown aboard and hauled taut, and the *Serapis*, forty minutes after the action had opened, was bound fast to us.

Now, if ever, was our last remaining chance. We must take that ship by boarding, or be soon sunk alongside her. Hurriedly Lieutenant Dale started to organize the boarding party but a dilemma confronted him. Should he arm our English seamen, he could be sure the moment they set foot aboard the *Serapis* they were more likely to turn to there cutting down their own shipmates than fighting Pearson's men. So there was some delay while Dale sorted out his boarders, eliminating all the English.

But Captain Pearson waited not to be boarded. Over the gunwale of the *Serapis*, outlined a moment against the moon, came a yelling mob of boarders to leap down on our quarter-deck.

In an instant, all up and down our starboard side we were fighting hand to hand on our own deck for our lives, pistols flaming, cutlasses, pikes, and knives flashing everywhere. Who was friend and who was foe in that melee in the dim light of the moon was hard to tell—all I knew was that in another second I found myself slashing madly with a cutlass at a half-naked seaman ferociously lunging at me with a pike. Fortunately my first wild cut shot his point aside, so that ere he could recover for another thrust, I had cut him down with a desperate slash that laid his head wide open.

The whole encounter was lightning in its swiftness. The boarders, finding themselves confronted by at least an equal number, had evidently no stomach for staying to face at such close quarters the evil-looking knives flashing out in the hands of our Algerines and Maltese, and hurriedly retreated over the rails back to their own deck.

Immediately Dale, yelling for his men to follow him, swept across after them, only to find himself there in no better case. Reenforced by seamen pouring up from below, the English far outnumbered him, having suffered but slightly in the gunnery action, so that he and his men were shortly driven back in their turn, leaving half a dozen dead on deck the *Serapis*.

For another moment the fight raged on the gunwales between the ships with pikes and cutlasses clashing loudly in the night, then both sides retired behind their own bulwarks and the action on deck ended.

Our last forlorn hope, the attempt to take the *Serapis* by boarding now that we had her alongside, had failed.

54

FROM on board the *Serapis*, we heard Captain Pearson roaring out to his First Lieutenant,

"Stanhope! Man the guns again! Damn their eyes, we'll sink those Yankees now!"

Immediately on the *Serapis*, Lieutenant Stanhope herded his cheering seamen back to their great guns to reopen fire on us. But at once he was in difficulty. What previously had been the unengaged starboard side of the *Serapis* was now toward us, and the gun port shutters on that side, still closed, could not be opened, so close to each other were the two hulls.

In vain the English strove to raise their port sills that they might run out their guns. There was no clearance to permit it. But the broadside came nevertheless. Stanhope fired with his guns run in, to rip his heavy port sills from their hinges and send them tearing into us along with the volley of solid shot.

Now with the muzzles of their great guns literally touching our starboard side, the enemy began firing rapidly, to send broadside after broadside crashing into the *Bon Homme Richard's* already shattered hulk, tearing huge holes in our timbers. In way of their lower range of eighteen-pounders, so thoroughly did those massive shot rend our weak hull that soon from one side to the other they had opened such a vast gap aft in our planking just above our waterline that a coach and six might easily have been driven in to starboard and out to larboard without touching anything! Why our quarterdeck did not collapse into that cavern below it, I could not fathom.

The only reason this savage bombardment did not sink

[569]

us out of hand was that the *Serapis*, being too close, could not depress the muzzles of her guns low enough to catch us below the waterline. So she was reduced perforce to cutting our ship asunder just above it, which Captain Pearson methodically set out to do.

Amidst all these thunderous salvos, Paul Jones, grim but undismayed, received Dale's report of his abortive boarding party.

"Can't carry 'em by boarding, Captain. They're hardly hurt on the *Serapis* yet! And in thirty minutes more with all that cannonading, they'll knock our topsides out from under us!"

"Aye, Dick," replied our skipper, "but they're going to be hurt now. We'll slow their fire! Get your men down on our gun decks again with pikes. Every time an English gunner leans out a port to ram home his charge, run him through!"

"Aye, aye, sir." Richard Dale turned to arming what men he had left as he had been directed, and soon, divided into small squads, they were down on our middle and lower gun decks again, spread out amongst our smashed gun carriages. Bandaged, bloody, half-naked, like demons out of hell amidst the flames of the enemy's guns they lunged fiercely across the slight gap between the ships with their boarding pikes each time a British tar ran his rammer out into our ship in order to sponge out or ram his gun.

Shortly in self-defense, Lieutenant Stanhope on the *Serapis* was compelled to arm some of his gunners likewise. So that with pikemen stationed on both sides, ere the enemy could load any gun a fierce battle was fought out with spears through every gun port amidships where the vessels touched. There, as in the days of Alexander of Macedon, the fight swiftly turned into a clash of infuriated spearmen, with sailors slaying each other through the ports to the serious detriment of the *Serapis'* gunfire.

So savagely did Richard Dale and his embattled seamen press home this novel defence that soon every lower deck gun amidships on the *Serapis* was silenced, with no Englishman daring to lean out the ports to load lest he be instantly pierced by a lance. As a consequence, Lieutenant Stanhope of the *Serapis* had to run his guns aside to clear the ports and thereafter fight with pikes alone.

Only at the bow and stern where the sides of the ships curved away from each other so far as to make pikes useless, was the *Serapis* able to maintain her fire below. At bow and stern therefore, with four heavy guns at each end, she kept up an incessant fire on us, relentlessly battering in our ends. And there was no way of stopping it on our part.

Simultaneously with Dale's departure for our lower decks, the battle burst out in a new quarter. With great foresight, Jones had heavily armed and heavily manned the platforms topping each of our three masts, and now our tops burst out into furious action.

Since the ships were side by side and their yards interlocked, hardly fifty feet separated our tops from those of the *Serapis*. At once, Lieutenant Edward Stack of the French marines, commanding in the maintop and ably seconded by Midshipman Fanning, took advantage of that situation. Jones had fitted larger platforms atop the masts of the *Bon Homme Richard* than were usual for any ship, and jammed them all—fore, main, and mizzen—with far more men than could be accommodated similarly on the *Serapis*.

With muskets, blunderbusses, pistols and swivels flaming luridly out in the moonlight, our seamen aloft poured such a hot fire at practically point-blank range into the enemy's tops as shortly to overwhelm the English marines stationed there. One by one, clawing wildly for support in empty air, the British pitched drunkenly off their tops to go sprawling out into space, crashing to the deck far below, limp corpses.

So murderous was this fire from our tops that in a few minutes the enemy's tops were entirely silenced, not one man being left alive aloft. When that was achieved, and our men were no longer exposed to any danger from the tops of the *Serapis*, they were left free to turn their whole attention to the enemy's decks.

[571]

Being in their elevated stations particularly well placed to look down over the bulwarks of the *Serapis*, Lieutenant Stack and his men began a deliberate and galling fire on the gun crews manning every great gun the *Serapis* had in the open, whether on forecastle, quarterdeck, or waist. This fire, seconded by fierce volleys of musketry from Chamillard's marines on our deck directed into the enemy's upper ports, and further aided by showers of grape from our two quarterdeck six-pounders, gradually cut down the crews of the *Serapis'* upper range of guns and somewhat slackened their fire.

Amidships on our upper deck, Matthew Mease, our fighting purser, who commanded the two six-pounders still in action in our waist, fell, wounded in the head by a grapeshot. Immediately his place was taken by Paul Jones himself, there to cheer the faltering seamen and hold up the fire of the last few guns we had.

But what Paul Jones expected to gain from this save to prolong defeat, I could not see. It was plain that we must soon strike or sink. From our hold came the report of the carpenter that the water was gaining fast, reaching already five feet above our keel and rising in spite of all his efforts at the pumps. Evidently we should shortly founder, even without more damage from the *Serapis*.

And still from the guns at bow and stern and on the upper deck of the *Serapis* came smashing into us a steady hail of round shot and of grape, gnawing away at our shivering hulk, with every discharge sending more splintered timbers to join the heaps of wreckage strewn about 'tween decks over our dead.

Now to add to our miseries came a new enemy—fire. The light sails of the *Serapis*, stowed atop her cranes on her quarterdeck, took fire from a hand grenade tossed aboard her from our tops. This set off her rigging, and the fire was there instantly communicated to ours, where it spread immediately to our splintered bulwarks, impregnated with pitch. In a moment, on deck and aloft we were ablaze, a vast

[572]

pillar of flame in the night, and the *Serapis,* though to a lesser degree, likewise.

At once on both ships, all firing ceased, with the seamen turned from fighting each other to fighting the flames. On the *Bon Homme Richard,* with water aplenty pouring up from our bilges through the pumps, we had fair means of combating it, so that we had our flames extinguished shortly. This the enemy also succeeded in achieving at about the same moment.

Seeing that a large number of men were gathered on the *Serapis'* quarterdeck who might again try to board us, Paul Jones rushed forward to our forecastle to muster there a party to oppose them. Gathering hastily up Red Jerry's gun crew and the forecastle gang under Mr. Caswell, master's mate, he armed them all with pikes, and drawing his own pistols, stood by to repel boarders.

At this moment came treachery. Down in the hold spread a rumor that Paul Jones and Richard Dale were dead, together with practically all hands on the topside, and that the gunner, Mr. Conner, was therefore Captain. No longer hearing any firing on deck, Conner concluded our resistance had ceased. He was discussing with Burbank, master-at-arms, what next to do, when into the magazine where Conner held forth sending up the powder charges for our last few six-pounders, came running Gunnison, the carpenter, shrieking,

"The hold's full of water! We're sinking!"

Instantly Conner, panic-stricken, acted.

"Come on, mates! If we want to save our lives, we must strike the flag before she sinks under us!" and followed by Gunnison and Burbank, he went scrambling wildly up the ladder from the magazine for that purpose.

Up from the hold, through the debris of our shattered gunrooms, and out on deck raced these three poltroons. Seeing nothing on the quarterdeck but heaps of dead and dying seamen, their worst fears were confirmed, and pausing not to look elsewhere for their Captain or Lieutenant, one and all they fled aft to strike our flag.

[573]

Coming out atop the poop, they ran to the stern to haul down the colors on the *Bon Homme Richard*, but to their dismay found themselves unable. Fortunately for us, a cannon ball from the *Serapis* had long since rendered us that service, and there remained neither staff nor flag for them to strike.

Hysterical that they might be slain on deck ere they could surrender the wreck of the *Bon Homme Richard*, they turned, all three, and fled for the waist, bawling out to the *Serapis* at the top of their lungs,

"Quarters! Quarters! For God's sake, quarters! Our ship is sinking!"

Instantly at that cowardly cry, Paul Jones, who had just discharged both his pistols over the rail at the men on the *Serapis*, leaped from our forecastle to run aft, roaring,

"What damned rascals are these? Shoot them! Kill them!"

The carpenter and the master-at-arms, hearing Jones' voice and well realizing what now might happen to them for their treachery, skulked immediately below, vanishing like shadows down the main hatch. Conner, the gunner, in mortal terror at this sudden resurrection of our Captain, attempted also to do the same but ere he could reach the hatch, Paul Jones, whose weapons were both discharged, hurled his empty pistols down the deck at the fleeing gunner.

One of them caught Conner fair in the head, fracturing his skull, and tumbled him senseless down the hatchway, where at the foot of the ladder he lay till the action was over.

At this moment, the relentless fire of the great guns from the *Serapis* began again, and having as yet no powder on deck for our remaining three insignificant six-pounders, we were perforce constrained for the moment to bear it in silence.

Seeing that their fire was not returned, and having heard the cries for quarter from our deck, the enemy concluded that, realizing we were fairly beaten, we had finally struck. As a consequence, Captain Pearson sang out to us across the bulwarks,

"Have you surrendered?"

From the silent deck of the sinking *Bon Homme Richard,* loud and clear in a deep voice fit to raise the dead lying all about and echoing over both ships through the roar of the English guns, came Paul Jones' answer,

"NEVER! I HAVE JUST BEGUN TO FIGHT!"

55

FROM the *Serapis* another broadside came blazing into us, and Captain Pearson, since we would not surrender while yet we might, doggedly set about the business of battering what was left of the *Bon Homme Richard* to splinters. Paul Jones countered by playing his last card.

We could not board the enemy with our much decimated crew in the face of his superior numbers waiting to receive us, but Paul Jones saw another way of taking her. He called me to him.

"Tom," he ordered brusquely. "Up to the maintop with you! Tell Stack and Fanning there to lay out on our yards into the enemy's tops, and then from there to clear her decks! All depends now on that! Turn loose everything they have from aloft on the *Serapis* herself!"

"Aye, aye, sir!" I sprang into the main rigging, went scrambling up the shrouds to the maintop. There on the crowded platform was Midshipman Fanning as black as a runaway negro, with his jacket which he had used in beating out the flames in the rigging, half burned away. Behind him, his gorgeous marine uniform coat in as bad a state, stood Lieutenant Stack, coolly directing his men in firing diagonally downward over the enemy's gunwales at the gun crews far below.

"Lieutenant! Captain's orders!" I burst out, panting violently from my exertions in getting aloft. "Get all your men and guns out on the yards and take possession of the enemy's tops you've cleared. From there, clear her decks! Give 'em everything you've got from musket balls to stinkpots!"

"Aye, aye!"

Stack motioned to Fanning, and immediately, seamen

first, all hands started to lay out our main yard, which was locked with *Serapis'* fore yard and thus led to her foretop.

Strung out thus on the yards far above the flaming decks below us, they balanced themselves like monkeys, busily engaged in sending across their muskets, grenades, swivel guns, and combustibles. I called out to Midshipman Coram in our foretop to do likewise.

Since our fore yard lay close to the main yard of the *Serapis*, he had no difficulty in his task, and shortly without resistance our men were ensconced in both the fore and main tops of the *Serapis*, from which excellent positions they had the entire upper decks of the *Serapis* at their mercy.

They swiftly improved their opportunity to hurl down a veritable shower of hand grenades and musket balls amongst the sweating gun crews serving the deck guns of the enemy. The bulwarks of the *Serapis* no longer afforded those exposed crews the slightest protection to this unexpected assault from their own tops.

Taken thus in reverse, with man after man in the very act of loading those deck guns pierced by a musket ball or knocked down by an exploding grenade coming from aloft, the British broke from the guns and fled to the shelter of their covered forecastle and quarterdeck. In twenty minutes, we had completely cleared their upper deck and silenced every gun in the open, so that only from such guns as were shielded by quarterdeck and forecastle from our attack, could any fire be maintained.

At this, matters began to look better for us. Urging on his dispirited men, Paul Jones (chiefly through the giant strength of Reuben Chase) managed to roll over from our larboard side another six-pounder, so that now we had three in our waist playing on the enemy. Hurriedly he brought Red Jerry aft to direct this fresh gun, his piece on the forecastle having at last been dismounted.

Again on both sides, the firing burst out in full fury.

Below, the *Serapis* savagely poured solid shot into us with four eighteen-pounders and four nine-pounders, all now well served by reenforcements from on deck.

Above, with two of our six-pounders and our fire from aloft, we raked the *Serapis'* upper deck continuously, keeping such a hail of grape and musket balls spraying over all as to discourage any attempt to man her topside battery again. And with our third six-pounder, directed now by Paul Jones himself and loaded with double-headed shot, a steady fire was played on the enemy's mainmast, standing sharply out against the moon. Jones wanted to cripple her fatally for maneuver should she by any chance break free of our embrace.

While both vessels were thus busily engaged, the *Serapis* in tearing apart what was left of our hull, and we in destroying her topsides, there now showed up for the first time since action had opened, our consort, the *Alliance*, sailing ghostlike out of the night into plain view in the moonlight off our lee quarter!

Immediately I pointed her out to the Commodore, who had eyes only for the *Serapis*.

"Thank God!" he cried joyfully, leaping for our poop to hail her. "Now this carnage on our decks will soon be over!" and in a full voice carrying clear across the water, he shouted,

"Lay the enemy aboard on the other side!"

"Aye, aye!" came back from the *Alliance*, and for the first time in some three hours, my spirits rose. With the *Alliance* pouring solid shot low down into the *Serapis* from one side the while we raked her decks from the other, Pearson must swiftly strike or have his men all slaughtered. This was the end at last, now that the timid Captain of the *Alliance* dared bring his ship to action.

But alas for my hopes! The *Alliance* had scarcely answered when she sheered in under our stern, presenting to us her starboard broadside, and let drive at the *Bon Homme Richard* with a volley of grapeshot that came raking down our deck!

Horrorstricken, I stood mute, wondering what was wrong, when from Midshipman Mayrant in our waist came the cry,

"The *Alliance* is manned with Englishmen and is firing on us!"

But I was under no such illusion, nor was Paul Jones. Pierre Landais, Captain of the *Alliance,* well knew what he was doing, though his men below at the guns might not. For in the bright light of a full moon now high in the heavens, by no possibility could Landais mistake the *Bon Homme Richard* with her high poop and her black sides for the *Serapis* with no such tower on her stern and her sides a bright yellow. What the vindictive Landais was now deliberately doing was of a piece with all his treachery before!

The *Alliance,* falling off again before the wind, stood on past our larboard side at no great distance, to give us another broadside when fairly abeam, of solid shot this time. These, catching us at short range on or under our waterline, went tearing through our unresisting side, immediately to add greatly to the water flooding into our holds.

Thus caught in a crossfire of solid shot from friend and foe alike, on deck and aloft the *Bon Homme Richard* became a bedlam of hoarse cries. In agonized French, Colonel Chamillard on our quarterdeck and Lieutenant Stack from the tops implored Landais not to sink us. In thunderous English, Paul Jones roared out they were firing into the wrong ship. From bow to stern, every tongue cried out, begging them for God's sake to forbear firing into the *Bon Homme Richard.* And as a last desperate resource, Paul Jones hung out our private recognition signal, three lanterns peculiarly arranged over our lee rail.

But nothing availed. Still the *Alliance* kept on, to sheer in near our bow and give us another broadside of grapeshot which raked our forecastle, killing Mr. Caswell, who commanded there, as well as many of his men.

Then, leaving our decks strewn with fresh heaps of dead and with dying men cursing with their last breaths our treacherous consort, the *Alliance* hauled by the wind and stood away to larboard. A mile or so off, Landais hove his ship to in the moonlight, satisfied, no doubt, that the issue had now been placed beyond dispute.

On deck the *Bon Homme Richard* all was demoralization with hope lost amongst our men. What little discipline was left vanished. Of what use to fight on in a hopeless battle, when nearby lay the *Alliance*, on which we could bring no gun to bear, ready at some unexpected moment to come back and slaughter what few of us remained?

Savagely with roaring voice and menacing pistols, Paul Jones drove our panic-stricken deck force back to their three guns and their musketry. With Reuben Chase, Red Jerry, and me as gun crew, as a start we three together loaded and ran out the six-pounder in the waist gangway. With his own hands Paul Jones sighted and fired it to inspire his men the battle was not over. Then rushing to the quarterdeck, with fierce imprecations and terrible oaths he rallied there the remnants of our French marines, once more to send a volley of musket balls to sweep the quarterdeck on the *Serapis*.

Slowly, raggedly, under Jones' tremendous voice roaring encouragement and threatening instant death to all who skulked, our fire started to pick up in answer to that of the *Serapis* which had never slackened in this interlude with the *Alliance*. Once again, between our renewed fire and the shower of grenades rained down upon the *Serapis* from her own tops, we managed to clear her decks of those who had ventured out preparing to board us. After half an hour more of fierce fighting with small arms above and pikes below, with the rattle of musketry, the explosion of grenades, and the barking of our three six-pounders lost almost in the thunder of the eighteen-pounders on the *Serapis* tearing at our vitals, we had at last about reestablished our control of the enemy's upper decks.

At that, Paul Jones, ranging our decks from forecastle to poop rallying even the wounded to rise and fight again, began to scent victory. The mainmast of the *Serapis* was shaking, nearly cut in two by our fire. Her decks were cleared. A sizeable boarding party could surely take her now, but where in our cut to pieces crew should he get the men to board?

There were too few left on our deck. If he should call up

[580]

Dale and his pikemen from below, the men of the *Serapis* there might easily step across into our unguarded ports and take us from below, immediately ending the battle.

While Paul Jones' eyes were roaming speculatively over our deck, taking count of what few seamen and marines might be gathered for boarders, suddenly every hatch on the *Bon Homme Richard* leading from below started to spew forth into the moonlight streams of water-soaked Englishmen!

In a moment our astounded Captain found himself smothered almost in a mass of struggling, raving seamen, some hundreds of them, unhurt, unwounded, shrieking out in terror,

"The ship's sinking!"

Now for the first time did fear strike home in Paul Jones' heart. All seemed lost. For Burbank, our traitorous master-at-arms, had released all the English prisoners from our flooding hold!

There they were, over two hundred of them, outnumbering by four to one what men we had left on deck, crazed with fear, anxious only to deliver us to the enemy. And though they were unarmed, they had but to stretch forth their hands to grab up from the decks and the arms rack what cutlasses and boarding pikes they wished, to sweep all before them and take immediate possession of our ship!

But even in that mad moment Paul Jones did not lose his head. Those fear-crazed men about him would respond to but one thing—fear. Instantly, louder than I had ever heard his voice before, it rose above the tumult and the roar of battle,

"The *Serapis* is sinking alongside us! If you want to save your lives, man the pumps on the *Richard!* It's your last hope!"

That deep voice, firm with authority, carried conviction with it. Immediately most of the panic-stricken prisoners broke for the pump handles, frantically eager to get to work. Shortly our carpenter, Mr. Gunnison, who had been making but sorry progress in that business with the few men he could get for his four pumps, found himself swamped with frenzied Englishmen, struggling only to get their hands on a pump lever that they might hold down the water in our holds and live!

Some few of the prisoners failed to respond, and these Paul Jones herded immediately to the pumps with his pistols, where Richard Dale took charge of all, and ended that danger. And indeed what Burbank had done proved by our Captain's quick wit to be a blessing after all, for so rapidly had the water been rising in our hull since the *Alliance* had holed us, that without these unwearied new hundreds to keep the pump handles flying for us, I verily believe we should shortly have foundered.

One prisoner, however, got away from us, and his escape went far toward nullifying what aid we received from his compatriots. This man, Captain Johnston of the English letter of marque *Union* which we had taken off northern Scotland, much bolder than his mates, had leaped through one of our lower deck ports into the *Serapis*, shouting he was an Englishman, there to be received with open arms by Lieutenant Stanhope.

Immediately he was escorted up above on the *Serapis* to Captain Pearson, to find that worthy looking gloomily out from under the shelter of his quarterdeck upon his deserted upper deck guns. Pearson, discouraged completely that we should ever strike and despairing that we should soon sink, was on the point of striking himself, when Captain Johnston appeared to change his mind for him.

"Look ye, sir!" exclaimed Johnston, pointing to himself. He was soaked to the waist. "The water's arising fast in all 'er holds! A few more broadsides're bound to sink 'er!"

With that, Pearson took fresh heart and Stanhope too, so that the flagging fire of the *Serapis* was accelerated, with every muzzle depressed as far as its carriage would permit, to hole us near our waterline. So sure were they from Johnston's story of our waterlogged hold, and from what their own eyes showed them, that a few more racking volleys would certainly sink us, that in a fury Stanhope doubled up

[582]

the pikemen at his lower ports to guard the loading and brought into action again many of his abandoned eighteen-pounders.

Once more were those terrible eighteen-pounders served at top speed by their sweating gun crews encouraged to believe the end was near. Full volleys of huge round shot came hurtling into our lower hull, some to fly harmlessly through us from one side to the other, touching naught but empty air, others to tear great masses of planking from our already blasted sides.

One of our four pumps was soon smashed, the water in our holds started to gain on us again. Smoke, flame, and the thunderous explosions of those guns tearing us to pieces filled our holds. We caught fire below from the flash of the guns. Splintered planks and oakum soaked in pitch and tar blazed everywhere along our battered gunrooms. Richard Dale, struggling to organize fire-fighting parties amongst some of his men to keep the fire away from our magazine the while the rest fought on with pikes, was fair driven to distraction by the multitude of the enemies he must fight—fire, water, and the Britons.

To Paul Jones on the topside one hopeless report after another came from below. It was impossible to put out the fire—throwing water on burning wood oozing hot tar and pitch merely spread about the blazing liquid. Any moment now we might be blown up should that devastating blaze, swirling already about its bulkheads, eat through the planking into the powder magazine. Once again, despite our pumping, the flood in the holds was rising. We were losing in our battle of the pikemen at the gun ports to slow the loading of that lower tier of eighteen-pounders fast reducing us to heaps of chips.

Our cockpit where Doctor Brooks held forth was already so jammed with wounded waiting amputation of shattered arms and legs, it was useless even to attempt to send any more below. So the wounded lay about the decks terribly mangled already by shot and splinters, feebly trying to drag their bleeding bodies out of the line of fire, groaning, shriek-

[583]

ing, begging for the aid no one could render. From bow to stern, from waterline to upper deck, the *Bon Homme Richard* was a shambles of horribly torn flesh and splintered wreckage—a scene dreadful beyond any power of description.

Our officers began to crack. Lieutenant Colonel Weibert, both of whose junior marine officers, young French ensigns, had died below at his side, torn almost to shreds by hurtling cannon balls, now came on deck to plead with Paul Jones to strike. But the Commodore was obdurate.

"I will never strike, *monsieur*. We cannot fail. Soon the enemy will lose heart and strike to us. Courage, *mon ami*, but a little longer!" and with a friendly pat, he sent the smoke-begrimed Colonel below again to back up Dale.

But whether the enemy would lose heart before we lost all buoyancy and sank under that terrible cannonading, I much doubted. Furtively I began to look about to see what was available on deck to keep my wearied limbs afloat when once the torn remnants of the *Bon Homme Richard* submerged beneath my feet. While I was thus engaged, Paul Jones who had been as keenly eyeing the *Serapis*, saw another opportunity, grasped my arm, twisted me about to look at what he saw.

"Tom," he exclaimed, "we must silence their lower deck battery! Look," and he pointed a long arm at the enemy alongside us. "There's the main hatch of the *Serapis* wide open directly beneath our fore yardarm! Get a bucket of hand grenades and heave them down that open hatch onto her gun deck!"

"Aye, aye, sir!"

Soberly I tossed aside the cutlass I had been wearing that I might not be encumbered on the yard. Then calling the sweating Red Jerry from his gun to get up the grenades for me, I scrambled up our fore shrouds into our top, holding a lighted slow match in my teeth. Behind me up the ratlines toiled Red Jerry with the bucket.

Once aloft, I looked about an instant before I started out on the yard. The full moon, riding high above, flooded the calm surface of the sea with a glorious silver radiance. Clearly outlined in the moonlight a mile away lay the *Alliance*, like a foul vulture hovering nearby waiting to pick the bones of the exhausted victor once we had struck to the *Serapis*. A little closer floated the *Vengeance*, afraid apparently to come to our assistance, and close aboard her was our little tender with Lieutenant Lunt and twenty seamen we desperately needed, likewise keeping prudently out of harm's way.

Somewhat farther off was the *Pallas* with the smaller English man-of-war alongside her, taken by Captain Cottineau after a short sharp struggle. Far off lay Flamborough Head glistening in the soft light of the moon, its heights covered with spectators gazing out to sea. All about was quiet—the clear sky, the ocean smooth as any millpond, the idle ships near and far.

But beneath me, locked tightly together the *Bon Homme Richard* and the *Serapis* rocked and shuddered from the recoil of the great guns and the impact of round shot. Lurid flashes like lightning flamed brilliantly out between their hulls.

The deafening explosions of the broadsides roared endlessly over the water, and on our lee side, the ocean sprayed up continuously where solid shot, tearing through us, splashed into the sea beyond to send up foaming geysers. Directly under me, with her every hatch glowing red in the night from the flames below, lay the torn wreck of the foundering *Richard*.

Red Jerry pushed the bucket of hand grenades up through the lubber's hole of the foretop, with a grunt scrambled over the futtock shrouds to land on the top beside me.

I waited no longer lest the *Bon Homme Richard* blow up under my feet. With the slow match in my teeth, I crawled carefully out the fore yard, followed closely by Red Jerry pushing the heavily laden bucket ahead of him.

Foot by foot we edged outward, with the spar swaying drunkenly about, no longer properly secured since all the braces had been shot away from it. Still farther we went till

[585]

we were over the *Serapis*, with her decks, so far as I could see, completely deserted and kept so in an endless fire of musketry directed by our shipmates on every bulkhead door and hatch leading into the open.

Finally, far out on the tapered end of our fore yard, I could look down amidships on the *Serapis*. There was her main hatch directly below me, but I lost hope when I looked down it. For from spar deck to hold, the canny English had removed every ladder and every grating, leaving a clear trunk so that anything pitched down it by our men from the enemy tops, might fall with no obstruction all the way to the open hold where the burst would injure nobody!

Red Jerry passed me the first grenade. I blew on my match till it glowed, then stretched precariously full length out on the yard, I lighted the fuse with one hand, instantly tossed the grenade with the other.

As I feared, it dropped clear down the hatchway, striking nothing on its way, to explode far below me, useless to damage the *Serapis*, still less to affect the gunners blasting us apart. Two more I hurled with no better results, while to add to my aggravations, I could see down 'tween decks the powder monkeys on the *Serapis* scurrying about, carelessly laying out fresh cartridges of powder on the deck behind those eighteen-pounders which we must silence or die.

Frenziedly, leaning first forward, then aft, I tried to get some angle on my grenades to get them in between decks amongst those invitingly laid out powder bags. I hurled half a dozen more, but all to no purpose. Every one fell harmlessly into the hold, and I was down to my last missile.

Red Jerry fished out the last grenade we had, tossed the bucket away, but instead of passing the grenade to me, motioned me contemptuously aside and slid out past me to the yardarm, shoving me inboard toward our own mast.

"You no make good harpooner, Tom," he scowled. "Too much miss! I show you," and he snatched from my hand the slow match. "Look!"

But Red Jerry neither lighted nor threw that last grenade. Instead, straddling the yard, that crazy Indian began

[586]

to swing his half naked body and his huge chest rhythmically fore and aft, chanting wildly all the while in an increasing frenzy till he had that spar beneath us swaying horizontally about our mast in a great arc, so that no longer was its end poised over the hatchway but sweeping back and forth over it. I began to see some method in his madness.

And now Red Jerry laid himself out flat on the gyrating yard, blew on the match an instant till it glowed brightly. The yard swung forward, stopped, started to swing aft again.

Instantly Red Jerry touched the match to the fuse, and as the powder train started to crackle, hurled the grenade downward toward the hatch at a considerable angle from forward.

Marked by a trail of hissing powder in the night, that grenade shot from the yardarm to go hurtling through the opening below us, strike on the lower deck hatch coaming, and bounce inward from our sight, landed fairly 'tween decks!

A second perhaps we clung to the yard holding our breaths and then below us the main hatch of the *Serapis* burst out in eruption. From that hatch, from every hatch aft of it, from every gun port in the side of the *Serapis* shot vast columns of fire to leap high in the night, vividly lighting up the skies in livid colors as if Vesuvius had burst forth beneath us. Our exploding grenade had touched off a whole string of powder cartridges laid out along the *Serapis'* deck behind those eighteen-pounders, to convert the lower gun deck of the *Serapis* into a veritable inferno! That murderous battery of eighteen-pounders was silenced at last!

Singed and choking from the flames and smoke which even fifty feet above her deck had shot from the *Serapis* to envelop us on the yardarm, we crawled slowly inboard. No longer did the thunder of heavy guns from the *Serapis* rend our eardrums. Save for the muffled shrieks of seared and dying gunners strewn about her silent guns below, for the moment all was quiet on the enemy.

But immediately from the *Bon Homme Richard* beneath

[587]

us burst out savagely the fire of our three six-pounders and the wild yells of our marines. Leaping by me from the yard to the foretop, disdaining the ratlines Red Jerry slid down a backstay to the deck, exultantly shrieking out in a weird battle chant, fearful he might lose a few rounds at his beloved gun.

In another moment he was back behind his piece, sighting and firing in mad abandon, sending chain shot flying at the gouged and battered base of the mainmast of the *Serapis*. Beside him, firing faster than ever, were Reuben Chase and Paul Jones, wildly urging on their men.

No guns save four far forward beneath the forecastle of the *Serapis* answered us, and their fire was obviously slackening. The end could not be far off now.

Paul Jones motioned Chase to mind his gun also and stepped to our main hatch. Calling up our First Lieutenant from below, he sang out,

"Boarders away!"

Dale seized a cutlass, I grabbed another. With Midshipman Mayrant helping us, by stripping our gun crews we gathered up perhaps two dozen men, Americans all lately from English gaols, armed them with pikes. Crouching low behind our bulwarks, Dale gave us our orders,

"Mayrant! Take half the men and get in to their fo'c'sle! Silence those forward guns! Folger! Come aft with me and the rest of the party to clear out their quarterdeck! Ready all! Remember Portsea prison!"

With our party thus divided and all ready, Dale looked expectantly inboard toward our Captain. Paul Jones looked at the *Serapis*. Her tottering mainmast started to go by the board. Now was the moment when the enemy would surely lose all hope.

"Go in, Dick!" roared out Paul Jones.

Instantly the fire of our guns ceased.

Over our shattered gunwales leaped our boarders, with Red Jerry, leaving his gun to seize a pike, scrambling madly up ahead of Mayrant to rush forward.

Up on the gunwale myself in one huge leap right behind

Dale, I saw him grab the enemy's main brace pendant and swing himself inboard to drop down on her deck. I was about to follow when on the quarterdeck of the *Serapis* aft by her ensign staff, I saw Captain Richard Pearson, standing starkly out against the moonlit sky, hauling down the flag of England!

The *Serapis* had struck to us and Paul Jones was of the Kings of the Sea!

56

WHAT need to go into the melancholy sequel? How amidst our heaps of dead and wounded, comprising two-thirds of our whole crew, we strove vainly for thirty hours in a rising gale against fire and water to save the remnants of our shattered ship? Or how in agony, despite the aid of the crews of our consorts in removing powder to keep her from blowing up, of the efforts of all the carpenters in the squadron in plugging shot holes, of frantic pumping by reliefs of seamen from all the ships, on the second morning we watched with tear-dimmed eyes from aboard the captured *Serapis* the blood-soaked hulk of the *Bon Homme Richard*, still carrying the bodies of our shipmates who had died valiantly upon her decks, plunge beneath the stormy waves to vanish forever from the sight of men?

With jury masts rigged up on the *Serapis* in place of all three of her masts which had gone by the board immediately the vessels had been separated after the battle, we set out across the tempestuous North Sea for the Texel in Holland. Under shot-torn canvas spread on makeshift spars we logged hardly two knots, no great speed with which to escape the squadrons of frigates and the huge ships-of-the-line the British had out scouring all the seas about to retake their lost *Serapis*.

So jammed were we with the wounded of both ships spread out amongst the guns of the *Serapis* that not a gun carriage could we have got into action. Any trifling cutter could have taken us with ease had she but fallen in with us alone. And had we encountered even one British frigate, God knows what save instant flight we might have expected from our consorts.

But with the Stars of Liberty floating proudly above the conquered *Serapis*, Paul Jones firmly held the squadron together and outguessed the men-of-war searching for us. Ten days after the battle he brought us all safely into the Texel in neutral Holland.

Now did the entire world ring with the name of Paul Jones! In France and in Holland he was immediately hailed as never a sea captain had been before. In England likewise his name was on every tongue but linked to epithets of which buccaneer was perhaps the mildest. Such a terror did his daring cruise inspire amongst the British Isles that at the mere rumor thereafter that Paul Jones was on the seas again, all shipping fled to harbor, unwilling to rely on convoying ships-of-war to protect them. And from the British nation, never enthusiastic over the war to subdue the colonies, came an ever-increasing demand that their inept Ministry make peace with America ere Paul Jones come back to burn the entire coast!

In the Texel, Paul Jones became the center of swirling intrigue. The British Ambassador demanded of the Dutch, who did not recognize America as an independent nation, that the *Serapis*, her consort, the *Countess of Scarborough*, and the five hundred British prisoners Jones had brought in, be all restored immediately to His Britannic Majesty, together with the rebellious pirates who had dared take them on the high seas.

The Dutch, overawed by threats, were inclined to comply. Skillfully Paul Jones, whose prizes were so battered they could not yet go to sea, countered by citing international law to such good purpose that the enraged British Ambassador was threatening war with Britain if it were not done, and the befuddled Dutch found themselves facing a war with France if it were. And all the while repairs were being rushed on the *Serapis*, refitting her into the powerful warship she had been.

When matters became at last acute, and a decision must be made, Franklin stepped forward with a master stroke to outmaneuver the British and give the Dutch a way out. He

[591]

relieved the treacherous Landais of command of the *Alliance*, placed Paul Jones on her as Captain, and put Captain Cottineau of the *Pallas* on the *Serapis* with the French flag hoisted on the latter. That ended the argument, for even the British could not demand of the Dutch the surrender of a vessel claimed by the King of France.

Thus all was shortly settled to everyone's satisfaction with the *Serapis* sailing under Captain Cottineau for L'Orient, and the *Alliance* soon following under Paul Jones. To everybody's satisfaction perhaps, except that of Captain Pierre Landais. This villain, removed in disgrace by Franklin and ordered to hold himself in readiness for transfer to America for court-martial, slipped off to Paris to see what he could do there with Franklin's enemies to regain his command.

The *Alliance* had hardly arrived in L'Orient with her new Captain than Paul Jones was ordered by Doctor Franklin to Paris in order that by royal command he might attend upon the King. So he left his frigate in Richard Dale's hands, and set out for the French capital. As before I accompanied him.

All Paris went literally mad over Paul Jones. Louis XVI received him in audience to knight him, making him Chevalier, and bestowing on him the Cross of Military Merit. Frenzied crowds followed him everywhere. Not the King himself excited such enthusiasm and wild cheering amongst the populace as did this valiant American Captain fighting for the liberty of his country—the Captain who after the most savage battle in the annals of the sea had so astonishingly come home victor aboard the enemy ship which had sunk his own! And shortly to crown all, Louis XVI presented him with a magnificent gold-hilted sword, inscribed,

"TO THE STRENUOUS DEFENDER OF THE RIGHTS OF THE SEA."

But the men of France with their swords, their titles, and their cheers were not left alone to honor Paul Jones. From the Queen down, Paul Jones captured all hearts amongst the women.

Young Marie Antoinette received him in private audience,

anxious to see this stout warrior who had so humbled the British, and to her astonishment found herself entertaining a gay and debonair knight indeed whose manners gave no slightest hint of the rough sea dog, and whose charm captivated all the ladies of her Court.

Now Paul Jones was in good truth fairly swamped with feminine attentions. The Duchesse de Chartres, whose golden gift had made possible the fitting out of the *Bon Homme Richard*, installed him as an honored guest in the Palais Royal, where between this great lady as his godmother in royal circles and the lovely young Queen herself as his patroness, the titled beauties of the French Court fairly fought each other for his smiles. As one such put it,

"If I am in love with him, for love I may die; I have as many rivals as there are ladies. He is the most agreeable sea wolf one could wish to meet with."

Truly was it so. His fame, his irresistible smile, his handsome face, brought to Paul Jones, scarce thirty-two and such a man as the French Court had never seen, the eager attention of every lady waiting on the Queen. Even in the atmosphere of that licentious Court where infidelity was a jest, it was almost beyond belief the manner in which all hands amongst the Queen's attendants flung themselves passionately upon Paul Jones.

They caught him in an auspicious moment. His youthful faith in the constancy of woman had long since been sadly shaken out of him by Dorothea Dandridge whose hand in marriage he had been barred from asking in the beginning by, forsooth, his humble birth. Now by the irony of Fate the titled ladies of the proudest Court in Europe were intriguing to fling themselves into his arms! Paul Jones would have been far more than human had he been able to resist.

But into these amours martial affairs intruded, even in Paris. With unexampled effrontery, Pierre Landais demanded of Ben Franklin the restoration to him of the *Alliance!* To which my cousin, ever a good judge of men, replied,

"If I had twenty ships-of-war at my disposal, I should not give one of them to Captain Landais. The same temper which excluded you from the French marine weighs equally with me. Of course I shall not replace you on the *Alliance*." And with that settled, the good Doctor, indulgently watching over his beloved Paul Jones that his head be not turned by the adulation of the French, began to consider how best to use this unexampled Captain and the fine frigate he now commanded.

Affairs in America, as well I knew, were again critical. The British were besieging Charleston, where most of our men-of-war lay blockaded. Washington's armies were sadly in need of military stores. So having obtained after great effort hundreds of stands of arms and desperately needed clothing for Washington's relief, Franklin sent them to L'Orient to be transported home aboard the *Alliance*, and bade Paul Jones stand ready to sail when all were aboard.

To this order, my Captain, of course, gave whole-hearted acquiescence. It was with less joy, however, that he received from Ben Franklin the news that he was to take Arthur Lee as a passenger back to America—Arthur Lee, now relieved as Commissioner in France, Jones' inveterate enemy whose intrigues had gone far to ruin all his efforts.

Now came far more trouble, for hardly had Jones agreed to that, when Lee called on him in Paris to request transportation on the *Alliance* for all his personal effects also, which were mountainous in amount, including of all things, a huge coach!

To this absurd request, Paul Jones gave flat refusal, since it was obvious that the holds of the *Alliance* would need every foot of storage space for the military stores. In high dudgeon over what he was pleased to consider this insult to his dignity Arthur Lee left him to set off for L'Orient.

I was myself a witness to this astonishing demand by him who considered himself the only pure patriot America had abroad. And knowing his capacity for intrigue, I was in no way surprised when Jones beckoned me after Arthur Lee slammed the door behind him,

"Tom, depart immediately for L'Orient and order Lieutenant Dale that Mr. Lee shall take aboard the *Alliance* naught save what he may get into his stateroom! I have the matters of our prize money, yet unpaid, to try to settle with the vacillating Monsieur de Chaumont here ere I come myself to L'Orient, which, however, should be within the week. Command Dale for me that he have all the stores for General Washington loaded so we may sail immediately I arrive."

"Aye, Captain," I agreed, and with a thankful heart I packed my slight effects and set off for L'Orient. Homeward bound at last, after two desperate years abroad!

57

IN L'Orient I passed along to Richard Dale our Captain's orders. It was with difficulty, however, that even that excellent officer was able to turn the disgruntled crew of the *Alliance* to in loading the stands of arms and the cases of clothing which encumbered the quay alongside us in vast heaps. For not a penny of prize money had any seaman yet received from the cruise of the *Bon Homme Richard*, and little in pay.

All over the ship, grumbling was rife. I knew well that with all the skill and diplomacy my cousin, Ben Franklin, could command, backed up with what influence through devious feminine channels Paul Jones had at Court, every effort was being made in Paris to extort a settlement from de Chaumont. But it was impossible to make sailors who had lost arms and legs in the taking of our prizes, as well as those who were still whole, believe that.

The glaring fact remained that across the basin from us in the hands of the King of France lay the *Serapis* and the *Countess of Scarborough* which we had taken from the English at the cost of so much blood. And many a fat merchantman had we sent in with prize crews to be sold by the agents of de Chaumont. Where was all that money if Paul Jones in Paris, with the connivance of Dr. Franklin, was not playing ducks and drakes with it?

Manfully Richard Dale struggled with insubordinate seamen mumbling threats if they did not receive their pay ere sailing, and ripe for mutiny. How he ever got the stores aboard at all under those circumstances was a miracle, but load her at last he did.

Arthur Lee arrived, moved on board the *Alliance*. John

Adams came also to L'Orient to see him off. Nothing was wanting to our departure save our Captain, due in some few days from Paris.

I was busy myself stowing my few odds and ends below in the steerage, when hearing some cheering and commotion on deck, I came up to run into an almost unbelievable scene.

There on our quarterdeck stood Pierre Landais, taking command of the *Alliance* in flat defiance of Franklin who had cashiered him! Amidst the shouts of cheering seamen, he read the crew orders from Arthur Lee confirming him as their legal Captain, and an opinion from John Adams backing that view with a statement Franklin had had no right to deprive him of the command!

Almost in a daze, I saw Richard Dale hustled unceremoniously over the side, our hatches broached, stands of arms and bales of uniforms for Washington's army heaved up out of our holds to be dumped indiscriminately on the quay, and in their room come aboard case after case of Arthur Lee's personal belongings, topped off at last by his private coach!

And in that state, with yards braced over and sails filling away, with Pierre Landais in command the *Alliance* shortly stood out of L'Orient for America!

That the infamous Arthur Lee should conspire with our disgruntled crew and the treacherous Pierre Landais to avenge himself thus on Franklin and on Jones, I could have guessed. But never should I have suspected that even he would sink to such a depth as to place the transportation of his private baggage above the needs of our struggling armies for the guns and the clothes he so contemptibly heaved overside to make way for his belongings!

We sailed thus for home, with the beautiful *Alliance*, America's most powerful man-of-war, in the hands of these two villains, each of whom in his own way had done his best to insure America's defeat in her struggle for liberty.

Never was there such a homeward voyage. Hardly had these two scamps got clear the coast of France when they fell foul of each other. Arthur Lee, considering he had put Landais in command, felt himself owner of the ship. Landais, who never in his turbulent career had ever got along with anyone, French or American, resented that, and soon the two were quarrelling like cats and dogs.

A trifle brought on open warfare. Lee presumed to help himself first at dinner to such tidbits as pleased him on the platter of meat. Landais seized a carving knife and with gleaming eyes threatened then and there to slay him for that presumption. Lee, in mortal terror, dropped his fork to let the Captain then have first choice.

But Arthur Lee swiftly avenged that insult. Claiming to have some medical knowledge (which perhaps he did) he declared Landais insane (which in good truth I think he was). And with that announcement, he persuaded the officers to recognize the First Lieutenant, Degge, and not Landais, as Captain. The result was that for some time the ship literally was a madhouse, with the perplexed seamen knowing not whom to obey, and sails being alternately spread and furled in rapid succession as the contending Captains countermanded each other's orders!

Where all this would have ended with the *Alliance* in the hands of these opposed scoundrels headed one moment west, the next east, God alone knows had not Landais, bursting suddenly into tears like a spoiled child denied a plaything, retired to his cabin, there to sulk the remainder of the voyage.

We finally arrived at Boston. Hardly had Arthur Lee got his goods ashore than he denounced to the authorities the precious confederate whom he had used to steal an American man-of-war for his private purposes.

Pierre Landais was promptly court-martialed for having absconded from France with the *Alliance* contrary to Doctor Franklin's orders. And Arthur Lee, who should have been in the dock beside him as a criminal, had the brazenness to appear as the principal witness to his guilt!

Landais was, of course, found guilty and broke, never again to be permitted to serve under the United States, but that was small reparation for the grave injuries that crazy Frenchman had done Paul Jones and all America.

58

I TOOK slight interest in what happened to Pierre Landais once we made port in Boston. All that mattered to me was that, almost three years since I had sailed away in the *Ranger*, I was home again!

Even the fact that some weeks later I was discharged with most the rest of the crew of the *Alliance* (our term of service being long since over) without a penny of the pay due me, worried me no great amount. I was alive, I was whole, I was home!

With my discharge in my pocket, with the only clothes I had the worn uniform upon my back, and with my purse as light as when long before I had left there, I set out afoot for Nantucket. Now I was twenty-two, a man grown, and a competent seaman. Save for one thing, I had no worries, for I well knew that nothing I might ever encounter would equal the distresses I had, by God's grace, come safely through.

Save for one thing. Would I fare no better after my long absence with Delight than Paul Jones had with Dorothea? As I plodded along the dusty road between Boston and New Bedford, endlessly I pondered that. If Paul Jones, than whom never a man was more attractive to a woman, had fared thus with Dorothea Dandridge, what chance for plain Tom Folger? My heart ached over that.

I also had some worried moments as to how I might get back to Nantucket from the mainland. Well I knew the British held New York, and from that point maintained a close blockade all along the shores thereabouts, which my Aunt Keziah had shrewdly turned to her own account against her starving neighbors. With Nantucket thus cut off, I stood fair prospect of landing in a British prison ship till the war was over if I were taken on the passage by a British cruiser.

So it may well be believed I started with much caution in New Bedford to investigate how I might best evade that hazard. However, the first fisherman I questioned on the New Bedford docks about the danger looked incredulously at me.

"Danger? There ain't no danger goin' to Nantucket, man! Where ye been all this time? Ain't ye heard naught o' what's happened on Nantucket?"

I had to confess to him I had been in France of late and was grossly ignorant.

"Well, sailor, rest yer mind of all yer fears. Nantucket's issued a Proclamation o' Neutrality in this war between these United States and King George and she ain't atakin' no part neither way. Smart folks, them Quakers on Nantucket! Ye won't have no trouble gittin' there so far's the British is concerned now. Just ask any fisherman going out to land ye on the island. No danger at all!"

It was even as he said. Without molestation from or even sight of any man-of-war cruising off Nantucket, I stepped from a little fishing smack running out of New Bedford to land on old Straight Wharf.

What meant this neutrality declared by Nantucket, I wondered? Could whaling have come back by any chance?

On that wharf from which first I had sailed aboard the *Beaver*, I looked about anxiously for any sign of spouters fitting out, but not a vessel showed the old familiar try-pots, though a few small schooners were obviously discharging cargo at the piers nearby. Whatever my little island of Nantucket had achieved by thus sturdily declaring herself neutral and defying both the Continent and King George, she had certainly not brought back the crowding hulls of spouters fitting out to hunt the spermaceti.

Slowly I started down the wharf, still puzzling over this neutrality, with my lagging feet of two minds—should they take me boldly to Centre Street that I might know the worst at once, or should they show some discretion by taking me to Debbie Chase's, for instance, where Reuben's gigantic sister might inform me of what had happened on our island?

They did neither, for the matter was oddly resolved for them. Coming out of Captain Rotch's counting house strode a tall figure, angular, unmistakable. Ere I could find anything on that deserted wharf to shelter me from observation, the sharp eyes of my Aunt Keziah had lighted on me and her bony fingers were imperiously beckoning me to her.

"I see thou art come back to us again, Tom Folger!" She looked me keenly up and down, missing no detail of my dusty clothes, well-worn from long use. "I judge from thy ragamuffin appearance thou hast not brought back from all thy wanderings the seventy pounds thou owest me?"

"Nay, Aunt Keziah," I answered, shamefaced. "I have earned it and in France it is indeed due me and much more, but when I shall receive my due that I may repay thee, I know not."

"Good!" exclaimed Keziah Coffin, her glum face relaxing into a smile. "I had feared when my eye first lighted on thee, thou might repay me and thus further aid the enemies of the King. Now am I spared thus comforting my enemies as well as his."

I looked blankly into my Aunt Keziah's countenance. Good? Aid the enemies of the King by repaying her? Was she sarcastic that I could not repay or had she lost her mind? But there was no doubt, incomprehensible as it might be, she meant what she said. For God knows what reason, Keziah Coffin who never in her life had let a shilling slip away from her that seemed within her grasp, positively glowed in triumph that I was not tendering her the seventy pounds sterling long her due. But I got no explanation. What had happened to that woman who I knew had practically all the property in Nantucket already mortgaged to her and was grasping for the rest? Why was she stalking off, rubbing her ungainly hands in satisfaction at being unable to collect from me?

Dumbfounded I watched her stride away. That she should take such unholy joy in my misfortune and her loss could only be that somehow it placed Delight beyond my reach.

[601]

With a sinking heart I gazed motionless on her retreating figure till I saw she was bound for her warehouse next to Captain Rotch's and not for home. I waited then only till she had vanished through its door to turn and fairly run for Centre Street.

With only one vicious bang at the knocker I paused not for anyone to answer, but flung back that door and burst into the hall. Now should I see!

I did. Almost petrified I looked about me at the bare walls of a house completely stripped of all its furniture, empty, deserted! What meant this? With the same sick feeling that had overcome me when I had gazed out in the moonlight from the *Bon Homme Richard's* blasted gun port to see the *Serapis* unmasking her deadly battery of eighteen-pounders on us, I stared about at those blank walls. Delight then was married and long since gone, my Aunt Keziah's grand house abandoned probably as beyond her needs now!

Sunk completely in spirit, my shoulders sagged as I turned about to leave, forlornly wondering why one of those shrieking round shot crashing through the *Richard's* sides had not mercifully taken me with it to spare me this last misery. My heavy steps echoed hollowly through that empty house as I faced around to go. What was left for me now of my homecoming?

Lightly, like a second echo to my clattering shoes came a footfall from above. I paused uncertainly, looked back over my shoulder at the deserted stairs. There peering down over the banister was Delight!

"Tom! Oh, Tom!" and like a tempest sweeping down those stairs she came flying down to fling both arms fiercely about my neck. Rapturously I lifted her clean off her feet to clutch her to me, smothering her almost as fiercely, kissing her lips upturned to mine in a wild surge of happiness.

"Delight, darling! You are still free?"

In doubt I held her off to look into her brown eyes while in starry rapture she gazed into mine.

"Goose!" She nestled close against my pounding heart. "Did I not tell thee, forever I should wait for thee? But I had long since ceased to hope thou hadst escaped the death that took so many others in that bloody battle on the sea! Now I can bear all else since the Lord hath spared thee to me!" Ecstatically I felt her soft cheek caressing mine, her arms encircling me as if she never meant to let me go again. For long in that empty hall caring naught for anything save to gaze into those heavenly brown eyes glowing happily into mine, I stood there, forgetful of time, oblivious of all else. Neither war nor my glowering Aunt Keziah should separate us again!

At last, fair drunk with ardent kisses, I spoke,

"You'll marry me now, Delight, though still I'm poor as when I saw you last?"

"Aye, Tom, an' thou wilt have me now when I can bring thee naught at all. Thou knowest what has happened to us?" and as if it mattered, she looked anxiously up at me.

"Happened?" and then suddenly I came back to earth again, recalling the vacant house in which I stood. I looked about at the bare walls. "What's happened?"

"Hast thou not heard?"

I shook my head.

"No, dearest, save I met your mother this morning and what she said of my debt to her left me perplexed as to whether she had lost her senses or I had. She seemed overjoyed I could not repay the seventy pounds I still owed!"

Delight sighed.

"Aye, mother's heart has changed no whit in her adversity. 'Twas that neutrality. The moment the British agreed to that, others could trade with the Continent and mother's monopoly on supply here instantly collapsed. Not one person on this island would buy a penny's worth again from her, and she was left with huge stocks in her warehouse and large debts to merchants in New York to whom she had given notes in payment for their goods. Our neighbors here, Captain Rotch and the other good people she had sore oppressed by her outrageous prices and on whose houses she held mortgages, on their own credit bought up all those

[603]

notes in New York and brought them here, demanding instant payment."

I laughed outright. So Keziah Coffin's Quaker neighbors had caught her then in her own trap!

"Mother had not the cash, of course, to pay," continued Delight soberly; "and when she sought to raise some by foreclosure on any mortgage that she held, no man stepped forth to bid upon the property save one agreed upon by her creditors who bid in the house for some such price as one pound only for a house worth perhaps a thousand. And thus in swift succession they stripped her of every mortgage that she held, returning it to its owner, and still she was in their debt on her notes. At that perhaps, they might have stopped had mother shown any sign of repentance, but breathing only fire she threatened vengeance on them all for conspiracy when the courts sat here again, so they went further. Seest thou what's happened?" Delight swept her eyes unhappily around the vacant house. "Against her unpaid notes they've seized our furniture, our house at Quaise, and tomorrow this house goes too. Mother hath not a shilling left to her name. Understandest thou now why she was glad thou couldst not repay her? That money also would straightway have been seized by her creditors, an' she would not have them have that satisfaction!"

Delight began to sob, with tear-stained eyes looked up to me. "I care not so much we have lost all, for that is but the judgment of the Lord on mother's oppression of our neighbors when she had them in her power. But now, Tom, if still thou dost desire me, I come to thee today, the poorest maid on all this island of Nantucket!"

Rapturously in the abandon of youth I kissed away those tears. Now my impoverished Aunt Keziah could not interpose.

"Aye, Delight, my dear! Today! Truly need we wait no longer now!"

59

NEVER again did I see Paul Jones, which was perhaps as well for me. How I might have stood the spectacle of his glorious strength wasted away and his indomitable will broken, not by an enemy but by his country, which could not find means amidst its wranglings and its petty politics ever to get him another man-of-war, I know not. Three weary years more the war dragged along, with what few ships we had left frittering away their opportunities under the Captains who had superseded him in rank, while Paul Jones was left ingloriously without a ship!

When peace came at last and with it the independence for which Paul Jones had valiantly drawn his sword and fought with brilliance, fortitude, and success matched by no man amongst us in that struggle, still America was as blind as ever to its interests.

Despite Paul Jones' forceful arguments and his anguished pleadings for the establishment of a proper Navy to support the very existence of our new nation, despite his plans for its organization and its growth, so blind were we that naught but strength could guard our liberty in a distressed world, that we allowed our Navy wholly to decay after the peace. Our last ship-of-war, the *Alliance*, was sold as a West India-man, and with no Navy left, the best use we could find for the finest seaman of our age was to send him back to Europe as collection agent, to extort from unwilling foreign courts the monies due us for the prizes he had captured.

After infinite vexation and toil he collected it, but to what end? Instead of Paul Jones or any man he led in battle receiving then or since a cent of what was long due him, with

[605]

such chicanery as might have been expected from Arthur
Lee, perhaps, he was ordered to turn all over to our new
Ambassador in France, Thomas Jefferson. It was to serve as
a fund from which to pay, forsooth, the salaries of Jefferson
and his fellow diplomats in European courts, since otherwise
these United States had not the wherewithal to pay its repre-
sentatives abroad!

And what of Paul Jones once he had been used thus that
Ambassadors might be paid the money due his seamen? A
quarter of a century has passed and Jones is long since
gone, dead at the age of forty-five, a broken-hearted victim
of his country's neglect, cast aside to perish of inaction in
foreign lands once he had been made the tool of this last
piece of vile injustice to himself and to the men he led in
battle.

Now are we paying and for long years yet to come shall
we pay for our disregard of what Paul Jones urged on his
heedless countrymen. In succession for lack of warships we
have been despoiled by the Algerines and the Barbary corsairs; by the grasping French who have taken our ships on
our very coasts; and now by the British who impress our
seamen and seize our goods on every sea!

In agony I look out now over our idle ships crowding
Nantucket harbor, held there by Jefferson's embargo, fit
symbol of our folly now or ever to resist the tyrants of this
earth by acquiescence in their tyrannies.

Paul Jones, dead these many years, lies in an unmarked
grave in an abandoned Parisian cemetery, neglected and forgotten by the country of his adoption. Never had we more
need of his rebellious spirit than today. In these hours of our
national disgrace when we can find no better means of re-
sisting oppression than like hermits to endeavor to cut ourselves off from all the world that our existence give no offense to these modern Caesars, I mournfully set down before
I die these recollections of my life with Captain Paul.

Humbly do I pray that I, Tom Folger, merchant of Nantucket, may thus fulfill my destiny on this earth. For no

other purpose could it have pleased God to cast me into the path of this strange Captain who as Paul Jones flamed across the dark night of our Revolution to strike the fear of free men to the hearts of tyrants in the only language these Caesars ever have or ever will understand—the thunder of rebellious guns.

THE END

HISTORICAL NOTE

THE body of John Paul Jones was at last brought back from France in 1905. It lies now enshrined in what is probably the most magnificent tomb in all America, at the Naval Academy in Annapolis, where I as a Midshipman in 1913 took part in Paul Jones' final funeral procession.

In every case where there are conflicting theories respecting Captain Paul's movements, I have used that theory which to me seems most probable in the light of everything known. I have, however, for the purposes of my story deviated from known fact in a few minor instances and these deviations are here noted. I have shifted the scene of Captain Paul's landing from the Spanish corsair in 1773 to bury his slain skipper, from Marthas Vineyard where he actually landed, to Nantucket. The names of the Spanish ship figuring in this incident, of the British warship which engaged her, and of the mutinous seaman whom Captain Paul killed in Tobago, are not known. I have given them such names as seemed appropriate. The occurrence related of the *Bon Homme Richard* in the storm off Ireland, where the terror-stricken French marines sought to leave the pumps to pray and were held at their posts only by bared cutlasses, actually took place later on Jones' first homeward voyage from France in the *Ariel*. As that later voyage forms no part of my narrative, I have taken the liberty of transposing that episode to the storm encountered by the *Bon Homme Richard*, which storm is otherwise correctly recounted.

The incidents in Tom Folger's disastrous adventure with the great whale, and particularly the manner of Jared Macy's death, may seem incredible. They are nevertheless authentic, being based on actual tragedies recorded in the whale fishery.

EDWARD ELLSBERG.

"I HAVE NOT YET BEGUN TO FIGHT"

CHAS. ROSNER